SEVENTH EDITION

Biochemistry

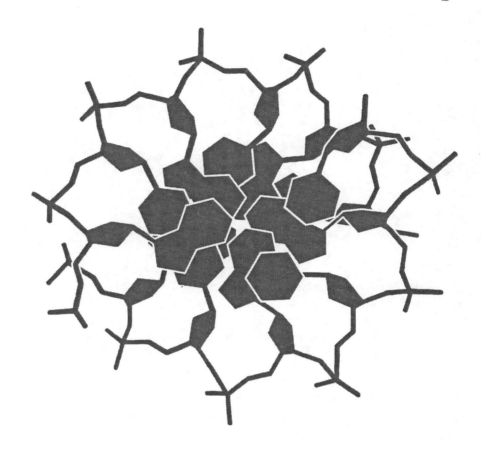

Jeremy M. Berg

John L. Tymoczko

Lubert Stryer

with
Gregory J. Gatto, Jr.

Custom Edition for McGill University

 **FREEMAN**
Custom Publishing

D1224071

ISBN-13: 978-1-4641-3772-3
ISBN-10: 1-4641-3772-2

Printed in the United States of America

Custom Publishing Division
W. H. Freeman and Company
41 Madison Avenue
New York, NY 10010

www.whfreeman.com/custompub

To our teachers and our students

ABOUT THE AUTHORS

JEREMY M. BERG received his B.S. and M.S. degrees in Chemistry from Stanford (where he did research with Keith Hodgson and Lubert Stryer) and his Ph.D. in Chemistry from Harvard with Richard Holm. He then completed a postdoctoral fellowship with Carl Pabo in Biophysics at Johns Hopkins University School of Medicine. He was an Assistant Professor in the Department of Chemistry at Johns Hopkins from 1986 to 1990. He then moved to Johns Hopkins University School of Medicine as Professor and Director of the Department of Biophysics and Biophysical Chemistry, where he remained until 2003. He then became Director of the National Institute of General Medical Sciences at the National Institutes of Health. He is an elected Fellow of the American Association for the Advancement of Science and an elected member of the Institute of Medicine of the National Academy of Sciences. He received the American Chemical Society Award in Pure Chemistry (1994) and the Eli Lilly Award for Fundamental Research in Biological Chemistry (1995), was named Maryland Outstanding Young Scientist of the Year (1995), received the Harrison Howe Award (1997), the Distinguished Service Award from the Biophysical Society (2009), and the Howard K. Schachman Public Service Award from the American Society for Biochemistry and Molecular Biology (2011). He also received numerous teaching awards, including the W. Barry Wood Teaching Award (selected by medical students), the Graduate Student Teaching Award, and the Professor's Teaching Award for the Preclinical Sciences. He is coauthor, with Stephen J. Lippard, of the textbook *Principles of Bioinorganic Chemistry*.

JOHN L. TYMOCZKO is Towsley Professor of Biology at Carleton College, where he has taught since 1976. He currently teaches Biochemistry, Biochemistry Laboratory, Oncogenes and the Molecular Biology of Cancer, and Exercise Biochemistry and coteaches an introductory course, Energy Flow in Biological Systems. Professor Tymoczko received his B.A. from the University of Chicago in 1970 and his Ph.D. in Biochemistry from the University of Chicago with Shutsung Liao at the Ben May Institute for Cancer Research. He then had a postdoctoral position with Hewson Swift of the Department of Biology at the University of Chicago. The focus of his research has been on steroid receptors, ribonucleoprotein particles, and proteolytic processing enzymes.

LUBERT STRYER is Winzer Professor of Cell Biology, Emeritus, in the School of Medicine and Professor of Neurobiology, Emeritus, at Stanford University, where he has been on the faculty since 1976. He received his M.D. from Harvard Medical School. Professor Stryer has received many awards for his research on the interplay of light and life, including the Eli Lilly Award for Fundamental Research in Biological Chemistry, the Distinguished Inventors Award of the Intellectual Property Owner Association, and election to the National Academy Sciences and the American Philosophical Society. He was awarded the National Medal of Science in 200 The publication of his first edition of *Biochemistry* 1975 transformed the teaching of biochemistry.

GREGORY J. GATTO, JR., received his A.B. in Chemistry from Princeton University, where he worked with Martin F. Semmelhack and was aw the Everett S. Wallis Prize in Organic Chemistr 2003, he received his M.D. and Ph.D. degrees Johns Hopkins University School of Medicine studied the structural biology of peroxisomal signal recognition with Jeremy M. Berg and Michael A. Shanoff Young Investigator Res He then completed a postdoctoral fellowsh with Christopher T. Walsh at Harvard M where he studied the biosynthesis of the immunosuppressants. He is currently an in the Heart Failure Discovery Perform GlaxoSmithKline Pharmaceuticals.

ABOUT THE AUTHORS

JEREMY M. BERG received his B.S. and M.S. degrees in Chemistry from Stanford (where he did research with Keith Hodgson and Lubert Stryer) and his Ph.D. in Chemistry from Harvard with Richard Holm. He then completed a postdoctoral fellowship with Carl Pabo in Biophysics at Johns Hopkins University School of Medicine. He was an Assistant Professor in the Department of Chemistry at Johns Hopkins from 1986 to 1990. He then moved to Johns Hopkins University School of Medicine as Professor and Director of the Department of Biophysics and Biophysical Chemistry, where he remained until 2003. He then became Director of the National Institute of General Medical Sciences at the National Institutes of Health. He is an elected Fellow of the American Association for the Advancement of Science and an elected member of the Institute of Medicine of the National Academy of Sciences. He received the American Chemical Society Award in Pure Chemistry (1994) and the Eli Lilly Award for Fundamental Research in Biological Chemistry (1995), was named Maryland Outstanding Young Scientist of the Year (1995), received the Harrison Howe Award (1997), the Distinguished Service Award from the Biophysical Society (2009), and the Howard K. Schachman Public Service Award from the American Society for Biochemistry and Molecular Biology (2011). He also received numerous teaching awards, including the W. Barry Wood Teaching Award (selected by medical students), the Graduate Student Teaching Award, and the Professor's Teaching Award for the Preclinical Sciences. He is coauthor, with Stephen J. Lippard, of the textbook *Principles of Bioinorganic Chemistry*.

JOHN L. TYMOCZKO is Towsley Professor of Biology at Carleton College, where he has taught since 1976. He currently teaches Biochemistry, Biochemistry Laboratory, Oncogenes and the Molecular Biology of Cancer, and Exercise Biochemistry and coteaches an introductory course, Energy Flow in Biological Systems. Professor Tymoczko received his B.A. from the University of Chicago in 1970 and his Ph.D. in Biochemistry from the University of Chicago with Shutsung Liao at the Ben May Institute for Cancer Research. He then had a postdoctoral position with Hewson Swift of the Department of Biology at the University of Chicago. The focus of his research has been on steroid receptors, ribonucleoprotein particles, and proteolytic processing enzymes.

LUBERT STRYER is Winzer Professor of Cell Biology, Emeritus, in the School of Medicine and Professor of Neurobiology, Emeritus, at Stanford University, where he has been on the faculty since 1976. He received his M.D. from Harvard Medical School. Professor Stryer has received many awards for his research on the interplay of light and life, including the Eli Lilly Award for Fundamental Research in Biological Chemistry, the Distinguished Inventors Award of the Intellectual Property Owners' Association, and election to the National Academy of Sciences and the American Philosophical Society. He was awarded the National Medal of Science in 2006. The publication of his first edition of *Biochemistry* in 1975 transformed the teaching of biochemistry.

GREGORY J. GATTO, JR., received his A.B. degree in Chemistry from Princeton University, where he worked with Martin F. Semmelhack and was awarded the Everett S. Wallis Prize in Organic Chemistry. In 2003, he received his M.D. and Ph.D. degrees from the Johns Hopkins University School of Medicine, where he studied the structural biology of peroxisomal targeting signal recognition with Jeremy M. Berg and received the Michael A. Shanoff Young Investigator Research Award. He then completed a postdoctoral fellowship in 2006 with Christopher T. Walsh at Harvard Medical School, where he studied the biosynthesis of the macrolide immunosuppressants. He is currently an Investigator in the Heart Failure Discovery Performance Unit at GlaxoSmithKline Pharmaceuticals.

To our teachers and our students

PREFACE

In writing this seventh edition of *Biochemistry*, we have balanced the desire to present up-to-the minute advances with the need to make biochemistry as clear and engaging as possible for the student approaching the subject for the first time. Instructors and students have long relied on *Biochemistry* for:

- **Clear writing**   The language of biochemistry is made as accessible as possible. A straightforward and logical organization leads the reader through processes and helps navigate complex pathways and mechanisms.

- **Single-concept illustrations**   Illustrations in this book address one point at a time so that each illustration clearly tells the story of a mechanism, pathway, or process without the distraction of excess detail.

- **Physiological relevance**   Biochemistry is the study of life on the smallest scale, and it has always been our goal to help students connect biochemistry to their own lives. Pathways and processes are presented in a physiological context so that the reader can see how biochemistry works in different parts of the body and under different environmental and hormonal conditions.

- **Clinical insights**   Wherever appropriate, pathways and mechanisms are applied to health and disease. These applications show students how biochemistry is relevant to them while reinforcing the concepts that they have just learned. (For a full list, see p. xi.)

- **Evolutionary perspective**   Evolution is evident in the structures and pathways of biochemistry and is woven into the narrative of the textbook. (For a full list, see p. x.)

New to This Edition

Researchers are making new discoveries in biochemistry every day. The seventh edition takes into account the discoveries that have changed how we think about the fundamental concepts in biochemistry and human health. New aspects of the book include:

- **Metabolism integrated in a new context**   New information about the role of leptins in hunger and satiety has greatly influenced how we think about obesity and the growing epidemic of diabetes. In this edition, we cover the integration of metabolism in the context of diet and obesity.

- **New chapters on gene regulation**   To relate to the rapidly growing understanding of the biochemical aspect of eukaryotic gene regulation, we have greatly expanded our discussion of regulation and have split the chapter in the preceding editions into two: Chapter 31, "The Control of Gene Expression in Prokaryotes," and Chapter 32, "The Control of Gene Expression in Eukaryotes." These chapters address recent discoveries such as quorum sensing in prokaryotes, induced pluripotent stem cells, and the role of microRNAs in regulating gene expression.

- **Experimental techniques updated and clarified**   We have revised Chapters 3 ("Exploring Proteins and Proteomes"), 5 ("Exploring Genes and Genomes"), and 6 ("Exploring Evolution and Bioinformatics") to give students a practical understanding of the benefits and limitations of the techniques that they will be using in the laboratory. We have expanded explanations of mass spectrometry and x-ray crystallography, for instance, and made them even clearer for the first-time student. We explain new techniques such as next-generation sequencing and real-time PCR in the context of their importance to modern research in biochemistry. (For a full list, see p. xii.)

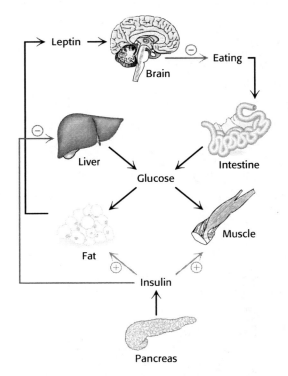

Chapter 27 A schematic representation illustrates a few of the many metabolic pathways that must be coordinated to meet the demands of living.

Recent Advances

Some of the exciting advances and new topics that we present in the seventh edition include:

- Osteogenesis imperfecta, or brittle bone disease (Chapter 2)
- Intrinsically unstructured proteins and metamorphic proteins (Chapter 2)
- Recent updates in protein-misfolding diseases (Chapter 2)
- The use of recombinant DNA technology in protein purification (Chapter 3)
- Expanded discussion of mass spectrometry and x-ray crystallography (Chapter 3)
- Next-generation sequencing methods (Chapter 5)
- Real-time PCR (Chapter 5)
- DNA microarrays (Chapter 5)
- Carbon monoxide poisoning (Chapter 7)
- Single-molecule studies of enzyme kinetics (Chapter 8)
- Myosins as a model of a catalytic strategy for ATP hydrolysis (Chapter 9)
- Glycobiology and glycomics (Chapter 11)
- Hurler disease (Chapter 11)
- Avian influenza H5N1 (Chapter 11)
- Lipid rafts (Chapter 12)
- Transferrin as an example of receptor-mediated endocytosis (Chapter 12)
- Long QT syndrome and arrhythmia caused by the inhibition of potassium channels (Chapter 13)
- Defects in the citric acid cycle and the development of cancer (Chapter 17)
- Synthesizing a more efficient rubisco (Chapter 20)
- The structure of mammalian fatty acid synthetase (Chapter 22)
- Pyrimidine salvage pathways (Chapter 25)
- Physical association of enzymes in metabolic pathways (Chapter 25)
- Phosphatidic acid phosphatase in the regulation of lipid metabolism (Chapter 26)
- The regulation of SCAP-SREBP movement in cholesterol metabolism (Chapter 26)
- Mutations in the LDL receptor (Chapter 26)
- The role of HDL in protecting against arteriosclerosis (Chapter 26)

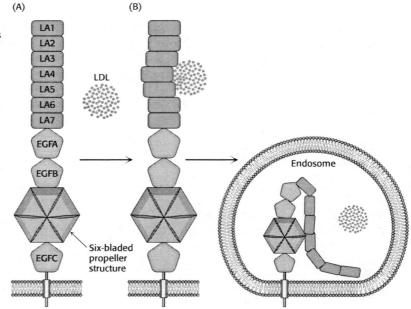

Figure 26.24 LDL receptor releases LDL in the endosomes. [After I. D. Campbell, *Biochem. Soc. Trans.* 31:1107–1114, 2003, Fig 1A.]

- Aromatase inhibitors in the treatment of breast and ovarian cancer (Chapter 26)
- The role of leptin in long-term caloric homeostasis (Chapter 27)
- Obesity and diabetes (Chapter 27)
- Exercise and its effects on cellular biochemistry (Chapter 27)
- Updated detailed mechanism of helicase's action (Chapter 28)
- Updated detailed mechanism of topoisomerase's action (Chapter 28)
- Riboswitches (Chapter 29)
- The production of small regulatory RNAs (Chapter 29)
- Vanishing white matter disease (Chapter 30)
- Quorum sensing (Chapter 31)
- Biofilms (Chapter 31)
- Induced pluripotent stem cells (Chapter 32)
- The role of microRNAs in gene regulation (Chapter 32)
- How vaccines work (Chapter 34)
- The structure of myosin head domains (Chapter 35)

Figure 32.27 MicroRNA action.

New End-of-Chapter Problems

Biochemistry is best learned by practicing it and, to help students practice biochemistry, we have increased the number of end-of-chapter problems by 50%. In addition to many traditional problems that test biochemical knowledge and the ability to use this knowledge, we have three categories of problems to address specific problem-solving skills.

- **Mechanism problems** ask students to suggest or elaborate a chemical mechanism.

- **Data interpretation problems** ask questions about a set of data provided in tabulated or graphic form. These problems give students a sense of how scientific conclusions are reached.

- **Chapter integration problems** require students to use information from several chapters to reach a solution. These problems reinforce a student's awareness of the interconnectedness of the different aspects of biochemistry.

Brief solutions to these problems are presented at the end of the book; expanded solutions are available in the accompanying *Student Companion*.

Visualizing Molecular Structure

All molecular structures have been selected and rendered by Jeremy Berg and Gregory Gatto. To help students read and understand these structures, we include the following tools:

- A **molecular-model "primer"** explains the different types of protein models and examines their strengths and weaknesses (see appendices to Chapters 1 and 2).

- **Figure legends** direct students explicitly to the key features of a model.

- A **great variety of types of molecular structures** are represented, including clearer renderings of membrane proteins.

- For most molecular models, the **PDB number** at the end of the figure legend gives the reader easy access to the file used in generating the structure from the Protein Data Bank Web site (www.pdb.org). At this site, a variety of tools for visualizing and analyzing the structure are available.

- **Living figures** for most molecular structures now appear on the Web site in Jmol to allow students to **rotate three-dimensional molecules** and view alternative renderings online.

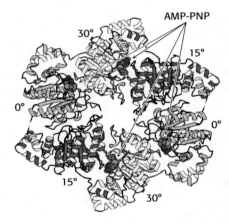

Figure 28.12 Helicase asymmetry. *Notice* that only four of the subunits, those shown in blue and yellow, bind AMP-PNP. [Drawn from 1E0K.pdb.]

Media and Supplements

A full package of media resources and supplements provides instructors and students with innovative tools to support a variety of teaching and learning approaches.

eBook

http://ebooks.bfwpub.com/berg7e

This online version of the textbook combines the contents of the printed book, electronic study tools, and a full complement of student media specifically created to support the text. Problems and resources from the printed textbook are incorporated throughout the eBook, to ensure that students can easily review specific concepts. The eBook enables students to:

- Access the complete book and its electronic study tools from any internet-connected computer by using a standard Web browser;

- Navigate quickly to any section or subsection of the book or any page number of the printed book;

- Add their own bookmarks, notes, and highlighting;

- Access all the fully integrated media resources associated with the book;

- Review quizzes and personal notes to help prepare for exams; and

- Search the entire eBook instantly, including the index and spoken glossary.

Instructors teaching from the eBook can assign either the entire textbook or a **custom version** that includes only the chapters that correspond to their syllabi. They can choose to add notes to any page of the eBook and share these notes with their students. These notes may include text, Web links, animations, or photographs.

BIOCHEM PORTAL

http://courses.bfwpub.com/berg7e

BiochemPortal is a dynamic, fully integrated learning environment that brings together all of our teaching and learning resources in one place. It features easy-to-use assessment tracking and grading tools that enable instructors to assign problems for practice, as homework, quizzes, or tests. A personalized calendar, an announcement center, and communication tools help instructors manage the course. In addition to all the resources found on the Companion Web site, BiochemPortal includes several other features:

- The **interactive eBook** integrates the complete text with all relevant media resources.

- Hundreds of **self-graded practice problems** allow students to test their understanding of concepts explained in the text, with immediate feedback.

- The **metabolic map** helps students understand the principles and applications of the core metabolic pathways. Students can work through guided tutorials with embedded assessment questions, or explore the Metabolic Map on their own using the dragging and zooming functionality of the map.

- **Jmol tutorials** by Jeffrey Cohlberg, California State University at Long Beach, teach students how to create models of proteins in Jmol based on data from the Protein Database. By working through the tutorial and answering assessment questions at the end of each exercise, students learn to use this important database and fully realize the relationship between structure and function of enzymes.

- **Animated techniques** illustrate laboratory techniques described in the text.

- **Concept tutorials** walk students through complex ideas in enzyme kinetics and metabolism.

BiochemPortal.

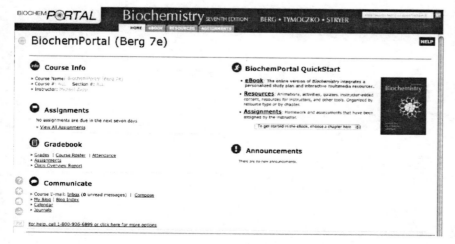

Companion Web Site
www.whfreeman.com/berg7e

For students

- **Living figures** allow students to explore protein structure in 3-D. Students can zoom and rotate the "live" structures to get a better understanding of their three-dimensional nature and can experiment with different display styles (space-filling, ball-and-stick, ribbon, backbone) by means of a user-friendly interface.

- **Concept-based tutorials** by Neil D. Clarke help students build an intuitive understanding of some of the more difficult concepts covered in the textbook.

- **Animated techniques** help students grasp experimental techniques used for exploring genes and proteins.

- The **self-assessment tool** helps students evaluate their progress. Students can test their understanding by taking an online multiple-choice quiz provided for each chapter, as well as a general chemistry review.

- The **glossary** of key terms.

- **Web links** connect students with the world of biochemistry beyond the classroom.

For Instructors

All of the student resources plus:

- All **illustrations and tables** from the textbook, in jpeg and PowerPoint formats optimized for classroom projection.

- The **Assessment Bank** offers more than 1500 questions in editable Microsoft Word format.

Instructor's Resource DVD
[1-4292-8411-0]

The CD includes all the instructor's resources from the Web site.

Overhead Transparencies
[1-4292-8412-9]

200 full-color illustrations from the textbook, optimized for classroom projection

Student Companion
[1-4292-3115-7]

For each chapter of the textbook, the *Student Companion* includes:

- Chapter Learning Objectives and Summary

- Self-Assessment Problems, including multiple-choice, short-answer, matching questions, and challenge problems, and their answers

- Expanded Solutions to end-of-chapter problems in the textbook

Molecular Evolution

 This icon signals the start of the many discussions that highlight protein commonalities or other molecular evolutionary insights.

Clinical Applications

 This icon signals the start of a clinical application in the text. Additional, briefer clinical correlations appear in the text as appropriate.

Tools and Techniques

The seventh edition of *Biochemistry* offers three chapters that present the tools and techniques of biochemistry: "Exploring Proteins and Proteomes" (Chapter 3), "Exploring Genes and Genomes" (Chapter 5), and "Exploring Evolution and Bioinformatics" (Chapter 6). Additional experimental techniques are presented throughout the book, as appropriate.

⚲ Animated Techniques

Animated explanations of experimental techniques used for exploring genes and proteins are available at www.whfreeman.com/berg7e.

Acknowledgments

Thanks go first and foremost to our students. Not a word was written or an illustration constructed without the knowledge that bright, engaged students would immediately detect vagueness and ambiguity. We also thank our colleagues who supported, advised, instructed, and simply bore with us during this arduous task. We are also grateful to our colleagues throughout the world who patiently answered our questions and shared their insights into recent developments. We thank Susan J. Baserga and Erica A. Champion of the Yale University School of Medicine for their outstanding contributions in the sixth edition's revision of Chapter 29. We also especially thank those who served as reviewers for this new edition. Their thoughtful comments, suggestions, and encouragement have been of immense help to us in maintaining the excellence of the preceding editions. These reviewers are:

Fareed Aboul-Ela
Louisiana State University

Paul Adams
University of Arkansas, Fayetteville

Kevin Ahern
Oregon State University

Edward Behrman
Ohio State University

Donald Beitz
Iowa State University

Sanford Bernstein
San Diego State University

Martin Brock
Eastern Kentucky University

W. Malcom Byrnes
Howard University College of Medicine

C. Britt Carlson
Brookdale Community College

Graham Carpenter
Vanderbilt University

Jun Chung
Louisiana State University

Michael Cusanovich
University of Arizona

David Daleke
Indiana University

Margaret Daugherty
Colorado College

Dan Davis
University of Arkansas, Fayetteville

Mary Farwell
East Carolina University

Brent Feske
Armstrong Atlantic University

Wilson Francisco
Arizona State University

Masaya Fujita
University of Houston, University Park

Peter Gegenheimer
University of Kansas

John Goers
California Polytechnic University, San Luis Obispo

Neena Grover
Colorado College

Paul Hager
East Carolina University

Frans Huijing
University of Miami

Nitin Jain
University of Tennessee

Gerwald Jogl
Brown University

Kelly Johanson
Xavier University of Louisiana

Todd Johnson
Weber State University

Michael Kalafatis
Cleveland State University

Mark Kearly
Florida State University

Sung-Kun Kim
Baylor University

Roger Koeppe
University of Arkansas, Fayetteville

Dmitry Kolpashchikov
University of Central Florida

John Koontz
University of Tennessee

Glen Legge
University of Houston, University Park

John Stephen Lodmell
University of Montana

Timothy Logan
Florida State University

Michael Massiah
Oklahoma State University

Diana McGill
Northern Kentucky University

Michael Mendenhall
University of Kentucky

David Merkler
University of South Florida

Gary Merrill
Oregon State University

Debra Moriarity
University of Alabama, Huntsville

Patricia Moroney
Louisiana State University

M. Kazem Mostafapour
University of Michigan, Dearborn

Duarte Mota de Freitas
Loyola University of Chicago

Stephen Munroe
Marquette University

Xiaping Pan
East Carolina University

Scott Pattison
Ball State University

Stefan Paula
Northern Kentucky University

David Pendergrass
University of Kansas

Reuben Peters
Iowa State University

Wendy Pogozelski
State University of New York, Geneseo

Geraldine Prody
Western Washington University

Greg Raner
University of North Carolina, Greensboro

Joshua Rausch
Elmhurst College

Tanea Reed
Eastern Kentucky University

Lori Robins
California Polytechnic University, San Luis Obispo

Douglas Root
University of North Texas

Theresa Salerno
Minnesota State University, Mankato

Scott Samuels
University of Montana, Missoula

Benjamin Sandler
Oklahoma State University

Joel Schildbach
Johns Hopkins University

Hua Shi
State University of New York, University at Albany

Kerry Smith
Clemson University

Robert Stach
University of Michigan, Flint

Scott Stagg
Florida State University

Wesley Stites
University of Arkansas, Fayetteville

Paul Straight
Texas A&M University

Gerald Stubbs
Vanderbilt University

Takita Felder Sumter
Winthrop University

Jeremy Thorner
University of California, Berkeley

Liang Tong
Columbia University

Kenneth Traxler
Bemidji State University

Peter Van Der Geer
San Diego State University

Nagarajan Vasumathi
Jacksonville State University

Stefan Vetter
Florida Atlantic University

Edward Walker
Weber State University

Xuemin Wang
University of Missouri, St. Louis

Kevin Williams
Western Kentucky University

Warren Williams
University of British Columbia

Shiyong Wu
Ohio University

Laura Zapanta
University of Pittsburgh

Three of us have had the pleasure of working with the folks at W. H. Freeman and Company on a number of projects, whereas one of us is new to the Freeman family. Our experiences have always been delightful and rewarding. Writing and producing the seventh edition of *Biochemistry* was no exception. The Freeman team has a knack for undertaking stressful, but exhilarating, projects and reducing the stress without reducing the exhilaration and a remarkable ability to coax without ever nagging. We have many people to thank for this experience. First, we would like to acknowledge the encouragement, patience, excellent advice, and good humor of Kate Ahr Parker, Publisher. Her enthusiasm is source of energy for all of us. Lisa Samols is our wonderful developmental editor. Her insight, patience, and understanding contributed immensely to the success of this project. Beth Howe and Erica Champion assisted Lisa by developing several chapters, and we are grateful to them for their help. Georgia Lee Hadler, Senior Project Editor, managed the flow of the entire project, from copyediting through bound book, with her usual admirable efficiency. Patricia Zimmerman and Nancy Brooks, our manuscript editors, enhanced the literary consistency and clarity of the text. Vicki Tomaselli, Design Manager, produced a design and layout that makes the book exciting and eye-catching while maintaining the link to past editions. Photo Editor Christine Beuse and Photo Researcher Jacalyn Wong found the photographs that we hope make the text more inviting. Janice Donnola, Illustration Coordinator, deftly directed the rendering of new illustrations. Paul Rohloff, Production Coordinator, made sure that the significant difficulties of scheduling, composition, and manufacturing were smoothly overcome. Andrea Gawrylewski, Patrick Shriner, Marni Rolfes, and Rohit Phillip did a wonderful job in their management of the media program. Amanda Dunning ably coordinated the print supplemants plan. Special thanks also to editorial assistant Anna Bristow. Debbie Clare, Associate Director of Marketing, enthusiastically introduced this newest edition of *Biochemistry* to the academic world. We are deeply appreciative of the sales staff for their enthusiastic support. Without them, all of our excitement and enthusiasm would ultimately come to naught. Finally, we owe a deep debt of gratitude to Elizabeth Widdicombe, President of W. H. Freeman and Company. Her vision for science textbooks and her skill at gathering exceptional personnel make working with W. H. Freeman and Company a true pleasure.

Thanks also to our many colleagues at our own institutions as well as throughout the country who patiently answered our questions and encouraged us on our quest. Finally, we owe a debt of gratitude to our families— our wives, Wendie Berg, Alison Unger, and Megan Williams, and our children, Alex, Corey, and Monica Berg, Janina and Nicholas Tymoczko, and Timothy and Mark Gatto. Without their support, comfort, and understanding, this endeavor could never have been undertaken, let alone successfully completed.

CONTENTS

Metabolism: Basic Concepts and Design

Hummingbirds are capable of prodigious feats of endurance. For instance, the tiny ruby-throated hummingbird can store enough fuel to fly across the Gulf of Mexico, a distance of some 500 miles, without resting. This achievement is possible because of the ability to convert fuels into the cellular energy currency, ATP, represented by the model at the right. [(Left) William Leaman/Alamy.]

The concepts of conformation and dynamics developed in Part I—especially those dealing with the specificity and catalytic power of enzymes, the regulation of their catalytic activity, and the transport of molecules and ions across membranes—enable us to now ask questions fundamental to biochemistry:

1. *How does a cell extract energy and reducing power from its environment?*

2. *How does a cell synthesize the building blocks of its macromolecules and then the macromolecules themselves?*

These processes are carried out by a highly integrated network of chemical reactions that are collectively known as *metabolism* or *intermediary metabolism*.

More than a thousand chemical reactions take place in even as simple an organism as *Escherichia coli*. The array of reactions may seem overwhelming at first glance. However, closer scrutiny reveals that metabolism has a *coherent design containing many common motifs*. These motifs include the use of an energy currency and the repeated appearance of a limited number of activated intermediates. In fact, a group of about 100 molecules play central roles in all forms of life. Furthermore, although the number of reactions in metabolism is large, the number of *kinds* of reactions is small and the mechanisms of these reactions are usually quite simple. Metabolic pathways are also regulated in common ways. The purpose of this chapter is to introduce some general principles and motifs of metabolism to provide a foundation for the more detailed studies to follow. These principles are:

1. Fuels are degraded and large molecules are constructed step by step in a series of linked reactions called *metabolic pathways.*

2. An energy currency common to all life forms, adenosine triphosphate (ATP), links energy-releasing pathways with energy-requiring pathways.

3. The oxidation of carbon fuels powers the formation of ATP.

4. Although there are many metabolic pathways, a limited number of types of reactions and particular intermediates are common to many pathways.

5. Metabolic pathways are highly regulated.

15.1 Metabolism Is Composed of Many Coupled, Interconnecting Reactions

Living organisms require a continual input of free energy for three major purposes: (1) the performance of mechanical work in muscle contraction and cellular movements, (2) the active transport of molecules and ions, and (3) the synthesis of macromolecules and other biomolecules from simple precursors. The free energy used in these processes, which maintain an organism in a state that is far from equilibrium, is derived from the environment. Photosynthetic organisms, or *phototrophs,* obtain this energy by trapping sunlight, whereas *chemotrophs,* which include animals, obtain energy through the oxidation of foodstuffs generated by phototrophs.

Metabolism consists of energy-yielding and energy-requiring reactions

Metabolism is essentially a linked series of chemical reactions that begins with a particular molecule and converts it into some other molecule or molecules in a carefully defined fashion (Figure 15.1). There are many such defined pathways in the cell (Figure 15.2), and we will examine a few of them in some detail later. These pathways are interdependent, and their activity is coordinated by exquisitely sensitive means of communication in which allosteric enzymes are predominant (Section 10.1). We considered the principles of this communication in Chapter 14.

We can divide metabolic pathways into two broad classes: (1) those that convert energy from fuels into biologically useful forms and (2) those that require inputs of energy to proceed. Although this division is often imprecise, it is nonetheless a useful distinction in an examination of metabolism. Those reactions that transform fuels into cellular energy are called *catabolic reactions* or, more generally, *catabolism.*

$$\text{Fuel (carbohydrates, fats)} \xrightarrow{\text{Catabolism}} CO_2 + H_2O + \text{useful energy}$$

Those reactions that require energy—such as the synthesis of glucose, fats, or DNA—are called *anabolic reactions* or *anabolism.* The useful forms of energy that are produced in catabolism are employed in anabolism to generate complex structures from simple ones, or energy-rich states from energy-poor ones.

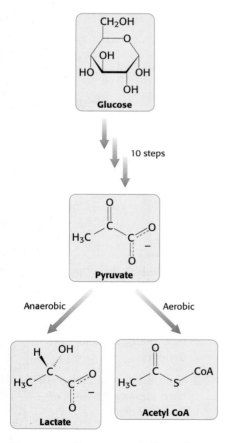

Figure 15.1 Glucose metabolism. Glucose is metabolized to pyruvate in 10 linked reactions. Under anaerobic conditions, pyruvate is metabolized to lactate and, under aerobic conditions, to acetyl CoA. The glucose-derived carbons of acetyl CoA are subsequently oxidized to CO_2.

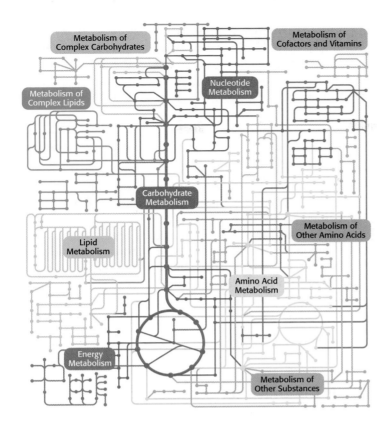

Figure 15.2 Metabolic pathways. [From the Kyoto Encyclopedia of Genes and Genomes (www.genome.ad.jp/kegg).]

$$\text{Useful energy + simple precursors} \xrightarrow{\text{Anabolism}} \text{complex molecules}$$

Some pathways can be either anabolic or catabolic, depending on the energy conditions in the cell. These pathways are referred to as *amphibolic pathways*.

An important general principle of metabolism is that *biosynthetic and degradative pathways are almost always distinct*. This separation is necessary for energetic reasons, as will be evident in subsequent chapters. It also facilitates the control of metabolism.

A thermodynamically unfavorable reaction can be driven by a favorable reaction

How are specific pathways constructed from individual reactions? A pathway must satisfy minimally two criteria: (1) the individual reactions must be *specific* and (2) the entire set of reactions that constitute the pathway must be *thermodynamically favored*. A reaction that is specific will yield only one particular product or set of products from its reactants. As discussed in Chapter 8, a function of enzymes is to provide this specificity. The thermodynamics of metabolism is most readily approached in relation to free energy, which was also discussed in Chapter 8. A reaction can occur spontaneously only if ΔG, the change in free energy, is negative. Recall that ΔG for the formation of products C and D from substrates A and B is given by

$$\Delta G = \Delta G^{\circ\prime} + RT \ln\frac{[\text{C}][\text{D}]}{[\text{A}][\text{B}]}$$

Thus, the ΔG of a reaction depends on the *nature* of the reactants and products (expressed by the $\Delta G^{\circ\prime}$ term, the standard free-energy change) and on their *concentrations* (expressed by the second term).

An important thermodynamic fact is that *the overall free-energy change for a chemically coupled series of reactions is equal to the sum of the free-energy changes of the individual steps.* Consider the following reactions:

$$A \rightleftharpoons B + C \qquad \Delta G^{\circ\prime} = +21 \text{ kJ mol}^{-1} \, (+5 \text{ kcal mol}^{-1})$$

$$\underline{B \rightleftharpoons D \qquad\qquad \Delta G^{\circ\prime} = -34 \text{ kJ mol}^{-1} \, (-8 \text{ kcal mol}^{-1})}$$

$$A \rightleftharpoons C + D \qquad \Delta G^{\circ\prime} = -13 \text{ kJ mol}^{-1} \, (-3 \text{ kcal mol}^{-1})$$

Under standard conditions, A cannot be spontaneously converted into B and C, because $\Delta G^{\circ\prime}$ is positive. However, the conversion of B into D under standard conditions is thermodynamically feasible. Because free-energy changes are additive, the conversion of A into C and D has a $\Delta G^{\circ\prime}$ of -13 kJ mol^{-1} (-3 kcal mol^{-1}), which means that it can occur spontaneously under standard conditions. Thus, *a thermodynamically unfavorable reaction can be driven by a thermodynamically favorable reaction to which it is coupled.* In this example, the reactions are coupled by the shared chemical intermediate B. Thus, metabolic pathways are formed by the coupling of enzyme-catalyzed reactions such that the overall free energy of the pathway is negative.

15.2 ATP Is the Universal Currency of Free Energy in Biological Systems

Just as commerce is facilitated by the use of a common currency, the commerce of the cell—metabolism—is facilitated by the use of a common energy currency, *adenosine triphosphate* (ATP). Part of the free energy derived from the oxidation of foodstuffs and from light is transformed into this highly accessible molecule, which acts as the free-energy donor in most energy-requiring processes such as motion, active transport, and biosynthesis. Indeed, most of catabolism consists of reactions that extract energy from fuels such as carbohydrates and fats and convert it into ATP.

ATP hydrolysis is exergonic

ATP is a nucleotide consisting of adenine, a ribose, and a triphosphate unit (Figure 15.3). The active form of ATP is usually a complex of ATP with Mg^{2+} or Mn^{2+}. In considering the role of ATP as an energy carrier, we can focus on its triphosphate moiety. *ATP is an energy-rich molecule because its triphosphate unit contains two phosphoanhydride bonds.* A large amount of free energy is liberated when ATP is hydrolyzed to adenosine diphosphate (ADP) and orthophosphate (P_i) or when ATP is hydrolyzed to adenosine monophosphate (AMP) and pyrophosphate (PP_i).

$$\text{ATP} + H_2O \rightleftharpoons \text{ADP} + P_i$$
$$\Delta G^{\circ\prime} = -30.5 \text{ kJ mol}^{-1} \, (-7.3 \text{ kcal mol}^{-1})$$

$$\text{ATP} + H_2O \rightleftharpoons \text{AMP} + PP_i$$
$$\Delta G^{\circ\prime} = -45.6 \text{ kJ mol}^{-1} \, (-10.9 \text{ kcal mol}^{-1})$$

The precise $\Delta G^{\circ\prime}$ for these reactions depends on the ionic strength of the medium and on the concentrations of Mg^{2+} and other metal ions. Under typical cellular concentrations, the actual ΔG for these hydrolyses is approximately -50 kJ mol^{-1} (-12 kcal mol^{-1}).

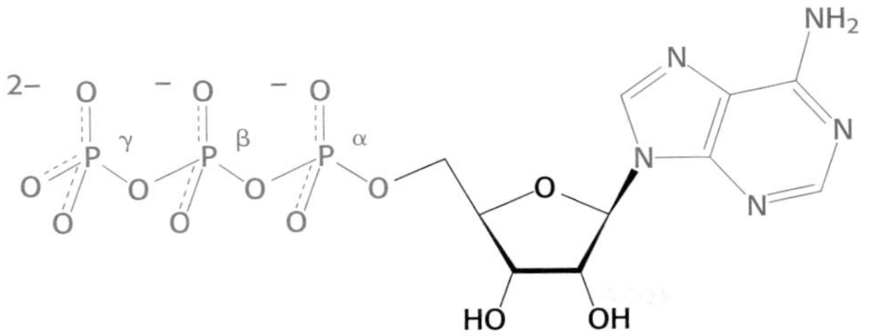

Adenosine triphosphate (ATP)

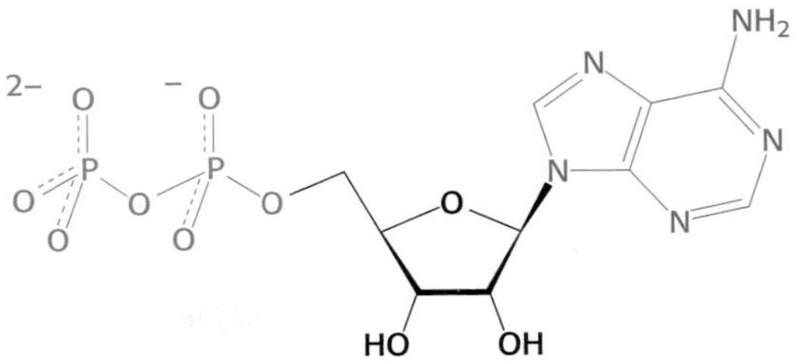

Adenosine diphosphate (ADP)

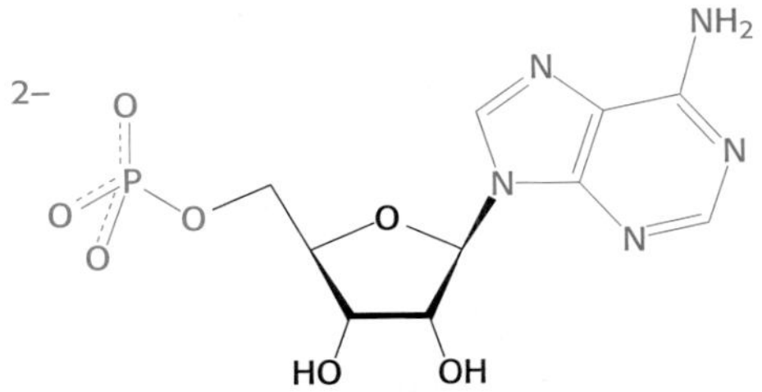

Adenosine monophosphate (AMP)

Figure 15.3 Structures of ATP, ADP, and AMP. These adenylates consist of adenine (blue), a ribose (black), and a tri-, di-, or monophosphate unit (red). The innermost phosphorus atom of ATP is designated P_α, the middle one P_β, and the outermost one P_γ.

The free energy liberated in the hydrolysis of ATP is harnessed to drive reactions that require an input of free energy, such as muscle contraction. In turn, ATP is formed from ADP and P_i when fuel molecules are oxidized in chemotrophs or when light is trapped by phototrophs. *This ATP–ADP cycle is the fundamental mode of energy exchange in biological systems.*

Some biosynthetic reactions are driven by the hydrolysis of nucleoside triphosphates that are analogous to ATP—namely, guanosine triphosphate (GTP), uridine triphosphate (UTP), and cytidine triphosphate (CTP). The diphosphate forms of these nucleotides are denoted by GDP, UDP, and CDP, and the monophosphate forms are denoted by GMP, UMP, and CMP. Enzymes catalyze the transfer of the terminal phosphoryl group from one nucleotide to another. The phosphorylation of nucleoside monophosphates is catalyzed by a family of *nucleoside monophosphate kinases*, as discussed in Section 9.4. The phosphorylation of nucleoside diphosphates is catalyzed by *nucleoside diphosphate kinase*, an enzyme with broad specificity.

$$\text{NMP} + \text{ATP} \underset{\text{Nucleoside monophosphate kinase}}{\rightleftharpoons} \text{NDP} + \text{ADP}$$

Nucleoside monophosphate

$$\text{NDP} + \text{ATP} \underset{\text{Nucleoside diphosphate kinase}}{\rightleftharpoons} \text{NTP} + \text{ADP}$$

Nucleoside diphosphate

It is intriguing to note that although all of the nucleotide triphosphates are energetically equivalent, ATP is nonetheless the primary cellular energy carrier. In addition, two important electron carriers, NAD^+ and FAD, are derivatives of ATP. *The role of ATP in energy metabolism is paramount.*

ATP hydrolysis drives metabolism by shifting the equilibrium of coupled reactions

An otherwise unfavorable reaction can be made possible by coupling to ATP hydrolysis. Consider a chemical reaction that is thermodynamically unfavorable without an input of free energy, a situation common to many biosynthetic reactions. Suppose that the standard free energy of the conversion of compound A into compound B is $+16.7$ kJ mol^{-1} ($+4.0$ kcal mol^{-1}):

$$A \rightleftharpoons B \qquad \Delta G^{\circ\prime} = +16.7 \text{ kJ mol}^{-1} (+4 \text{ kcal mol}^{-1})$$

The equilibrium constant K'_{eq} of this reaction at 25°C is related to $\Delta G^{\circ\prime}$ (in units of kilojoules per mole) by

$$K'_{eq} = [B]_{eq}/[A]_{eq} = 10^{-\Delta G^{\circ\prime}/5.69} = 1.15 \times 10^{-3}$$

Thus, net conversion of A into B cannot take place when the molar ratio of B to A is equal to or greater than 1.15×10^{-3}. However, A can be converted into B under these conditions if the reaction is coupled to the hydrolysis of ATP. Under standard conditions, the $\Delta G^{\circ\prime}$ of hydrolysis is approximately -30.5 kJ mol^{-1} (-7.3 kcal mol^{-1}). The new overall reaction is

$$A + ATP + H_2O \rightleftharpoons B + ATP + P_i$$
$$\Delta G^{\circ\prime} = -13.8 \text{ kJ mol}^{-1} (-3.3 \text{ kcal mol}^{-1})$$

Its free-energy change of -13.8 kJ mol^{-1} (-3.3 kcal mol^{-1}) is the sum of the value of $\Delta G^{\circ\prime}$ for the conversion of A into B [$+16.7$ kJ mol^{-1} ($+4.0$ kcal mol^{-1})] and the value of $\Delta G^{\circ\prime}$ for the hydrolysis of ATP [-30.5 kJ mol^{-1} (-7.3 kcal mol^{-1})]. At pH 7, the equilibrium constant of this coupled reaction is

$$K'_{eq} = \frac{[B]_{eq}}{[A]_{eq}} \times \frac{[ADP]_{eq}[P_i]_{eq}}{[ATP]_{eq}} = 10^{13.8/5.69} = 2.67 \times 10^2$$

At equilibrium, the ratio of [B] to [A] is given by

$$\frac{[B]_{eq}}{[A]_{eq}} = K'_{eq}\frac{[ATP]_{eq}}{[ADP]_{eq}[P_i]_{eq}}$$

which means that the hydrolysis of ATP enables A to be converted into B until the [B]/[A] ratio reaches a value of 2.67×10^2. This equilibrium ratio is strikingly different from the value of 1.15×10^{-3} for the reaction A $\rightarrow$ B in the absence of ATP hydrolysis. In other words, coupling the hydrolysis of ATP with the conversion of A into B under standard conditions has changed the equilibrium ratio of B to A by a factor of about 10^5. If we were to use the ΔG of hydrolysis of ATP under cellular conditions [-50.2 kJ mol^{-1} (-12 kcal mol^{-1})] in our calculations instead of $\Delta G^{\circ\prime}$, the change in the equilibrium ratio would be even more dramatic, on the order of 10^8.

We see here the thermodynamic essence of ATP's action as an *energy-coupling agent*. Cells maintain a high level of ATP by using oxidizable substrates or light as sources of free energy for synthesizing the molecule. In the cell, the hydrolysis of an ATP molecule in a coupled reaction then changes the equilibrium ratio of products to reactants by a very large factor, of the order of 10^8. More generally, the hydrolysis of n ATP molecules changes the equilibrium ratio of a coupled reaction (or sequence of reactions) by a factor of 10^{8n}. For example, the hydrolysis of three ATP molecules in a coupled reaction changes the equilibrium ratio by a factor of 10^{24}. Thus, *a thermodynamically unfavorable reaction sequence can be converted into a favorable one by coupling it to the hydrolysis of a sufficient number of ATP molecules in a new reaction*. It should also be emphasized that A and B in the preceding coupled reaction may be interpreted very generally, not only as different chemical species. For example, A and B may represent activated and unactivated conformations of a protein that is activated by phosphorylation with ATP. Through such changes in protein conformation, molecular motors such as myosin, kinesin, and dynein convert the chemical energy of ATP into mechanical energy (Chapter 34). Indeed, this conversion is the basis of muscle contraction.

Alternatively, A and B may refer to the concentrations of an ion or molecule on the outside and inside of a cell, as in the active transport of a nutrient. The active transport of Na^+ and K^+ across membranes is driven by the phosphorylation of the sodium–potassium pump by ATP and its subsequent dephosphorylation (Section 13.2).

The high phosphoryl potential of ATP results from structural differences between ATP and its hydrolysis products

What makes ATP a particularly efficient phosphoryl-group donor? Let us compare the standard free energy of hydrolysis of ATP with that of a phosphate ester, such as glycerol 3-phosphate:

$$ATP + H_2O \rightleftharpoons ADP + P_i$$
$$\Delta G^{\circ\prime} = -30.5 \text{ kJ mol}^{-1} (-7.3 \text{ kcal mol}^{-1})$$
$$\text{Glycerol 3-phosphate} + H_2O \rightleftharpoons \text{glycerol} + P_i$$
$$\Delta G^{\circ\prime} = -9.2 \text{ kJ mol}^{-1} (-2.2 \text{ kcal mol}^{-1})$$

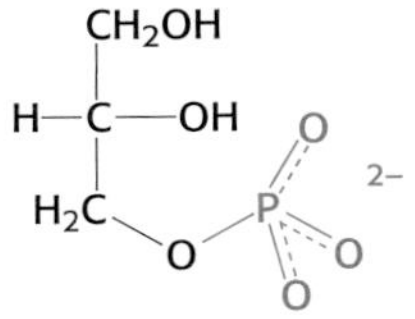

The magnitude of $\Delta G^{\circ\prime}$ for the hydrolysis of glycerol 3-phosphate is much smaller than that of ATP, which means that ATP has a stronger tendency to transfer its terminal phosphoryl group to water than does glycerol 3-phosphate. In other words, ATP has a higher *phosphoryl-transfer potential* (*phosphoryl-group-transfer potential*) than does glycerol 3-phosphate.

The high phosphoryl-transfer potential of ATP can be explained by features of the ATP structure. Because $\Delta G^{\circ\prime}$ depends on the *difference* in free energies of the products and reactants, we need to examine the structures of both ATP and its hydrolysis products, ADP and P_i, to answer this question. Three factors are important: *resonance stabilization, electrostatic repulsion,* and *stabilization due to hydration.*

1. *Resonance Stabilization.* ADP and, particularly, P_i, have greater resonance stabilization than does ATP. Orthophosphate has a number of resonance forms of similar energy (Figure 15.4), whereas the γ phosphoryl group of ATP has a smaller number. Forms like that shown in Figure 15.5 are unfavorable because a positively charged oxygen atom is adjacent to a positively charged phosphorus atom, an electrostatically unfavorable juxtaposition.

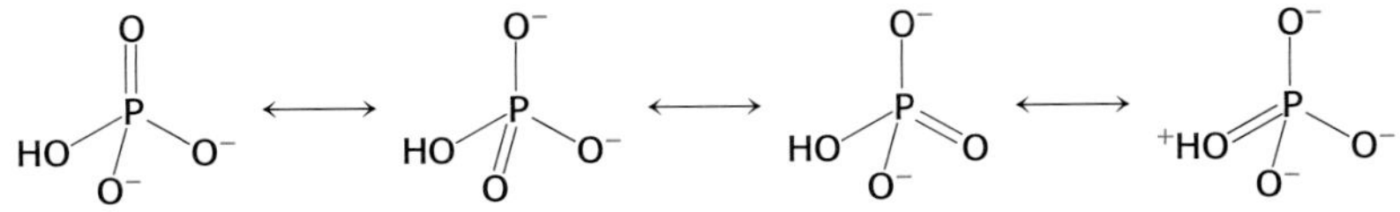

Glycerol 3-phosphate

Figure 15.4 Resonance structures of orthophosphate.

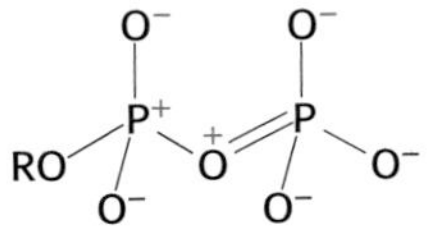

Figure 15.5 Improbable resonance structure. The structure contributes little to the terminal part of ATP, because two positive charges are placed adjacent to each other.

2. *Electrostatic Repulsion.* At pH 7, the triphosphate unit of ATP carries about four negative charges. These charges repel one another because they are in close proximity. The repulsion between them is reduced when ATP is hydrolyzed.

3. *Stabilization Due to Hydration.* More water can bind more effectively to ADP and P_i than can bind to the phosphoanhydride part of ATP, stabilizing the ADP and P_i by hydration.

ATP is often called a high-energy phosphate compound, and its phosphoanhydride bonds are referred to as high-energy bonds. Indeed, a

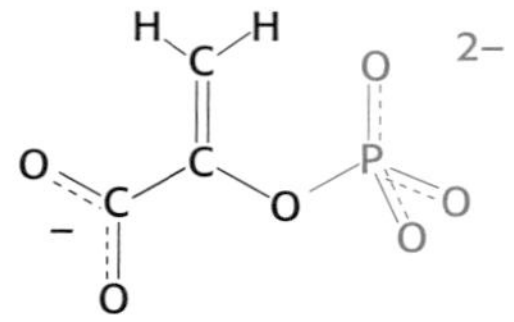

Phosphoenolpyruvate (PEP)

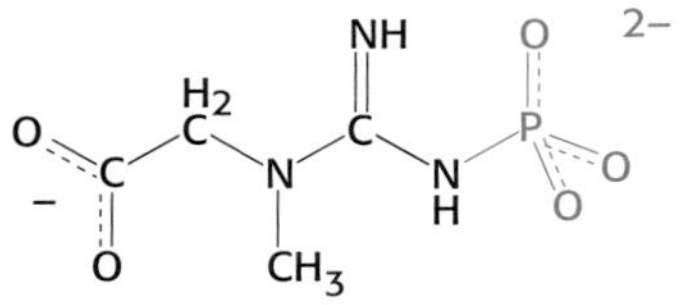

Creatine phosphate

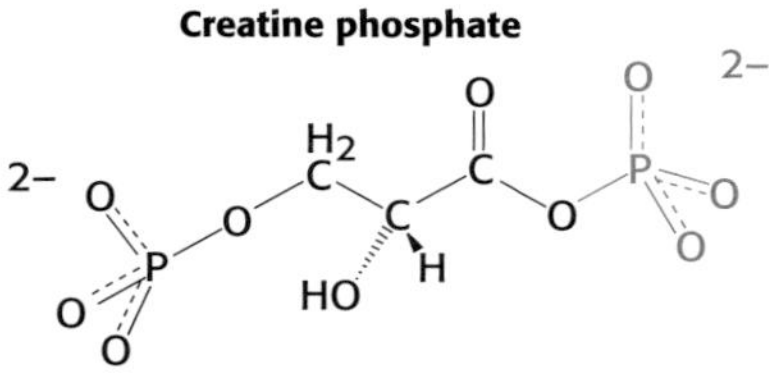

1,3-Bisphosphoglycerate (1,3-BPG)

Figure 15.6 Compounds with high phosphoryl-transfer potential. These compounds have a higher phosphoryl-transfer potential than that of ATP and can be used to phosphorylate ADP to form ATP.

"squiggle" ($\sim P$) is often used to indicate such a bond. Nonetheless, there is nothing special about the bonds themselves. *They are high-energy bonds in the sense that much free energy is released when they are hydrolyzed*, for the reasons listed in factors 1 through 3.

Phosphoryl-transfer potential is an important form of cellular energy transformation

The standard free energies of hydrolysis provide a convenient means of comparing the phosphoryl-transfer potential of phosphorylated compounds. Such comparisons reveal that ATP is not the only compound with a high phosphoryl-transfer potential. In fact, some compounds in biological systems have a higher phosphoryl-transfer potential than that of ATP. These compounds include phosphoenolpyruvate (PEP), 1,3-bisphosphoglycerate (1,3-BPG), and creatine phosphate (Figure 15.6). Thus, PEP can transfer its phosphoryl group to ADP to form ATP. Indeed, this transfer is one of the ways in which ATP is generated in the breakdown of sugars (Chapter 16). It is significant that ATP has a phosphoryl-transfer potential that is intermediate among the biologically important phosphorylated molecules (Table 15.1). *This intermediate position enables ATP to function efficiently as a carrier of phosphoryl groups.*

The amount of ATP in muscle suffices to sustain contractile activity for less than a second. Creatine phosphate in vertebrate muscle serves as a reservoir of high-potential phosphoryl groups that can be readily transferred to ADP. Indeed, we use creatine phosphate to regenerate ATP from ADP every time that we exercise strenuously. This reaction is catalyzed by *creatine kinase*.

$$\text{Creatine phosphate} + \text{ADP} \xrightleftharpoons{\text{Creatine kinase}} \text{ATP} + \text{creatine}$$

At pH 7, the standard free energy of hydrolysis of creatine phosphate is -43.1 kJ mol^{-1} (-10.3 kcal mol^{-1}), compared with -30.5 kJ mol^{-1} (-7.3 kcal mol^{-1}) for ATP. Hence, the standard free-energy change in forming ATP from creatine phosphate is -12.6 kJ mol^{-1} (-3.0 kcal mol^{-1}), which corresponds to an equilibrium constant of 162.

$$K_{eq} = \frac{[\text{ATP}][\text{creatine}]}{[\text{ADP}][\text{creatine phosphate}]} = 10^{-\Delta G^{\circ\prime}/5.69} = 10^{12.6/5.69} = 162$$

In resting muscle, typical concentrations of these metabolites are [ATP] = 4 mM, [ADP] = 0.013 mM [creatine phosphate] = 25 mM, and [creatine] = 13 mM. Because of its abundance and high phosphoryl-transfer potential relative to that of ATP, creatine phosphate is a highly effective phosphoryl

Table 15.1 Standard free energies of hydrolysis of some phosphorylated compounds

Compound	kJ mol^{-1}	kcal mol^{-1}
Phosphoenolpyruvate	-61.9	-14.8
1,3-Bisphosphoglycerate	-49.4	-11.8
Creatine phosphate	-43.1	-10.3
ATP (to ADP)	-30.5	-7.3
Glucose 1-phosphate	-20.9	-5.0
Pyrophosphate	-19.3	-4.6
Glucose 6-phosphate	-13.8	-3.3
Glycerol 3-phosphate	-9.2	-2.2

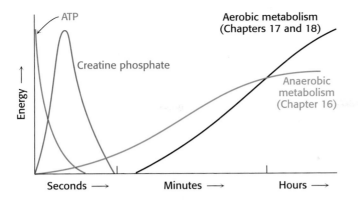

Figure 15.7 Sources of ATP during exercise. In the initial seconds, exercise is powered by existing high-phosphoryl-transfer compounds (ATP and creatine phosphate). Subsequently, the ATP must be regenerated by metabolic pathways.

buffer. Indeed, creatine phosphate is the major source of phosphoryl groups for ATP regeneration for a runner during the first 4 seconds of a 100-meter sprint. The fact that creatine phosphate can replenish ATP pools is the basis of the use of creatine as a dietary supplement by athletes in sports requiring short bursts of intense activity. After the creatine phosphate pool is depleted, ATP must be generated through metabolism (Figure 15.7).

15.3 The Oxidation of Carbon Fuels Is an Important Source of Cellular Energy

ATP serves as the principal *immediate donor of free energy* in biological systems rather than as a long-term storage form of free energy. In a typical cell, an ATP molecule is consumed within a minute of its formation. Although the total quantity of ATP in the body is limited to approximately 100 g, *the turnover of this small quantity of ATP is very high.* For example, a resting human being consumes about 40 kg of ATP in 24 hours. During strenuous exertion, the rate of utilization of ATP may be as high as 0.5 kg/minute. For a 2-hour run, 60 kg (132 pounds) of ATP is utilized. Clearly, having mechanisms for regenerating ATP is vital. Motion, active transport, signal amplification, and biosynthesis can take place only if ATP is continually regenerated from ADP (Figure 15.8). The generation of ATP is one of the primary roles of catabolism. The carbon in fuel molecules—such as glucose and fats—is oxidized to CO_2. The resulting electrons are captured and used to regenerate ATP from ADP and P_i.

In aerobic organisms, the ultimate electron acceptor in the oxidation of carbon is O_2 and the oxidation product is CO_2. Consequently, the more reduced a carbon is to begin with, the more free energy is released by its oxidation. Figure 15.9 shows the $\Delta G^{\circ\prime}$ of oxidation for one-carbon compounds.

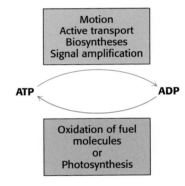

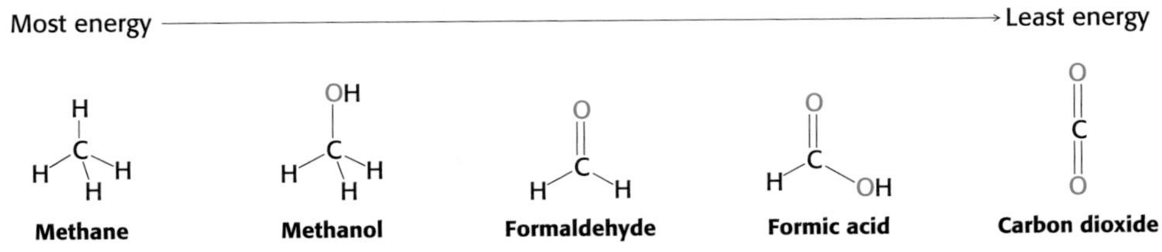

Figure 15.8 ATP–ADP cycle. This cycle is the fundamental mode of energy exchange in biological systems.

Most energy ──────────────────────────→ Least energy

	Methane	Methanol	Formaldehyde	Formic acid	Carbon dioxide
$\Delta G^{\circ\prime}$ oxidation (kJ mol^{-1})	−820	−703	−523	−285	0
$\Delta G^{\circ\prime}$ oxidation (kcal mol^{-1})	−196	−168	−125	−68	0

Figure 15.9 Free energy of oxidation of single-carbon compounds.

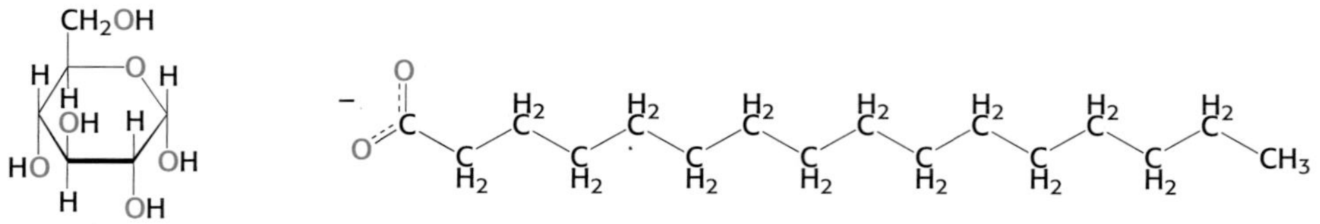

Figure 15.10 Prominent fuels. Fats are a more efficient fuel source than carbohydrates such as glucose because the carbon in fats is more reduced.

Glucose

Fatty acid

Glyceraldehyde 3-phosphate (GAP)

Although fuel molecules are more complex (Figure 15.10) than the single-carbon compounds depicted in Figure 15.9, when a fuel is oxidized the oxidation takes place one carbon at a time. The carbon-oxidation energy is used in some cases to create a compound with high phosphoryl-transfer potential and in other cases to create an ion gradient. In either case, the end point is the formation of ATP.

Compounds with high phosphoryl-transfer potential can couple carbon oxidation to ATP synthesis

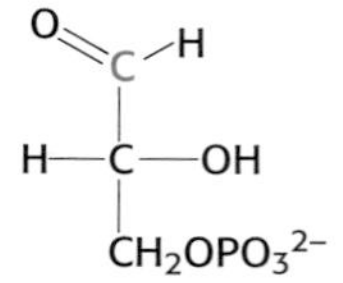

How is the energy released in the oxidation of a carbon compound converted into ATP? As an example, consider glyceraldehyde 3-phosphate (shown in the margin), which is a metabolite of glucose formed in the oxidation of that sugar. The C-1 carbon (shown in red) is at the aldehyde-oxidation level and is not in its most oxidized state. Oxidation of the aldehyde to an acid will release energy.

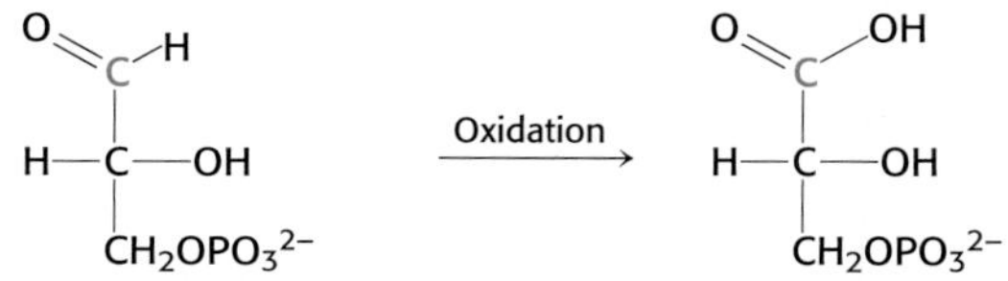

Glyceraldehyde 3-phosphate — Oxidation → 3-Phosphoglyceric acid

However, the oxidation does not take place directly. Instead, the carbon oxidation generates an acyl phosphate, 1,3-bisphosphoglycerate. The electrons released are captured by NAD^+, which we will consider shortly.

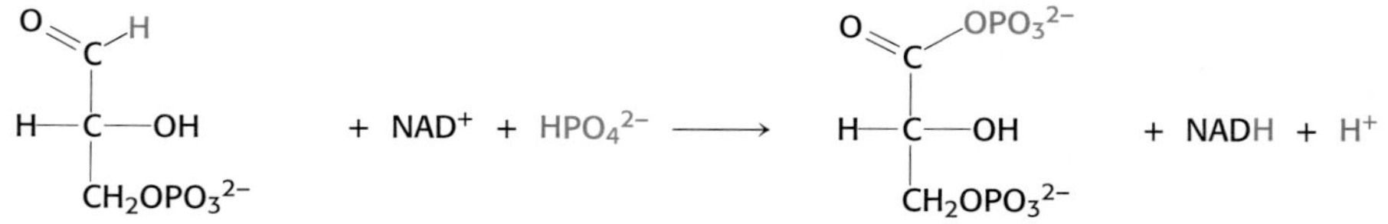

Glyceraldehyde 3-phosphate (GAP) $+ NAD^+ + HPO_4^{2-} \longrightarrow$ 1,3-Bisphosphoglycerate (1,3-BPG) $+ NADH + H^+$

For reasons similar to those discussed for ATP, 1,3-bisphosphoglycerate has a high phosphoryl-transfer potential. Thus, the cleavage of 1,3-BPG can be coupled to the synthesis of ATP.

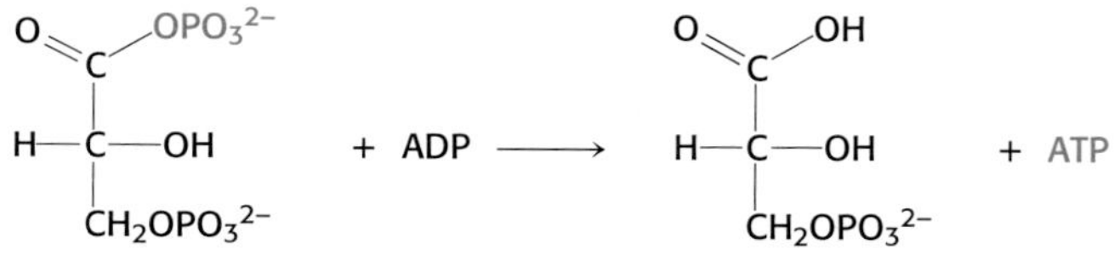

1,3-Bisphosphoglycerate $+ ADP \longrightarrow$ 3-Phosphoglyceric acid $+ ATP$

The energy of oxidation is initially trapped as a high-phosphoryl-transfer-potential compound and then used to form ATP. The oxidation energy of a carbon atom is transformed into phosphoryl-transfer potential, first as 1,3-bisphosphoglycerate and ultimately as ATP. We will consider these reactions in mechanistic detail in Chapter 16.

Ion gradients across membranes provide an important form of cellular energy that can be coupled to ATP synthesis

As described in Chapter 13, electrochemical potential is an effective means of storing free energy. Indeed, the electrochemical potential of *ion gradients across membranes*, produced by the oxidation of fuel molecules or by photosynthesis, ultimately powers the synthesis of most of the ATP in cells. In general, ion gradients are versatile means of coupling thermodynamically unfavorable reactions to favorable ones. Indeed, in animals, *proton gradients* generated by the oxidation of carbon fuels account for more than 90% of ATP generation (Figure 15.11). This process is called *oxidative phosphorylation* (Chapter 18). ATP hydrolysis can then be used to form ion gradients of different types and functions. The electrochemical potential of a Na^+ gradient, for example, can be tapped to pump Ca^{2+} out of cells or to transport nutrients such as sugars and amino acids into cells.

Energy from foodstuffs is extracted in three stages

Let us take an overall view of the processes of energy conversion in higher organisms before considering them in detail in subsequent chapters. Hans Krebs described three stages in the generation of energy from the oxidation of foodstuffs (Figure 15.12).

In the first stage, large molecules in food are broken down into smaller units. This process is *digestion*. Proteins are hydrolyzed to their 20 different amino acids, polysaccharides are hydrolyzed to simple sugars such as glucose, and fats are hydrolyzed to glycerol and fatty acids. The degradation products are then absorbed by the cells of the intestine and distributed throughout the body. This stage is strictly a preparation stage; no useful energy is captured in this phase.

In the second stage, these numerous small molecules are degraded to a few simple units that play a central role in metabolism. In fact, most of them—sugars, fatty acids, glycerol, and several amino acids—are converted into the acetyl unit of acetyl CoA. Some ATP is generated in this stage, but the amount is small compared with that obtained in the third stage.

In the third stage, ATP is produced from the complete oxidation of the acetyl unit of acetyl CoA. The third stage consists of the citric acid cycle and oxidative phosphorylation, which are *the final common pathways in the oxidation of fuel molecules.* Acetyl CoA brings acetyl units into the citric acid cycle [also called the tricarboxylic acid (TCA) cycle or Krebs cycle], where they are completely oxidized to CO_2. Four pairs of electrons are transferred (three to NAD^+ and one to FAD) for each acetyl group that is oxidized. Then, a

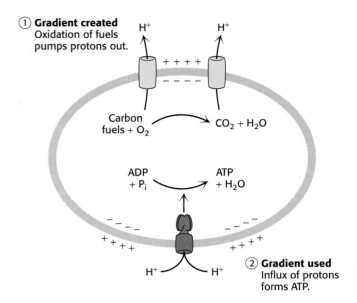

Figure 15.11 Proton gradients. The oxidation of fuels can power the formation of proton gradients by the action of specific proton pumps. These proton gradients can in turn drive the synthesis of ATP when the protons flow through an ATP-synthesizing enzyme.

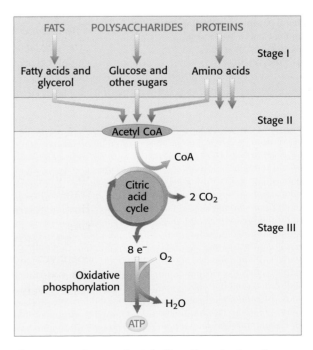

Figure 15.12 Stages of catabolism. The extraction of energy from fuels can be divided into three stages.

proton gradient is generated as electrons flow from the reduced forms of these carriers to O_2, and this gradient is used to synthesize ATP.

15.4 Metabolic Pathways Contain Many Recurring Motifs

At first glance, metabolism appears intimidating because of the sheer number of reactants and reactions. Nevertheless, there are unifying themes that make the comprehension of this complexity more manageable. These unifying themes include common metabolites, reactions, and regulatory schemes that stem from a common evolutionary heritage.

Activated carriers exemplify the modular design and economy of metabolism

We have seen that phosphoryl transfer can be used to drive otherwise endergonic reactions, alter the energy of conformation of a protein, or serve as a signal to alter the activity of a protein. The phosphoryl-group donor in all of these reactions is ATP. In other words, *ATP is an activated carrier of phosphoryl groups because phosphoryl transfer from ATP is an exergonic process.* The use of activated carriers is a recurring motif in biochemistry, and we will consider several such carriers here. Many such activated carriers function as coenzymes:

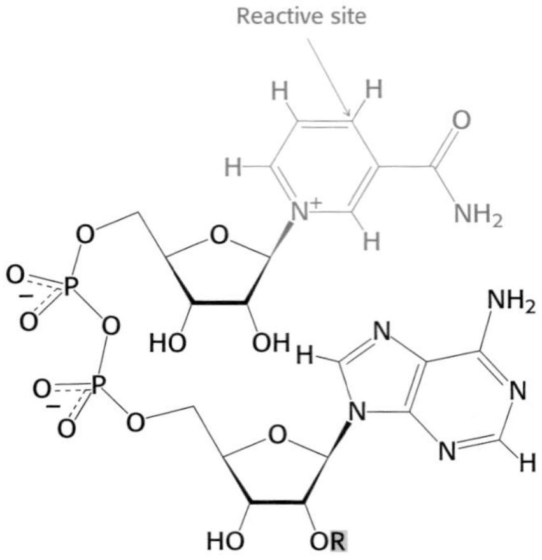

Reactive site

Figure 15.13 Structures of the oxidized forms of nicotinamide-derived electron carriers. Nicotinamide adenine dinucleotide (NAD$^+$) and nicotinamide adenine dinucleotide phosphate (NADP$^+$) are prominent carriers of high-energy electrons. In NAD$^+$, R = H; in NADP$^+$, R = PO$_3^{2-}$.

1. *Activated Carriers of Electrons for Fuel Oxidation.* In aerobic organisms, the ultimate electron acceptor in the oxidation of fuel molecules is O_2. However, electrons are not transferred directly to O_2. Instead, fuel molecules transfer electrons to special carriers, which are either *pyridine nucleotides* or *flavins*. The reduced forms of these carriers then transfer their high-potential electrons to O_2.

Nicotinamide adenine dinucleotide is a major electron carrier in the oxidation of fuel molecules (Figure 15.13). The reactive part of NAD$^+$ is its nicotinamide ring, a pyridine derivative synthesized from the vitamin niacin. *In the oxidation of a substrate, the nicotinamide ring of NAD$^+$ accepts a hydrogen ion and two electrons, which are equivalent to a hydride ion* (H:$^-$). The reduced form of this carrier is called *NADH*. In the oxidized form, the nitrogen atom carries a positive charge, as indicated by NAD$^+$. NAD$^+$ is the electron acceptor in many reactions of the type

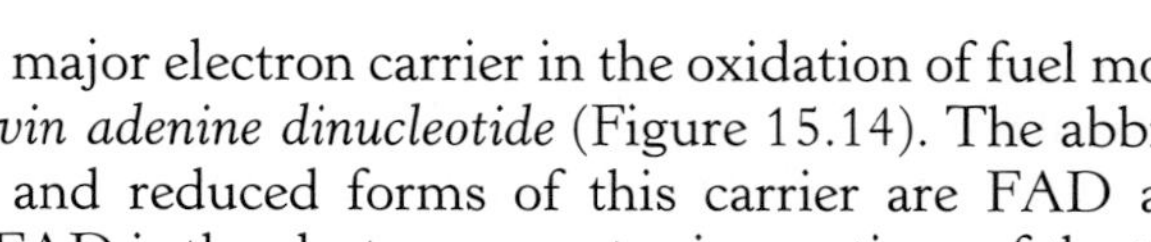

In this dehydrogenation, one hydrogen atom of the substrate is directly transferred to NAD$^+$, whereas the other appears in the solvent as a proton. Both electrons lost by the substrate are transferred to the nicotinamide ring.

The other major electron carrier in the oxidation of fuel molecules is the coenzyme *flavin adenine dinucleotide* (Figure 15.14). The abbreviations for the oxidized and reduced forms of this carrier are FAD and FADH$_2$, respectively. FAD is the electron acceptor in reactions of the type

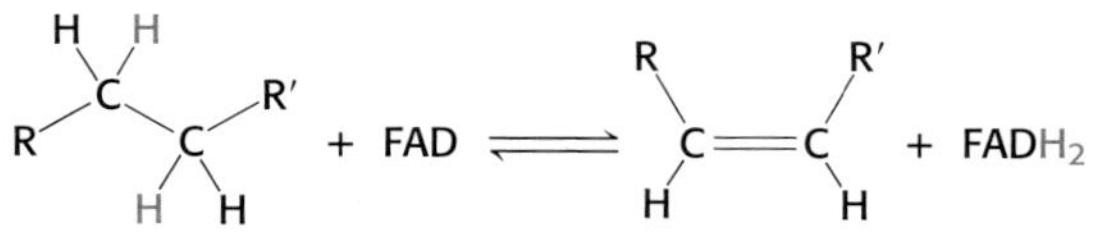

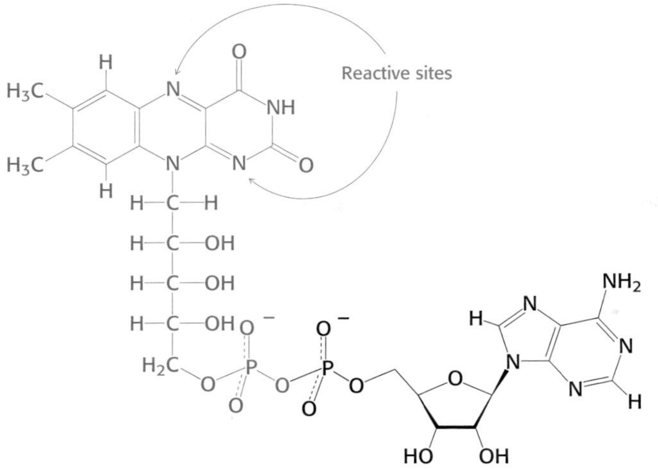

Figure 15.14 Structure of the oxidized form of flavin adenine dinucleotide (FAD). This electron carrier consists of a flavin mononucleotide (FMN) unit (shown in blue) and an AMP unit (shown in black).

The reactive part of FAD is its isoalloxazine ring, a derivative of the vitamin riboflavin (Figure 15.15). FAD, like NAD^+, can accept two electrons. In doing so, FAD, unlike NAD^+, takes up two protons. These carriers of high-potential electrons as well as flavin mononucleotide (FMN), an electron similar to FAD but lacking the adenine nucleotide, will be considered further in Chapter 18.

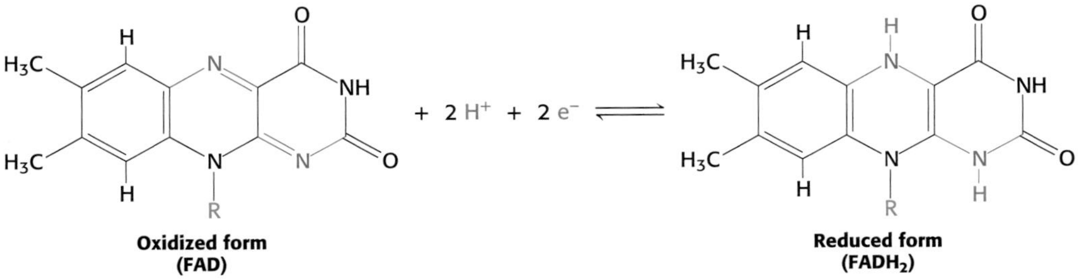

Figure 15.15 Structures of the reactive parts of FAD and FADH₂. The electrons and protons are carried by the isoalloxazine ring component of FAD and FADH₂.

2. An Activated Carrier of Electrons for Reductive Biosynthesis. High-potential electrons are required in most biosyntheses because the precursors are more oxidized than the products. Hence, reducing power is needed in addition to ATP. For example, in the biosynthesis of fatty acids, the keto group of an added two-carbon unit is reduced to a methylene group in several steps. This sequence of reactions requires an input of four electrons.

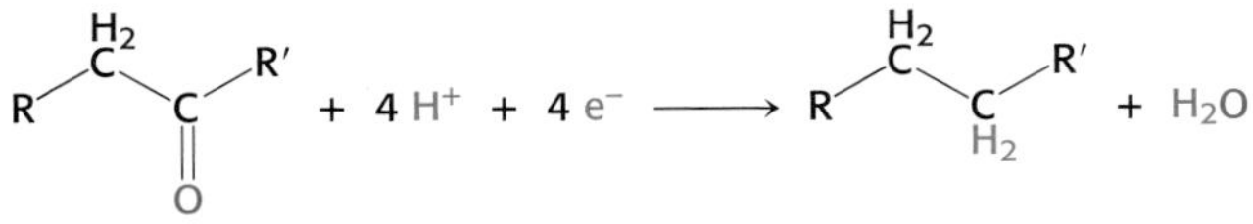

The electron donor in most reductive biosyntheses is NADPH, the reduced form of nicotinamide adenine dinucleotide phosphate ($NADP^+$; see Figure 15.13). NADPH differs from NADH in that the $2'$-hydroxyl group of its adenosine moiety is esterified with phosphate. NADPH carries electrons in the same way as NADH. However, *NADPH is used almost exclusively for reductive biosyntheses, whereas NADH is used primarily for the generation of ATP.* The extra phosphoryl group on NADPH is a tag that enables enzymes to distinguish between high-potential electrons to be used in anabolism and those to be used in catabolism.

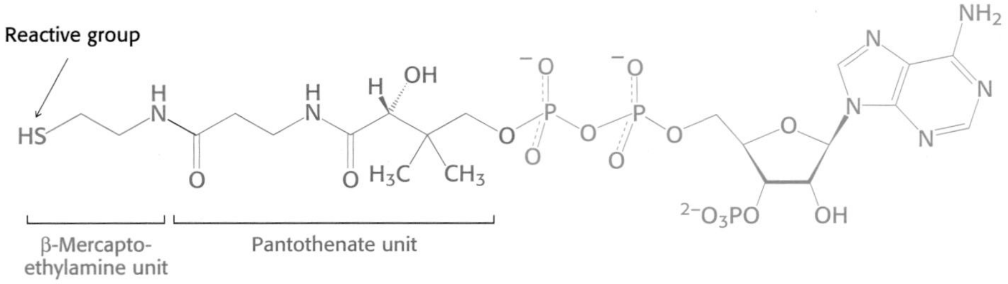

Reactive group

Figure 15.16 Structure of coenzyme A (CoA-SH).

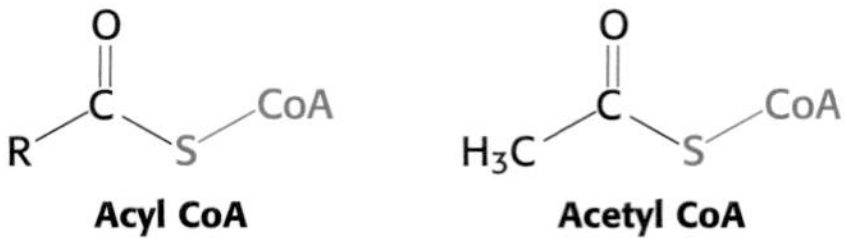

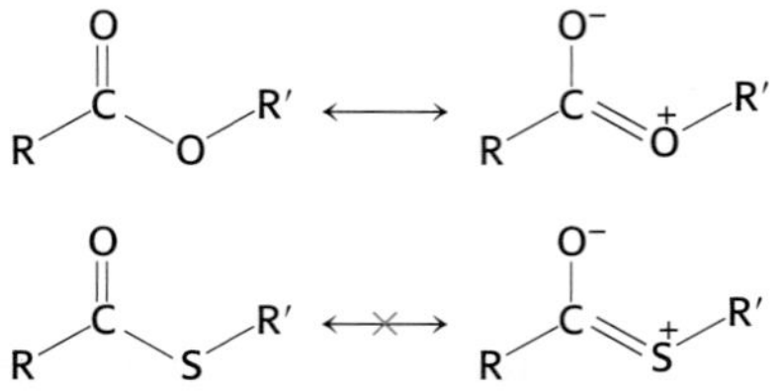

β-Mercapto-ethylamine unit   Pantothenate unit

Acyl CoA   **Acetyl CoA**

Oxygen esters are stabilized by resonance structures not available to thioesters.

3. *An Activated Carrier of Two-Carbon Fragments.* Coenzyme A, another central molecule in metabolism, is a carrier of acyl groups derived from the vitamin pantothenate (Figure 15.16). Acyl groups are important constituents both in catabolism, as in the oxidation of fatty acids, and in anabolism, as in the synthesis of membrane lipids. The terminal sulfhydryl group in CoA is the reactive site. Acyl groups are linked to CoA by thioester bonds. The resulting derivative is called an *acyl CoA*. An acyl group often linked to CoA is the acetyl unit; this derivative is called *acetyl CoA*. The $\Delta G^{\circ\prime}$ for the hydrolysis of acetyl CoA has a large negative value:

$$\text{Acetyl CoA} + H_2O \rightleftharpoons \text{acetate} + \text{CoA} + H^+$$
$$\Delta G^{\circ\prime} = -31.4 \text{ kJ mol}^{-1} (-7.5 \text{ kcal mol}^{-1})$$

The hydrolysis of a thioester is thermodynamically more favorable than that of an oxygen ester because the electrons of the C=O bond cannot form resonance structures with the C—S bond that are as stable as those that they can form with the C—O bond. Consequently, *acetyl CoA has a high acetyl-group-transfer potential because transfer of the acetyl group is exergonic.* Acetyl CoA carries an activated acetyl group, just as ATP carries an activated phosphoryl group.

The use of activated carriers illustrates two key aspects of metabolism. First, NADH, NADPH, and $FADH_2$ react slowly with O_2 in the absence of a catalyst. Likewise, ATP and acetyl CoA are hydrolyzed slowly (in times of many hours or even days) in the absence of a catalyst. These molecules are kinetically quite stable in the face of a large thermodynamic driving force for reaction with O_2 (in regard to the electron carriers) and H_2O (for ATP and acetyl CoA). *The kinetic stability of these molecules in the absence of specific catalysts is essential for their biological function because it enables enzymes to control the flow of free energy and reducing power.*

Second, *most interchanges of activated groups in metabolism are accomplished by a rather small set of carriers* (Table 15.2). The existence of a recurring set

Table 15.2 Some activated carriers in metabolism

Carrier molecule in activated form	Group carried	Vitamin precursor
ATP	Phosphoryl	
NADH and NADPH	Electrons	Nicotinate (niacin)
$FADH_2$	Electrons	Riboflavin (vitamin B_2)
$FMNH_2$	Electrons	Riboflavin (vitamin B_2)
Coenzyme A	Acyl	Pantothenate
Lipoamide	Acyl	
Thiamine pyrophosphate	Aldehyde	Thiamine (vitamin B_1)
Biotin	CO_2	Biotin
Tetrahydrofolate	One-carbon units	Folate
S-Adenosylmethionine	Methyl	
Uridine diphosphate glucose	Glucose	
Cytidine diphosphate diacylglycerol	Phosphatidate	
Nucleoside triphosphates	Nucleotides	

Note: Many of the activated carriers are coenzymes that are derived from water-soluble vitamins.

Table 15.3 The B vitamins

441

15.4 Recurring Motifs

Vitamin	Coenzyme	Typical reaction type	Consequences of deficiency
Thiamine (B$_1$)	Thiamine pyrophosphate	Aldehyde transfer	Beriberi (weight loss, heart problems, neurological dysfunction)
Riboflavin (B$_2$)	Flavin adenine dinucleotide (FAD)	Oxidation–reduction	Cheliosis and angular stomatitis (lesions of the mouth), dermatitis
Pyridoxine (B$_6$)	Pyridoxal phosphate	Group transfer to or from amino acids	Depression, confusion, convulsions
Nicotinic acid (niacin)	Nicotinamide adenine dinucleotide (NAD$^+$)	Oxidation–reduction	Pellagra (dermatitis, depression, diarrhea)
Pantothenic acid	Coenzyme A	Acyl-group transfer	Hypertension
Biotin	Biotin–lysine adducts (biocytin)	ATP-dependent carboxylation and carboxyl-group transfer	Rash about the eyebrows, muscle pain, fatigue (rare)
Folic acid	Tetrahydrofolate	Transfer of one-carbon components; thymine synthesis	Anemia, neural-tube defects in development
B$_{12}$	5′-Deoxyadenosyl cobalamin	Transfer of methyl groups; intramolecular rearrangements	Anemia, pernicious anemia, methylmalonic acidosis

of activated carriers in all organisms is one of the unifying motifs of biochemistry. Furthermore, it illustrates the modular design of metabolism. A small set of molecules carries out a very wide range of tasks. Metabolism is readily comprehended because of the economy and elegance of its underlying design.

Many activated carriers are derived from vitamins

Almost all the activated carriers that act as coenzymes are derived from *vitamins*. Vitamins are organic molecules that are needed in small amounts in the diets of some higher animals. Table 15.3 lists the vitamins that act as coenzymes and Figure 15.17 shows the structures of some. This series of vitamins is known as the vitamin B group. Note that, in all cases, the vitamin must be modified before it can serve its function. We have already touched on the roles of niacin, riboflavin, and pantothenate. We will see these three and the other B vitamins many times in our study of biochemistry.

Vitamins serve the same roles in nearly all forms of life, but higher animals lost the capacity to synthesize them in the course of evolution. For instance, whereas *E. coli* can thrive on glucose and organic salts,

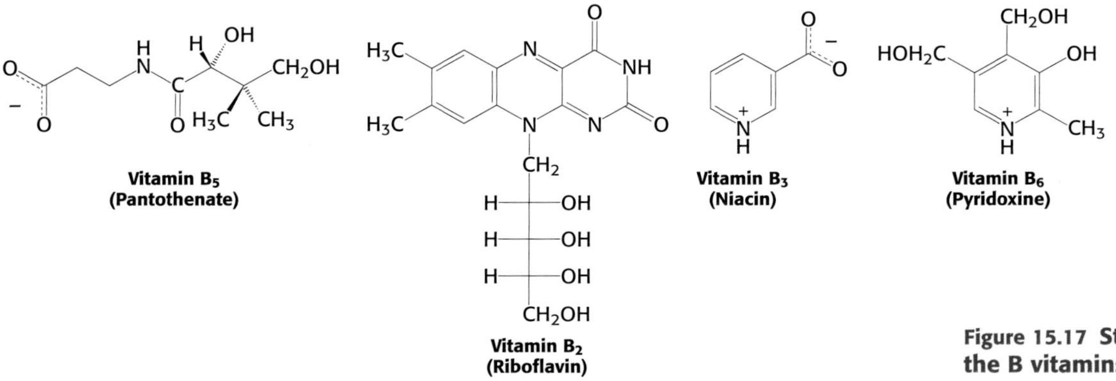

Figure 15.17 Structures of some of the B vitamins.

Table 15.4 Noncoenzyme vitamins

Vitamin	Function	Deficiency
A	Roles in vision, growth, reproduction	Night blindness, cornea damage, damage to respiratory and gastrointestinal tract
C (ascorbic acid)	Antioxidant	Scurvy (swollen and bleeding gums, subdermal hemorrhaging)
D	Regulation of calcium and phosphate metabolism	Rickets (children): skeletal deformities, impaired growth Osteomalacia (adults): soft, bending bones
E	Antioxidant	Inhibition of sperm production; lesions in muscles and nerves (rare)
K	Blood coagulation	Subdermal hemorrhaging

human beings require at least 12 vitamins in their diet. The biosynthetic pathways for vitamins can be complex; thus, it is biologically more efficient to ingest vitamins than to synthesize the enzymes required to construct them from simple molecules. This efficiency comes at the cost of dependence on other organisms for chemicals essential for life. Indeed, vitamin deficiency can generate diseases in all organisms requiring these molecules (see Tables 15.3 and 15.4).

Not all vitamins function as coenzymes. Vitamins designated by the letters A, C, D, E, and K (Figure 15.18 and Table 15.4) have a diverse array of functions. Vitamin A (retinol) is the precursor of retinal, the light-sensitive group in rhodopsin and other visual pigments (Section 32.3), and retinoic acid, an important signaling molecule. A deficiency of this vitamin leads to night blindness. In addition, young animals require vitamin A for growth. Vitamin C, or ascorbate, acts as an antioxidant. A deficiency in vitamin C can lead to scurvy, a disease due to malformed collagen and characterized by skin lesions and blood-vessel fragility (Section 27.6). A metabolite of vitamin D is a hormone that regulates the metabolism of calcium and phosphorus. A deficiency in vitamin D impairs bone formation in growing animals. Infertility in rats is a consequence of vitamin E (α-tocopherol) deficiency. This vitamin reacts with reactive oxygen species such as hydroxyl radicals and inactivates them before they can oxidize unsaturated membrane lipids, damaging cell structures. Vitamin K is required for normal blood clotting (Section 10.4).

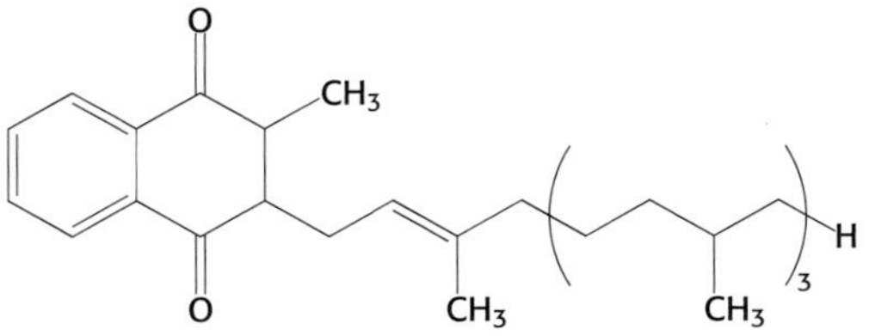

Vitamin K₁

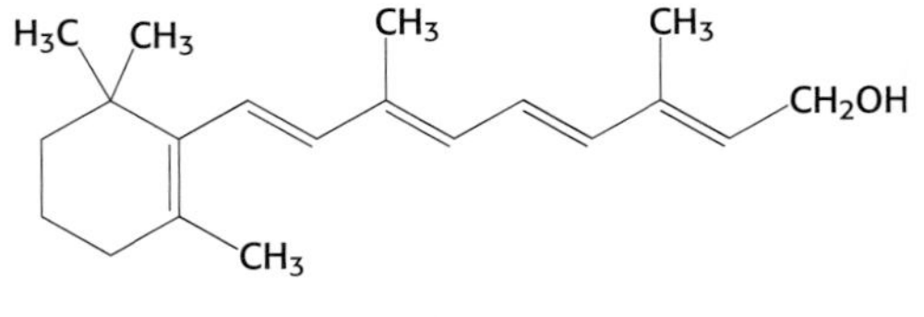

Vitamin A (Retinol)

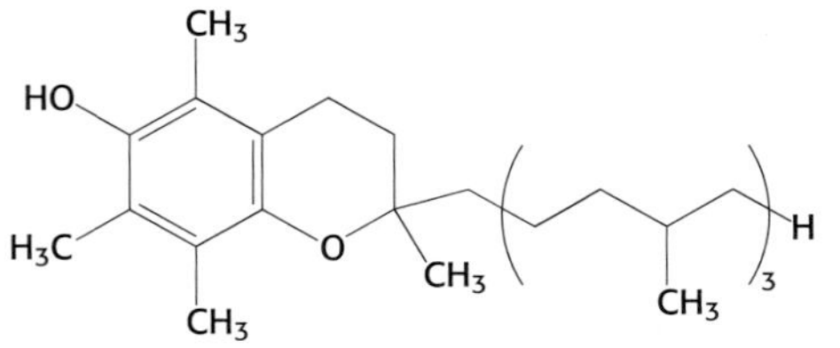

Vitamin E (α-Tocopherol)

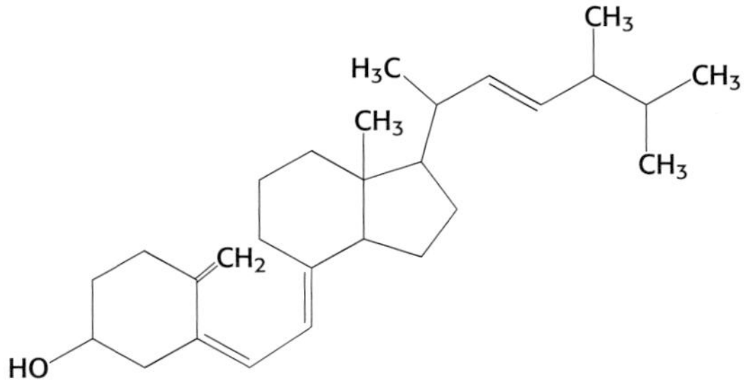

Vitamin D₂ (Ergocalciferol)

Figure 15.18 Structures of some vitamins that do not function as coenzymes.

Table 15.5 Types of chemical reactions in metabolism

Type of reaction	Description
Oxidation–reduction	Electron transfer
Ligation requiring ATP cleavage	Formation of covalent bonds (i.e., carbon–carbon bonds)
Isomerization	Rearrangement of atoms to form isomers
Group transfer	Transfer of a functional group from one molecule to another
Hydrolytic	Cleavage of bonds by the addition of water
Addition or removal of functional groups	Addition of functional groups to double bonds or their removal to form double bonds

Key reactions are reiterated throughout metabolism

Just as there is an economy of design in the use of activated carriers, so is there an economy of design in biochemical reactions. The thousands of metabolic reactions, bewildering at first in their variety, can be subdivided into just six types (Table 15.5). Specific reactions of each type appear repeatedly, reducing the number of reactions that a student needs to learn.

1. *Oxidation–reduction reactions* are essential components of many pathways. Useful energy is often derived from the oxidation of carbon compounds. Consider the following two reactions:

Succinate + FAD ⇌ **Fumarate** + FADH$_2$ (1)

Malate + NAD$^+$ ⇌ **Oxaloacetate** + NADH + H$^+$ (2)

These two oxidation–reduction reactions are components of the citric acid cycle (Chapter 17), which completely oxidizes the activated two-carbon fragment of acetyl CoA to two molecules of CO_2. In reaction 1, FADH$_2$ carries the electrons, whereas, in reaction 2, electrons are carried by NADH.

2. *Ligation reactions* form bonds by using free energy from ATP cleavage. Reaction 3 illustrates the ATP-dependent formation of a carbon–carbon bond, necessary to combine smaller molecules to form larger ones. Oxaloacetate is formed from pyruvate and CO_2.

Pyruvate + CO_2 + ATP + H_2O ⇌ **Oxaloacetate** + ADP + P$_i$ + H$^+$ (3)

The oxaloacetate can be used in the citric acid cycle, or converted into
glucose or amino acids such as aspartic acid.

3. *Isomerization reactions* rearrange particular atoms within a molecule.
Their role is often to prepare the molecule for subsequent reactions such as
the oxidation–reduction reactions described in point 1.

Citrate   Isocitrate   (4)

Reaction 4 is, again, a component of the citric acid cycle. This isomerization
prepares the molecule for subsequent oxidation and decarboxylation by
moving the hydroxyl group of citrate from a tertiary to a secondary
position.

4. *Group-transfer reactions* play a variety of roles. Reaction 5 is representa-
tive of such a reaction. A phosphoryl group is transferred from the activated
phosphoryl-group carrier, ATP, to glucose, the initial step in glycolysis, a
key pathway for extracting energy from glucose (Chapter 16). This reaction
traps glucose in the cell so that further catabolism can take place.

Glucose   ATP

Glucose 6-phosphate   ADP   (5)
(G-6P)

As stated earlier, group-transfer reactions are used to synthesize ATP. We
also saw examples of their use in signaling pathways (Chapter 14).

5. *Hydrolytic reactions* cleave bonds by the addition of water. Hydrolysis is
a common means employed to break down large molecules, either to facilitate further metabolism or to reuse some of the components for biosynthetic purposes. Proteins are digested by hydrolytic cleavage (Chapters 9
and 10). Reaction 6 illustrates the hydrolysis of a peptide to yield two
smaller peptides.

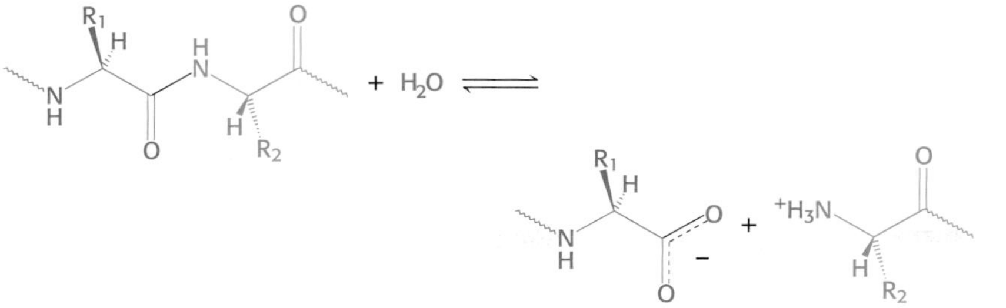

$$\text{(peptide + H}_2\text{O)} \rightleftharpoons \tag{6}$$

6. *Functional groups may be added to double bonds to form single bonds or removed from single bonds to form double bonds.* The enzymes that catalyze these types of reaction are classified as *lyases*. An important example, illustrated in reaction 7, is the conversion of the six-carbon molecule fructose 1,6-bisphosphate into two three-carbon fragments: dihydroxyacetone phosphate and glyceraldehyde 3-phosphate.

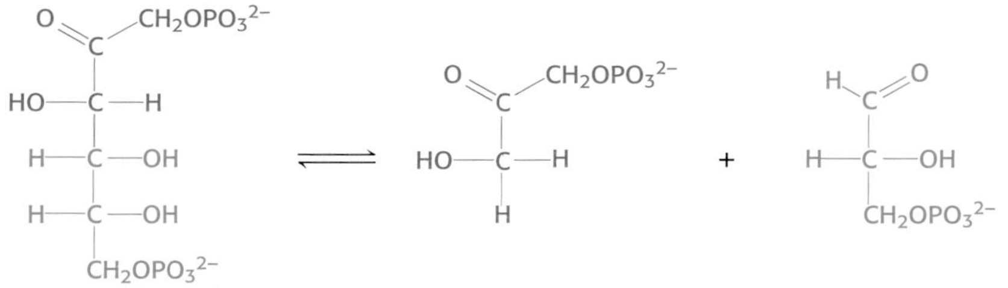

$$\text{(reaction 7)} \tag{7}$$

Fructose 1,6-bisphosphate   **Dihydroxyacetone phosphate**   **Glyceraldehyde 3-phosphate**
(F-1,6-BP)   **(DHAP)**   **(GAP)**

This reaction is a critical step in glycolysis (Chapter 16). Dehydrations to form double bonds, such as the formation of phosphoenolpyruvate (see Table 15.1) from 2-phosphoglycerate (reaction 8), are important reactions of this type.

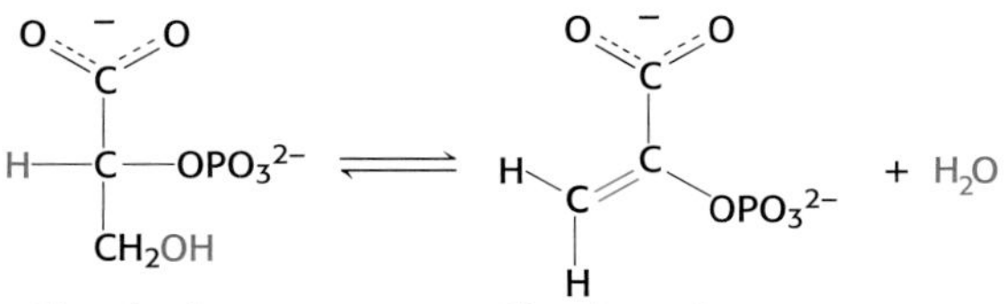

$$\text{(reaction 8)} \qquad + \text{ H}_2\text{O} \tag{8}$$

2-Phosphoglycerate   **Phosphoenolpyruvate**
(PEP)

The dehydration sets up the next step in the pathway, a group-transfer reaction that uses the high phosphoryl-transfer potential of the product PEP to form ATP from ADP.

These six fundamental reaction types are the basis of metabolism. Remember that all six types can proceed in either direction, depending on the standard free energy for the specific reaction and the concentrations of the reactants and products inside the cell. An effective way to learn is to look for commonalities in the diverse metabolic pathways that we will be examining. There is a chemical logic that, when exposed, renders the complexity of the chemistry of living systems more manageable and reveals its elegance.

Metabolic processes are regulated in three principal ways

It is evident that the complex network of metabolic reactions must be rigorously regulated. At the same time, metabolic control must be flexible, to adjust metabolic activity to the constantly changing external environments of cells. Metabolism is regulated through control of (1) *the amounts of enzymes,* (2) *their catalytic activities,* and (3) *the accessibility of substrates.*

Controlling the amounts of enzymes.   The amount of a particular enzyme depends on both its rate of synthesis and its rate of degradation. The level of many enzymes is adjusted primarily by a change in the *rate of transcription* of the genes encoding them (Chapters 29 and 31). In *E. coli,* for example, the presence of lactose induces within minutes a more than 50-fold increase in the rate of synthesis of β-galactosidase, an enzyme required for the breakdown of this disaccharide.

Controlling catalytic activity.   The catalytic activity of enzymes is controlled in several ways. *Reversible allosteric control* is especially important. For example, the first reaction in many biosynthetic pathways is allosterically inhibited by the ultimate product of the pathway. The inhibition of aspartate transcarbamoylase by cytidine triphosphate (Section 10.1) is a well-understood example of *feedback inhibition.* This type of control can be almost instantaneous. Another recurring mechanism is *reversible covalent modification.* For example, glycogen phosphorylase, the enzyme catalyzing the breakdown of glycogen, a storage form of sugar, is activated by the phosphorylation of a particular serine residue when glucose is scarce (Section 21.1).

Hormones coordinate metabolic relations between different tissues, often by regulating the reversible modification of key enzymes. For instance, the hormone epinephrine triggers a signal-transduction cascade in muscle, resulting in the phosphorylation and activation of key enzymes and leading to the rapid degradation of glycogen to glucose, which is then used to supply ATP for muscle contraction. As described in Chapter 14, many hormones act through intracellular messengers, such as cyclic AMP and calcium ion, that coordinate the activities of many target proteins.

Many reactions in metabolism are controlled by the *energy status* of the cell. One index of the energy status is the *energy charge,* which is proportional to the mole fraction of ATP plus half the mole fraction of ADP, given that ATP contains two anhydride bonds, whereas ADP contains one. Hence, the energy charge is defined as

$$\text{Energy charge} = \frac{[\text{ATP}] + \frac{1}{2}[\text{ADP}]}{[\text{ATP}] + [\text{ADP}] + [\text{AMP}]}$$

The energy charge can have a value ranging from 0 (all AMP) to 1 (all ATP). Daniel Atkinson showed that *ATP-generating (catabolic) pathways are inhibited by a high energy charge, whereas ATP-utilizing (anabolic) pathways are stimulated by a high energy charge.* In plots of the reaction rates of such pathways versus the energy charge, the curves are steep near an energy charge of 0.9, where they usually intersect (Figure 15.19). It is evident that

Figure 15.19 Energy charge regulates metabolism. High concentrations of ATP inhibit the relative rates of a typical ATP-generating (catabolic) pathway and stimulate the typical ATP-utilizing (anabolic) pathway.

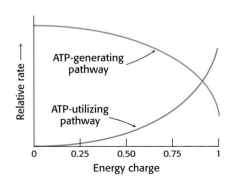

the control of these pathways has evolved to maintain the energy charge within rather narrow limits. In other words, *the energy charge, like the pH of a cell, is buffered.* The energy charge of most cells ranges from 0.80 to 0.95. An alternative index of the energy status is the *phosphorylation potential,* which is defined as

$$\text{Phosphorylation potential} = \frac{[\text{ATP}]}{[\text{ADP}] + [\text{P}_i]}$$

The phosphorylation potential, in contrast with the energy charge, depends on the concentration of P_i and is directly related to the free-energy storage available from ATP.

Controlling the accessibility of substrates. In eukaryotes, metabolic regulation and flexibility are enhanced by compartmentalization. For example, fatty acid oxidation takes place in mitochondria, whereas fatty acid synthesis takes place in the cytoplasm. *Compartmentalization segregates opposed reactions.*

Controlling the *flux of substrates* is another means of regulating metabolism. Glucose breakdown can take place in many cells only if insulin is present to promote the entry of glucose into the cell. The transfer of substrates from one compartment of a cell to another (e.g., from the cytoplasm to mitochondria) can serve as a control point.

Aspects of metabolism may have evolved from an RNA world

How did the complex pathways that constitute metabolism evolve? The current thinking is that RNA was an early biomolecule and that, in an early RNA world, RNA served as catalysts and information-storage molecules.

Why do activated carriers such as ATP, NADH, $FADH_2$, and coenzyme A contain adenosine diphosphate units (Figure 15.20)? A possible explanation is that these molecules evolved from the early RNA catalysts. Non-RNA units such as the isoalloxazine ring may have been recruited to serve as efficient carriers of activated electrons and chemical units, a function not readily performed by RNA itself. We can picture the adenine ring of $FADH_2$ binding to a uracil unit in a niche of an RNA enzyme (ribozyme) by base-pairing, whereas the isoalloxazine ring protrudes and functions as an electron carrier. When the more versatile proteins replaced RNA as the major catalysts, the ribonucleotide coenzymes stayed essentially unchanged because they were already well suited to their metabolic roles. The nicotinamide unit of NADH, for example, can readily transfer electrons irrespective of whether the adenine unit interacts with a base in an RNA enzyme or with amino acid residues in a protein enzyme. With the advent of protein enzymes, these important cofactors evolved as free molecules without losing the adenosine diphosphate vestige of their RNA-world ancestry. That molecules and motifs of metabolism are common to all forms of life testifies to their common origin and to the retention of functioning modules through billions of years of evolution. Our understanding of metabolism, like that of other biological processes, is enriched by inquiry into how these beautifully integrated patterns of reactions came into being.

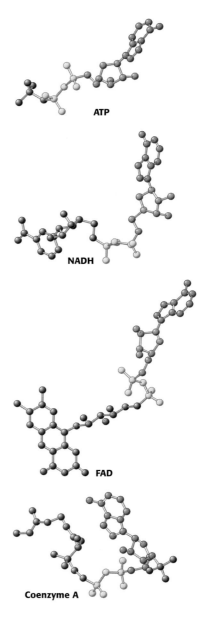

ATP

NADH

FAD

Coenzyme A

Figure 15.20 Adenosine diphosphate (ADP) is an ancient module in metabolism. This fundamental building block is present in key molecules such as ATP, NADH, FAD, and coenzyme A. The adenine unit is shown in blue, the ribose unit in red, and the diphosphate unit in yellow.

Summary

All cells transform energy. They extract energy from their environment and use this energy to convert simple molecules into cellular components.

15.1 Metabolism Is Composed of Many Coupled, Interconnecting Reactions

The process of energy transduction takes place through metabolism, a highly integrated network of chemical reactions. Metabolism can be subdivided into catabolism (reactions employed to extract energy from fuels) and anabolism (reactions that use this energy for biosynthesis). The most valuable thermodynamic concept for understanding bioenergetics is free energy. A reaction can occur spontaneously only if the change in free energy (ΔG) is negative. A thermodynamically unfavorable reaction can be driven by a thermodynamically favorable one, which is the hydrolysis of ATP in many cases.

15.2 ATP Is the Universal Currency of Free Energy in Biological Systems

The energy derived from catabolism is transformed into adenosine triphosphate. ATP hydrolysis is exergonic and the energy released can be used to power cellular processes, including motion, active transport, and biosynthesis. Under cellular conditions, the hydrolysis of ATP shifts the equilibrium of a coupled reaction by a factor of 10^8. ATP, the universal currency of energy in biological systems, is an energy-rich molecule because it contains two phosphoanhydride bonds.

15.3 The Oxidation of Carbon Fuels Is an Important Source of Cellular Energy

ATP formation is coupled to the oxidation of carbon fuels, either directly or through the formation of ion gradients. Photosynthetic organisms can use light to generate such gradients. ATP is consumed in muscle contraction and other motions of cells, in active transport, in signal-transduction processes, and in biosyntheses. The extraction of energy from foodstuffs by aerobic organisms comprises three stages. In the first stage, large molecules are broken down into smaller ones, such as amino acids, sugars, and fatty acids. In the second stage, these small molecules are degraded to a few simple units that have pervasive roles in metabolism. One of them is the acetyl unit of acetyl CoA, a carrier of activated acyl groups. The third stage of metabolism is the citric acid cycle and oxidative phosphorylation, in which ATP is generated as electrons flow to O_2, the ultimate electron acceptor, and fuels are completely oxidized to CO_2.

15.4 Metabolic Pathways Contain Many Recurring Motifs

Metabolism is characterized by common motifs. A small number of recurring activated carriers, such as ATP, NADH, and acetyl CoA, transfer activated groups in many metabolic pathways. NADPH, which carries two electrons at a high potential, provides reducing power in the biosynthesis of cell components from more-oxidized precursors. Many activated carriers are derived from vitamins, small organic molecules required in the diets of many higher organisms. Moreover, key reaction types are used repeatedly in metabolic pathways.

Metabolism is regulated in a variety of ways. The amounts of some critical enzymes are controlled by regulation of the rate of synthesis and degradation. In addition, the catalytic activities of many enzymes are regulated by allosteric interactions (as in feedback inhibition) and by covalent modification. The movement of many substrates into cells and subcellular compartments also is controlled. The energy charge, which depends on the relative amounts of ATP, ADP, and AMP, plays a role in metabolic regulation. A high energy charge inhibits ATP-generating (catabolic) pathways, whereas it stimulates ATP-utilizing (anabolic) pathways.

Key Terms

metabolism or intermediary metabolism (p. 427)

phototroph (p. 428)

chemotroph (p. 428)

catabolism (p. 428)

anabolism (p. 428)

amphibolic pathway (p. 429)

adenosine triphosphate (ATP) (p. 430)

phosphoryl-transfer potential (p. 433)

oxidative phosphorylation (p. 437)

activated carrier (p. 438)

vitamin (p. 441)

oxidation–reduction reaction (p. 443)

ligation reaction (p. 443)

isomerization reaction (p. 444)

group-transfer reaction (p. 444)

hydrolytic reaction (p. 444)

addition to or formation of double-bond reaction (p. 445)

lyase (p. 445)

energy charge (p. 446)

phosphorylation potential (p. 447)

Problems

1. *Complex patterns.* What is meant by *intermediary metabolism?*

2. *Opposites.* Differentiate between anabolism and catabolism.

3. *Why bother to eat?* What are the three primary uses for cellular energy?

4. *Match 'em.*

1. Cellular energy currency	a. NAD$^+$
2. Anabolic electron carrier	b. Coenzyme A
3. Phototroph	c. Precursor to coenzymes
4. Catabolic electron carrier reaction	d. Yields energy
5. Oxidation-reduction reaction	e. Requires energy
6. Activated carrier of two carbon fragments	f. ATP
7. Vitamin	g. Transfers electrons
8. Anabolism	h. NADP$^+$
9. Amphibolic reaction	i. Converts light energy to chemical energy
10. Catabolism	j. Used in anabolism and catabolism

5. *Energy to burn.* What factors account for the high-phosphoryl transfer potential of nucleoside triphosphates?

6. *Back in time.* Account for the fact that ATP, and not another nucleoside triphosphate, is the cellular energy currency.

7. *Currency Issues.* Why does it make good sense to have a single nucleotide, ATP, function as the cellular energy currency?

8. *Environmental conditions.* The standard free energy of hydrolysis for ATP is -30.5 kJ mol^{-1} (-7.3 kcal mol^{-1}).

$$\text{ATP} + \text{H}_2\text{O} \rightleftharpoons \text{ADP} + \text{P}_i$$

What conditions might be changed to alter the free energy of hydrolysis?

9. *Brute force?* Metabolic pathways frequently contain reactions with positive standard free energy values, yet the reactions still take place. How is this possible?

10. *Energy flow.* What is the direction of each of the following reactions when the reactants are initially present in equimolar amounts? Use the data given in Table 15.1.

(a) ATP + creatine $\rightleftharpoons$ creatine phosphate + ADP

(b) ATP + glycerol $\rightleftharpoons$ glycerol 3-phosphate + ADP

(c) ATP + pyruvate $\rightleftharpoons$ phosphoenolpyruvate + ADP

(d) ATP + glucose $\rightleftharpoons$ glucose 6-phosphate + ADP

11. *A proper inference.* What information do the $\Delta G^{\circ\prime}$ data given in Table 15.1 provide about the relative rates of hydrolysis of pyrophosphate and acetyl phosphate?

12. *A potent donor.* Consider the following reaction:

ATP + pyruvate $\rightleftharpoons$ phosphoenolpyruvate + ADP

(a) Calculate $\Delta G^{\circ\prime}$ and K'_{eq} at 25°C for this reaction by using the data given in Table 15.1.

(b) What is the equilibrium ratio of pyruvate to phosphoenolpyruvate if the ratio of ATP to ADP is 10?

13. *Isomeric equilibrium.* Calculate $\Delta G^{\circ\prime}$ for the isomerization of glucose 6-phosphate to glucose 1-phosphate. What is the equilibrium ratio of glucose 6-phosphate to glucose 1-phosphate at 25°C?

14. *Activated acetate.* The formation of acetyl CoA from acetate is an ATP-driven reaction:

Acetate + ATP + CoA $\rightleftharpoons$ acetyl CoA + AMP + PP$_i$

(a) Calculate $\Delta G^{\circ\prime}$ for this reaction by using data given in this chapter.

(b) The PP$_i$ formed in the preceding reaction is rapidly hydrolyzed in vivo because of the ubiquity of inorganic pyrophosphatase. The $\Delta G^{\circ\prime}$ for the hydrolysis of PP$_i$ is -19.2 kJ mol^{-1} (-4.6 kcal mol^{-1}). Calculate the $\Delta G^{\circ\prime}$ for the overall reaction, including pyrophosphate hydrolysis.

What effect does the hydrolysis of PP_i have on the formation of acetyl CoA?

15. *Acid strength.* The pK of an acid is a measure of its proton-group-transfer potential.

(a) Derive a relation between $\Delta G°'$ and pK.

(b) What is the $\Delta G°'$ for the ionization of acetic acid, which has a pK of 4.8?

16. *Raison d'être.* The muscles of some invertebrates are rich in arginine phosphate (phosphoarginine). Propose a function for this amino acid derivative.

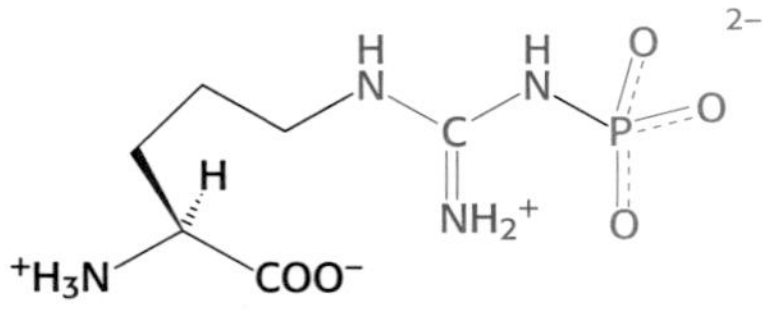

Arginine phosphate

17. *Recurring motif.* What is the structural feature common to ATP, FAD, NAD^+, and CoA?

18. *Ergogenic help or hindrance?* Creatine is a popular, but untested, dietary supplement.

(a) What is the biochemical rationale for the use of creatine?

(b) What type of exercise would most benefit from creatine supplementation?

19. *Standard conditions versus real life 1.* The enzyme aldolase catalyzes the following reaction in the glycolytic pathway:

Fructose 1, 6-bisphosphate $\overset{\text{Aldolase}}{\rightleftharpoons}$
dihydroxyacetone phosphate +
glyceraldehyde 3-phosphate

The $\Delta G°'$ for the reaction is $+ 23.8$ kJ mol^{-1} ($+ 5.7$ kcal mol^{-1}), whereas the ΔG in the cell is -1.3 kJ mol^{-1} (-0.3 kcal mol^{-1}). Calculate the ratio of reactants to products under equilibrium and intracellular conditions. Using your results, explain how the reaction can be endergonic under standard conditions and exergonic under intracellular conditions.

20. *Standard conditions versus real life 2.* On page 430, we showed that a reaction, $A \rightleftharpoons B$, with a $\Delta G'= +13$ kJ mol^{-1} ($+ 4.0$ kcal mol^{-1}) has an K_{eq} of 1.15×10^{-3}. The K_{eq} is increased to 2.67×10^2 if the reaction is coupled to ATP hydrolysis under standard conditions. The ATP-generating system of cells maintains the $[ATP]/[ADP][P_i]$ ratio at a high level, typically of the order of 500 M^{-1}. Calculate the ratio of B/A under cellular conditions.

21. *Not all alike.* The concentrations of ATP, ADP, and P_i differ with cell type. Consequently, the release of free energy with the hydrolysis of ATP will vary with cell type. Using the following table, calculate the ΔG for the hydroly-

sis of ATP in liver, muscle, and brain cells. In which cell type is the free energy of ATP hydrolysis most negative?

	ATP (mM)	ADP (mM)	P_i (mM)
Liver	3.5	1.8	5.0
Muscle	8.0	0.9	8.0
Brain	2.6	0.7	2.7

22. *Oxidation issues.* Examine the pairs of molecules and identify the more-reduced molecule in each pair.

(a) Ethanol   Acetaldehyde

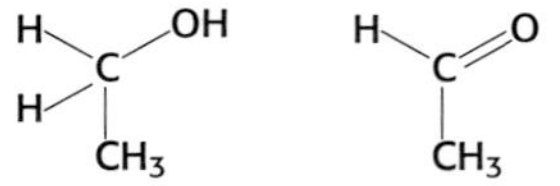

(b) Lactate   Pyruvate

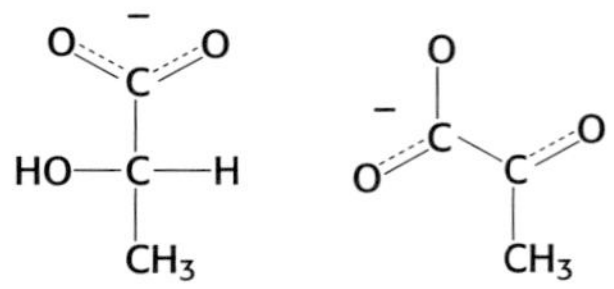

(c) Succinate   Fumarate

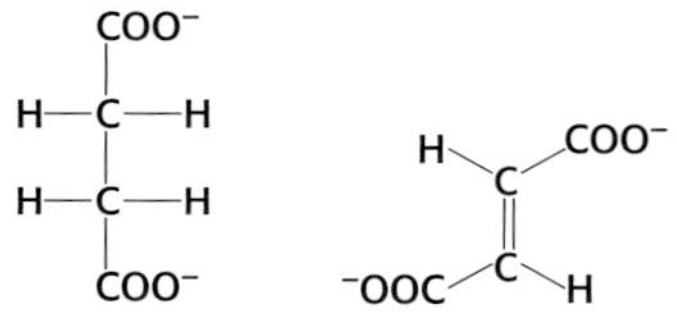

(d) Oxalosuccinate   Isocitrate

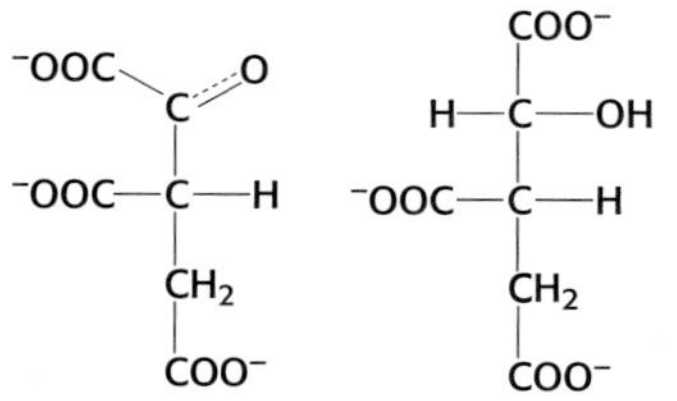

(e) Malate   Oxaloacetate

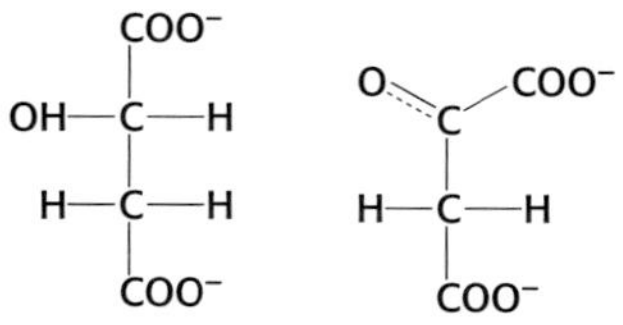

(f) Pyruvate   2-Phosphoglycerate

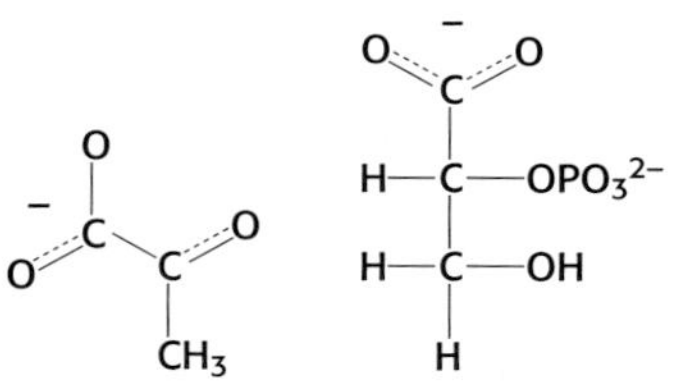

23. *Running downhill.* Glycolysis is a series of 10 linked reactions that convert one molecule of glucose into two molecules of pyruvate with the concomitant synthesis of two molecules of ATP (Chapter 16). The $\Delta G^{\circ\prime}$ for this set of reactions is $-35.6 \text{ kJ mol}^{-1}$ ($-8.5 \text{ kcal mol}^{-1}$), whereas the ΔG is $-76.6 \text{ kJ mol}^{-1}$ ($-18.3 \text{ kcal mol}^{-1}$). Explain why the free-energy release is so much greater under intracellular conditions than under standard conditions.

24. *Breakdown products.* Digestion is the first stage in the extraction of energy from food, but no useful energy is acquired during this stage. Why is digestion considered a stage in energy extraction?

25. *High-energy electrons.* What are the activated electron carriers for catabolism? For anabolism?

26. *Less reverberation.* Thioesters, common in biochemistry, are more unstable (energy-rich) than oxygen esters. Explain why this is the case.

27. *Classifying reactions.* What are the six common types of reactions seen in biochemistry?

28. *Staying in control.* What are the three principal means of controlling metabolic reactions?

Chapter Integration Problems

29. *Kinetic vs. thermodynamic.* The reaction of NADH with oxygen to produce NAD^+ and H_2O is very exergonic, yet the reaction of NADH and oxygen takes place very slowly. Why does a thermodynamically favorable reaction not occur rapidly?

30. *Activated sulfate.* Fibrinogen contains tyrosine-*O*-sulfate. Propose an activated form of sulfate that could react in vivo with the aromatic hydroxyl group of a tyrosine residue in a protein to form tyrosine-*O*-sulfate.

Data Interpretation Problem

31. *Opposites attract.* The following graph shows how the ΔG for the hydrolysis of ATP varies as a function of the Mg^{2+} concentration (pMg $= -\log[Mg^{2+}]$).

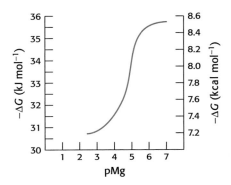

(a) How does decreasing $[Mg^{2+}]$ affect the ΔG of hydrolysis for ATP?

(b) Explain this effect.

CHAPTER 16

Glycolysis and Gluconeogenesis

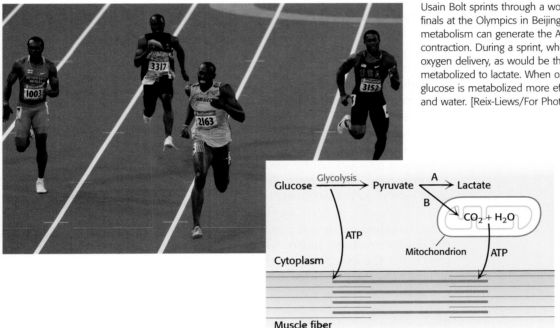

Usain Bolt sprints through a world record in the 200-meter finals at the Olympics in Beijing in 2008. Glucose metabolism can generate the ATP to power muscle contraction. During a sprint, when the ATP needs outpace oxygen delivery, as would be the case for Bolt, glucose is metabolized to lactate. When oxygen delivery is adequate, glucose is metabolized more efficiently to carbon dioxide and water. [Reix-Liews/For Photo/Corbis.]

A. Low O_2
(last seconds of a sprint)

B. Normal
(long slow run)

The first metabolic pathway that we encounter is *glycolysis*, an ancient pathway employed by a host of organisms. *Glycolysis is the sequence of reactions that metabolizes one molecule of glucose to two molecules of pyruvate with the concomitant net production of two molecules of ATP.* This process is anaerobic (i.e., it does not require O_2) because it evolved before substantial amounts of oxygen accumulated in the atmosphere. Pyruvate can be further processed anaerobically to lactate (*lactic acid fermentation*) or ethanol (*alcoholic fermentation*). Under aerobic conditions, pyruvate can be completely oxidized to CO_2, generating much more ATP, as will be described in Chapters 17 and 18. Figure 16.1 shows some possible fates of pyruvate produced by glycolysis.

Because glucose is such a precious fuel, metabolic products, such as pyruvate and lactate, are salvaged to synthesize glucose in the process of *gluconeogenesis.* Although glycolysis and gluconeogenesis have some enzymes in common, the two pathways are not simply the reverse of each other. In particular, the highly exergonic, irreversible steps of glycolysis are bypassed in gluconeogenesis. The two pathways are reciprocally regulated so that glycolysis and gluconeogenesis do not take place simultaneously in the same cell to a significant extent.

Our understanding of glucose metabolism, especially glycolysis, has a rich history. Indeed, the development of biochemistry and the delineation of

Glycolysis
Derived from the Greek stem *glyk-*, "sweet," and the word *lysis,* "dissolution."

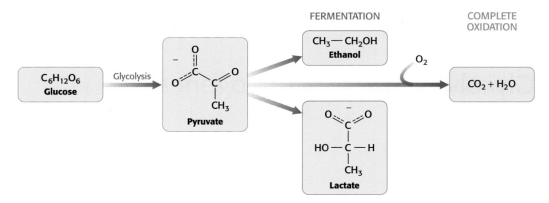

Figure 16.1 Some fates of glucose.

glycolysis went hand in hand. A key discovery was made by Hans Buchner and Eduard Buchner in 1897, quite by accident. The Buchners were interested in manufacturing cell-free extracts of yeast for possible therapeutic use. These extracts had to be preserved without the use of antiseptics such as phenol, and so they decided to try sucrose, a commonly used preservative in kitchen chemistry. They obtained a startling result: sucrose was rapidly fermented into alcohol by the yeast juice. The significance of this finding was immense. *The Buchners demonstrated for the first time that fermentation could take place outside living cells.* The accepted view of their day, asserted by Louis Pasteur in 1860, was that fermentation is inextricably tied to living cells. The chance discovery by the Buchners refuted this dogma and opened the door to modern biochemistry. The Buchners' discovery inspired the search for the biochemicals that catalyze the conversion of sucrose into alcohol. *The study of metabolism became the study of chemistry.*

Studies of muscle extracts then showed that many of the reactions of lactic acid fermentation were the same as those of alcoholic fermentation. *This exciting discovery revealed an underlying unity in biochemistry.* The complete glycolytic pathway was elucidated by 1940, largely through the pioneering contributions of Gustav Embden, Otto Meyerhof, Carl Neuberg, Jacob Parnas, Otto Warburg, Gerty Cori, and Carl Cori. Glycolysis is also known as the *Embden–Meyerhof pathway.*

Glucose is generated from dietary carbohydrates

We typically consume in our diets a generous amount of starch and a smaller amount of glycogen. These complex carbohydrates must be converted into simpler carbohydrates for absorption by the intestine and transport in the blood. Starch and glycogen are digested primarily by the pancreatic enzyme *α-amylase* and to a lesser extent by salivary α-amylase. Amylase cleaves the α-1,4 bonds of starch and glycogen, but not the α-1,6 bonds. The products are the di- and trisaccharides maltose and maltotriose. The material not digestible because of the α-1,6 bonds is called the *limit dextrin.*

Maltase cleaves maltose into two glucose molecules, whereas *α-glucosidase* digests maltotriose and any other oligosaccharides that may have escaped digestion by the amylase. *α-Dextrinase* further digests the limit dextrin. Maltase and α-glucosidase are located on the surface of the intestinal cells, as is *sucrase,* an enzyme that degrades the sucrose contributed by vegetables to fructose and glucose. The enzyme *lactase* is responsible for degrading the milk sugar lactose into glucose and galactose. The monosaccharides are transported into the cells lining the intestine and then into the bloodstream.

Enzyme

A term coined by Friedrich Wilhelm Kühne in 1878 to designate catalytically active substances that had formerly been called ferments. Derived from the Greek words *en,* "in," and *zyme,* "leaven."

Glucose is an important fuel for most organisms

Glucose is a common and important fuel. In mammals, glucose is the only fuel that the brain uses under nonstarvation conditions and the only fuel that red blood cells can use at all. Indeed, almost all organisms use glucose, and most that do process it in a similar fashion. Recall from Chapter 11 that there are many carbohydrates. Why is glucose instead of some other monosaccharide such a prominent fuel? We can speculate on the reasons. First, glucose is one of several monosaccharides formed from formaldehyde under prebiotic conditions, and so it may have been available as a fuel source for primitive biochemical systems. Second, glucose has a low tendency, relative to other monosaccharides, to nonenzymatically glycosylate proteins. In their open-chain forms, monosaccharides contain carbonyl groups that can react with the amino groups of proteins to form Schiff bases, which rearrange to form a more stable amino–ketone linkage. Such nonspecifically modified proteins often do not function effectively. Glucose has a strong tendency to exist in the ring conformation and, consequently, relatively little tendency to modify proteins. Recall that all the hydroxyl groups in the ring conformation of β-glucose are equatorial, contributing to the sugar's high relative stability (Section 11.1).

16.1 Glycolysis Is an Energy-Conversion Pathway in Many Organisms

We now begin our consideration of the glycolytic pathway. This pathway is common to virtually all cells, both prokaryotic and eukaryotic. In eukaryotic cells, glycolysis takes place in the cytoplasm. This pathway can be thought of as comprising two stages (Figure 16.2). Stage 1 is the trapping and preparation phase. No ATP is generated in this stage. Stage 1 begins with the conversion of glucose into fructose 1,6-bisphosphate, which consists of three steps: a phosphorylation, an isomerization, and a second phosphorylation reaction. *The strategy of these initial steps in glycolysis is to trap the glucose in the cell and form a compound that can be readily cleaved into phosphorylated three-carbon units.* Stage 1 is completed with the cleavage of the fructose 1,6-bisphosphate into two three-carbon fragments. These resulting three-carbon units are readily interconvertible. In stage 2, ATP is harvested when the three-carbon fragments are oxidized to pyruvate.

Hexokinase traps glucose in the cell and begins glycolysis

Glucose enters cells through specific transport proteins (p. 477) and has one principal fate: *it is phosphorylated by ATP to form glucose 6-phosphate.* This step is notable for two reasons: (1) glucose 6-phosphate cannot pass through the membrane because it is not a substrate for the glucose transporters, and (2) the addition of the phosphoryl group acts to destabilize glucose, thus facilitating its further metabolism. The transfer of the phosphoryl group from ATP to the hydroxyl group on carbon 6 of glucose is catalyzed by *hexokinase.*

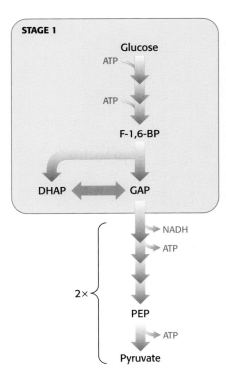

First stage of glycolysis. The first stage of glycolysis begins with the phosphorylation of glucose by hexokinase and ends with the isomerization of dihydroxyacetone phosphate to glyceraldehyde 3-phosphate.

Glucose   **Glucose 6-phosphate (G-6P)**

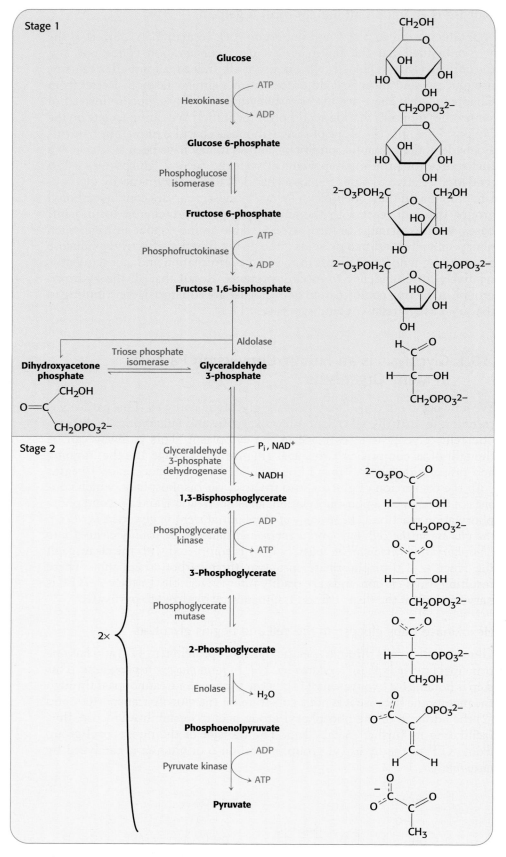

Figure 16.2 Stages of glycolysis. The glycolytic pathway can be divided into two stages: (1) glucose is trapped, destabilized, and cleaved into two interconvertible three-carbon molecules generated by cleavage of six-carbon fructose; and (2) ATP is generated.

Phosphoryl transfer is a fundamental reaction in biochemistry. *Kinases* are enzymes that catalyze the transfer of a phosphoryl group from ATP to an acceptor. Hexokinase, then, catalyzes the transfer of a phosphoryl group from ATP to a variety of six-carbon sugars (*hexoses*), such as glucose and mannose. *Hexokinase, like adenylate kinase (Section 9.4) and all other kinases, requires Mg^{2+} (or another divalent metal ion such as Mn^{2+}) for activity.* The divalent metal ion forms a complex with ATP.

X-ray crystallographic studies of yeast hexokinase revealed that the binding of glucose induces a large conformational change in the enzyme. Hexokinase consists of two lobes, which move toward each other when glucose is bound (Figure 16.3). On glucose binding, one lobe rotates 12 degrees with respect to the other, resulting in movements of the polypeptide backbone of as much as 8 Å. The cleft between the lobes closes, and the bound glucose becomes surrounded by protein, except for the hydroxyl group of carbon 6, which will accept the phosphoryl group from ATP. The closing of the cleft in hexokinase is a striking example of the role *of induced fit* in enzyme action (Section 8.3).

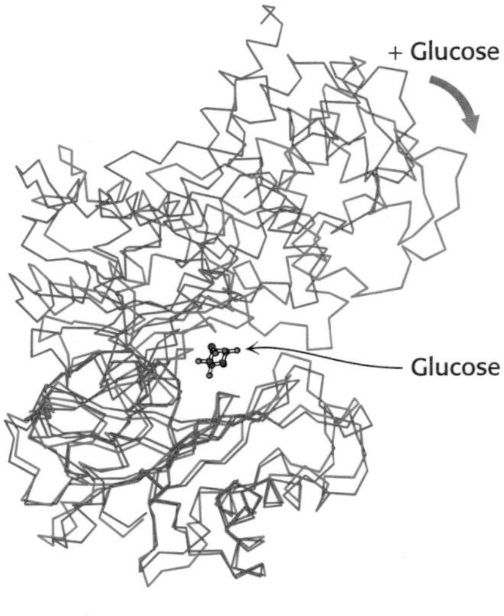

The glucose-induced structural changes are significant in two respects. First, the environment around the glucose becomes more nonpolar, which favors reaction between the hydrophilic hydroxyl group of glucose and the terminal phosphoryl group of ATP. Second, the conformational changes enable the kinase to discriminate against H$_2$O as a substrate. The closing of the cleft keeps water molecules away from the active site. If hexokinase were rigid, a molecule of H$_2$O occupying the binding site for the —CH$_2$OH of glucose could attack the γ phosphoryl group of ATP, forming ADP and P$_i$. In other words, a rigid kinase would likely also be an ATPase. It is interesting to note that other kinases taking part in glycolysis—phosphofructokinase, phosphoglycerate kinase, and pyruvate kinase—also contain clefts between lobes that close when substrate is bound, although the structures of these enzymes are different in other regards. *Substrate-induced cleft closing is a general feature of kinases.*

Fructose 1,6-bisphosphate is generated from glucose 6-phosphate

The next step in glycolysis is the *isomerization of glucose 6-phosphate to fructose 6-phosphate.* Recall that the open-chain form of glucose has an aldehyde group at carbon 1, whereas the open-chain form of fructose has a keto group at carbon 2. Thus, the isomerization of glucose 6-phosphate to fructose 6-phosphate is a *conversion of an aldose into a ketose.* The reaction catalyzed by *phosphoglucose isomerase* takes several steps because both glucose 6-phosphate and fructose 6-phosphate are present primarily in the cyclic forms. The enzyme must first open the six-membered ring of glucose 6-phosphate, catalyze the isomerization, and then promote the formation of the five-membered ring of fructose 6-phosphate.

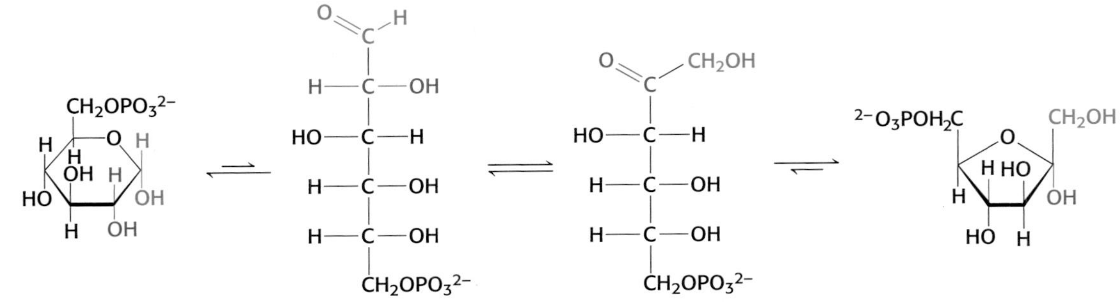

Figure 16.3 Induced fit in hexokinase. As shown in blue, the two lobes of hexokinase are separated in the absence of glucose. The conformation of hexokinase changes markedly on binding glucose, as shown in red. *Notice* that two lobes of the enzyme come together and surround the substrate, creating the necessary environment for catalysis. [Courtesy of Dr. Thomas Steitz.]

Glucose 6-phosphate (G-6P) · Glucose 6-phosphate (open-chain form) · Fructose 6-phosphate (open-chain form) · Fructose 6-phosphate (F-6P)

(open-chain forms)

A second phosphorylation reaction follows the isomerization step. *Fructose 6-phosphate is phosphorylated at the expense of ATP to fructose 1,6-bisphosphate* (F-1,6-BP). The prefix *bis-* in bisphosphate means that two separate monophosphoryl groups are present, whereas the prefix *di-* in diphosphate (as in adenosine diphosphate) means that two phosphoryl groups are present and are connected by an anhydride bond.

Fructose 6-phosphate
(F-6P)

Fructose 1,6-bisphosphate
(F-1, 6-BP)

This reaction is catalyzed by *phosphofructokinase* (PFK), an allosteric enzyme that sets the pace of glycolysis. As we will learn, this enzyme plays a central role in the metabolism of many molecules in all parts of the body.

The six-carbon sugar is cleaved into two three-carbon fragments

The newly formed fructose 1,6-bisphosphate is cleaved into *glyceraldehyde 3-phosphate* (GAP) and *dihydroxyacetone phosphate* (DHAP), completing stage 1 of glycolysis. The products of the remaining steps in glycolysis consist of three-carbon units rather than six-carbon units.

Dihydroxyacetone phosphate (DHAP)

Glyceraldehyde 3-phosphate (GAP)

Fructose 1,6-bisphosphate (F-1, 6-BP)

This reaction, which is readily reversible, is catalyzed by *aldolase*. This enzyme derives its name from the nature of the reverse reaction, an aldol condensation.

Glyceraldehyde 3-phosphate is on the direct pathway of glycolysis, whereas dihydroxyacetone phosphate is not. Unless a means exists to convert dihydroxyacetone phosphate into glyceraldehyde 3-phosphate, a three-carbon fragment useful for generating ATP will be lost. These compounds are isomers that can be readily interconverted: dihydroxyacetone phosphate is a ketose, whereas glyceraldehyde 3-phosphate is an aldose. The isomerization of these three-carbon phosphorylated sugars is catalyzed by *triose phosphate isomerase* (TPI, sometimes abbreviated TIM; Figure 16.4).

Dihydroxyacetone phosphate

Glyceraldehyde 3-phosphate

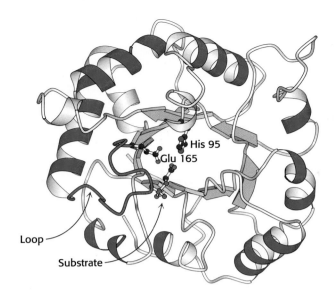

Figure 16.4 Structure of triose phosphate isomerase. This enzyme consists of a central core of eight parallel β strands (orange) surrounded by eight α helices (blue). This structural motif, called an αβ barrel, is also found in the glycolytic enzymes aldolase, enolase, and pyruvate kinase. *Notice* that histidine 95 and glutamate 165, essential components of the active site of triose phosphate isomerase, are located in the barrel. A loop (red) closes off the active site on substrate binding. [Drawn from 2YPI.pdb.]

This reaction is rapid and reversible. At equilibrium, 96% of the triose phosphate is dihydroxyacetone phosphate. However, the reaction proceeds readily from dihydroxyacetone phosphate to glyceraldehyde 3-phosphate because the subsequent reactions of glycolysis remove this product.

We now see the significance of the isomerization of glucose 6-phosphate to fructose 6-phosphate and its subsequent phosphorylation to form fructose 1,6-bisphosphate. Had the aldol cleavage taken place in the aldose glucose, a two-carbon and a four-carbon fragment would have resulted. Two different metabolic pathways, one to process the two-carbon fragment and one for the four-carbon fragment, would have been required to extract energy. Isomerization to the ketose fructose followed by aldol cleavage yields two phosphorylated interconvertible three-carbon fragments that will be oxidized in the later steps of glycolysis to capture energy in the form of ATP.

Mechanism: Triose phosphate isomerase salvages a three-carbon fragment

Much is known about the catalytic mechanism of triose phosphate isomerase. TPI catalyzes the transfer of a hydrogen atom from carbon 1 to carbon 2, an intramolecular oxidation–reduction. This isomerization of a ketose into an aldose proceeds through an *enediol intermediate* (Figure 16.5).

X-ray crystallographic and other studies showed that glutamate 165 plays the role of a general acid–base catalyst: it abstracts a proton (H^+) from carbon 1 and then donates it to carbon 2. However, the carboxylate group of glutamate 165 by itself is not basic enough to pull a proton away from a carbon atom adjacent to a carbonyl group. Histidine 95 assists catalysis by donating a proton to stabilize the negative charge that develops on the C-2 carbonyl group.

Two features of this enzyme are noteworthy. First, TPI displays great catalytic prowess. It accelerates isomerization by a factor of 10^{10} compared with the rate obtained with a simple base catalyst such as acetate ion. Indeed, the k_{cat}/K_M ratio for the isomerization of glyceraldehyde 3-phosphate is $2 \times 10^8 \ M^{-1} \ s^{-1}$, which is close to the diffusion-controlled limit. In other words, catalysis takes place every time that enzyme and substrate meet. The diffusion-controlled encounter of substrate and enzyme is thus the rate-limiting step in catalysis. TPI is an example of a *kinetically perfect enzyme* (Section 8.4). Second, TPI suppresses an undesired side

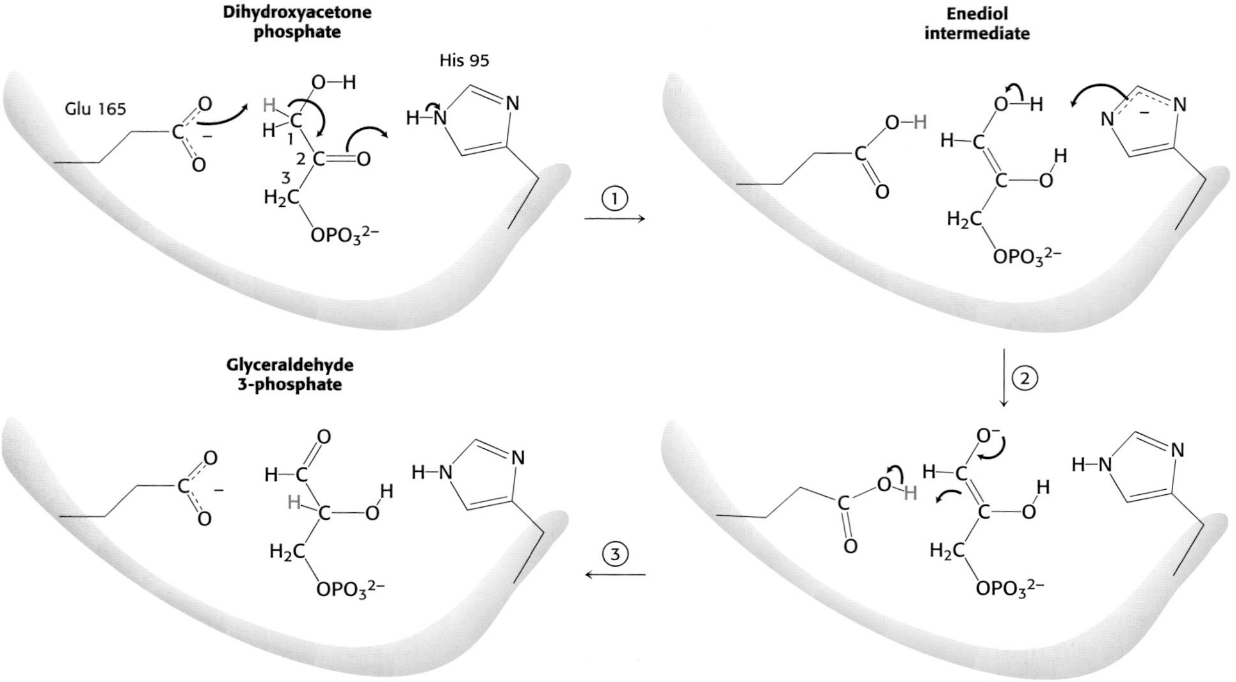

Figure 16.5 Catalytic mechanism of triose phosphate isomerase. (1) Glutamate 165 acts as a general base by abstracting a proton (H⁺) from carbon 1. Histidine 95, acting as a general acid, donates a proton to the oxygen atom bonded to carbon 2, forming the enediol intermediate. (2) Glutamic acid, now acting as a general acid, donates a proton to C-2 while histidine removes a proton from the OH group of C-l. (3) The product is formed, and glutamate and histidine are returned to their ionized and neutral forms, respectively.

reaction, the decomposition of the enediol intermediate into methyl glyoxal and orthophosphate.

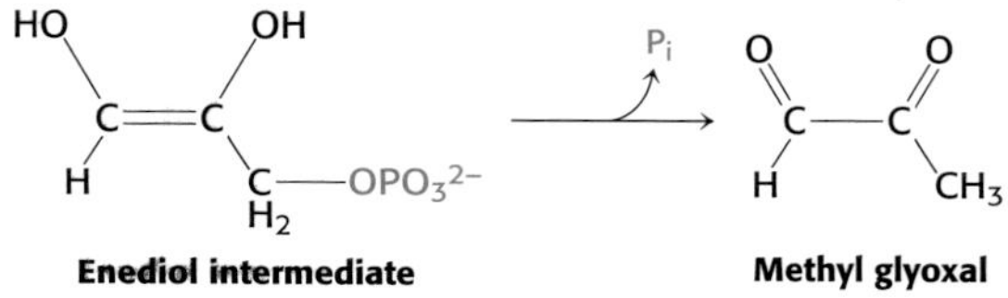

In solution, this physiologically useless reaction is 100 times as fast as isomerization. Moreover, methyl glyoxal is a highly reactive compound that can modify the structure and function of a variety of biomolecules, including proteins and DNA. The reaction of methyl glyoxal with a biomolecule is an example of deleterious reactions called advance glycation end products, discussed earlier (AGEs, Section 11.1). Hence, TPI must prevent the enediol from leaving the enzyme. This labile intermediate is trapped in the active site by the movement of a loop of 10 residues (see Figure 16.4). This loop serves as a lid on the active site, shutting it when the enediol is present and reopening it when isomerization is completed. *We see here a striking example of one means of preventing an undesirable alternative reaction: the active site is kept closed until the desirable reaction takes place.*

Thus, two molecules of glyceraldehyde 3-phosphate are formed from one molecule of fructose 1,6-bisphosphate by the sequential action of aldolase and triose phosphate isomerase. The economy of metabolism is evident in this reaction sequence. The isomerase funnels dihydroxyacetone phosphate into the main glycolytic pathway; a separate set of reactions is not needed.

The oxidation of an aldehyde to an acid powers the formation of a compound with high phosphoryl-transfer potential

The preceding steps in glycolysis have transformed one molecule of glucose into two molecules of glyceraldehyde 3-phosphate, but no energy has yet been extracted. On the contrary, thus far, two molecules of ATP have been invested. We come now to the second stage of glycolysis, a series of steps that harvest some of the energy contained in glyceraldehyde 3-phosphate as ATP. The initial reaction in this sequence is the *conversion of glyceraldehyde 3-phosphate into 1,3-bisphosphoglycerate* (1,3-BPG), a reaction catalyzed by *glyceraldehyde 3-phosphate dehydrogenase.*

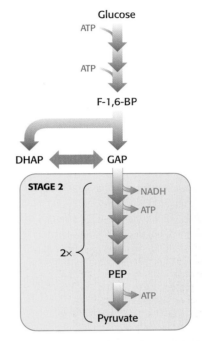

Second stage of glycolysis. The oxidation of three-carbon fragments yields ATP.

1,3-Bisphosphoglycerate is an acyl phosphate, which is a mixed anhydride of phosphoric acid and a carboxylic acid. Such compounds have a high phosphoryl-transfer potential; one of its phosphoryl groups is transferred to ADP in the next step in glycolysis.

The reaction catalyzed by glyceraldehyde 3-phosphate dehydrogenase can be viewed as the sum of two processes: the *oxidation* of the aldehyde to a carboxylic acid by NAD^+ and the *joining* of the carboxylic acid and orthophosphate to form the acyl-phosphate product.

The first reaction is thermodynamically quite favorable, with a standard free-energy change, $\Delta G°'$, of approximately -50 kJ mol^{-1} ($-12 \text{ kcal mol}^{-1}$), whereas the second reaction is quite unfavorable, with a standard free-energy change of the same magnitude but the opposite sign. If these two reactions simply took place in succession, the second reaction would have a very large activation energy and thus not take place at a biologically significant rate. These two processes *must be coupled* so that the favorable aldehyde oxidation can be used to drive the formation of the acyl phosphate. How are these reactions coupled? *The key is an intermediate, formed as a result of the aldehyde oxidation, that is linked to the enzyme by a thioester bond.* Thioesters are high-energy compounds found in many biochemical pathways (Section 15.4). This intermediate reacts with orthophosphate to form the high-energy compound 1,3-bisphosphoglycerate.

The thioester intermediate is higher in free energy than the free carboxylic acid is. The favorable oxidation and unfavorable phosphorylation reactions are coupled by the thioester intermediate, which preserves much of the free energy released in the oxidation reaction. We see here the *use of a covalent enzyme-bound intermediate as a mechanism of energy coupling.* A free-energy profile of the glyceraldehyde 3-phosphate dehydrogenase reaction, compared

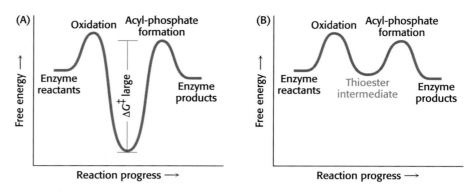

Figure 16.6 Free-energy profiles for glyceraldehyde oxidation followed by acyl-phosphate formation. (A) A hypothetical case with no coupling between the two processes. The second step must have a large activation barrier, making the reaction very slow. (B) The actual case with the two reactions coupled through a thioester intermediate.

with a hypothetical process in which the reaction proceeds without this intermediate, reveals how this intermediate allows a favorable process to drive an unfavorable one (Figure 16.6).

Mechanism: Phosphorylation is coupled to the oxidation of glyceraldehyde 3-phosphate by a thioester intermediate

The active site of glyceraldehyde 3-phosphate dehydrogenase includes a reactive cysteine residue, as well as NAD^+ and a crucial histidine (Figure 16.7). Let us consider in detail how these components cooperate in the reaction mechanism (Figure 16.8). In step 1, the aldehyde substrate reacts with the sulfhydryl group of cysteine 149 on the enzyme to form a hemithioacetal. Step 2 is the *transfer of a hydride ion to a molecule of NAD^+ that is tightly bound to the enzyme and is adjacent to the cysteine residue.* This reaction is favored by the deprotonation of the hemithioacetal by histidine 176. The products of this reaction are the reduced coenzyme NADH and a thioester intermediate. *This thioester intermediate has a free energy close to that of the reactants* (see Figure 16.6). In step 3, the NADH formed from the aldehyde oxidation leaves the enzyme and is replaced by a second molecule of NAD^+. This step is important because the positive charge on NAD^+ polarizes the thioester intermediate to facilitate the attack by orthophosphate. In step 4, orthophosphate attacks the thioester to form

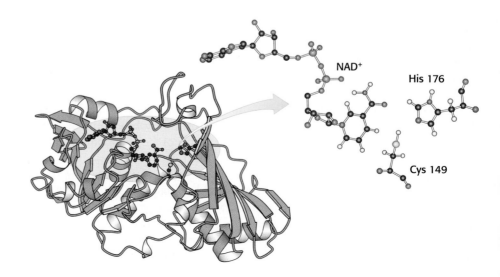

Figure 16.7 Structure of glyceraldehyde 3-phosphate dehydrogenase. *Notice* that the active site includes a cysteine residue and a histidine residue adjacent to a bound NAD^+ molecule. The sulfur atom of cysteine will link with the substrate to form a transitory thioester intermediate. [Drawn from 1GAD.pdb.]

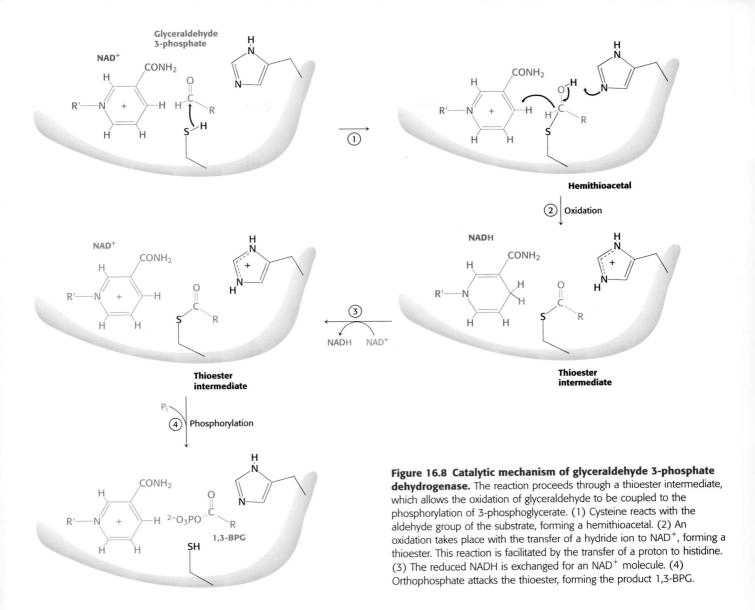

Figure 16.8 Catalytic mechanism of glyceraldehyde 3-phosphate dehydrogenase. The reaction proceeds through a thioester intermediate, which allows the oxidation of glyceraldehyde to be coupled to the phosphorylation of 3-phosphoglycerate. (1) Cysteine reacts with the aldehyde group of the substrate, forming a hemithioacetal. (2) An oxidation takes place with the transfer of a hydride ion to NAD^+, forming a thioester. This reaction is facilitated by the transfer of a proton to histidine. (3) The reduced NADH is exchanged for an NAD^+ molecule. (4) Orthophosphate attacks the thioester, forming the product 1,3-BPG.

1,3-BPG and free the cysteine residue. This example illustrates the essence of energy transformations and of metabolism itself: energy released by carbon oxidation is converted into high phosphoryl-transfer potential.

ATP is formed by phosphoryl transfer from 1,3-bisphosphoglycerate

1,3-Bisphosphoglycerate is an energy-rich molecule with a greater phosphoryl-transfer potential than that of ATP (Section 15.2). Thus, 1,3-BPG can be used to power the synthesis of ATP from ADP. *Phosphoglycerate kinase* catalyzes the transfer of the phosphoryl group from the acyl phosphate of 1,3-bisphosphoglycerate to ADP. ATP and 3-phosphoglycerate are the products.

The formation of ATP in this manner is referred to as *substrate-level phosphorylation* because the phosphate donor, 1,3-BPG, is a substrate with high phosphoryl-transfer potential. We will contrast this manner of ATP formation with the formation of ATP from ionic gradients in Chapters 18 and 19.

Thus, the outcomes of the reactions catalyzed by glyceraldehyde 3-phosphate dehydrogenase and phosphoglycerate kinase are as follows:

1. Glyceraldehyde 3-phosphate, an aldehyde, is oxidized to 3-phosphoglycerate, a carboxylic acid.

2. NAD^+ is concomitantly reduced to NADH.

3. ATP is formed from P_i and ADP at the expense of carbon-oxidation energy.

In essence, the energy released during the oxidation of glyceraldehyde 3-phosphate to 3-phosphoglycerate is temporarily trapped as 1,3-bisphosphoglycerate. This energy powers the transfer of a phosphoryl group from 1,3-bisphosphoglycerate to ADP to yield ATP. Keep in mind that, because of the actions of aldolase and triose phosphate isomerase, two molecules of glyceraldehyde 3-phosphate were formed and hence two molecules of ATP were generated. These ATP molecules make up for the two molecules of ATP consumed in the first stage of glycolysis.

Additional ATP is generated with the formation of pyruvate

In the remaining steps of glycolysis, 3-phosphoglycerate is converted into pyruvate, and a second molecule of ATP is formed from ADP.

3-Phosphoglycerate   2-Phosphoglycerate   Phosphenolpyruvate   Pyruvate

The first reaction is a rearrangement. The position of the phosphoryl group shifts in the *conversion of 3-phosphoglycerate into 2-phosphoglycerate*, a reaction catalyzed by *phosphoglycerate mutase*. In general, a *mutase* is an enzyme that catalyzes the intramolecular shift of a chemical group, such as a phosphoryl group. The phosphoglycerate mutase reaction has an interesting mechanism: the phosphoryl group is not simply moved from one carbon atom to another. This enzyme requires catalytic amounts of 2,3-bisphosphoglycerate (2,3-BPG) to maintain an active-site histidine residue in a phosphorylated form. This phosphoryl group is transferred to 3-phosphoglycerate to re-form 2,3-bisphosphoglycerate.

Enz-His-phosphate + 3-phosphoglycerate $\Longrightarrow$

Enz-His + 2,3-bisphosphoglycerate

The mutase then functions as a phosphatase: it converts 2,3-bisphosphoglycerate into 2-phosphoglycerate. The mutase retains the phosphoryl group to regenerate the modified histidine.

Enz-His + 2,3-bisphosphoglycerate $\Longrightarrow$

Enz-His-phosphate + 2-phosphoglycerate

The sum of these reactions yields the mutase reaction:

$$\text{3-Phosphoglycerate} \rightleftharpoons \text{2-phosphoglycerate}$$

In the next reaction, the dehydration of 2-phosphoglycerate introduces a double bond, creating an *enol*. *Enolase* catalyzes this formation of the enol phosphate *phosphoenolpyruvate* (PEP). This dehydration markedly elevates the transfer potential of the phosphoryl group. An *enol phosphate* has a high phosphoryl-transfer potential, whereas the phosphate ester of an ordinary alcohol, such as 2-phosphoglycerate, has a low one. The $\Delta G°'$ of the hydrolysis of a phosphate ester of an ordinary alcohol is -13 kJ mol^{-1} (-3 kcal mol^{-1}), whereas that of phosphoenolpyruvate is -62 kJ mol^{-1} (-15 kcal mol^{-1}).

Why does phosphoenolpyruvate have such a high phosphoryl-transfer potential? The phosphoryl group traps the molecule in its unstable enol form. When the phosphoryl group has been donated to ATP, the enol undergoes a conversion into the more stable ketone—namely, pyruvate.

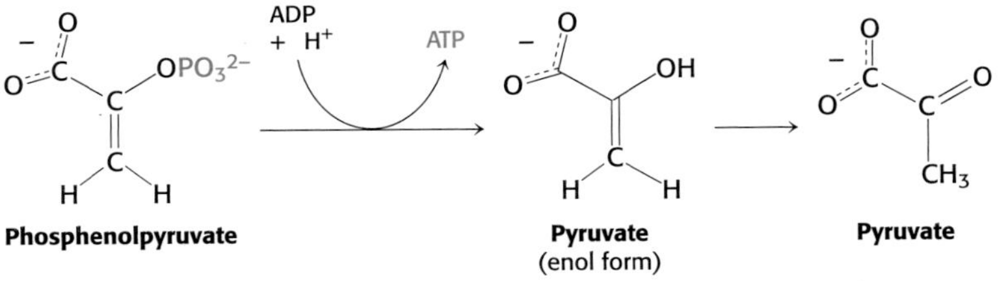

Phosphenolpyruvate   **Pyruvate**   **Pyruvate**
                                (enol form)

Thus, *the high phosphoryl-transfer potential of phosphoenolpyruvate arises primarily from the large driving force of the subsequent enol–ketone conversion.* Hence, pyruvate is formed, and ATP is generated concomitantly. The virtually irreversible transfer of a phosphoryl group from phosphoenolpyruvate to ADP is catalyzed *by pyruvate kinase.* What is the energy source for the formation of phosphoenolpyruvate? The answer to this question becomes clear when we compare the structures of 2-phosphoglycerate and pyruvate. The formation of pyruvate from 2-phosphoglycerate is, in essence, an internal oxidation–reduction reaction; carbon 3 takes electrons from carbon 2 in the conversion of 2-phosphoglycerate into pyruvate. Compared with 2-phosphoglycerate, C-3 is more reduced in pyruvate, whereas C-2 is more oxidized. Once again, carbon oxidation powers the synthesis of a compound with high phosphoryl-transfer potential, phosphoenolpyruvate here and 1,3-bisphosphoglycerate earlier, which allows the synthesis of ATP.

Because the molecules of ATP used in forming fructose 1,6-bisphosphate have already been regenerated, the two molecules of ATP generated from phosphoenolpyruvate are "profit."

Two ATP molecules are formed in the conversion of glucose into pyruvate

The net reaction in the transformation of glucose into pyruvate is

$$\text{Glucose} + 2\,\text{P}_i + 2\,\text{ADP} + 2\,\text{NAD}^+ \rightarrow$$
$$\text{2 pyruvate} + 2\,\text{ATP} + 2\,\text{NADH} + 2\,\text{H}^+ + 2\,\text{H}_2\text{O}$$

Thus, *two molecules of ATP are generated in the conversion of glucose into two molecules of pyruvate.* The reactions of glycolysis are summarized in Table 16.1.

The energy released in the anaerobic conversion of glucose into two molecules of pyruvate is about -96 kJ mol^{-1} (-23 kcal mol^{-1}). We shall see

Table 16.1 Reactions of glycolysis

Step	Reaction
1	Glucose + ATP $\longrightarrow$ glucose 6-phosphate + ADP + H$^+$
2	Glucose 6-phosphate $\rightleftharpoons$ fructose 6-phosphate
3	Fructose 6-phosphate + ATP $\longrightarrow$ fructose 1,6-bisphosphate + ADP + H$^+$
4	Fructose 1,6-bisphosphate $\rightleftharpoons$ dihydroxyacetone phosphate + glyceraldehyde 3-phosphate
5	Dihydroxyacetone phosphate $\rightleftharpoons$ glyceraldehyde 3-phosphate
6	Glyceraldehyde 3-phosphate + P$_i$ + NAD$^+$ $\rightleftharpoons$ 1,3-bisphosphoglycerate + NADH + H$^+$
7	1,3-Bisphosphoglycerate + ADP $\rightleftharpoons$ 3-phosphoglycerate + ATP
8	3-Phosphoglycerate $\rightleftharpoons$ 2-phosphoglycerate
9	2-Phosphoglycerate $\rightleftharpoons$ phosphoenolpyruvate + H$_2$O
10	Phosphoenolpyruvate + ADP + H$^+$ $\longrightarrow$ pyruvate + ATP

Note: ΔG, the actual free-energy change, has been calculated from $\Delta G°'$ and known concentrations of reactants under typical physiological conditions. Glycolysis can proceed only if the ΔG values of all reactions are negative. The smalls positive ΔG values of three of the above reactions indicate that the concentrations of metabolites in vivo in cells undergoing glycolysis are not precisely known.

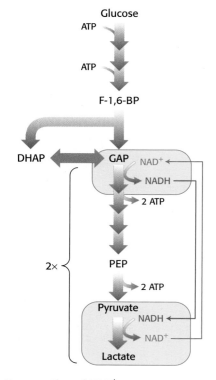

Regeneration of NAD$^+$.

in Chapters 17 and 18 that much more energy can be released from glucose in the presence of oxygen.

NAD$^+$ is regenerated from the metabolism of pyruvate

The conversion of glucose into two molecules of pyruvate has resulted in the net synthesis of ATP. However, an energy-converting pathway that stops at pyruvate will not proceed for long, because redox balance has not been maintained. As we have seen, the activity of glyceraldehyde 3-phosphate dehydrogenase, in addition to generating a compound with high phosphoryl-transfer potential, of necessity leads to the reduction of NAD$^+$ to NADH. In the cell, there are limited amounts of NAD$^+$, which is derived from the vitamin niacin, a dietary requirement for human beings. Consequently, NAD$^+$ must be regenerated for glycolysis to proceed. Thus, the final process in the pathway is the regeneration of NAD$^+$ through the metabolism of pyruvate.

The sequence of reactions from glucose to pyruvate is similar in most organisms and most types of cells. In contrast, the fate of pyruvate is variable. Three reactions of pyruvate are of primary importance: conversion into ethanol, lactate, or carbon dioxide (Figure 16.9). The first two reactions are fermentations that take place in the absence of oxygen. A *fermentation* is an ATP-generating process in which organic compounds act both as the donor and as the acceptor of electrons. In the presence of oxygen, the most common situation in multicellular organisms and in many unicellular ones, pyruvate is metabolized to carbon dioxide and water through the citric acid cycle and the electron-transport chain with oxygen serving as the final electron acceptor. We now take a closer look at these three possible fates of pyruvate.

1.   *Ethanol* is formed from pyruvate in yeast and several other microorganisms. The first step is the decarboxylation of pyruvate. This reaction is catalyzed by *pyruvate decarboxylase*, which requires the coenzyme thiamine pyrophosphate. This coenzyme, derived from the vitamin thiamine (B$_1$), also participates in reactions catalyzed by other enzymes (Section 17.1). The second step is the reduction of

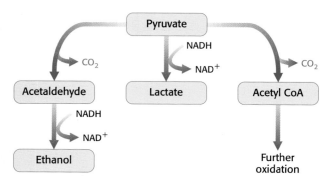

Figure 16.9 Diverse fates of pyruvate. Ethanol and lactate can be formed by reactions that include NADH. Alternatively, a two-carbon unit from pyruvate can be coupled to coenzyme A (Chapter 17) to form acetyl CoA.

Enzyme	Reaction type	$\Delta G^{\circ\prime}$ in kJ mol^{-1} (kcal mol^{-1})	ΔG in kJ mol^{-1} (kcal mol^{-1})
Hexokinase	Phosphoryl transfer	$-16.7\ (-4.0)$	$-33.5\ (-8.0)$
Phosphoglucose isomerase	Isomerization	$+1.7\ (+0.4)$	$-2.5\ (-0.6)$
Phosphofructokinase	Phosphoryl transfer	$-14.2\ (-3.4)$	$-22.2\ (-5.3)$
Aldolase	Aldol cleavage	$+23.8\ (+5.7)$	$-1.3\ (-0.3)$
Triose phosphate isomerase	Isomerization	$+7.5\ (+1.8)$	$+2.5\ (+0.6)$
Glyceraldehyde 3-phosphate dehydrogenase	Phosphorylation coupled to oxidation	$+6.3\ (+1.5)$	$-1.7\ (-0.4)$
Phosphoglycerate kinase	Phosphoryl transfer	$-18.8\ (-4.5)$	$+1.3\ (+0.3)$
Phosphoglycerate mutase	Phosphoryl shift	$+4.6\ (+1.1)$	$+0.8\ (+0.2)$
Enolase	Dehydration	$+1.7\ (+0.4)$	$-3.3\ (-0.8)$
Pyruvate kinase	Phosphoryl transfer	$-31.4\ (-7.5)$	$-16.7\ (-4.0)$

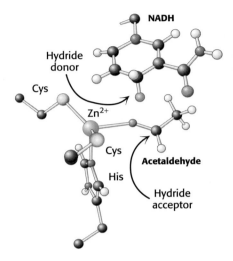

Figure 16.10 Active site of alcohol dehydrogenase. The active site contains a zinc ion bound to two cysteine residues and one histidine residue. *Notice* that the zinc ion binds the acetaldehyde substrate through its oxygen atom, polarizing the substrate so that it more easily accepts a hydride from NADH. Only the nicotinamide ring of NADH is shown.

acetaldehyde to ethanol by NADH, in a reaction catalyzed by *alcohol dehydrogenase*. This process regenerates NAD$^+$.

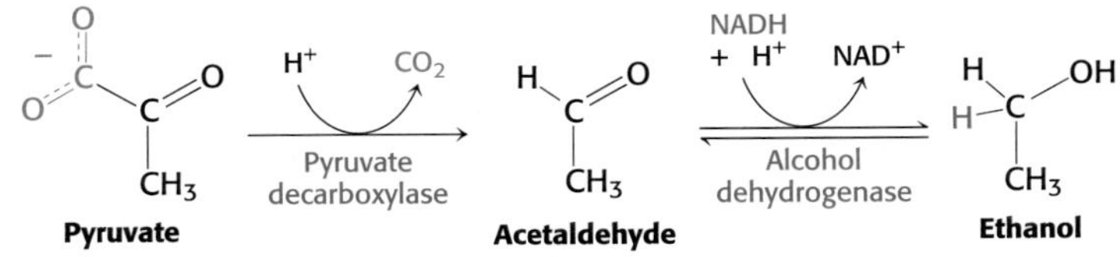

The active site of alcohol dehydrogenase contains a zinc ion that is coordinated to the sulfur atoms of two cysteine residues and a nitrogen atom of histidine (Figure 16.10). This zinc ion polarizes the carbonyl group of the substrate to favor the transfer of a hydride from NADH.

The conversion of glucose into ethanol is an example *of alcoholic fermentation*. The net result of this anaerobic process is

$$\text{Glucose} + 2\ P_i + 2\ \text{ADP} + 2\ \text{H}^+ \rightarrow$$
$$2\ \text{ethanol} + 2\ \text{CO}_2 + 2\ \text{ATP} + 2\ \text{H}_2\text{O}$$

Note that NAD$^+$ and NADH do not appear in this equation, even though they are crucial for the overall process. NADH generated by the oxidation of glyceraldehyde 3-phosphate is consumed in the reduction of acetaldehyde to ethanol. Thus, *there is no net oxidation–reduction in the conversion of glucose into ethanol* (Figure 16.11). The ethanol formed in alcoholic fermentation provides a key ingredient for brewing and winemaking.

2. *Lactate* is formed from pyruvate in a variety of microorganisms in a process called *lactic acid fermentation*. The reaction also takes place in the cells of higher organisms when the amount of oxygen is limiting, as in

Figure 16.11 Maintaining redox balance. The NADH produced by the glyceraldehyde 3-phosphate dehydrogenase reaction must be reoxidized to NAD$^+$ for the glycolytic pathway to continue. In alcoholic fermentation, alcohol dehydrogenase oxidizes NADH and generates ethanol. In lactic acid fermentation (not shown), lactate dehydrogenase oxidizes NADH while generating lactic acid.

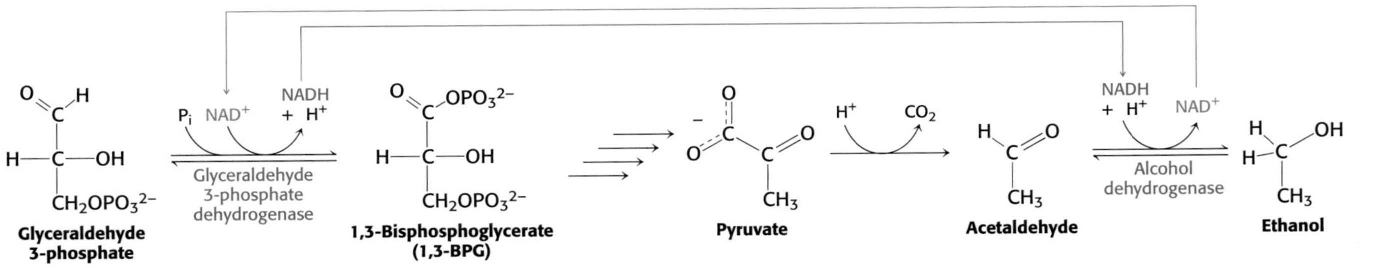

muscle cells during intense activity. The reduction of pyruvate by NADH to form lactate is catalyzed by *lactate dehydrogenase*.

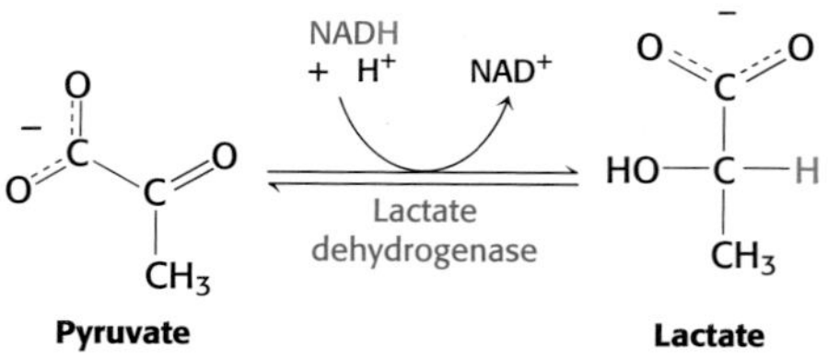

The overall reaction in the conversion of glucose into lactate is

$$\text{Glucose} + 2\,P_i + 2\,\text{ADP} \rightarrow 2\,\text{lactate} + 2\,\text{ATP} + 2\,H_2O$$

As in alcoholic fermentation, there is no net oxidation–reduction. The NADH formed in the oxidation of glyceraldehyde 3-phosphate is consumed in the reduction of pyruvate. *The regeneration of NAD$^+$ in the reduction of pyruvate to lactate or ethanol sustains the continued process of glycolysis under anaerobic conditions.*

3. Only a fraction of the energy of glucose is released in its anaerobic conversion into ethanol or lactate. Much more energy can be extracted aerobically by means of the citric acid cycle and the electron-transport chain. The entry point to this oxidative pathway is *acetyl coenzyme A* (acetyl CoA), which is formed inside mitochondria by the oxidative decarboxylation of pyruvate.

$$\text{Pyruvate} + \text{NAD}^+ + \text{CoA} \rightarrow \text{acetyl CoA} + CO_2 + \text{NADH} + \text{H}$$

This reaction, which is catalyzed by the pyruvate dehydrogenase complex, will be considered in detail in Chapter 17. The NAD$^+$ required for this reaction and for the oxidation of glyceraldehyde 3-phosphate is regenerated when NADH ultimately transfers its electrons to O_2 through the electron-transport chain in mitochondria.

Fermentations provide usable energy in the absence of oxygen

Fermentations yield only a fraction of the energy available from the complete combustion of glucose. Why is a relatively inefficient metabolic pathway so extensively used? The fundamental reason is that oxygen is not required. The ability to survive without oxygen affords a host of living accommodations such as soils, deep water, and skin pores. Some organisms, called *obligate anaerobes*, cannot survive in the presence of O_2, a highly reactive compound. The bacterium *Clostridium perfringens*, the cause of gangrene, is an example of an obligate anaerobe. Other pathogenic obligate anaerobes are listed in Table 16.2. Skeletal muscles in most animals can function anaerobically for short periods. For example, when animals perform bursts of intense exercise, their ATP needs rise faster than the ability of the body

Table 16.2 Examples of pathogenic obligate anaerobes

Bacterium	Result of infection
Clostridium tetani	Tetanus (lockjaw)
Clostridium botulinum	Botulism (an especially severe type of food poisoning)
Clostridium perfringens	Gas gangrene (gas is produced as an end point of the fermentation, distorting and destroying the tissue)
Bartonella hensela	Cat scratch fever (flu-like symptoms)
Bacteroides fragilis	Abdominal, pelvic, pulmonary, and blood infections

to provide oxygen to the muscle. The muscle functions anaerobically until fatigue sets in, which is caused, in part, by lactate buildup.

Although we have considered only lactic acid and alcoholic fermentation, microorganisms are capable of generating a wide array of molecules as end points of fermentation (Table 16.3). Indeed, many food products, including sour cream, yogurt, various cheeses, beer, wine, and sauerkraut, result from fermentation.

The binding site for NAD⁺ is similar in many dehydrogenases

The three dehydrogenases—glyceraldehyde 3-phosphate dehydrogenase, alcohol dehydrogenase, and lactate dehydrogenase—have quite different three-dimensional structures. However, their NAD^+-binding domains are strikingly similar (Figure 16.12). This nucleotide-binding region is made up of four α helices and a sheet of six parallel β strands. Moreover, in all cases, the bound NAD^+ displays nearly the same conformation. This common structural domain was one of the first recurring structural domains to be discovered. It is often called a *Rossmann fold* after Michael Rossmann, who first recognized it. This fold likely represents a primordial dinucleotide-binding domain that recurs in the dehydrogenases of glycolysis and other enzymes because of their descent from a common ancestor.

Table 16.3 Starting and ending points of various fermentations

Glucose	→	lactate
Lactate	→	acetate
Glucose	→	ethanol
Ethanol	→	acetate
Arginine	→	carbon dioxide
Pyrimidines	→	carbon dioxide
Purines	→	formate
Ethylene glycol	→	acetate
Threonine	→	propionate
Leucine	→	2-alkylacetate
Phenylalanine	→	propionate

Note: The products of some fermentations are the substrates for others.

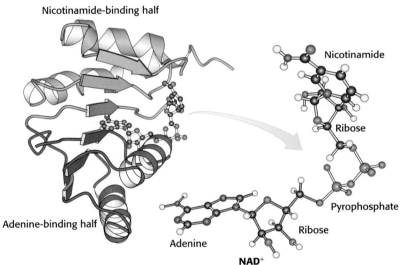

Nicotinamide-binding half

Nicotinamide

Ribose

Pyrophosphate

Ribose

Adenine-binding half

Adenine

NAD⁺

Figure 16.12 NAD⁺-binding region in dehydrogenases. *Notice* that the nicotinamide-binding half (yellow) is structurally similar to the adenine-binding half (red). The two halves together form a structural motif called a Rossmann fold. The NAD^+ molecule binds in an extended conformation. [Drawn from 3LDH.pdb.]

Fructose and galactose are converted into glycolytic intermediates

Although glucose is the most widely used monosaccharide, others also are important fuels. Let us consider how two abundant sugars—fructose and galactose—can be funneled into the glycolytic pathway (Figure 16.13). There are no catabolic pathways for metabolizing fructose or galactose, and so the strategy is to convert these sugars into a metabolite of glucose.

Fructose can take one of two pathways to enter the glycolytic pathway. Much of the ingested fructose is metabolized by the liver, using *the fructose 1-phosphate pathway* (Figure 16.14). The first step is the phosphorylation of *fructose* to *fructose 1-phosphate* by *fructokinase*. Fructose 1-phosphate is then split into *glyceraldehyde* and *dihydroxyacetone phosphate,* an

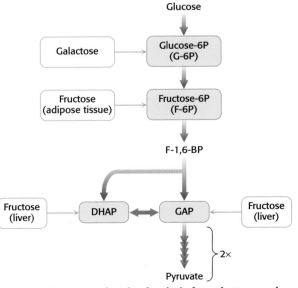

Figure 16.13 Entry points in glycolysis for galactose and fructose.

469

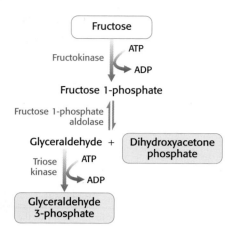

Figure 16.14 Fructose metabolism.
Fructose enters the glycolytic pathway in the liver through the fructose 1-phosphate pathway.

intermediate in glycolysis. This aldol cleavage is catalyzed by a specific *fructose 1-phosphate aldolase.* Glyceraldehyde is then phosphorylated to *glyceraldehyde 3-phosphate,* a glycolytic intermediate, by *triose kinase.* In other tissues, *fructose can be phosphorylated to fructose 6-phosphate by hexokinase.*

Galactose is converted into *glucose 6-phosphate* in four steps. The first reaction in the *galactose–glucose interconversion pathway* is the phosphorylation of galactose to galactose 1-phosphate by *galactokinase.*

Galactose 1-phosphate then acquires a uridyl group from uridine diphosphate glucose (UDP-glucose), an activated intermediate in the synthesis of carbohydrates (Section 21.4).

The products of this reaction, which is catalyzed by *galactose 1-phosphate uridyl transferase,* are UDP-galactose and glucose 1-phosphate. The galactose moiety of UDP-galactose is then epimerized to glucose. The configuration of the hydroxyl group at carbon 4 is inverted by *UDP-galactose 4-epimerase.*

The sum of the reactions catalyzed by galactokinase, the transferase, and the epimerase is

$$\text{Galactose} + \text{ATP} \longrightarrow \text{glucose 1-phosphate} + \text{ADP} + \text{H}^+$$

Note that UDP-glucose is not consumed in the conversion of galactose into glucose, because it is regenerated from UDP-galactose by the epimerase. This reaction is reversible, and the product of the reverse direction also is important. *The conversion of UDP-glucose into UDP-galactose is essential for the synthesis of galactosyl residues in complex polysaccharides and glyco-proteins if the amount of galactose in the diet is inadequate to meet these needs.*

Finally, glucose 1-phosphate, formed from galactose, is isomerized to glucose 6-phosphate by *phosphoglucomutase*. We shall return to this reaction when we consider the synthesis and degradation of glycogen, which proceeds through glucose 1-phosphate, in Chapter 21.

Many adults are intolerant of milk because they are deficient in lactase

Many adults are unable to metabolize the milk sugar lactose and experience gastrointestinal disturbances if they drink milk. *Lactose intolerance,* or hypolactasia, is most commonly caused by a deficiency of the enzyme lactase, which cleaves lactose into glucose and galactose.

Lactose + H_2O $\xrightleftharpoons{\text{Lactase}}$ **Galactose** + **Glucose**

"Deficiency" is not quite the appropriate term, because a decrease in lactase is normal in the course of development in all mammals. As children are weaned and milk becomes less prominent in their diets, lactase activity normally declines to about 5% to 10% of the level at birth. This decrease is not as pronounced with some groups of people, most notably Northern Europeans, and people from these groups can continue to ingest milk without gastrointestinal difficulties. With the appearance of milk-producing domesticated animals, an adult with active lactase would have a selective advantage in being able to consume calories from the readily available milk. Because dairy farming originated only about 10,000 years ago, the evolutionary selective pressure on lactase persistence must have been substantial, attesting to the biochemical value of being able to use milk as an energy source into adulthood.

What happens to the lactose in the intestine of a lactase-deficient person? The lactose is a good energy source for microorganisms in the colon, and they ferment it to lactic acid while generating methane (CH_4) and hydrogen gas (H_2). The gas produced creates the uncomfortable feeling of gut distension and the annoying problem of flatulence. The lactate produced by the microorganisms is osmotically active and draws water into the intestine, as does any undigested lactose, resulting in diarrhea. If severe enough, the gas and diarrhea hinder the absorption of other nutrients such as fats and proteins. The simplest treatment is to avoid the consumption of products containing much lactose. Alternatively, the enzyme lactase can be ingested with milk products.

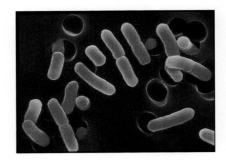

Scanning electron micrograph of *Lactobacillus.* The anaerobic bacterium *Lactobacillus* is shown here (artificially colored) at a magnification of 22.245×. As suggested by its name, this genus of bacteria ferments glucose into lactic acid and is widely used in the food industry. *Lactobacillus* is also a component of the normal human bacterial flora of the urogenital tract where, because of its ability to generate an acidic environment, it prevents the growth of harmful bacteria. [Dr. Dennis Kunkel/PhotoTake.]

Galactose is highly toxic if the transferase is missing

Less common than lactose intolerance are disorders that interfere with the metabolism of galactose. The disruption of galactose metabolism is referred to as *galactosemia*. The most common form, called classic galactosemia, is an inherited deficiency in galactose 1-phosphate uridyl transferase activity. Afflicted infants fail to thrive. They vomit or have diarrhea after consuming milk, and enlargement of the liver and jaundice are common, sometimes progressing to cirrhosis. Cataracts will form, and lethargy and retarded mental development also are common. The blood-galactose level is markedly elevated, and galactose is found in the urine. The absence of the transferase in red blood cells is a definitive diagnostic criterion.

The most common treatment is to remove galactose (and lactose) from the diet. An enigma of galactosemia is that, although elimination of galactose from the diet prevents liver disease and cataract development, the majority of patients still suffer from central nervous system malfunction, most commonly a delayed acquisition of language skills. Female patients also display ovarian failure.

Cataract formation is better understood. A cataract is the clouding of the normally clear lens of the eye (Figure 16.15). If the transferase is not active in the lens of the eye, the presence of aldose reductase causes the accumulating galactose to be reduced to galactitol.

(A)

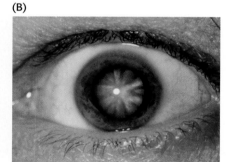

(B)

Figure 16.15 Cataracts are evident as the clouding of the lens. (A) A healthy eye. (B) An eye with a cataract. [(A) © Imageafter; (B) SPL/Photo Researchers.]

Galactitol is osmotically active, and water will diffuse into the lens, instigating the formation of cataracts. In fact, there is a high incidence of cataract formation with age in populations that consume substantial amounts of milk into adulthood.

16.2 The Glycolytic Pathway Is Tightly Controlled

The glycolytic pathway has a dual role: it degrades glucose to generate ATP and it provides building blocks for synthetic reactions, such as the formation of fatty acids. The rate of conversion of glucose into pyruvate is regulated to meet these two major cellular needs. *In metabolic pathways, enzymes catalyzing essentially irreversible reactions are potential sites of control.* In glycolysis, the reactions catalyzed by hexokinase, phosphofructokinase, and pyruvate kinase are virtually irreversible; hence, these enzymes would be expected to have regulatory as well as catalytic roles. In fact, each of them serves as a control site. These enzymes become more active or less so in response to the reversible binding of allosteric effectors or covalent modification. In addition, the amounts of these important enzymes are varied by the regulation of transcription to meet changing metabolic needs. The time required for reversible allosteric control, regulation by phosphorylation, and transcriptional control is measured typically in milliseconds, seconds,

Glycolysis in muscle is regulated to meet the need for ATP

Glycolysis in skeletal muscle provides ATP primarily to power contraction. Consequently, the primary control of muscle glycolysis is the energy charge of the cell—the ratio of ATP to AMP. Let us examine how each of the key regulatory enzymes responds to changes in the amounts of ATP and AMP present in the cell.

Phosphofructokinase. *Phosphofructokinase is the most important control site in the mammalian glycolytic pathway* (Figure 16.16). High levels of ATP allosterically inhibit the enzyme (a 340-kd tetramer). ATP binds to a specific regulatory site that is distinct from the catalytic site. The binding of ATP lowers the enzyme's affinity for fructose 6-phosphate. Thus, a high concentration of ATP converts the hyperbolic binding curve of fructose 6-phosphate into a sigmoidal one (Figure 16.17). AMP reverses the inhibitory action of ATP, and so *the activity of the enzyme increases when the ATP/AMP ratio is lowered.* In other words, *glycolysis is stimulated as the energy charge falls.* A decrease in pH also inhibits phosphofructokinase activity by augmenting the inhibitory effect of ATP. The pH might fall when muscle is functioning anaerobically, producing excessive quantities of lactic acid. The inhibitory effect protects the muscle from damage that would result from the accumulation of too much acid.

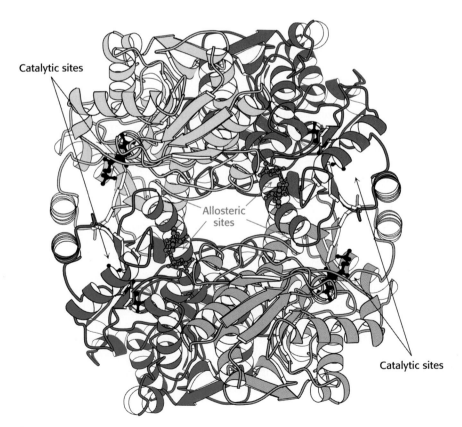

Catalytic sites

Allosteric sites

Catalytic sites

► Figure 16.16 Structure of phosphofructokinase. The structure of phosphofructokinase from *E. coli* comprises a tetramer of four identical subunits. *Notice* the separation of the catalytic and allosteric sites. Each subunit of the human liver enzyme consists of two domains that are similar to the *E. coli* enzyme. [Drawn from 1PFK.pdb.]

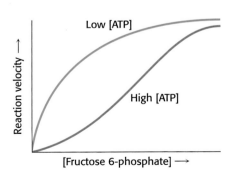

Low [ATP]

High [ATP]

Reaction velocity ⟶

[Fructose 6-phosphate] ⟶

Figure 16.17 Allosteric regulation of phosphofructokinase. A high level of ATP inhibits the enzyme by decreasing its affinity for fructose 6-phosphate. AMP diminishes and citrate enhances the inhibitory effect of ATP.

Why is AMP and not ADP the positive regulator of phosphofruc-tokinase? When ATP is being utilized rapidly, the enzyme *adenylate kinase* (Section 9.4) can form ATP from ADP by the following reaction:

$$\text{ADP} + \text{ADP} \rightleftharpoons \text{ATP} + \text{AMP}$$

Thus, some ATP is salvaged from ADP, and AMP becomes the signal for the low-energy state. Moreover, the use of AMP as an allosteric regulator provides an especially sensitive control. We can understand why by consid-ering, first, that the total adenylate pool ([ATP], [ADP], [AMP]) in a cell is constant over the short term and, second, that the concentration of ATP is greater than that of ADP and the concentration of ADP is, in turn, greater than that of AMP. Consequently, small-percentage changes in [ATP] result in larger-percentage changes in the concentrations of the other adenylate nucleotides. This magnification of small changes in [ATP] to larger changes in [AMP] leads to tighter control by increasing the range of sensitivity of phosphofructokinase.

Hexokinase. Phosphofructokinase is the most prominent regulatory enzyme in glycolysis, but it is not the only one. Hexokinase, the enzyme catalyzing the first step of glycolysis, is inhibited by its product, glucose 6-phosphate. High concentrations of this molecule signal that the cell no longer requires glucose for energy or for the synthesis of glycogen, a storage form of glucose (Chapter 21), and the glucose will be left in the blood. A rise in glucose 6-phosphate concentration is a means by which phosphofruc-tokinase communicates with hexokinase. When phosphofructokinase is inactive, the concentration of fructose 6-phosphate rises. In turn, the level of glucose 6-phosphate rises because it is in equilibrium with fructose 6-phosphate. Hence, *the inhibition of phosphofructokinase leads to the inhibi-tion of hexokinase.*

Why is phosphofructokinase rather than hexokinase the pacemaker of glycolysis? The reason becomes evident on noting that glucose 6-phosphate is not solely a glycolytic intermediate. In muscle, glucose 6-phosphate can also be converted into glycogen. The first irreversible reaction unique to the glycolytic pathway, the *committed step* (Section 10.1), is the phosphorylation of fructose 6-phosphate to fructose 1,6-bisphosphate. Thus, it is highly appropriate for phosphofructokinase to be the primary control site in glyco-lysis. In general, *the enzyme catalyzing the committed step in a metabolic sequence is the most important control element in the pathway.*

Pyruvate kinase. Pyruvate kinase, the enzyme catalyzing the third irre-versible step in glycolysis, controls the outflow from this pathway. This final step yields ATP and pyruvate, a central metabolic intermediate that can be oxidized further or used as a building block. ATP allosterically inhibits pyruvate kinase to slow glycolysis when the energy charge is high. Finally, alanine (synthesized in one step from pyruvate, Section 23.3) also allosterically inhibits pyruvate kinase—in this case, to signal that building blocks are abundant. When the pace of glycolysis increases, fructose 1,6-bisphosphate, the product of the preceding irreversible step in glycoly-sis, activates the kinase to enable it to keep pace with the oncoming high flux of intermediates. A summary of the regulation of glycolysis in resting and active muscle is shown in Figure 16.18.

The regulation of glycolysis in the liver illustrates the biochemical versatility of the liver

The liver has more-diverse biochemical functions than muscle. Significantly, the liver maintains blood-glucose levels: it stores glucose as glycogen when

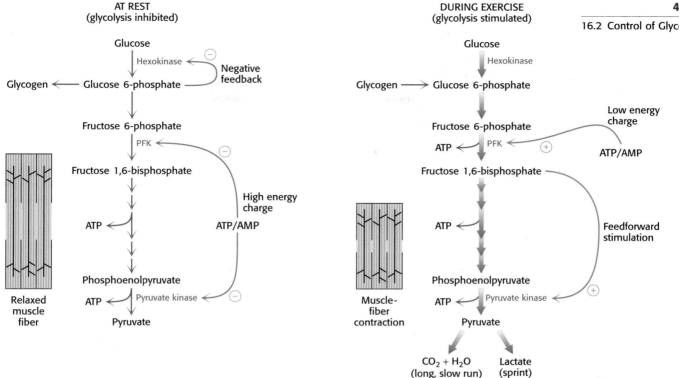

Figure 16.18 Regulation of glycolysis in muscle. At rest (left), glycolysis is not very active (thin arrows). The high concentration of ATP inhibits phosphofructokinase (PFK), pyruvate kinase, and hexokinase. Glucose 6-phosphate is converted into glycogen (Chapter 21). During exercise (right), the decrease in the ATP/AMP ratio resulting from muscle contraction activates phosphofructokinase and hence glycolysis. The flux down the pathway is increased, as represented by the thick arrows.

glucose is plentiful, and it releases glucose when supplies are low. It also uses glucose to generate reducing power for biosynthesis (Section 20.3) as well as to synthesize a host of biochemicals. So, although the liver has many of the regulatory features of muscle glycolysis, the regulation of glycolysis in the liver is more complex.

Phosphofructokinase. Regulation with respect to ATP is the same in the liver as in muscle. Low pH is not a metabolic signal for the liver enzyme, because lactate is not normally produced in the liver. Indeed, as we will see, lactate is converted into glucose in the liver.

Glycolysis also furnishes carbon skeletons for biosyntheses, and so a signal indicating whether building blocks are abundant or scarce should also regulate phosphofructokinase. In the liver, *phosphofructokinase is inhibited by citrate,* an early intermediate in the citric acid cycle (Chapter 17). A high level of citrate in the cytoplasm means that biosynthetic precursors are abundant, and so there is no need to degrade additional glucose for this purpose. Citrate inhibits phosphofructokinase by enhancing the inhibitory effect of ATP.

One means by which glycolysis in the liver responds to changes in blood glucose is through the signal molecule *fructose 2,6-bisphosphate* (F-2,6-BP), a potent activator of phosphofructokinase (Figure 16.19). In the liver, the concentration of fructose 6-phosphate rises when blood-glucose concentration is high, and the abundance of fructose 6-phosphate accelerates the synthesis of F-2,6-BP (Figure 16.20). Hence, *an abundance of fructose 6-phosphate leads to a higher concentration of F-2,6-BP.* The binding of

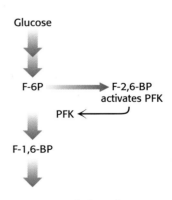

Figure 16.19 Regulation of phosphofructokinase by fructose 2,6-bisphosphate. In high concentrations, fructose 6-phosphate (F-6P) activates the enzyme phosphofructokinase (PFK) through an intermediary, fructose 2,6-bisphosphate (F-2,6-BP).

Figure 16.20 Activation of phosphofructokinase by fructose 2,6-bisphosphate. (A) The sigmoidal dependence of velocity on substrate concentration becomes hyperbolic in the presence of 1 μM fructose 2,6-bisphosphate. (B) ATP, acting as a substrate, initially stimulates the reaction. As the concentration of ATP increases, it acts as an allosteric inhibitor. The inhibitory effect of ATP is reversed by fructose 2,6-bisphosphate. [After E. Van Schaftingen, M. F. Jett, L. Hue, and H. G. Hers. *Proc. Natl. Acad. Sci. U. S. A.* 78:3483–3486, 1981.]

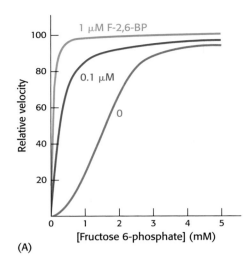
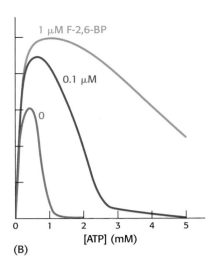

(A)

(B)

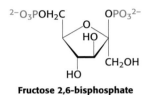

**Fructose 2,6-bisphosphate
(F-2,6-BP)**

fructose 2,6-bisphosphate increases the affinity of phosphofructokinase for fructose 6-phosphate and diminishes the inhibitory effect of ATP. Glycolysis is thus accelerated when glucose is abundant. Such a process is called *feedforward stimulation.* We will turn to the synthesis and degradation of this important regulatory molecule after we have considered gluconeogenesis.

Hexokinase. The hexokinase reaction in the liver is controlled as in the muscle. However, the liver, in keeping with its role as monitor of blood-glucose levels, possesses another specialized isozyme of hexokinase, called *glucokinase,* which is not inhibited by glucose 6-phosphate. Glucokinase phosphorylates glucose only when glucose is abundant because the affinity of glucokinase for glucose is about 50-fold lower than that of hexokinase. The role of glucokinase is to provide glucose 6-phosphate for the synthesis of glycogen and for the formation of fatty acids (Section 22.1). The low affinity of glucokinase for glucose in the liver gives the brain and muscles first call on glucose when its supply is limited, and it ensures that glucose will not be wasted when it is abundant. Glucokinase is also present in the β cells of the pancreas, where the increased formation of glucose 6-phosphate by glucokinase when blood-glucose levels are elevated leads to the secretion of the hormone insulin. Insulin signals the need to remove glucose from the blood for storage as glycogen or conversion into fat.

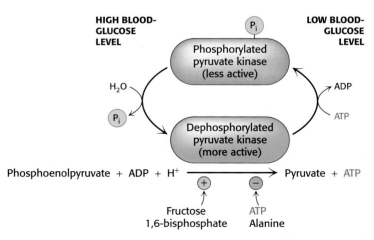

Figure 16.21 Control of the catalytic activity of pyruvate kinase.
Pyruvate kinase is regulated by allosteric effectors and covalent modification.

Pyruvate kinase. Several isozymic forms of pyruvate kinase (a tetramer of 57-kd subunits) encoded by different genes are present in mammals: the L type predominates in the liver, and the M type in muscle and the brain. The L and M forms of pyruvate kinase have many properties in common. Indeed, the liver enzyme behaves much like the muscle enzyme with regard to allosteric regulation. However, the isozymic forms differ in their susceptibility to covalent modification. The catalytic properties of the L form—but not of the M form—are also controlled by reversible phosphorylation (Figure 16.21). When the blood-glucose level is low, the glucagon-triggered cyclic AMP cascade (p. 487) leads to the phosphorylation of pyruvate kinase, which diminishes its activity. This hormone-triggered phosphorylation prevents

Table 16.4 Family of glucose transporters

Name	Tissue location	K_M	Comments
GLUT1	All mammalian tissues	1 mM	Basal glucose uptake
GLUT2	Liver and pancreatic β cells	15–20 mM	In the pancreas, plays a role in the regulation of insulin In the liver, removes excess glucose from the blood
GLUT3	All mammalian tissues	1 mM	Basal glucose uptake
GLUT4	Muscle and fat cells	5 mM	Amount in muscle plasma membrane increases with endurance training
GLUT5	Small intestine	—	Primarily a fructose transporter

the liver from consuming glucose when it is more urgently needed by the brain and muscle. We see here a clear-cut example of how isoenzymes contribute to the metabolic diversity of different organs. We will return to the control of glycolysis after considering gluconeogenesis.

A family of transporters enables glucose to enter and leave animal cells

Several glucose transporters mediate the thermodynamically downhill movement of glucose across the plasma membranes of animal cells. Each member of this protein family, named GLUT1 to GLUT5, consists of a single polypeptide chain about 500 residues long (Table 16.4). Each glucose transporter has a 12-transmembrane-helix structure similar to that of lactose permease (Section 13.3).

The members of this family have distinctive roles:

1. GLUT1 and GLUT3, present in nearly all mammalian cells, are responsible for basal glucose uptake. Their K_M value for glucose is about 1 mM, significantly less than the normal serum-glucose level, which typically ranges from 4 mM to 8 mM. Hence, GLUT1 and GLUT3 continually transport glucose into cells at an essentially constant rate.

2. GLUT2, present in liver and pancreatic β cells, is distinctive in having a very high K_M value for glucose (15–20 mM). Hence, glucose enters these tissues at a biologically significant rate only when there is much glucose in the blood. The pancreas can sense the glucose level and accordingly adjust the rate of insulin secretion. The high K_M value of GLUT2 also ensures that glucose rapidly enters liver cells only in times of plenty.

3. GLUT4, which has a K_M value of 5 mM, transports glucose into muscle and fat cells. The number of GLUT4 transporters in the plasma membrane increases rapidly in the presence of insulin, which signals the fed state. Hence, insulin promotes the uptake of glucose by muscle and fat. Endurance exercise training increases the amount of this transporter present in muscle membranes.

4. GLUT5, present in the small intestine, functions primarily as a fructose transporter.

This family of transporters vividly illustrates how isoforms of a single protein can significantly shape the metabolic character of cells and contribute to their diversity and functional specialization. The transporters are members of a superfamily of transporters called the major facilitator (MF) superfamily. Members of this family transport sugars in organisms as diverse as *E. coli*, *Trypanosoma brucei* (a parasitic protozoan that causes sleeping sickness), and human beings. An elegant solution to the problem of fuel transport evolved early and has been tailored to meet the needs of different organisms and even different tissues.

Cancer and exercise training affect glycolysis in a similar fashion

Tumors have been known for decades to display enhanced rates of glucose uptake and glycolysis. Indeed, rapidly growing tumor cells will metabolize glucose to lactate even in the presence of oxygen, a process called *aerobic glycolysis* or the "Warburg effect," after Otto Warburg, the biochemist who first noted this characteristic of cancer cells in the 1920s. In fact, tumors with a high glucose uptake are particularly aggressive, and the cancer is likely to have a poor prognosis. A nonmetabolizable glucose analog, 2-^{18}F-2-D-deoxyglucose, detectable by a combination of positron emission tomography (PET) and computer-aided tomography (CAT), easily visualizes tumors (Figure 16.22).

What selective advantage does aerobic glycolysis offer the tumor over the energetically more efficient oxidative phosphorylation? Research is being actively pursued to answer the question, but we can speculate on the benefits. First, aerobic glycolysis generates lactic acid that is then secreted. Acidification of the tumor environment has been shown to facilitate tumor invasion and inhibit the immune system from attacking the tumor. Second, the increased uptake of glucose and formation of glucose 6-phosphate provides substrates for another metabolic pathway, the pentose phosphate

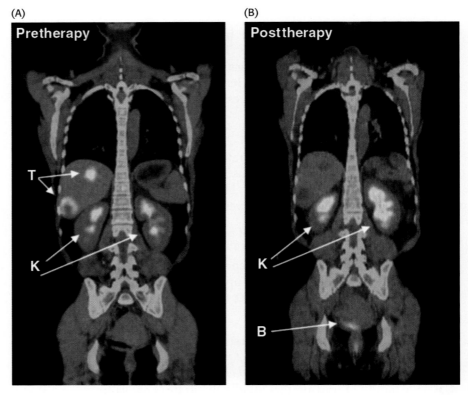

Figure 16.22 Tumors can be visualized with 2-^{18}F-2-D-deoxyglucose (FDG) and positron emission tomography. (A) A nonmetabolizable glucose analog infused into a patient and detected by a combination of positron emission and computer-aided tomography reveals the presence of a malignant tumor (T). (B) After 4 weeks of treatment with a tyrosine kinase inhibitor (Section 14.5), the tumor shows no uptake of FDG, indicating decreased metabolism. Excess FDG, which is excreted in the urine, also visualizes the kidney (K) and bladder (B). [Images courtesy of A. D. Van den Abbeele, Dana-Farber Cancer Institute, Boston.]

pathway (Chapter 20), that generates biosynthetic reducing power. Moreover, the pentose phosphate pathway, in cooperation with glycolysis, produces precursors for biomolecules necessary for growth, such as nucleotides. Finally, cancer cells grow more rapidly than the blood vessels that nourish them; thus, as solid tumors grow, the oxygen concentration in their environment falls. In other words, they begin to experience *hypoxia,* a deficiency of oxygen. The use of aerobic glycolysis reduces the dependence of cell growth on oxygen.

Hypoxia itself enhances tumor growth by activating a transcription factor, *hypoxia-inducible transcription factor* (HIF-1). HIF-1 increases the expression of most glycolytic enzymes and the glucose transporters GLUT1 and GLUT3 (Table 16.5). These adaptations by the cancer cells enable a tumor to survive until blood vessels can grow. HIF-1 also increases the expression of signal molecules, such as vascular endothelial growth factor (VEGF), that facilitate the growth of blood vessels that will provide nutrients to the cells (Figure 16.23). Without new blood vessels, a tumor would cease to grow and either die or remain harmlessly small. Efforts are underway to develop drugs that inhibit the growth of blood vessels in tumors.

What biochemical alterations facilitate the switch to aerobic glycolysis? Again, the answers are not complete, but changes in gene expression of isozymic forms of two glycolytic enzymes may be crucial. Tumor cells express an isozyme of hexokinase that binds to mitochondria. There, the enzyme has ready access to any ATP generated by oxidative phosphorylation and is no longer susceptible to feedback inhibition by its product, glucose 6-phosphate. An embryonic isozyme of pyruvate kinase also is expressed; it facilitates uses of glycolytic intermediates for biosynthetic reactions and is sensitive to growth-factor regulation.

Interestingly, anaerobic exercise training activates HIF-1, producing the same effects as those seen in the tumor—enhanced ability to generate ATP anaerobically and a stimulation of blood-vessel growth. These biochemical effects account for the improved athletic performance that results from training and demonstrate how behavior can affect biochemistry.

16.3 Glucose Can Be Synthesized from Noncarbohydrate Precursors

We now turn to the *synthesis of glucose from noncarbohydrate precursors,* a process called *gluconeogenesis.* Maintaining levels of glucose is important because the brain depends on glucose as its primary fuel and red blood cells use glucose as their only fuel. The daily glucose requirement of the brain in a typical adult human being is about 120 g, which accounts for most of the 160 g of glucose needed daily by the whole body. The amount of glucose present in body fluids is about 20 g, and that readily available from glycogen is approximately 190 g. Thus, the direct glucose reserves are sufficient to meet glucose needs for about a day. Gluconeogenesis is especially important during a longer period of fasting or starvation (Section 27.5).

The gluconeogenic pathway converts pyruvate into glucose. Noncarbohydrate precursors of glucose are first converted into pyruvate or enter the pathway at later intermediates such as oxaloacetate and dihydroxyacetone phosphate (Figure 16.24). The major noncarbohydrate precursors are *lactate, amino acids,* and *glycerol.* Lactate is formed by active skeletal muscle when the rate of glycolysis exceeds the rate of oxidative metabolism. Lactate is readily converted into pyruvate by the action of lactate dehydrogenase (p. 468). Amino acids are derived from proteins in the diet and,

Table 16.5 Proteins in glucose metabolism encoded by genes regulated by hypoxia-inducible factor

GLUT1
GLUT3
Hexokinase
Phosphofructokinase
Aldolase
Glyceraldehyde 3-phosphate dehydrogenase
Phosphoglycerate kinase
Enolase
Pyruvate kinase

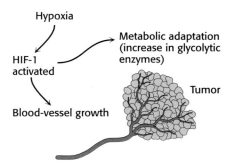

Figure 16.23 Alteration of gene expression in tumors owing to hypoxia. The hypoxic conditions inside a tumor mass lead to the activation of the hypoxia-inducible transcription factor (HIF-1), which induces metabolic adaptation (an increase in glycolytic enzymes) and activates angiogenic factors that stimulate the growth of new blood vessels. [After C. V. Dang and G. L. Semenza. *Trends Biochem. Sci.* 24:68–72, 1999.]

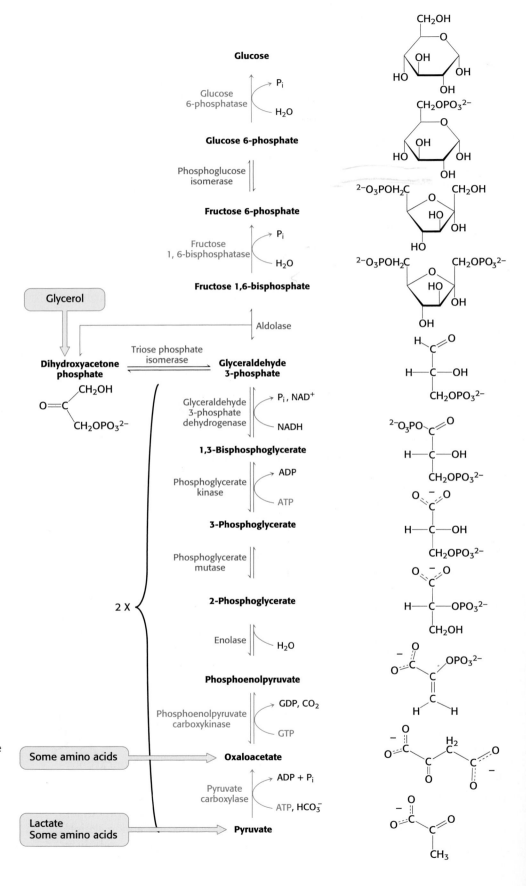

Glucose

Glucose
6-phosphatase
$\rightarrow P_i$
$\rightarrow H_2O$

Glucose 6-phosphate

Phosphoglucose
isomerase

Fructose 6-phosphate

Fructose
1, 6-bisphosphatase
$\rightarrow P_i$
$\rightarrow H_2O$

Fructose 1,6-bisphosphate

Glycerol

Aldolase

Triose phosphate
isomerase

Dihydroxyacetone phosphate ⇌ **Glyceraldehyde 3-phosphate**

Glyceraldehyde
3-phosphate
dehydrogenase
$\rightarrow P_i , NAD^+$
$\rightarrow NADH$

1,3-Bisphosphoglycerate

Phosphoglycerate
kinase
$\rightarrow ADP$
$\rightarrow ATP$

3-Phosphoglycerate

Phosphoglycerate
mutase

2-Phosphoglycerate

Enolase
$\rightarrow H_2O$

Phosphoenolpyruvate

Phosphoenolpyruvate
carboxykinase
$\rightarrow GDP, CO_2$
$\rightarrow GTP$

Some amino acids → **Oxaloacetate**

Pyruvate
carboxylase
$\rightarrow ADP + P_i$
$\rightarrow ATP, HCO_3^-$

Lactate
Some amino acids → **Pyruvate**

2 X

**Figure 16.24 Pathway of
gluconeogenesis.** The distinctive
reactions and enzymes of this pathway
are shown in red. The other reactions are
common to glycolysis. The enzymes for
gluconeogenesis are located in the
cytoplasm, except for pyruvate
carboxylase (in the mitochondria) and
glucose 6-phosphatase (membrane
bound in the endoplasmic reticulum).
The entry points for lactate, glycerol, and
amino acids are shown.

during starvation, from the breakdown of proteins in skeletal muscle (Section 23.1). The hydrolysis of triacylglycerols (Section 22.2) in fat cells yields glycerol and fatty acids. Glycerol is a precursor of glucose, but animals cannot convert fatty acids into glucose, for reasons that will be given later. Glycerol may enter either the gluconeogenic or the glycolytic pathway at dihydroxyacetone phosphate.

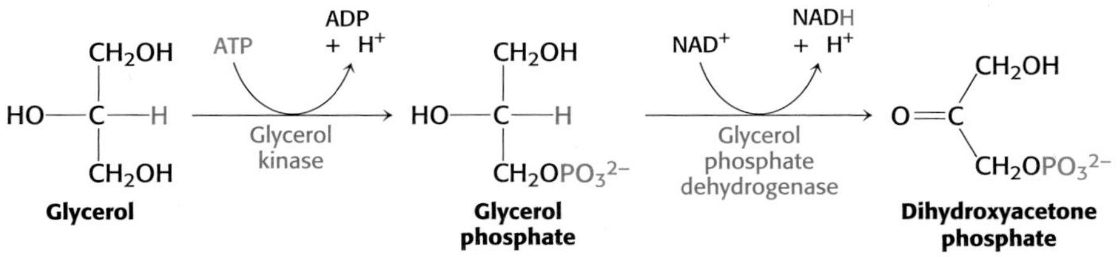

The major site of gluconeogenesis is the *liver,* with a small amount also taking place in the *kidney.* Little gluconeogenesis takes place in the brain, skeletal muscle, or heart muscle. Rather, *gluconeogenesis in the liver and kidney helps to maintain the glucose level in the blood so that the brain and muscle can extract sufficient glucose from it to meet their metabolic demands.*

Gluconeogenesis is not a reversal of glycolysis

In glycolysis, glucose is converted into pyruvate; in gluconeogenesis, pyruvate is converted into glucose. However, *gluconeogenesis is not a reversal of glycolysis.* Several reactions must differ because the equilibrium of glycolysis lies far on the side of pyruvate formation. The actual ΔG for the formation of pyruvate from glucose is about -84 kJ mol^{-1} (-20 kcal mol^{-1}) under typical cellular conditions. Most of the decrease in free energy in glycolysis takes place in the three essentially irreversible steps catalyzed by hexokinase, phosphofructokinase, and pyruvate kinase.

$$\text{Glucose} + \text{ATP} \xrightarrow{\text{Hexokinase}} \text{glucose 6-phosphate} + \text{ADP}$$
$$\Delta G = -33 \text{ kJ mol}^{-1} \ (-8.0 \text{ kcal mol}^{-1})$$

$$\text{Fructose 6-phosphate} + \text{ATP} \xrightarrow{\text{Phosphofructokinase}}$$
$$\text{fructose 1,6-bisphosphate} + \text{ADP}$$
$$\Delta G = -22 \text{ kJ mol}^{-1} \ (-5.3 \text{ kcal mol}^{-1})$$

$$\text{Phosphoenolpyruvate} + \text{ADP} \xrightarrow{\text{Pyruvate kinase}} \text{pyruvate} + \text{ATP}$$
$$\Delta G = -17 \text{ kJ mol}^{-1} \ (-4.0 \text{ kcal mol}^{-1})$$

In gluconeogenesis, the following new steps bypass these virtually irreversible reactions of glycolysis:

1. *Phosphoenolpyruvate is formed from pyruvate by way of oxaloacetate* through the action of pyruvate carboxylase and phosphoenolpyruvate carboxykinase.

$$\text{Pyruvate} + \text{CO}_2 + \text{ATP} + \text{H}_2\text{O} \xrightarrow{\text{Pyruvate carboxylase}}$$
$$\text{oxaloacetate} + \text{ADP} + \text{P}_i + 2 \text{ H}^+$$

$$\text{Oxaloacetate} + \text{GTP} \xrightarrow{\text{Phosphoenolpyruvate carboxykinase}}$$
$$\text{phosphoenolpyruvate} + \text{GDP} + \text{CO}_2$$

2. *Fructose 6-phosphate is formed from fructose 1,6-bisphosphate by hydrolysis of the phosphate ester at carbon 1.* Fructose 1,6-bisphosphatase catalyzes this exergonic hydrolysis.

$$\text{Fructose 1,6-bisphosphate} + H_2O \longrightarrow \text{fructose 6-phosphate} + P_i$$

3. *Glucose is formed by the hydrolysis of glucose 6-phosphate* in a reaction catalyzed by glucose 6-phosphatase.

$$\text{Glucose 6-phosphate} + H_2O \longrightarrow \text{glucose} + P_i$$

We will examine each of these steps in turn.

The conversion of pyruvate into phosphoenolpyruvate begins with the formation of oxaloacetate

The first step in gluconeogenesis is the carboxylation of pyruvate to form oxaloacetate at the expense of a molecule of ATP.

Pyruvate **Oxaloacetate**

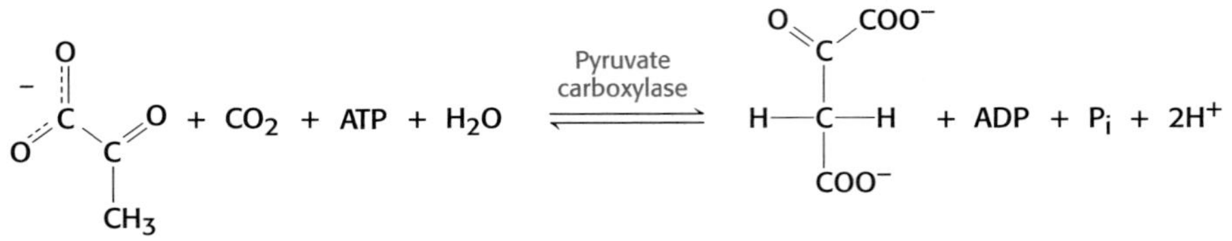

Then, oxaloacetate is decarboxylated and phosphorylated to yield phosphoenolpyruvate, at the expense of the high phosphoryl-transfer potential of GTP.

Oxaloacetate **Phosphoenolpyruvate**

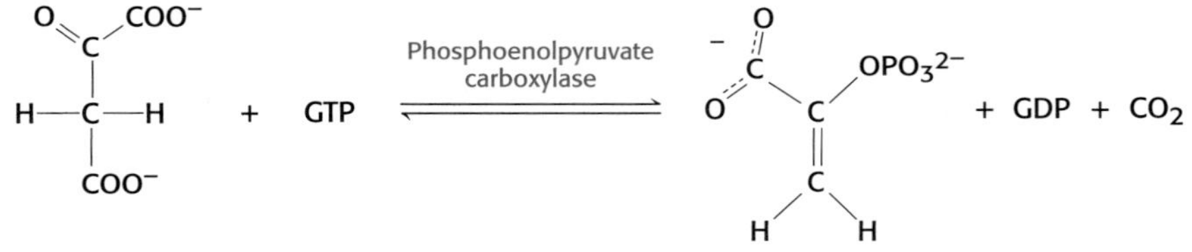

The first of these reactions takes place inside the mitochondria.

The first reaction is catalyzed by *pyruvate carboxylase* and the second by *phosphoenolpyruvate carboxykinase* (PEPCK). The sum of these reactions is

$$\text{Pyruvate} + \text{ATP} + \text{GTP} + H_2O \rightleftharpoons \text{phosphoenolpyruvate} + \text{ADP} + \text{GDP} + P_i + 2\,H^+$$

Pyruvate carboxylase is of special interest because of its structural, catalytic, and allosteric properties. The N-terminal 300 to 350 amino acids form an *ATP-grasp domain* (Figure 16.25), which is an ATP-activating domain found in many enzymes, to be considered in more detail when we examine nucleotide biosynthesis (Chapter 25). The C-terminal 80 amino acids constitute a biotin-binding domain (Figure 16.26) that we will see again in fatty acid synthesis (Section 22.4). *Biotin* is a covalently attached prosthetic

Figure 16.25 Domain structure of pyruvate carboxylase. The ATP-grasp domain activates HCO_3^- and transfers CO_2 to the biotin-binding domain. From there, the CO_2 is transferred to pyruvate generated in the central domain.

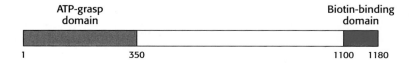

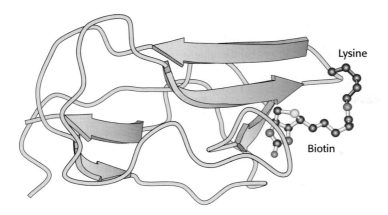

Figure 16.26 Biotin-binding domain of pyruvate carboxylase. This likely structure is based on the structure of the homologous domain of the enzyme acetyl CoA carboxylase (Section 22.4). *Notice* that the biotin is on a flexible tether, allowing it to move between the ATP-bicarbonate site and the pyruvate site. [Drawn from 1BDO.pdb.]

group, which serves as a *carrier of activated CO₂*. The carboxylate group of biotin is linked to the ε-amino group of a specific lysine residue by an amide bond (Figure 16.27). Note that biotin is attached to pyruvate carboxylase by a *long, flexible chain*.

The carboxylation of pyruvate takes place in three stages:

$$HCO_3^- + ATP \rightleftharpoons HOCO_2\text{-}PO_3^{2-} + ADP$$
$$\text{Biotin–enzyme} + HOCO_2\text{-}PO_3^{2-} \rightleftharpoons CO_2 - \text{biotin–enzyme} + P_i$$
$$CO_2 - \text{biotin–enzyme} + \text{pyruvate} \rightleftharpoons \text{biotin–enzyme} + \text{oxaloacetate}$$

Recall that, in aqueous solutions, CO_2 exists primarily as HCO_3^- with the aid of carbonic anhydrase (Section 9.2). HCO_3^- is activated to carboxyphosphate. This activated CO_2 is subsequently bonded to the N-l atom of the biotin ring to form the carboxybiotin–enzyme intermediate (see Figure 16.27). The CO_2 attached to biotin is quite activated. The $\Delta G^{\circ\prime}$ for its cleavage

$$CO_2\text{–biotin–enzyme} + H^+ \rightarrow CO_2 + \text{biotin–enzyme}$$

is -20 kJ mol^{-1} (-4.7 kcal mol^{-1}). This negative $\Delta G^{\circ\prime}$ indicates that carboxybiotin is able to transfer CO_2 to acceptors without the input of additional free energy.

The activated carboxyl group is then transferred from carboxybiotin to pyruvate to form oxaloacetate. The long, flexible link between biotin and the enzyme enables this prosthetic group to rotate from one active site of the enzyme (the ATP-bicarbonate site) to the other (the pyruvate site).

The first partial reaction of pyruvate carboxylase, the formation of carboxybiotin, depends on the presence of acetyl CoA. *Biotin is not carboxylated unless acetyl CoA is bound to the enzyme.* Acetyl CoA has no effect on the second partial reaction. The allosteric activation of pyruvate carboxylase by acetyl CoA is an important physiological control mechanism that will be discussed in Section 17.4.

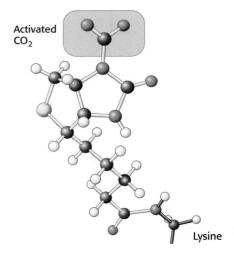

Activated CO_2

Lysine

Figure 16.27 Structure of carboxybiotin.

Oxaloacetate is shuttled into the cytoplasm and converted into phosphoenolpyruvate

Pyruvate carboxylase is a mitochondrial enzyme, whereas the other enzymes of gluconeogenesis are present primarily in the cytoplasm. Oxaloacetate, the product of the pyruvate carboxylase reaction, must thus be transported to the cytoplasm to complete the pathway. Oxaloacetate is transported from a mitochondrion in the form of malate: oxaloacetate is reduced to malate inside the mitochondrion by an NADH-linked malate dehydrogenase. After malate has been transported across the mitochondrial membrane, it is reoxidized to oxaloacetate by an NAD$^+$-linked malate dehydrogenase in the

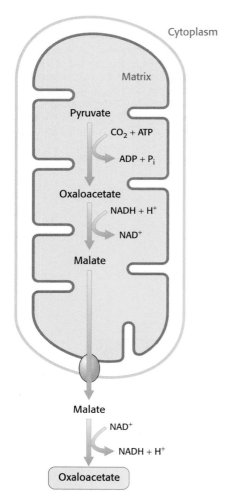

**Figure 16.28 Compartmental
cooperation.** Oxaloacetate used in the
cytoplasm for gluconeogenesis is formed in
the mitochondrial matrix by the carboxylation
of pyruvate. Oxaloacetate leaves the
mitochondrion by a specific transport system
(not shown) in the form of malate, which is
reoxidized to oxaloacetate in the cytoplasm.

cytoplasm (Figure 16.28). The formation of oxaloacetate from malate also provides NADH for use in subsequent steps in gluconeogenesis. Finally, oxaloacetate is simultaneously *decarboxylated* and *phosphorylated* by phosphoenolpyruvate carboxykinase to generate phosphoenolpyruvate. The phosphoryl donor is GTP. The CO_2 that was added to pyruvate by pyruvate carboxylase comes off in this step.

Why is a carboxylation and a decarboxylation required to form phosphoenolpyruvate from pyruvate? Recall that, in glycolysis, the presence of a phosphoryl group traps the unstable enol isomer of pyruvate as phosphoenolpyruvate (p. 465). However, the addition of a phosphoryl group to pyruvate is a highly unfavorable reaction: the $\Delta G^{\circ\prime}$ of the reverse of the glycolytic reaction catalyzed by pyruvate kinase is $+31$ kJ mol^{-1} ($+7.5$ kcal mol^{-1}). In gluconeogenesis, the use of the carboxylation and decarboxylation steps results in a much more favorable $\Delta G^{\circ\prime}$. The formation of phosphoenolpyruvate from pyruvate in the gluconeogenic pathway has a $\Delta G^{\circ\prime}$ of $+0.8$ kJ mol^{-1} ($+0.2$ kcal mol^{-1}). A molecule of ATP is used to power the addition of a molecule of CO_2 to pyruvate in the carboxylation step. That CO_2 is then removed to power the formation of phosphoenolpyruvate in the decarboxylation step. *Decarboxylations often drive reactions that are otherwise highly endergonic.* This metabolic motif is used in the citric acid cycle (Chapter 17), the pentose phosphate pathway (Chapter 20), and fatty acid synthesis (Section 22.4).

The conversion of fructose 1,6-bisphosphate into fructose 6-phosphate and orthophosphate is an irreversible step

On formation, phosphoenolpyruvate is metabolized by the enzymes of glycolysis but in the reverse direction. These reactions are near equilibrium under intracellular conditions; so, when conditions favor gluconeogenesis, the reverse reactions will take place until the next irreversible step is reached. This step is the hydrolysis of fructose 1,6-bisphosphate to fructose 6-phosphate and P_i.

$$\text{Fructose 1,6-bisphosphate} + H_2O \xrightarrow{\text{Fructose 1,6-bisphosphatase}} \text{fructose 6-phosphate} + P_i$$

The enzyme responsible for this step is fructose 1,6-bisphosphatase. Like its glycolytic counterpart, it is an allosteric enzyme that participates in the regulation of gluconeogenesis. We will return to its regulatory properties later in the chapter.

The generation of free glucose is an important control point

The fructose 6-phosphate generated by fructose 1,6-bisphosphatase is readily converted into glucose 6-phosphate. In most tissues, gluconeogenesis ends here. Free glucose is not generated; rather, the glucose 6-phosphate is processed in some other fashion, notably to form glycogen. One advantage to ending gluconeogenesis at glucose 6-phosphate is that, unlike free glucose, the molecule is not transported out of the cell. To keep glucose inside the cell, the generation of free glucose is controlled in two ways. First, the enzyme responsible for the conversion of glucose 6-phosphate into glucose, *glucose 6-phosphatase,* is regulated. Second, the enzyme is present only in tissues whose metabolic duty is to maintain blood-glucose homeostasis—tissues that release glucose into the blood. These tissues are the liver and to a lesser extent the kidney.

This final step in the generation of glucose does not take place in the cytoplasm. Rather, glucose 6-phosphate is transported into the lumen of the endoplasmic reticulum, where it is hydrolyzed to glucose by glucose

6-phosphatase, which is bound to the membrane (Figure 16.29). An associated Ca^{2+}-binding stabilizing protein is essential for phosphatase activity. Glucose and P_i are then shuttled back to the cytoplasm by a pair of transporters. The glucose transporter in the endoplasmic reticulum membrane is like those found in the plasma membrane. It is striking that five proteins are needed to transform cytoplasmic glucose 6-phosphate into glucose.

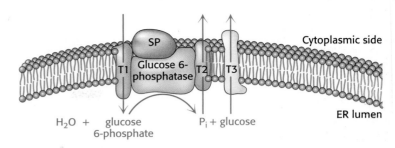

Figure 16.29 Generation of glucose from glucose 6-phosphate. Several endoplasmic reticulum (ER) proteins play a role in the generation of glucose from glucose 6-phosphate. T1 transports glucose 6-phosphate into the lumen of the ER, whereas T2 and T3 transport P_i and glucose, respectively, back into the cytoplasm. Glucose 6-phosphatase is stabilized by a Ca^{2+}-binding protein (SP). [After A. Buchell and I. D. Waddel. *Biochem. Biophys. Acta* 1092:129–137, 1991.]

Six high-transfer-potential phosphoryl groups are spent in synthesizing glucose from pyruvate

The formation of glucose from pyruvate is energetically unfavorable unless it is coupled to reactions that are favorable. Compare the stoichiometry of gluconeogenesis with that of the reverse of glycolysis.

The stoichiometry of gluconeogenesis is

$$2 \text{ Pyruvate} + 4 \text{ ATP} + 2 \text{ GTP} + 2 \text{ NADH} + 6 \text{ H}_2\text{O} \rightarrow$$
$$\text{glucose} + 4 \text{ ADP} + 2 \text{ GDP} + 6 \text{ P}_i + 2 \text{ NAD}^+ + 2 \text{ H}^+$$
$$\Delta G^{\circ\prime} = -48 \text{ kJ mol}^{-1}(-11 \text{ kcal mol}^{-1})$$

In contrast, the stoichiometry for the reversal of glycolysis is

$$2 \text{ Pyruvate} + 2 \text{ ATP} + \text{ NADH} + 2 \text{ H}_2\text{O} \rightarrow$$
$$\text{glucose} + 2 \text{ ADP} + 2 \text{ P}_i + 2 \text{ NAD}^+ + 2 \text{ H}^+$$
$$\Delta G^{\circ\prime} = +84 \text{ kJ mol}^{-1}(+20 \text{ kcal mol}^{-1})$$

Note that *six* nucleoside triphosphate molecules are hydrolyzed to synthesize glucose from pyruvate in gluconeogenesis, whereas only *two* molecules of ATP are generated in glycolysis in the conversion of glucose into pyruvate. Thus, the extra cost of gluconeogenesis is four high-phosphoryl-transfer-potential molecules for each molecule of glucose synthesized from pyruvate. The four additional molecules having high phosphoryl-transfer potential are needed to turn an energetically unfavorable process (the reversal of glycolysis) into a favorable one (gluconeogenesis). Here we have a clear example of the coupling of reactions: NTP hydrolysis is used to power an energetically unfavorable reaction. The reactions of gluconeogenesis are summarized in Table 16.6.

Table 16.6 Reactions of gluconeogenesis

Step	Reaction
1	Pyruvate + CO_2 + ATP + $H_2O \longrightarrow$ oxaloacetate + ADP + P_i + $2H^+$
2	Oxaloacetate + GTP $\rightleftharpoons$ phosphoenolpyruvate + GDP + CO_2
3	Phosphoenolpyruvate + $H_2O \rightleftharpoons$ 2-phosphoglycerate
4	2-Phosphoglycerate $\rightleftharpoons$ 3-phosphoglycerate
5	3-Phosphoglycerate + ATP $\rightleftharpoons$ 1,3-bisphosphoglycerate + ADP
6	1,3-Bisphosphoglycerate + NADH + $H^+ \rightleftharpoons$ glyceraldehyde 3-phosphate + NAD^+ + P_i
7	Glyceraldehyde 3-phosphate $\rightleftharpoons$ dihydroxyacetone phosphate
8	Glyceraldehyde 3-phosphate + dihydroxyacetone phosphate $\rightleftharpoons$ fructose 1,6-bisphosphate
9	Fructose 1,6-bisphosphate + $H_2O \longrightarrow$ fructose 6-phosphate + P_i
10	Fructose 6-phosphate $\rightleftharpoons$ glucose 6-phosphate
11	Glucose 6-phosphate + $H_2O \longrightarrow$ + glucose + P_i

16.4 Gluconeogenesis and Glycolysis Are Reciprocally Regulated

Gluconeogenesis and glycolysis are coordinated so that, within a cell, one pathway is relatively inactive while the other is highly active. If both sets of reactions were highly active at the same time, the net result would be the hydrolysis of four nucleoside triphosphates (two ATP molecules plus two GTP molecules) per reaction cycle. Both glycolysis and gluconeogenesis are highly exergonic under cellular conditions, and so there is no thermodynamic barrier to such simultaneous activity. However, the *amounts* and *activities* of the distinctive enzymes of each pathway are controlled so that both pathways are not highly active at the same time. The rate of glycolysis is also determined by the concentration of glucose, and the rate of gluconeogenesis by the concentrations of lactate and other precursors of glucose. The basic premise of the reciprocal regulation is that, when energy is needed, glycolysis will predominate. When there is a surplus of energy, gluconeogenesis will take over.

Energy charge determines whether glycolysis or gluconeogenesis will be most active

The first important regulation site is the interconversion of fructose 6-phosphate and fructose 1,6-bisphosphate (Figure 16.30). Consider first a situation in which energy is needed. In this case, the concentration of AMP is high. Under this condition, AMP stimulates phosphofructokinase but inhibits fructose 1,6-bisphosphatase. Thus, glycolysis is turned on and gluconeogenesis is inhibited. Conversely, high levels of ATP and citrate indicate that the energy charge is high and that biosynthetic intermediates

Figure 16.30 Reciprocal regulation of gluconeogenesis and glycolysis in the liver. The level of fructose 2,6-bisphosphate is high in the fed state and low in starvation. Another important control is the inhibition of pyruvate kinase by phosphorylation during starvation.

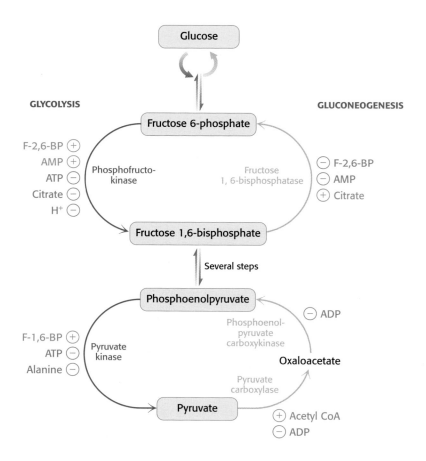

are abundant. ATP and citrate inhibit phosphofructokinase, whereas citrate activates fructose 1,6-bisphosphatase. Under these conditions, glycolysis is nearly switched off and gluconeogenesis is promoted. Why does citrate take part in this regulatory scheme? As we will see in Chapter 17, citrate reports on the status of the citric acid cycle, the primary pathway for oxidizing fuels in the presence of oxygen. High levels of citrate indicate an energy-rich situation and the presence of precursors for biosynthesis.

Glycolysis and gluconeogenesis are also reciprocally regulated at the interconversion of phosphoenolpyruvate and pyruvate in the liver. The glycolytic enzyme pyruvate kinase is inhibited by allosteric effectors ATP and alanine, which signal that the energy charge is high and that building blocks are abundant. Conversely, pyruvate carboxylase, which catalyzes the first step in gluconeogenesis from pyruvate, is inhibited by ADP. Likewise, ADP inhibits phosphoenolpyruvate carboxykinase. Pyruvate carboxylase is activated by acetyl CoA, which, like citrate, indicates that the citric acid cycle is producing energy and biosynthetic intermediates (Chapter 17). Hence, gluconeogenesis is favored when the cell is rich in biosynthetic precursors and ATP.

The balance between glycolysis and gluconeogenesis in the liver is sensitive to blood-glucose concentration

In the liver, rates of glycolysis and gluconeogenesis are adjusted to maintain blood-glucose levels. *The signal molecule fructose 2,6-bisphosphate strongly stimulates phosphofructokinase* (PFK) *and inhibits fructose 1,6-bisphosphatase* (p. 475). When blood glucose is low, fructose 2,6-bisphosphate loses a phosphoryl group to form fructose 6-phosphate, which no longer binds to PFK. How is the concentration of fructose 2,6-bisphosphate controlled to rise and fall with blood-glucose levels? Two enzymes regulate the concentration of this molecule: one phosphorylates fructose 6-phosphate and the other dephosphorylates fructose 2,6-bisphosphate. Fructose 2,6-bisphosphate is formed in a reaction catalyzed by *phosphofructokinase 2* (PFK2), a different enzyme from phosphofructokinase. Fructose 6-phosphate is formed through the hydrolysis of fructose 2,6-bisphosphate by a specific phosphatase, *fructose bisphosphatase 2* (FBPase2). The striking finding is that *both PFK2 and FBPase2 are present in a single 55-kd polypeptide chain* (Figure 16.31). This *bifunctional enzyme* contains an N-terminal *regulatory domain,* followed by a *kinase domain* and a *phosphatase domain.* PFK2 resembles adenylate kinase in having a P-loop NTPase domain (Section 9.4), whereas FBPase2 resembles phosphoglycerate mutase (p. 464). Recall that the mutase is essentially a phosphatase. In the bifunctional enzyme, the phosphatase activity evolved to become specific for F-2,6-BP. The bifunctional enzyme itself probably arose by the fusion of genes encoding the kinase and phosphatase domains.

What controls whether PFK2 or FBPase2 dominates the bifunctional enzyme's activities in the liver? The activities of PFK2 and FBPase2 are reciprocally controlled by *phosphorylation of a single serine residue.* When glucose is scarce, such as during a night's fast, a rise in the blood level of the hormone glucagon triggers a cyclic AMP signal cascade (Section 14.1), leading to the phosphorylation of this bifunctional enzyme by protein kinase A (Figure 16.32). This covalent modification activates FBPase2 and inhibits PFK2, lowering the level of F-2,6-BP. Gluconeogenesis

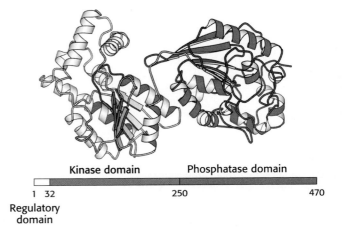

Kinase domain   Phosphatase domain

1 32   250   470

Regulatory
domain

▶ **Figure 16.31 Domain structure of the bifunctional enzyme phosphofructokinase 2.** The kinase domain (purple) is fused to the phosphatase domain (red). The kinase domain is a P-loop NTP hydrolase domain, as indicated by the purple shading (Section 9.4). The bar represents the amino acid sequence of the enzyme. [Drawn from 1BIF.pdb.]

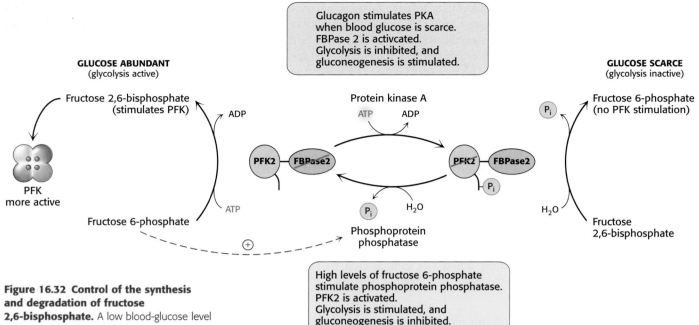

GLUCOSE ABUNDANT
(glycolysis active)

Glucagon stimulates PKA when blood glucose is scarce. FBPase 2 is activcated. Glycolysis is inhibited, and gluconeogenesis is stimulated.

GLUCOSE SCARCE
(glycolysis inactive)

Fructose 2,6-bisphosphate (stimulates PFK)

Fructose 6-phosphate (no PFK stimulation)

Protein kinase A

ADP

ATP   ADP

P_i

PFK
more active

PFK2 — FBPase2

PFK2 — FBPase2

P_i

ATP

P_i H_2O

H_2O

Fructose 6-phosphate

Phosphoprotein phosphatase

Fructose 2,6-bisphosphate

High levels of fructose 6-phosphate stimulate phosphoprotein phosphatase. PFK2 is activated. Glycolysis is stimulated, and gluconeogenesis is inhibited.

Figure 16.32 Control of the synthesis and degradation of fructose 2,6-bisphosphate. A low blood-glucose level as signaled by glucagon leads to the phosphorylation of the bifunctional enzyme and hence to a lower level of fructose 2,6-bisphosphate, slowing glycolysis. High levels of fructose 6-phosphate accelerate the formation of fructose 2,6-bisphosphate by facilitating the dephosphorylation of the bifunctional enzyme.

predominates. Glucose formed by the liver under these conditions is essential for the viability of the brain. Glucagon stimulation of protein kinase A also inactivates pyruvate kinase in the liver (p. 476).

Conversely, when blood-glucose levels are high, such as after a meal, gluconeogenesis is not needed. Insulin is secreted and initiates a signal pathway that activates a protein phosphatase, which removes the phosphoryl group from the bifunctional enzyme. This covalent modification activates PFK2 and inhibits FBPase2. The resulting rise in the level of F-2,6-BP accelerates glycolysis. The coordinated control of glycolysis and gluconeogenesis is facilitated by the location of the kinase and phosphatase domains on the same polypeptide chain as the regulatory domain.

The hormones insulin and glucagon also regulate the amounts of essential enzymes. These hormones alter gene expression primarily by changing the rate of transcription. Insulin levels rise subsequent to eating, when there is plenty of glucose for glycolysis. To encourage glycolysis, insulin stimulates the expression of phosphofructokinase, pyruvate kinase, and the bifunctional enzyme that makes and degrades F-2,6-BP. Glucagon rises during fasting, when gluconeogenesis is needed to replace scarce glucose. To encourage gluconeogenesis, glucagon inhibits the expression of the three regulated glycolytic enzymes and stimulates instead the production of two key gluconeogenic enzymes, phosphoenolpyruvate carboxykinase and fructose 1,6-bisphosphatase. Transcriptional control in eukaryotes is much slower than allosteric control, taking hours or days instead of seconds to minutes. The richness and complexity of hormonal control are graphically displayed by the promoter of the phosphoenolpyruvate carboxykinase gene, which contains regulatory sequences that respond to insulin, glucagon (through the cAMP response elements), glucocorticoids, and thyroid hormone (Figure 16.33).

Figure 16.33 The promoter of the phosphoenolpyruvate carboxykinase gene. This promoter is approximately 500 bp in length and contains regulatory sequences (response elements) that mediate the action of several hormones. Abbreviations: IRE, insulin response element; GRE, glucocorticoid response element; TRE, thyroid hormone response element; CREI and CREII, cAMP response elements. [After M. M. McGrane, J. S. Jun, Y. M. Patel, and R. W. Hanson. *Trends Biochem. Sci.* 17:40–44, 1992.]

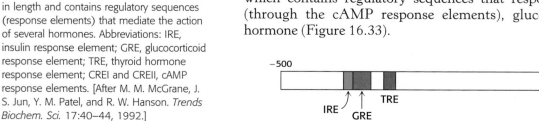

−500   1

IRE   GRE   TRE   CREI   CREII

Substrate cycles amplify metabolic signals and produce heat

A pair of reactions such as the phosphorylation of fructose 6-phosphate to fructose 1,6-bisphosphate and its hydrolysis back to fructose 6-phosphate is called a *substrate cycle*. As already mentioned, both reactions are not simultaneously fully active in most cells, because of reciprocal allosteric controls. However, isotope-labeling studies have shown that some fructose 6-phosphate is phosphorylated to fructose 1,6-bisphosphate even during gluconeogenesis. There also is a limited degree of cycling in other pairs of opposed irreversible reactions. This cycling was regarded as an imperfection in metabolic control, and so substrate cycles have sometimes been called *futile cycles*. Indeed, there are pathological conditions, such as malignant hyperthermia, in which control is lost and both pathways proceed rapidly. One result is the rapid, uncontrolled hydrolysis of ATP, which generates heat.

Despite such extraordinary circumstances, substrate cycles now seem likely to be biologically important. One possibility is that *substrate cycles amplify metabolic signals.* Suppose that the rate of conversion of A into B is 100 and of B into A is 90, giving an initial net flux of 10. Assume that an allosteric effector increases the A → B rate by 20% to 120 and reciprocally decreases the B → A rate by 20% to 72. The new net flux is 48, and so a 20% change in the rates of the opposing reactions has led to a 380% increase in the net flux. In the example shown in Figure 16.34, this amplification is made possible by the rapid hydrolysis of ATP. The flux down the glycolytic pathway has been suggested to increase as much as 1000-fold at the initiation of intense exercise. Because the allosteric activation of enzymes alone seems unlikely to explain this increased flux, the existence of substrate cycles may partly account for the rapid rise in the rate of glycolysis.

The other potential biological role of substrate cycles is the generation of heat produced by the hydrolysis of ATP. In European bumblebees, cycling is used for both signal amplification and heat generation. Phosphofructokinase and fructose 1,6-bisphosphatase in a bee's flight muscle are simultaneously active. The cycling augments other means of thermogenesis, such as shivering, and amplifies the flux down the glycolytic pathway in preparation for the transition from rest to flight.

Lactate and alanine formed by contracting muscle are used by other organs

Lactate produced by active skeletal muscle and erythrocytes is a source of energy for other organs. Erythrocytes lack mitochondria and can never oxidize glucose completely. In contracting skeletal muscle during vigorous exercise, the rate at which glycolysis produces pyruvate exceeds the rate at which the citric acid cycle oxidizes it. In these cells, lactate dehydrogenase reduces excess pyruvate to lactate to restore redox balance (p. 466). However, lactate is a dead end in metabolism. It must be converted back into pyruvate before it can be metabolized. Both pyruvate and lactate diffuse out of these cells through carriers into the blood. *In contracting skeletal muscle, the formation and release of lactate lets the muscle generate ATP in the absence of oxygen and shifts the burden of metabolizing lactate from muscle to other organs.* The pyruvate and lactate in the bloodstream have two fates. In one fate, the plasma membranes of some cells, particularly cells in cardiac muscle, contain carriers that make the cells highly permeable to lactate and pyruvate. These molecules diffuse from the blood into such permeable cells. Once inside these well-oxygenated cells, lactate can be reverted back to pyruvate and metabolized through the citric acid cycle and oxidative phosphorylation to generate ATP. The use of lactate in place of glucose by these

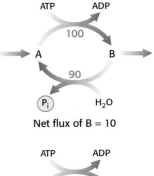

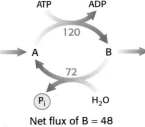

Figure 16.34 Substrate cycle. This ATP-driven cycle operates at two different rates. A small change in the rates of the two opposing reactions results in a large change in the *net* flux of product B.

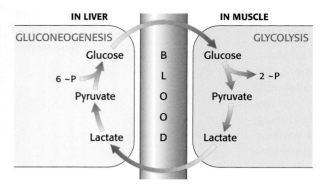

IN LIVER

GLUCONEOGENESIS

Glucose

6 ~P

Pyruvate

Lactate

B
L
O
O
D

IN MUSCLE

GLYCOLYSIS

Glucose

2 ~P

Pyruvate

Lactate

Figure 16.35 The Cori cycle. Lactate formed by active muscle is converted into glucose by the liver. This cycle shifts part of the metabolic burden of active muscle to the liver.

cells makes more circulating glucose available to the active muscle cells. In the other fate, excess lactate enters the liver and is converted first into pyruvate and then into glucose by the gluconeogenic pathway. *Contracting skeletal muscle supplies lactate to the liver, which uses it to synthesize and release glucose. Thus, the liver restores the level of glucose necessary for active muscle cells, which derive ATP from the glycolytic conversion of glucose into lactate. These reactions constitute the Cori cycle* (Figure 16.35).

Studies have shown that alanine, like lactate, is a major precursor of glucose in the liver. The alanine is generated in muscle when the carbon skeletons of some amino acids are used as fuels. The nitrogens from these amino acids are transferred to pyruvate to form alanine; the reverse reaction takes place in the liver. This process also helps maintain nitrogen balance. The interplay between glycolysis and gluconeogenesis is summarized in Figure 16.36, which shows how these pathways help meet the energy needs of different cell types.

Isozymic forms of lactate dehydrogenase in different tissues catalyze the interconversions of pyruvate and lactate (Section 10.2). Lactate dehydrogenase is a tetramer of two kinds of 35-kd subunits encoded by similar genes: the H type predominates in the heart, and the homologous M type in skeletal muscle and the liver. These subunits associate to form five types of tetramers: H_4, H_3M_1, H_2M_2, H_1M_3, and M_4. The H_4 isozyme (type 1) has higher affinity for substrates than that of the M_4 isozyme (type 5) and, unlike M_4, is allosterically inhibited by high levels of pyruvate. The other isozymes have intermediate properties, depending on

Figure 16.36 PATHWAY INTEGRATION: Cooperation between glycolysis and gluconeogenesis during a sprint.
Glycolysis and gluconeogenesis are coordinated, in a tissue-specific fashion, to ensure that the energy needs of all cells are met. Consider a sprinter. In skeletal leg muscle, glucose will be metabolized aerobically to CO_2 and H_2O or, more likely (thick arrows) during a sprint, anaerobically to lactate. In cardiac muscle, the lactate can be converted into pyruvate and used as a fuel, along with glucose, to power the heartbeats to keep the sprinter's blood flowing. Gluconeogenesis, a primary function of the liver, will be taking place rapidly (thick arrows) to ensure that enough glucose is present in the blood for skeletal and cardiac muscle, as well as for other tissues. Glycogen, glycerol, and amino acids are other sources of energy that we will learn about in later chapters.

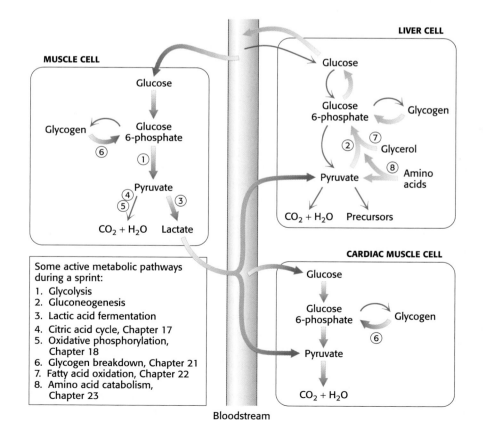

Some active metabolic pathways during a sprint:
1. Glycolysis
2. Gluconeogenesis
3. Lactic acid fermentation
4. Citric acid cycle, Chapter 17
5. Oxidative phosphorylation, Chapter 18
6. Glycogen breakdown, Chapter 21
7. Fatty acid oxidation, Chapter 22
8. Amino acid catabolism, Chapter 23

Bloodstream

the ratio of the two kinds of chains. The H_4 isozyme oxidizes lactate to pyruvate, which is then used as a fuel by the heart through aerobic metabolism. Indeed, heart muscle never functions anaerobically. In contrast, M_4 is optimized to operate in the reverse direction, to convert pyruvate into lactate to allow glycolysis to proceed under anaerobic conditions. We see here an example of how gene duplication and divergence generate a series of homologous enzymes that foster metabolic cooperation between organs.

Glycolysis and gluconeogenesis are evolutionarily intertwined

The metabolism of glucose has ancient origins. Organisms living in the early biosphere depended on the anaerobic generation of energy until significant amounts of oxygen began to accumulate 2 billion years ago. Glycolytic enzymes were most likely derived independently rather than by gene duplication, because glycolytic enzymes with similar properties do not have similar amino acid sequences. Although there are four kinases and two isomerases in the pathway, both sequence and structural comparisons do not suggest that these sets of enzymes are related to one another by divergent evolution. The common dinucleotide-binding domain found in the dehydrogenases (see Figure 16.12) and the αβ barrels are the only major recurring elements.

We can speculate on the relationship between glycolysis and gluconeogenesis if we think of glycolysis as consisting of two segments: the metabolism of hexoses (the upper segment) and the metabolism of trioses (the lower segment). The enzymes of the upper segment are different in some species and are missing entirely in some archaea, whereas enzymes of the lower segment are quite conserved. In fact, four enzymes of the lower segment are present in all species. *This lower part of the pathway is common to glycolysis and gluconeogenesis.* This common part of the two pathways may be the oldest part, constituting the core to which the other steps were added. The upper part would have varied according to the sugars that were available to evolving organisms in particular niches. Interestingly, this core part of carbohydrate metabolism can generate triose precursors for ribose sugars, a component of RNA and a critical requirement for the RNA world. Thus, we are left with the unanswered question, Was the original core pathway used for energy conversion or biosynthesis?

Summary

16.1 Glycolysis Is an Energy-Conversion Pathway in Many Organisms

Glycolysis is the set of reactions that converts glucose into pyruvate. The 10 reactions of glycolysis take place in the cytoplasm. In the first stage, glucose is converted into fructose 1,6-bisphosphate by a phosphorylation, an isomerization, and a second phosphorylation reaction. Fructose 1,6-bisphosphate is then cleaved by aldolase into dihydroxyacetone phosphate and glyceraldehyde 3-phosphate, which are readily interconvertible. Two molecules of ATP are consumed per molecule of glucose in these reactions, which are the prelude to the net synthesis of ATP. In the second stage, ATP is generated. Glyceraldehyde 3-phosphate is oxidized and phosphorylated to form 1,3-bisphosphoglycerate, an acyl phosphate with a high phosphoryl-transfer potential. This molecule transfers a phosphoryl group to ADP to form ATP and 3-phosphoglycerate. A phosphoryl shift and a dehydration form phosphoenolpyruvate, a second intermediate with a high phosphoryl-transfer potential. Another molecule of ATP is generated as phosphoenolpyruvate is converted into pyruvate. There is a net gain of two molecules of ATP in the formation of two molecules of pyruvate from one molecule of glucose.

The electron acceptor in the oxidation of glyceraldehyde 3-phosphate is NAD^+, which must be regenerated for glycolysis to continue. In aerobic organisms, the NADH formed in glycolysis transfers its electrons to O_2 through the electron-transport chain, which thereby regenerates NAD^+. Under anaerobic conditions and in some microorganisms, NAD^+ is regenerated by the reduction of pyruvate to lactate. In other microorganisms, NAD^+ is regenerated by the reduction of pyruvate to ethanol. These two processes are examples of fermentations.

16.2 The Glycolytic Pathway Is Tightly Controlled

The glycolytic pathway has a dual role: it degrades glucose to generate ATP, and it provides building blocks for the synthesis of cellular components. The rate of conversion of glucose into pyruvate is regulated to meet these two major cellular needs. Under physiological conditions, the reactions of glycolysis are readily reversible except for those catalyzed by hexokinase, phosphofructokinase, and pyruvate kinase. Phosphofructokinase, the most important control element in glycolysis, is inhibited by high levels of ATP and citrate, and it is activated by AMP and fructose 2,6-bisphosphate. In the liver, this bisphosphate signals that glucose is abundant. Hence, phosphofructokinase is active when either energy or building blocks are needed. Hexokinase is inhibited by glucose 6-phosphate, which accumulates when phosphofructokinase is inactive. ATP and alanine allosterically inhibit pyruvate kinase, the other control site, and fructose 1,6-bisphosphate activates the enzyme. Consequently, pyruvate kinase is maximally active when the energy charge is low and glycolytic intermediates accumulate.

16.3 Glucose Can Be Synthesized from Noncarbohydrate Precursors

Gluconeogenesis is the synthesis of glucose from noncarbohydrate sources, such as lactate, amino acids, and glycerol. Several of the reactions that convert pyruvate into glucose are common to glycolysis. Gluconeogenesis, however, requires four new reactions to bypass the essential irreversibility of three reactions in glycolysis. In two of the new reactions, pyruvate is carboxylated in mitochondria to oxaloacetate, which in turn is decarboxylated and phosphorylated in the cytoplasm to phosphoenolpyruvate. Two molecules having high phosphoryl-transfer potential are consumed in these reactions, which are catalyzed by pyruvate carboxylase and phosphoenolpyruvate carboxykinase. Pyruvate carboxylase contains a biotin prosthetic group. The other distinctive reactions of gluconeogenesis are the hydrolyses of fructose 1,6-bisphosphate and glucose 6-phosphate, which are catalyzed by specific phosphatases. The major raw materials for gluconeogenesis by the liver are lactate and alanine produced from pyruvate by active skeletal muscle. The formation of lactate during intense muscular activity buys time and shifts part of the metabolic burden from muscle to the liver.

16.4 Gluconeogenesis and Glycolysis Are Reciprocally Regulated

Gluconeogenesis and glycolysis are reciprocally regulated so that one pathway is relatively inactive while the other is highly active. Phosphofructokinase and fructose 1,6-bisphosphatase are key control points. Fructose 2,6-bisphosphate, an intracellular signal molecule present at higher levels when glucose is abundant, activates glycolysis and inhibits gluconeogenesis by regulating these enzymes. Pyruvate kinase and pyruvate carboxylase are regulated by other effectors so that both are not maximally active at the same time. Allosteric regulation and reversible phosphorylation, which are rapid, are complemented by transcriptional control, which takes place in hours or days.

Key Terms

glycolysis (p. 453)

lactic acid fermentation (p. 453)

alcoholic fermentation (p. 453)

gluconeogenesis (p. 453)

α-amylase (p. 454)

hexokinase (p. 455)

kinase (p. 457)

phosphofructokinase (PFK) (p. 458)

thioester intermediate (p. 462)

substrate-level phosphorylation (p. 464)

phosphoglycerate mutase (p. 464)

enol phosphate (p. 465)

pyruvate kinase (p. 465)

fermentation (p. 466)

obligate anaerobe (p. 468)

Rossmann fold (p. 469)

committed step (p. 474)

feedforward stimulation (p. 476)

aerobic glycolysis (p. 478)

pyruvate carboxylase (p. 482)

biotin (p. 482)

glucose 6-phosphatase (p. 484)

bifunctional enzyme (p. 487)

substrate cycle (p. 489)

Cori cycle (p. 490)

Problems

1. *Gross versus net.* The gross yield of ATP from the metabolism of glucose to two molecules of pyruvate is four molecules of ATP. However, the net yield is only two molecules of ATP. Why are the gross and net values different?

2. *Who takes? Who gives?* Lactic acid fermentation and alcoholic fermentation are oxidation–reduction reactions. Identify the ultimate electron donor and electron acceptor.

3. *ATP yield.* Each of the following molecules is processed by glycolysis to lactate. How much ATP is generated from each molecule?

(a) Glucose 6-phosphate
(b) Dihydroxyacetone phosphate
(c) Glyceraldehyde 3-phosphate
(d) Fructose
(e) Sucrose

4. *Enzyme redundancy?* Why is it advantageous for the liver to have both hexokinase and glucokinase to phosphorylate glucose?

5. *Corporate sponsors.* Some of the early research on glycolysis was supported by the brewing industry. Why would the brewing industry be interested in glycolysis?

6. *Recommended daily allowance.* The recommended daily allowance for the vitamin niacin is 15 mg per day. How would glycolysis be affected by niacin deficiency?

7. *Who's on first?* Although both hexokinase and phosphofructokinase catalyze irreversible steps in glycolysis and the hexokinase-catalyzed step is first, phosphofructokinase is nonetheless the pacemaker of glycolysis. What does this information tell you about the fate of the glucose 6-phosphate formed by hexokinase?

8. *The tortoise and the hare.* Why is the regulation of phosphofructokinase by energy charge not as important in the liver as it is in muscle?

9. *Running in reverse.* Why can't the reactions of the glycolytic pathway simply be run in reverse to synthesize glucose?

10. *Road blocks.* What reactions of glycolysis are not readily reversible under intracellular conditions?

11. *No pickling.* Why is it in the muscle's best interest to export lactic acid into the blood during intense exercise?

12. *Après vous.* Why is it physiologically advantageous for the pancreas to use GLUT2, with a high K_M, as the transporter that allows glucose entry into β cells?

13. *Bypass.* In the liver, fructose can be converted into glyceraldehyde 3-phosphate and dihydroxyacetone phosphate without passing through the phosphofructokinase-regulated reaction. Show the reactions that make this conversion possible. Why might ingesting high levels of fructose have deleterious physiological effects?

14. *Trouble ahead.* Suppose that a microorganism that was an obligate anaerobe suffered a mutation that resulted in the loss of triose phosphate isomerase activity. How would this loss affect the ATP yield of fermentation? Could such an organism survive?

15. *Kitchen chemistry.* Sucrose is commonly used to preserve fruits. Why is glucose not suitable for preserving foods?

16. *Tracing carbon atoms 1.* Glucose labeled with ^{14}C at C-1 is incubated with the glycolytic enzymes and necessary cofactors.

(a) What is the distribution of ^{14}C in the pyruvate that is formed? (Assume that the interconversion of glyceraldehyde 3-phosphate and dihydroxyacetone phosphate is very rapid compared with the subsequent step.)

(b) If the specific activity of the glucose substrate is 10 mCi mmol^{-1} (millicuries per mole, a measure of radioactivity per mole), what is the specific activity of the pyruvate that is formed?

17. *Lactic acid fermentation.* (a) Write a balanced equation for the conversion of glucose into lactate. (b) Calculate the standard free-energy change of this reaction by using the data given in Table 16.1 and the fact that $\Delta G^{\circ\prime}$ is -25 kJ mol^{-1} (-6 kcal mol^{-1}) for the following reaction:

$$\text{Pyruvate} + \text{NADH} + \text{H}^+ \rightleftharpoons \text{lactate} + \text{NAD}^+$$

What is the free-energy change (ΔG, not $\Delta G^{\circ\prime}$) of this reaction when the concentrations of reactants are: glucose, 5 mM; lactate, 0.05 mM; ATP, 2 mM; ADP, 0.2 mM; and Pi, 1 mM?

18. *High potential.* What is the equilibrium ratio of phosphoenolpyruvate to pyruvate under standard conditions when [ATP]/[ADP] = 10?

19. *Hexose–triose equilibrium.* What are the equilibrium concentrations of fructose 1,6-bisphosphate, dihydroxyacetone phosphate, and glyceraldehyde 3-phosphate when 1 mM fructose 1,6-bisphosphate is incubated with aldolase under standard conditions?

20. *Double labeling.* 3-Phosphoglycerate labeled uniformly with ^{14}C is incubated with 1,3-BPG labeled with ^{32}P at C-1. What is the radioisotope distribution of the 2,3-BPG that is formed on addition of BPG mutase?

21. *An informative analog.* Xylose has the same structure as that of glucose except that it has a hydrogen atom at G-5 in place of a hydroxymethyl group. The rate of ATP hydrolysis by hexokinase is markedly enhanced by the addition of xylose. Why?

22. *Distinctive sugars.* The intravenous infusion of fructose into healthy volunteers leads to a two- to fivefold increase in the level of lactate in the blood, a far greater increase than that observed after the infusion of the same amount of glucose.

(a) Why is glycolysis more rapid after the infusion of fructose?

(b) Fructose has been used in place of glucose for intravenous feeding. Why is this use of fructose unwise?

23. *It is not hard to meet expenses. They are everywhere.* What energetic barrier prevents glycolysis from simply running in reverse to synthesis glucose? What is the energetic cost to overcome this barrier?

24. *Waste not, want not.* Why is the conversion of lactic acid from the blood into glucose in the liver in an organism's best interest?

25. *Road blocks bypassed.* How are the irreversible reactions of glycolysis bypassed in gluconeogenesis?

26. *Pointlessness averted.* What are the regulatory means that prevent high levels of activity in glycolysis and gluconeogenesis simultaneously?

27. *Different needs.* Liver is primarily a gluconeogenic tissue, whereas muscle is primarily glycolytic. Why does this division of labor make good physiological sense?

28. *Metabolic mutants.* What would be the effect on an organism's ability to use glucose as an energy source if a mutation inactivated glucose 6-phosphatase in the liver?

29. *Never let me go.* Why does the lack of glucose 6-phosphatase activity in the brain and muscle make good physiological sense?

30. *Counting high-energy compounds 1.* How many NTP molecules are required for the synthesis of one molecule of glucose from two molecules of pyruvate? How many NADH molecules?

31. *Counting high-energy compounds 2.* How many NTP molecules are required to synthesize glucose from each of the following compounds?

(a) Glucose 6-phosphate
(b) Fructose 1,6-bisphosphate
(c) Two molecules of oxaloacetate
(d) Two molecules of dihydroxyacetone phosphate

32. *Lending a hand.* How might enzymes that remove amino groups from alanine and aspartate contribute to gluconeogenesis?

33. *More metabolic mutants.* Predict the effect of each of the following mutations on the pace of glycolysis in liver cells:

(a) Loss of the allosteric site for ATP in phosphofructokinase
(b) Loss of the binding site for citrate in phosphofructokinase
(c) Loss of the phosphatase domain of the bifunctional enzyme that controls the level of fructose 2,6-bisphosphate
(d) Loss of the binding site for fructose 1,6-bisphosphate in pyruvate kinase

34. *Yet another metabolic mutant.* What are the likely consequences of a genetic disorder rendering fructose 1,6-bisphosphatase in the liver less sensitive to regulation by fructose 2,6-bisphosphate?

35. *Biotin snatcher.* Avidin, a 70-kd protein in egg white, has very high affinity for biotin. In fact, it is a highly

specific inhibitor of biotin enzymes. Which of the following conversions would be blocked by the addition of avidin to a cell homogenate?

(a) Glucose $\rightarrow$ pyruvate
(b) Pyruvate $\rightarrow$ glucose
(c) Oxaloacetate $\rightarrow$ glucose
(d) Malate $\rightarrow$ oxaloacetate
(e) Pyruvate $\rightarrow$ oxaloacetate
(f) Glyceraldehyde 3-phosphate $\rightarrow$ fructose 1,6-bisphosphate

36. *Tracing carbon atoms 2.* If cells synthesizing glucose from lactate are exposed to CO_2 labeled with ^{14}C, what will be the distribution of label in the newly synthesized glucose?

37. *Arsenate poisoning.* Arsenate (AsO_4^{3-}) closely resembles P_i in structure and reactivity. In the reaction catalyzed by glyceraldehyde 3-phosphate dehydrogenase, arsenate can replace phosphate in attacking the energy-rich thioester intermediate. The product of this reaction, 1-arseno-3-phosphoglycerate, is unstable. It and other acyl arsenates are rapidly and spontaneously hydrolyzed. What is the effect of arsenate on energy generation in a cell?

38. *Reduce, reuse, recycle.* In the conversion of glucose into two molecules of lactate, the NADH generated earlier in the pathway is oxidized to NAD^+. Why is it not to the cell's advantage to simply make more NAD^+ so that the regeneration would not be necessary? After all, the cell would save much energy because it would no longer need to synthesize lactic acid dehydrogenase.

39. *Adenylate kinase again.* Adenylate kinase, an enzyme considered in great detail in Chapter 9, is responsible for interconverting the adenylate nucleotide pool:

$$ADP + ADP \rightleftharpoons ATP + AMP$$

The equilibrium constant for this reaction is close to 1, inasmuch as the number of phosphoanhydride bonds is the same on each side of the equation. Using the equation for the equilibrium constant for this reaction, show why changes in [AMP] are a more effective indicator of the adenylate pool than [ATP].

40. *Working at cross-purposes?* Gluconeogenesis takes place during intense exercise, which seems counterintuitive. Why would an organism synthesize glucose and at the same time use glucose to generate energy?

41. *Powering pathways.* Compare the stoichiometries of glycolysis and gluconeogenesis. Recall that the input of one ATP equivalent changes the equilibrium constant of a reaction by a factor of about 10^8 (Section 15.2). By what factor do the additional high-phosphoryl-transfer compounds alter the equilibrium constant of gluconeogenesis?

Mechanism Problem

42. *Argument by analogy.* Propose a mechanism for the conversion of glucose 6-phosphate into fructose 6-phosphate by phosphoglucose isomerase based on the mechanism of triose phosphate isomerase.

Chapter Integration Problems

43. *Not just for energy.* People with galactosemia display central nervous system abnormalities even if galactose is eliminated from the diet. The precise reason for it is not known. Suggest a plausible explanation.

44. *State function.* Fructose 2,6-bisphosphate is a potent stimulator of phosphofructokinase. Explain how fructose 2,6-bisphosphate might function in the concerted model for allosteric enzymes.

Data Interpretation Problems

45. *Now, that's unusual.* Phosphofructokinase has recently been isolated from the hyperthermophilic archaeon *Pyrococcus furiosus*. It was subjected to standard biochemical analysis to determine basic catalytic parameters. The processes under study were of the form

Fructose 6-phosphate + $(x - P_i) \rightarrow$
$\qquad$ fructose 1,6-bisphosphate + (x)

The assay measured the increase in fructose 1,6-bisphosphate. Selected results are shown in the adjoining graph.

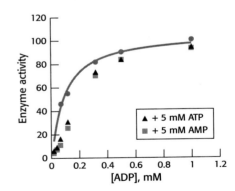

[Data from J. E. Tuininga et al. *J. Biol. Chem.* 274:21023–21028, 1999.]

(a) How does the *P. furiosus* phosphofructokinase differ from the phosphofructokinase considered in this chapter?
(b) What effects do AMP and ATP have on the reaction with ADP?

46. *Cool bees.* In principle, a futile cycle that includes phosphofructokinase and fructose 2,6-bisphosphatase could be used to generate heat. The heat could be used to warm tissues. For instance, certain bumblebees have been reported

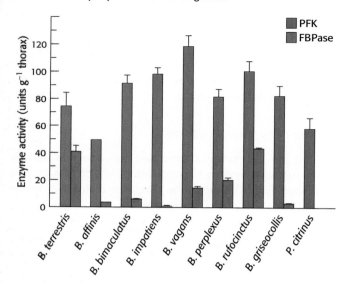

[After J. F. Staples, E. L. Koen, and T. M. Laverty, *J. Exp. Biol.* 207:749–754, 2004, p. 751.]

to use such a futile cycle to warm their flight muscles on cool mornings.

Scientists undertook a series of experiments to determine if a number of species of bumblebee use this futile cycle. Their approach was to measure the activity of PFK and F-1,6-BPase in flight muscle.

(a) What was the rationale for comparing the activities of these two enzymes?

(b) The data at the left show the activites of both enzymes for a variety of bumblebee species (genera *Bombus* and *Psithyrus*). Do these results support the notion that bumblebees use futile cycles to generate heat? Explain.

(c) In which species might futile cycling take place? Explain your reasoning.

(d) Do these results prove that futile cycling does not participate in heat generation?

The Citric Acid Cycle

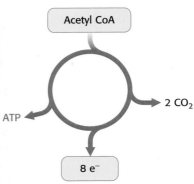

Roundabouts, or traffic circles, function as hubs to facilitate traffic flow. The citric acid cycle is the biochemical hub of the cell, oxidizing carbon fuels, usually in the form of acetyl CoA, as well as serving as a source of precursors for biosynthesis. [(Left) Lynn Saville/Getty Images.]

The metabolism of glucose to pyruvate in glycolysis, an anaerobic process, harvests but a fraction of the ATP available from glucose. Most of the ATP generated in metabolism is provided by the *aerobic* processing of glucose. This process starts with the complete oxidation of glucose derivatives to carbon dioxide. This oxidation takes place in a series of reactions called the *citric acid cycle*, also known as the *tricarboxylic acid* (TCA) *cycle* or the *Krebs cycle*. The citric acid cycle is the *final common pathway for the oxidation of fuel molecules*—carbohydrates, fatty acids, and amino acids. Most fuel molecules enter the cycle as *acetyl coenzyme A*.

OUTLINE

Acetyl coenzyme A (Acetyl CoA)

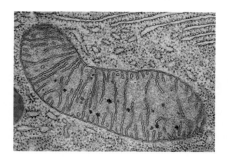

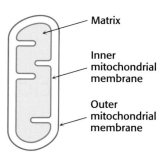

Matrix

Inner mitochondrial membrane

Outer mitochondrial membrane

Figure 17.1 Mitochondrion. The double membrane of the mitochondrion is evident in this electron micrograph. The numerous invaginations of the inner mitochondrial membrane are called cristae. The oxidative decarboxylation of pyruvate and the sequence of reactions in the citric acid cycle take place within the matrix. [(Left) Omikron/Photo Researchers.]

Under aerobic conditions, the pyruvate generated from glucose is oxidatively decarboxylated to form acetyl CoA. In eukaryotes, the reactions of the citric acid cycle take place inside mitochondria (Figure 17.1), in contrast with those of glycolysis, which take place in the cytoplasm.

The citric acid cycle harvests high-energy electrons

The citric acid cycle is the central metabolic hub of the cell. It is the gateway to the aerobic metabolism of any molecule that can be transformed into an acetyl group or a component of the citric acid cycle. The cycle is also an important source of precursors for the building blocks of many other molecules such as amino acids, nucleotide bases, and porphyrin (the organic component of heme). The citric acid cycle component, oxaloacetate, is also an important precursor to glucose (Section 16.3).

What is the function of the citric acid cycle in transforming fuel molecules into ATP? Recall that fuel molecules are carbon compounds that are capable of being oxidized—that is, of losing electrons (Chapter 15). The citric acid cycle includes a series of oxidation–reduction reactions that result in the oxidation of an acetyl group to two molecules of carbon dioxide. This oxidation generates high-energy electrons that will be used to power the synthesis of ATP. *The function of the citric acid cycle is the harvesting of high-energy electrons from carbon fuels.*

The overall pattern of the citric acid cycle is shown in Figure 17.2. A four-carbon compound (oxaloacetate) condenses with a two-carbon acetyl unit to yield a six-carbon tricarboxylic acid. The six-carbon compound releases CO_2 twice in two successive oxidative decarboxylations that yield high-energy electrons. A four-carbon compound remains. This four-carbon compound is further processed to regenerate oxaloacetate, which can initiate another round of the cycle. Two carbon atoms enter the cycle as an acetyl unit and two carbon atoms leave the cycle in the form of two molecules of CO_2.

Note that the citric acid cycle itself neither generates a large amount of ATP nor includes oxygen as a reactant (Figure 17.3). Instead, the citric acid cycle removes electrons from acetyl CoA and uses these electrons to form NADH and $FADH_2$. Three hydride ions (hence, six electrons) are transferred to three molecules of nicotinamide adenine dinucleotide (NAD^+), and one pair of hydrogen atoms (hence, two electrons) is transferred to one molecule of flavin adenine dinucleotide (FAD). These electron carriers yield nine molecules of ATP when they are oxidized by O_2 in *oxidative phosphorylation* (Chapter 18). Electrons released in the reoxidation of NADH and $FADH_2$ flow through a series of membrane proteins (referred to as the *electron-transport chain*) to generate a proton gradient across the membrane. These protons then flow through ATP synthase to generate ATP from ADP and inorganic phosphate.

The citric acid cycle, in conjunction with oxidative phosphorylation, provides the vast preponderance of energy used by aerobic cells—in human

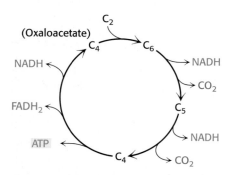

Figure 17.2 Overview of the citric acid cycle. The citric acid cycle oxidizes two-carbon units, producing two molecules of CO_2, one molecule of ATP, and high-energy electrons in the form of NADH and $FADH_2$.

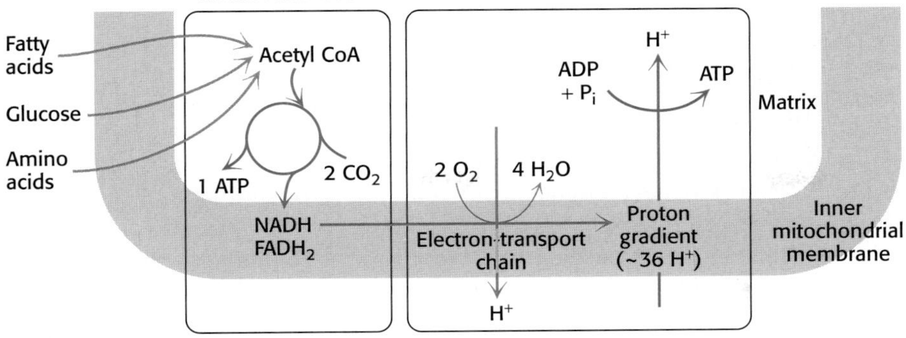

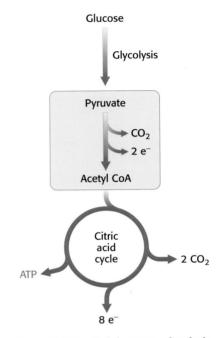

Figure 17.3 Cellular respiration. The citric acid cycle constitutes the first stage in cellular respiration, the removal of high-energy electrons from carbon fuels in the form of NADH and FADH$_2$ (left). These electrons reduce O$_2$ to generate a proton gradient (red pathway), which is used to synthesize ATP (green pathway). The reduction of O$_2$ and the synthesis of ATP constitute oxidative phosphorylation.

beings, greater than 90%. It is highly efficient because the oxidation of a limited number of citric acid cycle molecules can generate large amounts of NADH and FADH$_2$. Note in Figure 17.2 that the four-carbon molecule, oxaloacetate, that initiates the first step in the citric acid cycle is regenerated at the end of one passage through the cycle. Thus, one molecule of oxaloacetate is capable of participating in the oxidation of many acetyl molecules.

17.1 Pyruvate Dehydrogenase Links Glycolysis to the Citric Acid Cycle

Carbohydrates, most notably glucose, are processed by glycolysis into pyruvate (Chapter 16). Under anaerobic conditions, the pyruvate is converted into lactate or ethanol, depending on the organism. Under aerobic conditions, the pyruvate is transported into mitochondria by a specific carrier protein embedded in the mitochondrial membrane. In the mitochondrial matrix, pyruvate is oxidatively decarboxylated by the *pyruvate dehydrogenase complex* to form acetyl CoA.

$$\text{Pyruvate} + \text{CoA} + \text{NAD}^+ \longrightarrow \text{acetyl CoA} + \text{CO}_2 + \text{NADH} + \text{H}^+$$

This irreversible reaction is the link between glycolysis and the citric acid cycle (Figure 17.4). Note that the pyruvate dehydrogenase complex produces CO$_2$ and captures high-transfer-potential electrons in the form of NADH. Thus, the pyruvate dehydrogenase reaction has many of the key features of the reactions of the citric acid cycle itself.

The pyruvate dehydrogenase complex is a large, highly integrated complex of three distinct enzymes (Table 17.1). Pyruvate dehydrogenase complex is a member of a family of homologous complexes that include the citric acid cycle enzyme α-ketoglutarate dehydrogenase complex (p. 507). These complexes are giant, larger than ribosomes, with molecular masses ranging from 4 million to 10 million daltons (Figure 17.5). As we will see,

Figure 17.4 The link between glycolysis and the citric acid cycle. Pyruvate produced by glycolysis is converted into acetyl CoA, the fuel of the citric acid cycle.

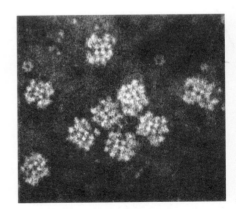

Figure 17.5 Electron micrograph of the pyruvate dehydrogenase complex from *E. coli*. [Courtesy of Dr. Lester Reed.]

Table 17.1 Pyruvate dehydrogenase complex of *E. coli*

Enzyme	Abbreviation	Number of chains	Prosthetic group	Reaction catalyzed
Pyruvate dehydrogenase component	E$_1$	24	TPP	Oxidative decarboxylation of pyruvate
Dihydrolipoyl transacetylase	E$_2$	24	Lipoamide	Transfer of acetyl group to CoA
Dihydrolipoyl dehydrogenase	E$_3$	12	FAD	Regeneration of the oxidized form of lipoamide

their elaborate structures allow groups to travel from one active site to another, connected by tethers to the core of the structure.

Mechanism: The synthesis of acetyl coenzyme A from pyruvate requires three enzymes and five coenzymes

The mechanism of the pyruvate dehydrogenase reaction is wonderfully complex, more so than is suggested by its simple stoichiometry. The reaction requires the participation of the three enzymes of the pyruvate dehydrogenase complex and five coenzymes. The coenzymes *thiamine pyrophosphate* (TPP), *lipoic acid,* and *FAD* serve as catalytic cofactors, and CoA and NAD^+ are stoichiometric cofactors, cofactors that function as substrates.

Thiamine pyrophosphate (TPP)   **Lipoic acid**

The conversion of pyruvate into acetyl CoA consists of three steps: decarboxylation, oxidation, and transfer of the resultant acetyl group to CoA.

Pyruvate   **Acetyl CoA**

These steps must be coupled to preserve the free energy derived from the decarboxylation step to drive the formation of NADH and acetyl CoA.

1. *Decarboxylation.* Pyruvate combines with TPP and is then decarboxylated to yield hydroxyethyl-TPP (Figure 17.6).

Carbanion   **Pyruvate**   **Hydroxyethyl-TPP**
of TPP

This reaction is catalyzed by the *pyruvate dehydrogenase component* (E_1) of the multienzyme complex. TPP is the prosthetic group of the pyruvate dehydrogenase component.

2. *Oxidation.* The hydroxyethyl group attached to TPP is *oxidized* to form an acetyl group while being simultaneously transferred to lipoamide, a derivative of lipoic acid that is linked to the side chain of a lysine residue by an amide linkage. Note that this transfer results in the formation of an energy-rich thioester bond.

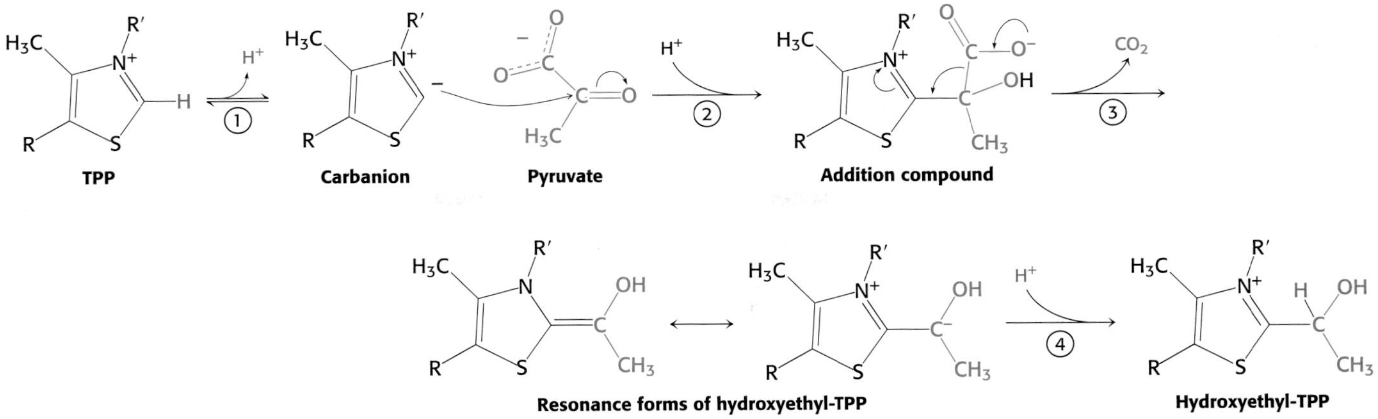

Figure 17.6 Mechanism of the E_1 decarboxylation reaction. E_1 is the pyruvate dehydrogenase component of the pyruvate dehydrogenase complex. A key feature of the prosthetic group, TPP, is that the carbon atom between the nitrogen and sulfur atoms in the thiazole ring is much more acidic than most =CH— groups, with a pK_a value near 10. (1) This carbon center ionizes to form a *carbanion.* (2) The carbanion readily adds to the carbonyl group of pyruvate. (3) This addition is followed by the decarboxylation of pyruvate. The positively charged ring of TPP acts as an electron sink that stabilizes the negative charge that is transferred to the ring as part of the decarboxylation. (4) Protonation yields hydroxyethyl-TPP.

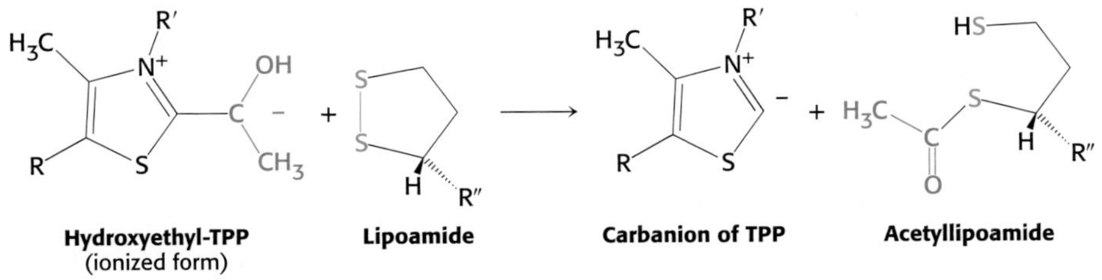

The oxidant in this reaction is the disulfide group of lipoamide, which is reduced to its disulfhydryl form. This reaction, also catalyzed by the pyruvate dehydrogenase component E_1, yields *acetyllipoamide.*

3. *Formation of Acetyl CoA.* The acetyl group is transferred from acetyllipoamide to CoA to form acetyl CoA.

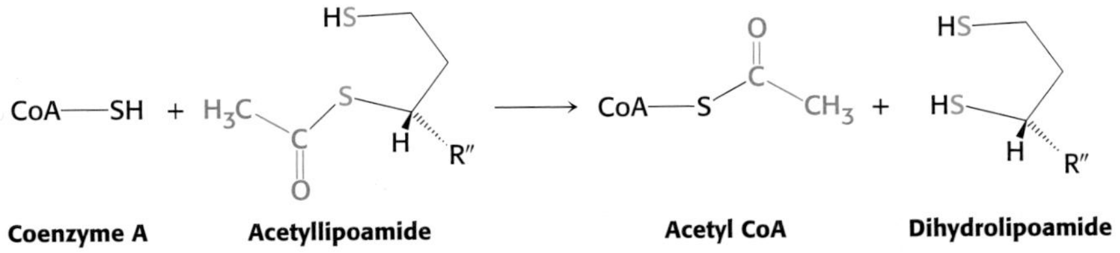

Dihydrolipoyl transacetylase (E_2) catalyzes this reaction. The energy-rich thioester bond is preserved as the acetyl group is transferred to CoA. Recall that CoA serves as a carrier of many activated acyl groups, of which acetyl is the simplest (Section 15.3). Acetyl CoA, the fuel for the citric acid cycle, has now been generated from pyruvate.

The pyruvate dehydrogenase complex cannot complete another catalytic cycle until the dihydrolipoamide is oxidized to lipoamide. In a fourth step, *the oxidized form of lipoamide is regenerated by dihydrolipoyl dehydrogenase* (E_3). Two electrons are transferred to an FAD prosthetic group of the enzyme and then to NAD^+.

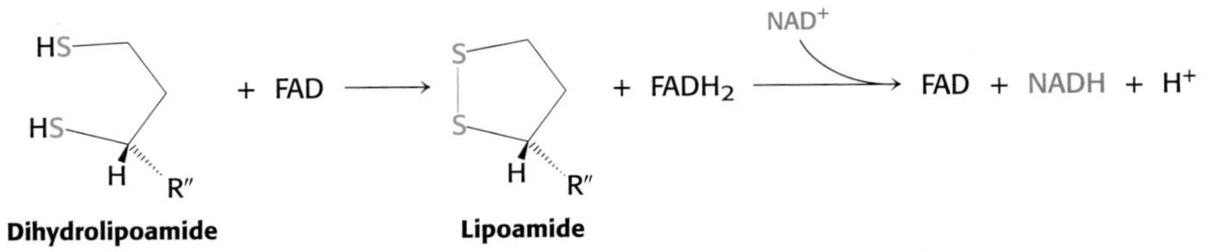

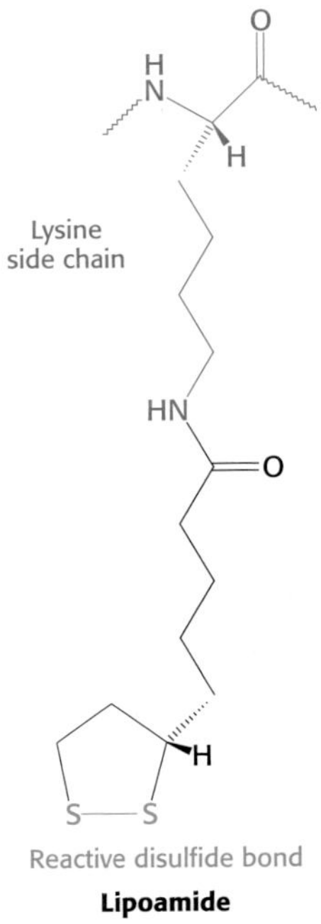

501

This electron transfer from FAD to NAD$^+$ is unusual because the common role for FAD is to receive electrons from NADH. The electron-transfer potential of FAD is increased by its chemical environment within the enzyme, enabling it to transfer electrons to NAD$^+$. Proteins tightly associated with FAD or flavin mononucleotide (FMN) are called *flavoproteins*.

Flexible linkages allow lipoamide to move between different active sites

The structures of all of the component enzymes of the pyruvate dehydrogenase complex are known, albeit from different complexes and species. Thus, it is now possible to construct an atomic model of the complex to understand its activity (Figure 17.7).

The core of the complex is formed by the transacetylase component E$_2$. Transacetylase consists of eight catalytic trimers assembled to form a hollow cube. Each of the three subunits forming a trimer has three major domains (Figure 17.8). At the amino terminus is a small domain that contains a bound flexible lipoamide cofactor attached to a lysine residue. This domain is homologous to biotin-binding domains such as that of pyruvate carboxylase (see Figure 16.26). The lipoamide domain is followed by a small domain that interacts with E$_3$ within the complex. A larger transacetylase domain completes an E$_2$ subunit. E$_1$ is an $\alpha_2\beta_2$ tetramer, and E$_3$ is an $\alpha\beta$ dimer. Multiples copies of E$_1$ and E$_3$ surround the E$_2$ core. How do the three distinct active sites work in concert (Figure 17.9)? The key is the long, flexible lipoamide arm of the E$_2$ subunit, which carries substrate from active site to active site.

1. Pyruvate is decarboxylated at the active site of E$_1$, forming the hydroxyethyl-TPP intermediate, and CO$_2$ leaves as the first product. This active site lies deep within the E$_1$ complex, connected to the enzyme surface by a 20-Å-long hydrophobic channel.

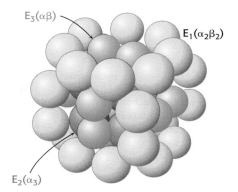

Figure 17.7 Schematic representation of the pyruvate dehydrogenase complex. The transacetylase core (E$_2$) is shown in red, the pyruvate dehydrogenase component (E$_1$) in yellow, and the dihydrolipoyl dehydrogenase (E$_3$) in green.

E$_3$($\alpha\beta$)

E$_1$($\alpha_2\beta_2$)

E$_2$(α_3)

Figure 17.8 Structure of the transacetylase (E$_2$) core. Each red ball represents a trimer of three E$_2$ subunits. *Notice* that each subunit consists of three domains: a lipoamide-binding domain, a small domain for interaction with E$_3$, and a large transacetylase catalytic domain. The transacetylase domain has three identical subunits, with one depicted in red and the others in white in the ribbon representation.

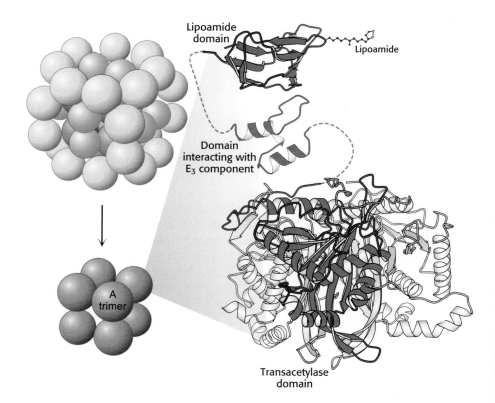

Lipoamide domain

Lipoamide

Domain interacting with E$_3$ component

A trimer

Transacetylase domain

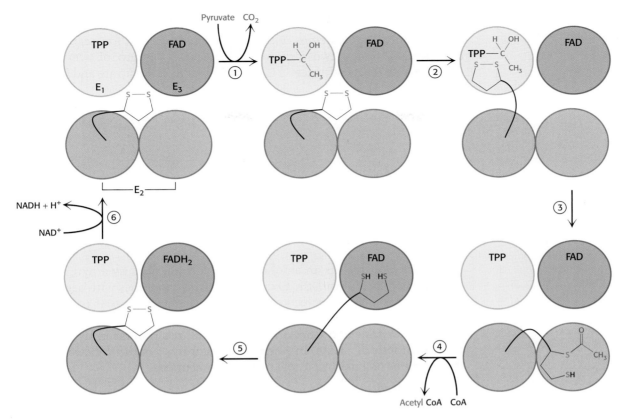

2. E_2 inserts the lipoamide arm of the lipoamide domain into the deep channel in E_1 leading to the active site.

3. E_1 catalyzes the transfer of the acetyl group to the lipoamide. The acetylated arm then leaves E_1 and enters the E_2 cube to visit the active site of E_2, located deep in the cube at the subunit interface.

4. The acetyl moiety is then transferred to CoA, and the second product, acetyl CoA, leaves the cube. The reduced lipoamide arm then swings to the active site of the E_3 flavoprotein.

5. At the E_3 active site, the lipoamide is oxidized by coenzyme FAD. The reactivated lipoamide is ready to begin another reaction cycle.

6. The final product, NADH, is produced with the reoxidation of $FADH_2$ to FAD.

The structural integration of three kinds of enzymes and the long, flexible lipoamide arm make the coordinated catalysis of a complex reaction possible. The proximity of one enzyme to another *increases the overall reaction rate and minimizes side reactions.* All the intermediates in the oxidative decarboxylation of pyruvate remain bound to the complex throughout the reaction sequence and are readily transferred as the flexible arm of E_2 calls on each active site in turn.

Figure 17.9 Reactions of the pyruvate dehydrogenase complex. At the top (left), the enzyme (represented by a yellow, a green, and two red spheres) is unmodified and ready for a catalytic cycle. (1) Pyruvate is decarboxylated to form hydroxyethyl-TPP. (2) The lipoamide arm of E_2 moves into the active site of E_1. (3) E_1 catalyzes the transfer of the two-carbon group to the lipoamide group to form the acetyl–lipoamide complex. (4) E_2 catalyzes the transfer of the acetyl moiety to CoA to form the product acetyl CoA. The dihydrolipoamide arm then swings to the active site of E_3. E_3 catalyzes (5) the oxidation of the dihydrolipoamide acid and (6) the transfer of the protons and electrons to NAD^+ to complete the reaction cycle.

17.2 The Citric Acid Cycle Oxidizes Two-Carbon Units

The conversion of pyruvate into acetyl CoA by the pyruvate dehydrogenase complex is the link between glycolysis and cellular respiration because *acetyl CoA is the fuel for the citric acid cycle.* Indeed, all fuels are ultimately metabolized to acetyl CoA or components of the citric acid cycle.

Citrate synthase forms citrate from oxaloacetate and acetyl coenzyme A

The citric acid cycle begins with the condensation of a four-carbon unit, oxaloacetate, and a two-carbon unit, the acetyl group of acetyl CoA. Oxaloacetate reacts with acetyl CoA and H_2O to yield citrate and CoA.

Oxaloacetate   Acetyl CoA   Citryl CoA   Citrate

This reaction, which is an aldol condensation followed by a hydrolysis, is catalyzed by *citrate synthase*. Oxaloacetate first condenses with acetyl CoA to form *citryl CoA,* a molecule that is energy rich because it contains the thioester bond that originated in acetyl CoA. The hydrolysis of citryl CoA thioester to citrate and CoA drives the overall reaction far in the direction of the synthesis of citrate. In essence, the hydrolysis of the thioester powers the synthesis of a new molecule from two precursors.

Mechanism: The mechanism of citrate synthase prevents undesirable reactions

Because the condensation of acetyl CoA and oxaloacetate initiates the citric acid cycle, it is very important that side reactions, notably the hydrolysis of acetyl CoA to acetate and CoA, be minimized. Let us briefly consider how the citrate synthase prevents the wasteful hydrolysis of acetyl CoA.

Mammalian citrate synthase is a dimer of identical 49-kd subunits. Each active site is located in a cleft between the large and the small domains of a subunit, adjacent to the subunit interface. X-ray crystallographic studies of citrate synthase and its complexes with several substrates and inhibitors revealed that the enzyme undergoes large conformational changes in the course of catalysis. Citrate synthase exhibits sequential, ordered kinetics: oxaloacetate binds first, followed by acetyl CoA. The reason for the ordered binding is that *oxaloacetate induces a major structural rearrangement leading to the creation of a binding site for acetyl CoA.* The binding of oxaloacetate converts the open form of the enzyme into a closed form (Figure 17.10). In each subunit, the small domain rotates 19 degrees relative to the large domain. *Movements as large as 15 Å are produced by the rotation of α helices elicited by quite small shifts of side chains around bound oxaloacetate.* These structural changes create a binding site for acetyl CoA. This conformational transition is reminiscent of the cleft closure in hexokinase induced by the binding of glucose (Section 16.1).

Citrate synthase catalyzes the condensation reaction by bringing the substrates into close proximity, orienting them, and polarizing certain bonds (Figure 17.11). The donation and removal of protons transforms acetyl CoA into an *enol intermediate.* The enol attacks oxaloacetate to form a carbon–carbon double bond linking acetyl CoA and oxaloacetate. The newly formed citryl CoA induces additional structural changes in the enzyme, causing the active site to become completely enclosed. The enzyme cleaves the citryl CoA thioester by hydrolysis. CoA leaves the enzyme, followed by citrate, and the enzyme returns to the initial open conformation.

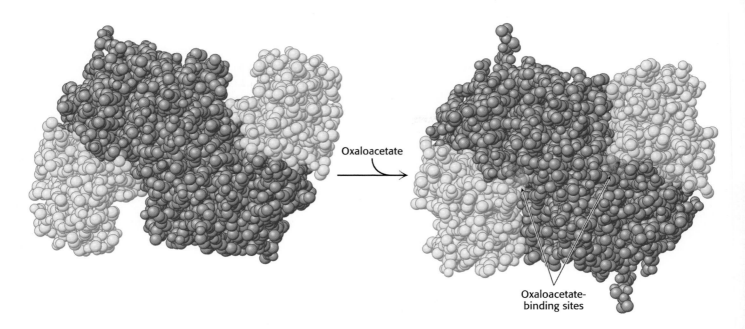

Oxaloacetate

Oxaloacetate-binding sites

Figure 17.10 Conformational changes in citrate synthase on binding oxaloacetate. The small domain of each subunit of the homodimer is shown in yellow; the large domains are shown in blue. (Left) Open form of enzyme alone. (Right) Closed form of the liganded enzyme. [Drawn from 5CSC.pdb and 4CTS.pdb.]

We can now understand how the wasteful hydrolysis of acetyl CoA is prevented. Citrate synthase is well suited to hydrolyze *citryl* CoA but not *acetyl* CoA. How is this discrimination accomplished? First, acetyl CoA does not bind to the enzyme until oxaloacetate is bound and ready for condensation. Second, the catalytic residues crucial for the hydrolysis of the thioester linkage are not appropriately positioned *until citryl CoA is formed*. As with hexokinase and triose phosphate isomerase (Section 16.1), *induced fit prevents an undesirable side reaction*.

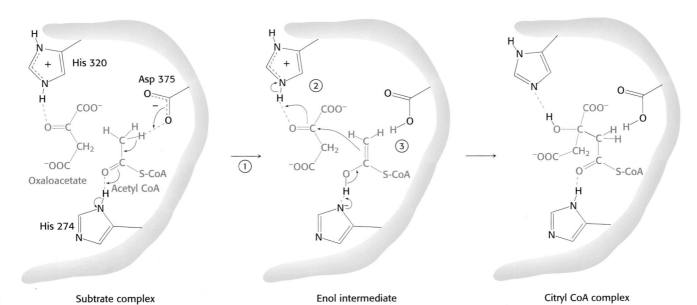

Subtrate complex   Enol intermediate   Citryl CoA complex

Figure 17.11 Mechanism of synthesis of citryl CoA by citrate synthase. (1) In the substrate complex (left), His 274 donates a proton to the carbonyl oxygen of acetyl CoA to promote the removal of a methyl proton by Asp 375 to form the enol intermediate (center). (2) Oxaloacetate is activated by the transfer of a proton from His 320 to its carbonyl carbon atom. (3) Simultaneously, the enol of acetyl CoA attacks the carbonyl carbon of oxaloacetate to form a carbon–carbon bond linking acetyl CoA and oxaloacetate. His 274 is reprotonated. Citryl CoA is formed. His 274 participates again as a proton donor to hydrolyze the thioester (not shown), yielding citrate and CoA.

Citrate is isomerized into isocitrate

The hydroxyl group is not properly located in the citrate molecule for the oxidative decarboxylations that follow. Thus, citrate is isomerized into isocitrate to enable the six-carbon unit to undergo oxidative decarboxylation. The isomerization of citrate is accomplished by a *dehydration* step followed by a *hydration* step. The result is an interchange of an H and an OH. The enzyme catalyzing both steps is called *aconitase* because cis-*aconitate* is an intermediate.

Aconitase is an *iron–sulfur protein*, or *nonheme-iron protein*, in that it contains iron that is not bonded to heme. Rather, its four iron atoms are complexed to four inorganic sulfides and three cysteine sulfur atoms, leaving one iron atom available to bind citrate through one of its COO^- groups and an OH group (Figure 17.12). This Fe-S cluster participates in dehydrating and rehydrating the bound substrate.

Isocitrate is oxidized and decarboxylated to alpha-ketoglutarate

We come now to the first of four oxidation–reduction reactions in the citric acid cycle. The oxidative decarboxylation of isocitrate is catalyzed by *isocitrate dehydrogenase*.

$$\text{Isocitrate} + \text{NAD}^+ \longrightarrow \alpha\text{-ketoglutarate} + CO_2 + \text{NADH}$$

The intermediate in this reaction is oxalosuccinate, an unstable β-ketoacid. While bound to the enzyme, it loses CO_2 to form α-ketoglutarate.

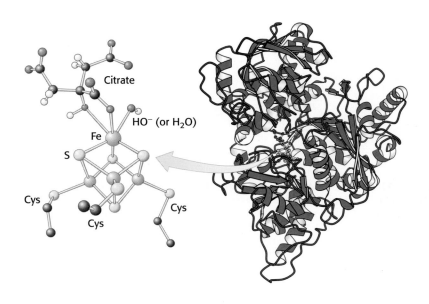

Figure 17.12 Binding of citrate to the iron–sulfur complex of aconitase. A 4Fe-4S iron–sulfur cluster is a component of the active site of aconitase. *Notice* that one of the iron atoms of the cluster binds to a COO^- group and an OH group of citrate. [Drawn from 1C96.pdb.]

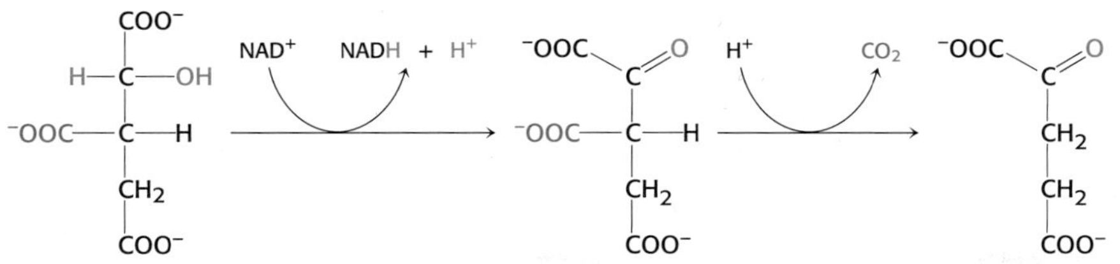

The structures shown depict the conversion of Isocitrate to Oxalosuccinate to α-Ketoglutarate, with NAD⁺ → NADH + H⁺ and release of H^+ and CO_2.

Isocitrate → **Oxalosuccinate** → **α-Ketoglutarate**

The rate of formation of α-ketoglutarate is important in determining the overall rate of the cycle, as will be discussed on page 514. This oxidation generates the first high-transfer-potential electron carrier, NADH, in the cycle.

Succinyl coenzyme A is formed by the oxidative decarboxylation of alpha-ketoglutarate

The conversion of isocitrate into α-ketoglutarate is followed by a second oxidative decarboxylation reaction, the formation of succinyl CoA from α-ketoglutarate.

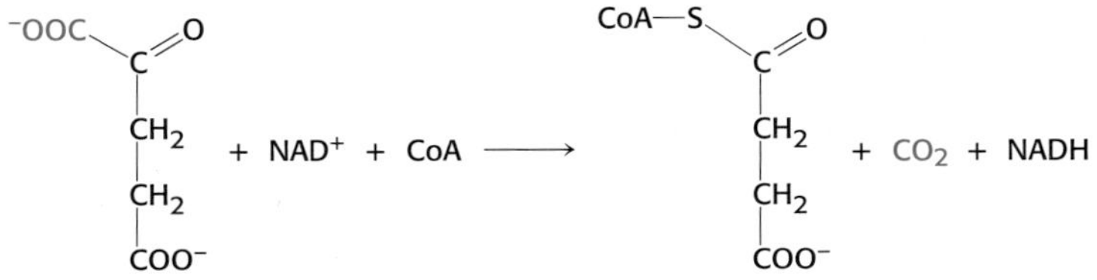

α-Ketoglutarate $+ NAD^+ + CoA \longrightarrow$ **Succinyl CoA** $+ CO_2 + NADH$

This reaction is catalyzed by the *α-ketoglutarate dehydrogenase complex,* an organized assembly of three kinds of enzymes that is homologous to the pyruvate dehydrogenase complex. In fact, the oxidative decarboxylation of α-ketoglutarate closely resembles that of pyruvate, also an α-ketoacid.

$$\text{Pyruvate} + \text{CoA} + \text{NAD}^+ \xrightarrow{\text{Pyruvate dehydrogenase complex}} \text{acetyl CoA} + \text{CO}_2 + \text{NADH} + \text{H}^+$$

$$\alpha\text{-Ketoglutarate} + \text{CoA} + \text{NAD}^+ \xrightarrow{\alpha\text{-Ketoglutarate dehydrogenase complex}} \text{succinyl CoA} + \text{CO}_2 + \text{NADH}$$

Both reactions include the decarboxylation of an α-ketoacid and the subsequent formation of a thioester linkage with CoA that has a high transfer potential. The reaction mechanisms are entirely analogous (p. 500).

A compound with high phosphoryl-transfer potential is generated from succinyl coenzyme A

Succinyl CoA is an energy-rich thioester compound. The $\Delta G^{\circ\prime}$ for the hydrolysis of succinyl CoA is about -33.5 kJ mol^{-1} (-8.0 kcal mol^{-1}), which is comparable to that of ATP (-30.5 kJ mol^{-1}, or -7.3 kcal mol^{-1}). In the citrate synthase reaction, the cleavage of the thioester bond powers the synthesis of the six-carbon citrate from the four-carbon oxaloacetate and the two-carbon fragment. *The cleavage of the thioester bond of succinyl CoA is coupled to the phosphorylation of a purine nucleoside diphosphate, usually ADP.* This reaction, which is readily reversible, is catalyzed by *succinyl CoA synthetase* (succinate thiokinase).

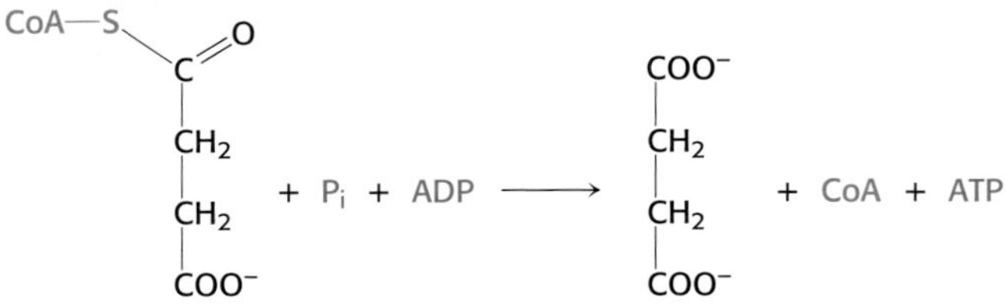

Succinyl CoA → **Succinate**

$$\text{Succinyl CoA} + P_i + ADP \longrightarrow \text{Succinate} + CoA + ATP$$

This reaction is the only step in the citric acid cycle that directly yields a compound with high phosphoryl-transfer potential. In mammals, there are two isozymic forms of the enzyme, one specific for ADP and one for GDP. In tissues that perform large amounts of cellular respiration, such as skeletal and heart muscle, the ADP-requiring isozyme predominates. In tissues that perform many anabolic reactions, such as the liver, the GDP-requiring enzyme is common. The GDP-requiring enzyme is believed to work in reverse of the direction observed in the TCA cycle; that is, GTP is used to power the synthesis of succinyl CoA, which is a precursor for heme synthesis. The *E. coli* enzyme uses either GDP or ADP as the phosphoryl-group acceptor.

Note that the enzyme *nucleoside diphosphokinase*, which catalyzes the following reaction,

$$GTP + ADP \rightleftharpoons GDP + ATP$$

allows the γ phosphoryl group to be readily transferred from GTP to form ATP, thereby allowing the adjustment of the concentration of GTP or ATP to meet the cell's need.

Mechanism: Succinyl coenzyme A synthetase transforms types of biochemical energy

The mechanism of this reaction is a clear example of an energy transformation: energy inherent in the thioester molecule is transformed into phosphoryl-group-transfer potential (Figure 17.13). The first step is the displacement of coenzyme A by orthophosphate, which generates another

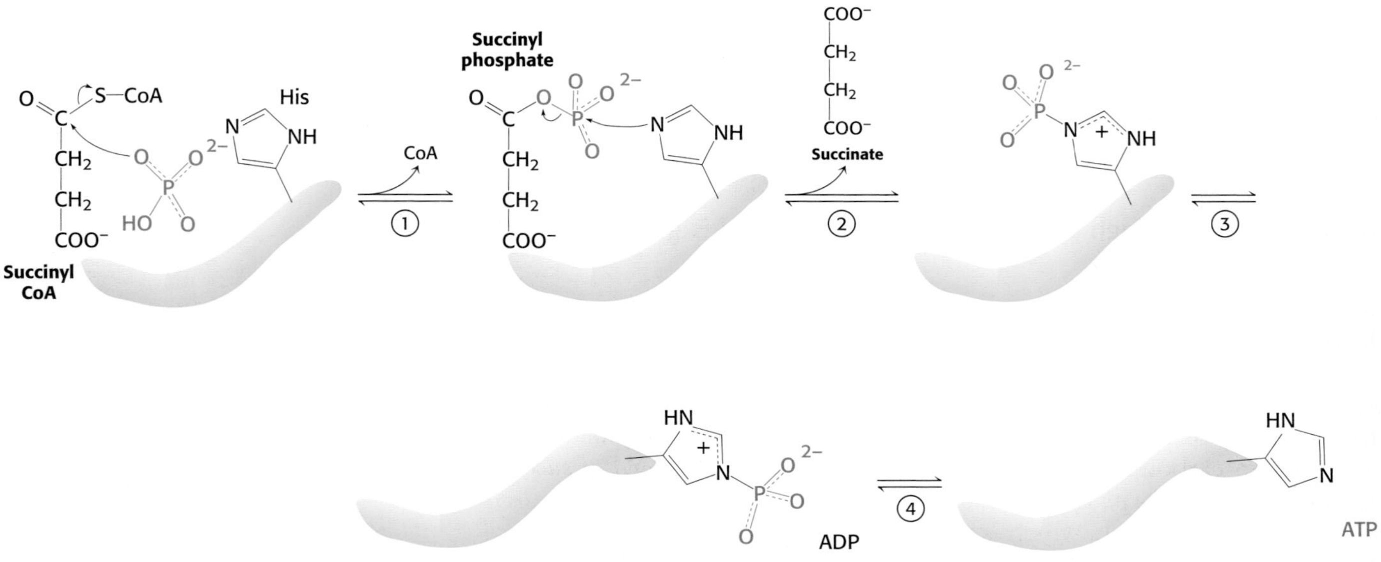

Figure 17.13 Reaction mechanism of succinyl CoA synthetase. The reaction proceeds through a phosphorylated enzyme intermediate. (1) Orthophosphate displaces coenzyme A, which generates another energy-rich compound, succinyl phosphate. (2) A histidine residue removes the phosphoryl group with the concomitant generation of succinate and phosphohistidine. (3) The phosphohistidine residue then swings over to a bound nucleoside diphosphate, and (4) the phosphoryl group is transferred to form the nucleoside triphosphate.

energy-rich compound, succinyl phosphate. A histidine residue plays a key role as a moving arm that detaches the phosphoryl group, then swings over to a bound nucleoside diphosphate and transfers the group to form the nucleoside triphosphate. The participation of high-energy compounds in all the steps is attested to by the fact that the reaction is readily reversible: $\Delta G°' = -3.4$ kJ mol^{-1} (-0.8 kcal mol^{-1}). The formation of ATP at the expense of succinyl CoA is an example of substrate-level phosphorylation.

Succinyl CoA synthetase is an $\alpha_2\beta_2$ heterodimer; the functional unit is one $\alpha\beta$ pair. The enzyme mechanism shows that a phosphoryl group is transferred first to succinyl CoA bound in the α subunit and then to a nucleoside diphosphate bound in the β subunit. Examination of the three-dimensional structure of succinyl CoA synthetase reveals that each subunit comprises two domains (Figure 17.14). The amino-terminal domains of the two subunits have different structures, each characteristic of its role in the mechanism. The amino-terminal domain of the α subunit forms a Rossmann fold (Section 16.1), which binds the ADP substrate of succinyl CoA synthetase. The amino-terminal domain of the β subunit is an ATP-grasp domain, found in many enzymes, which here binds and activates ADP. Succinyl CoA synthetase has evolved by adopting these domains and harnessing them to capture the energy associated with succinyl CoA cleavage, which is used to drive the generation of a nucleoside triphosphate.

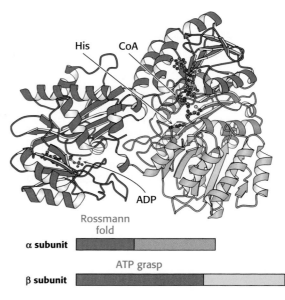

Figure 17.14 Structure of succinyl CoA synthetase. The enzyme is composed of two subunits. The α subunit contains a Rossmann fold that binds the ADP component of CoA, and the β subunit contains a nucleotide-activating region called the ATP-grasp domain. The ATP-grasp domain is shown here binding a molecule of ADP. *Notice* that the histidine residue is between the CoA and the ADP. This histidine residue picks up the phosphoryl group from near the CoA and swings over to transfer it to the nucleotide bound in the ATP-grasp domain. [Drawn from 1CGI.pdb.]

Oxaloacetate is regenerated by the oxidation of succinate

Reactions of four-carbon compounds constitute the final stage of the citric acid cycle: the regeneration of oxaloacetate.

The reactions constitute a metabolic motif that we will see again in fatty acid synthesis and degradation as well as in the degradation of some amino acids. A methylene group (CH_2) is converted into a carbonyl group (C=O) in three steps: an oxidation, a hydration, and a second oxidation reaction. Oxaloacetate is thereby regenerated for another round of the cycle, and more energy is extracted in the form of $FADH_2$ and NADH.

Succinate is oxidized to fumarate by *succinate dehydrogenase*. The hydrogen acceptor is FAD rather than NAD^+, which is used in the other three oxidation reactions in the cycle. FAD is the hydrogen acceptor in this reaction because the free-energy change is insufficient to reduce NAD^+. FAD is nearly always the electron acceptor in oxidations that remove two hydrogen *atoms* from a substrate. In succinate dehydrogenase, the isoalloxazine ring of FAD is covalently attached to a histidine side chain of the enzyme (denoted E-FAD).

$$\text{E-FAD} + \text{succinate} \rightleftharpoons \text{E-FADH}_2 + \text{fumarate}$$

Succinate dehydrogenase, like aconitase, is an iron–sulfur protein. Indeed, succinate dehydrogenase contains three different kinds of iron–sulfur clusters: 2Fe-2S (two iron atoms bonded to two inorganic sulfides), 3Fe-4S, and 4Fe-4S. Succinate dehydrogenase—which consists of a 70-kd and a 27-kd subunit—differs from other enzymes in the citric acid cycle in being embedded in the inner mitochondrial membrane. In fact, *succinate dehydrogenase is directly associated with the electron-transport chain, the link between the citric acid cycle and ATP formation.* $FADH_2$ produced by the oxidation of succinate does not dissociate from the enzyme, in contrast with NADH produced in other oxidation–reduction reactions. Rather, two electrons are transferred from $FADH_2$ directly to iron–sulfur clusters of the enzyme, which in turn passes the electrons to coenzyme Q (CoQ). Coenzyme Q, an important member of the electron-transport chain, passes electrons to the ultimate acceptor, molecular oxygen, as we shall see in Chapter 18.

The next step is the hydration of fumarate to form L-malate. *Fumarase* catalyzes a stereospecific trans addition of H^+ and OH^-. The OH^- group adds to only one side of the double bond of fumarate; hence, only the L isomer of malate is formed.

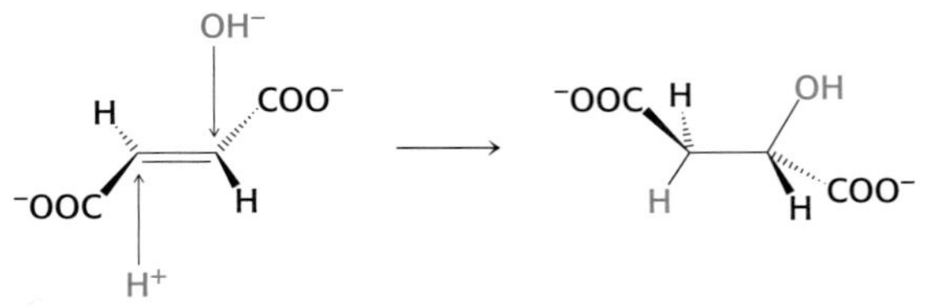

Fumarate   **L-Malate**

Finally, malate is oxidized to form oxaloacetate. This reaction is catalyzed by *malate dehydrogenase,* and NAD^+ is again the hydrogen acceptor.

$$\text{Malate} + NAD^+ \rightleftharpoons \text{oxaloacetate} + NADH + H^+$$

The standard free energy for this reaction, unlike that for the other steps in the citric acid cycle, is significantly positive ($\Delta G^{\circ\prime} = +29.7$ kJ mol^{-1}, or $+7.1$ kcal mol^{-1}). The oxidation of malate is driven by the use of the products—oxaloacetate by citrate synthase and NADH by the electron-transport chain.

The citric acid cycle produces high-transfer-potential electrons, ATP, and CO_2

The net reaction of the citric acid cycle is

$$\text{Acetyl CoA} + 3\,NAD^+ + FAD + ADP + P_i + 2\,H_2O \longrightarrow$$
$$2\,CO_2 + 3\,NADH + FADH_2 + ATP + 2\,H^+ + CoA$$

Let us recapitulate the reactions that give this stoichiometry (Figure 17.15 and Table 17.2):

1. Two carbon atoms enter the cycle in the condensation of an acetyl unit (from acetyl CoA) with oxaloacetate. Two carbon atoms leave the cycle in the form of CO_2 in the successive decarboxylations catalyzed by isocitrate dehydrogenase and α-ketoglutarate dehydrogenase.

2. Four pairs of hydrogen atoms leave the cycle in four oxidation reactions. Two NAD^+ molecules are reduced in the oxidative decarboxylations of isocitrate and α-ketoglutarate, one FAD molecule is reduced in the oxidation

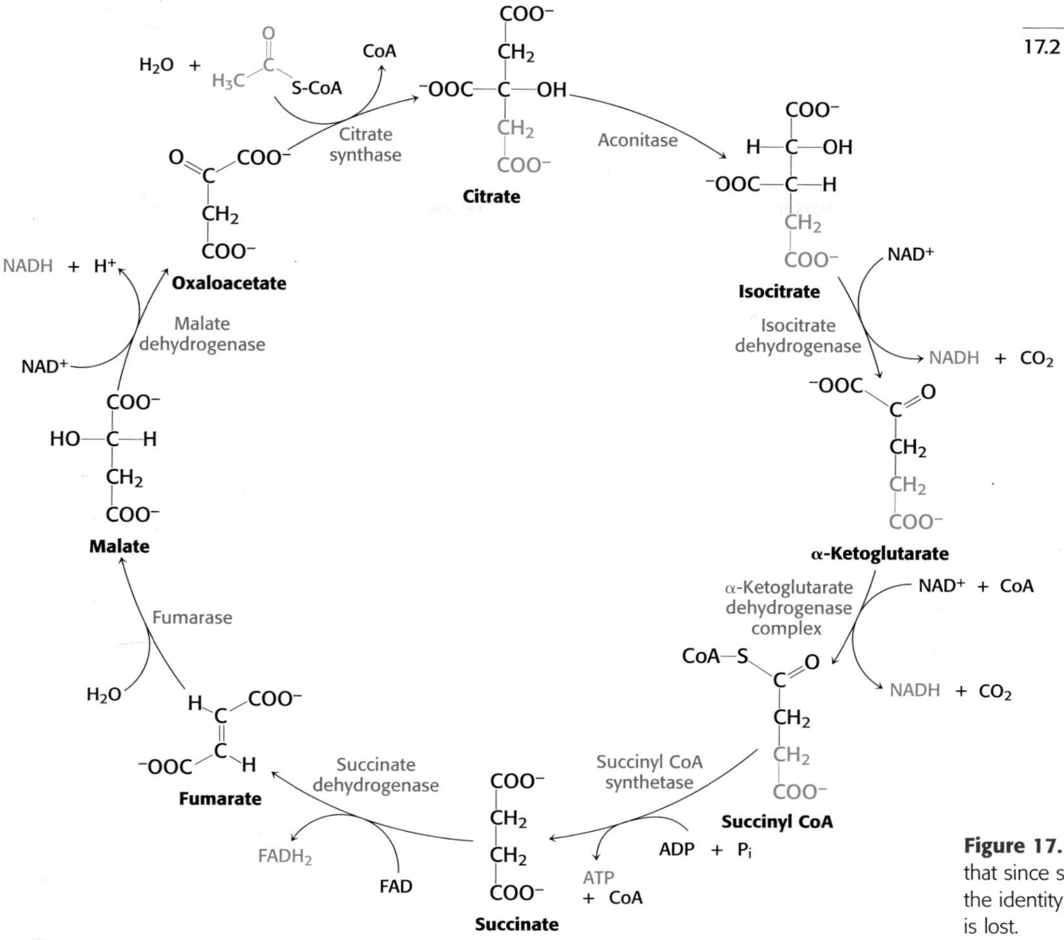

Figure 17.15 The citric acid cycle. *Notice that since succinate is a symmetric molecule, the identity of the carbons from the acetyl unit is lost.*

Table 17.2 Citric acid cycle

Step	Reaction	Enzyme	Prosthetic group	Type*	$\Delta G^{\circ\prime}$ kJ mol^{-1}	kcal mol^{-1}
1	Acetyl CoA + oxaloacetate + $H_2O \rightarrow$ citrate + CoA + H^+	Citrate synthase		a	−31.4	−7.5
2a	Citrate $\rightleftharpoons$ *cis*-aconitate + H_2O	Aconitase	Fe-S	b	+8.4	+2.0
2b	*cis*-Aconitate + $H_2O \rightleftharpoons$ isocitrate	Aconitase	Fe-S	c	−2.1	−0.5
3	Isocitrate + NAD$^+$ $\rightleftharpoons$ α-ketoglutarate + CO_2 + NADH	Isocitrate dehydrogenase		d + e	−8.4	−2.0
4	α-Ketoglutarate + NAD$^+$ + CoA $\rightleftharpoons$ succinyl CoA + CO_2 + NADH	α-Ketoglutarate dehydrogenase complex	Lipoic acid, FAD, TPP	d + e	−30.1	−7.2
5	Succinyl CoA + P_i + ADP $\rightleftharpoons$ succinate + ATP + CoA	Succinyl CoA synthetase		f	−3.3	−0.8
6	Succinate + FAD (enzyme-bound) $\rightleftharpoons$ fumarate + $FADH_2$(enzyme-bound)	Succinate dehydrogenase	FAD, Fe-S	e	0	0
7	Fumarate + $H_2O \rightleftharpoons$ L-malate	Fumarase		c	−3.8	−0.9
8	L-Malate + NAD$^+$ $\rightleftharpoons$ oxaloacetate + NADH + H^+	Malate dehydrogenase		e	+29.7	+7.1

*Reaction type: (a) condensation; (b) dehydration; (c) hydration; (d) decarboxylation; (e) oxidation; (f) substrate-level phosphorylation.

of succinate, and one NAD^+ molecule is reduced in the oxidation of malate. Recall also that one NAD^+ molecule is reduced in the oxidative decarboxylation of pyruvate to form acetyl CoA.

3. One compound with high phosphoryl-transfer potential, usually ATP, is generated from the cleavage of the thioester linkage in succinyl CoA.

4. Two water molecules are consumed: one in the synthesis of citrate by the hydrolysis of citryl CoA and the other in the hydration of fumarate.

Isotope-labeling studies revealed that the two carbon atoms that enter each cycle are not the ones that leave. The two carbon atoms that enter the cycle as the acetyl group are retained during the initial two decarboxylation reactions (see Figure 17.15) and then remain incorporated in the four-carbon acids of the cycle. Note that succinate is a symmetric molecule. Consequently, the two carbon atoms that enter the cycle can occupy any of the carbon positions in the subsequent metabolism of the four-carbon acids. The two carbons that enter the cycle as the acetyl group will be released as CO_2 in *subsequent* trips through the cycle. To understand why citrate is not processed as a symmetric molecule, see Problems 27 and 28.

Evidence is accumulating that the enzymes of the citric acid cycle are physically associated with one another. The close arrangement of enzymes enhances the efficiency of the citric acid cycle because a reaction product can pass directly from one active site to the next through connecting channels, a process called *substrate channeling*. The word *metabolon* has been suggested as the name for such multienzyme complexes.

As will be considered in Chapter 18, the electron-transport chain oxidizes the NADH and $FADH_2$ formed in the citric acid cycle. The transfer of electrons from these carriers to O_2, the ultimate electron acceptor, leads to the generation of a proton gradient across the inner mitochondrial membrane. This proton-motive force then powers the generation of ATP; the net stoichiometry is about 2.5 ATP per NADH, and 1.5 ATP per $FADH_2$. Consequently, nine high-transfer-potential phosphoryl groups are generated when the electron-transport chain oxidizes 3 NADH molecules and 1 $FADH_2$ molecule, and one high-transfer-potential phosphoryl group is directly formed in one round of the citric acid cycle. Thus, one acetyl unit generates approximately 10 molecules of ATP. In dramatic contrast, the anaerobic glycolysis of 1 glucose molecule generates only 2 molecules of ATP (and 2 molecules of lactate).

Recall that molecular oxygen does not participate directly in the citric acid cycle. However, the cycle operates only under aerobic conditions because NAD^+ and FAD can be regenerated in the mitochondrion only by the transfer of electrons to molecular oxygen. *Glycolysis has both an aerobic and an anaerobic mode, whereas the citric acid cycle is strictly aerobic.* Glycolysis can proceed under anaerobic conditions because NAD^+ is regenerated in the conversion of pyruvate into lactate or ethanol.

17.3 Entry to the Citric Acid Cycle and Metabolism Through It Are Controlled

The citric acid cycle is the final common pathway for the aerobic oxidation of fuel molecules. Moreover, as we will see shortly (Section 17.4) and repeatedly elsewhere in our study of biochemistry, the cycle is an important source of building blocks for a host of important biomolecules. As befits its role as the metabolic hub of the cell, entry into the cycle and the rate of the cycle itself are controlled at several stages.

The pyruvate dehydrogenase complex is regulated allosterically and by reversible phosphorylation

As stated earlier, glucose can be formed from pyruvate (Section 16.3). *However, the formation of acetyl CoA from pyruvate is an irreversible step in animals and thus they are unable to convert acetyl CoA back into glucose.* The oxidative decarboxylation of pyruvate to acetyl CoA commits the carbon atoms of glucose to one of two principal fates: oxidation to CO_2 by the citric acid cycle, with the concomitant generation of energy, or incorporation into lipid (Figure 17.16). As expected of an enzyme at a critical branch point in metabolism, the activity of the pyruvate dehydrogenase complex is stringently controlled. High concentrations of reaction products inhibit the reaction: acetyl CoA inhibits the transacetylase component (E_2) by binding directly, whereas NADH inhibits the dihydrolipoyl dehydrogenase (E_3). High concentrations of NADH and acetyl CoA inform the enzyme that the energy needs of the cell have been met or that fatty acids are being degraded to produce acetyl CoA and NADH. In either case, there is no need to metabolize pyruvate to acetyl CoA. This inhibition has the effect of sparing glucose, because most pyruvate is derived from glucose by glycolysis (Section 16.1).

The key means of regulation of the complex in eukaryotes is covalent modification (Figure 17.17). *Phosphorylation of the pyruvate dehydrogenase component (E_1) by pyruvate dehydrogenase kinase I (PDK) switches off the activity of the complex. Deactivation is reversed by the pyruvate dehydrogenase phosphatase (PDP).* The kinase is associated with the transacetylase component (E_2), again highlighting the structural and mechanistic importance of this core. Both the kinase and the phosphatase are regulated. To see how this regulation works in biological conditions, consider muscle that is becoming active after a period of rest (Figure 17.18). At rest, the muscle will not have significant energy demands. Consequently, the $NADH/NAD^+$, acetyl CoA/CoA, and ATP/ADP ratios will be high. These high ratios promote phosphorylation and, hence, deactivation of the pyruvate dehydrogenase complex. In other words, high concentrations of immediate (acetyl CoA and NADH) and ultimate (ATP) products inhibit the activity. Thus, *pyruvate dehydrogenase is switched off when the energy charge is high.*

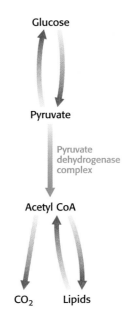

Figure 17.16 From glucose to acetyl CoA. The synthesis of acetyl CoA by the pyruvate dehydrogenase complex is a key irreversible step in the metabolism of glucose.

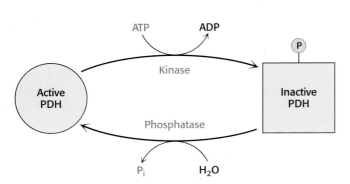

Figure 17.17 Regulation of the pyruvate dehydrogenase complex. A specific kinase phosphorylates and inactivates pyruvate dehydrogenase (PDH), and a phosphatase activates the dehydrogenase by removing the phosphoryl group. The kinase and the phosphatase also are highly regulated enzymes.

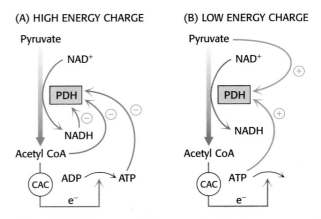

Figure 17.18 Response of the pyruvate dehydrogenase complex to the energy charge. The pyruvate dehydrogenase complex is regulated to respond to the energy charge of the cell. (A) The complex is inhibited by its immediate products, NADH and acetyl CoA, as well as by the ultimate product of cellular respiration, ATP. (B) The complex is activated by pyruvate and ADP, which inhibit the kinase that phosphorylates PDH.

As exercise begins, the concentrations of ADP and pyruvate will increase as muscle contraction consumes ATP and glucose is converted into pyruvate to meet the energy demands. Both ADP and pyruvate activate the dehydrogenase by inhibiting the kinase. Moreover, the phosphatase is stimulated by Ca^{2+}, the same signal that initiates muscle contraction. A rise in the cytoplasmic Ca^{2+} level (Section 35.2) elevates the mitochondrial Ca^{2+} level. The rise in mitochondrial Ca^{2+} activates the phosphatase, enhancing pyruvate dehydrogenase activity.

In some tissues, the phosphatase is regulated by hormones. In liver, epinephrine binds to the α-adrenergic receptor to initiate the phosphatidylinositol pathway (Section 14.1), causing an increase in Ca^{2+} concentration that activates the phosphatase. In tissues capable of fatty acid synthesis, such as the liver and adipose tissue, insulin, the hormone that signifies the fed state, stimulates the phosphatase, increasing the conversion of pyruvate into acetyl CoA. Acetyl CoA is the precursor for fatty acid synthesis (Section 22.4). In these tissues, the pyruvate dehydrogenase complex is activated to funnel glucose to pyruvate and then to acetyl CoA and ultimately to fatty acids.

In people with a phosphatase deficiency, pyruvate dehydrogenase is always phosphorylated and thus inactive. Consequently, glucose is processed to lactate rather than acetyl CoA. This condition results in unremitting lactic acidosis—high blood levels of lactic acid. In such an acidic environment, many tissues malfunction, most notably the central nervous system.

The citric acid cycle is controlled at several points

The rate of the citric acid cycle is precisely adjusted to meet an animal cell's needs for ATP (Figure 17.19). The primary control points are the allosteric enzymes isocitrate dehydrogenase and α-ketoglutarate dehydrogenase, the first two enzymes in the cycle to generate high-energy electrons.

The first control site is isocitrate dehydrogenase. The enzyme is allosterically stimulated by ADP, which enhances the enzyme's affinity for substrates. The binding of isocitrate, NAD^+, Mg^{2+}, and ADP is mutually cooperative. In contrast, ATP is inhibitory. The reaction product NADH also inhibits isocitrate dehydrogenase by directly displacing NAD^+. It is important to note that several steps in the cycle require NAD^+ or FAD, which are abundant only when the energy charge is low.

A second control site in the citric acid cycle is α-ketoglutarate dehydrogenase. Some aspects of this enzyme's control are like those of the pyruvate dehydrogenase complex, as might be expected from the homology of the two enzymes. α-Ketoglutarate dehydrogenase is inhibited by succinyl CoA and NADH, the products of the reaction that it catalyzes. In addition, α-ketoglutarate dehydrogenase is inhibited by a high energy charge. Thus, *the rate of the cycle is reduced when the cell has a high level of ATP.*

The use of isocitrate dehydrogenase and α-ketoglutarate dehydrogenase as control points integrates the citric acid cycle with other pathways and highlights the central role of the citric acid cycle in metabolism. For instance, the inhibition of isocitrate dehydrogenase leads to a buildup of citrate, because the interconversion of isocitrate and citrate is readily reversible under intracellular conditions. Citrate can be transported to the cytoplasm, where it signals phosphofructokinase to halt glycolysis (Section 16.2) and where it can serve as a source of acetyl CoA for fatty acid synthesis (Section 22.4). The α-ketoglutarate that accumulates when α-ketoglutarate

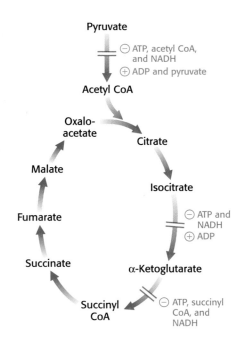

Figure 17.19 Control of the citric acid cycle. The citric acid cycle is regulated primarily by the concentration of ATP and NADH. The key control points are the enzymes isocitrate dehydrogenase and α-ketoglutarate dehydrogenase.

dehydrogenase is inhibited can be used as a precursor for several amino acids and the purine bases (Chapter 23 and Chapter 25).

In many bacteria, the funneling of two-carbon fragments into the cycle also is controlled. *The synthesis of citrate from oxaloacetate and acetyl CoA carbon units is an important control point in these organisms.* ATP is an allosteric inhibitor of citrate synthase. The effect of ATP is to increase the value of K_M for acetyl CoA. Thus, as the level of ATP increases, less of this enzyme is saturated with acetyl CoA and so less citrate is formed.

Defects in the citric acid cycle contribute to the development of cancer

Three enzymes crucial to cellular respiration are known to contribute to the development of cancer: succinate dehydrogenase, fumarase, and pyruvate dehydrogenase kinase. Mutations that alter the activity of all three of these enzymes enhance aerobic glycolysis. In aerobic glycolysis, cancer cells preferentially metabolize glucose to lactate even in the presence of oxygen. Defects in all of these enzymes share a common biochemical link: the transcription factor *hypoxia inducible factor 1* (HIF-1).

Normally, HIF-1 up-regulates the enzymes and transporters that enhance glycolysis only when oxygen concentration falls, a condition called hypoxia. Under normal conditions, HIF-1 is hydroxylated by prolyl hydroxylase 2 and is subsequently destroyed by the proteasome, a large complex of proteolytic enzymes (Chapter 23). The degradation of HIF-1 prevents the stimulation of glycolysis. Prolyl hydroxylase 2 requires α-ketoglutarate, ascorbate, and oxygen for activity. Thus, when oxygen concentration falls, the prolyl hydroxylase 2 is inactive, HIF-1 is not hydroxylated and not degraded, and the synthesis of proteins required for glycolysis is stimulated. As a result, the rate of glycolysis is increased.

Defects in the enzymes of the citric acid cycle can significantly affect the regulation of prolyl hydroxylase 2. When either succinate dehydrogenase or fumarase is defective, succinate and fumarate accumulate in the mitochondria and spill over into the cytoplasm. Both succinate and fumarate are competitive inhibitors of prolyl hydroxylase 2. The inhibition of prolyl hydroxylase 2 results in the stabilization of HIF-1, since HIF-1 is no longer hydroxylated. Lactate, the end product of glycolysis, also appears to inhibit prolyl hydroxylase 2 by interfering with the action of ascorbate. In addition to increasing the amount of the proteins required for glycolysis, HIF-1 also stimulates the production of pyruvate dehydrogenase kinase (PDK). The kinase inhibits the pyruvate dehydrogenase complex, preventing the conversion of pyruvate into acetyl CoA. The pyruvate remains in the cytoplasm, further increasing the rate of aerobic glycolysis. Moreover, mutations in PDK that lead to enhanced activity contribute to increased aerobic glycolysis and the subsequent development of cancer. By enhancing glycolysis and increasing the concentration of lactate, the mutations in PDK result in the inhibition of hydroxylase and the stabilization of HIF-1.

These observations linking citric acid cycle enzymes to cancer suggest that cancer is also a metabolic disease, not simply a disease of mutant growth factors and cell cycle control proteins. The realization that there is a metabolic component to cancer opens the door to new thinking about the control of cancer. Indeed, preliminary experiments suggest that if cancer cells undergoing aerobic glycolysis are forced by pharmacological manipulation to use oxidative phosphorylation, the cancer cells lose their malignant properties. It is also interesting to note that the citric acid cycle, which has been studied for decades, still has secrets to be revealed by future biochemists.

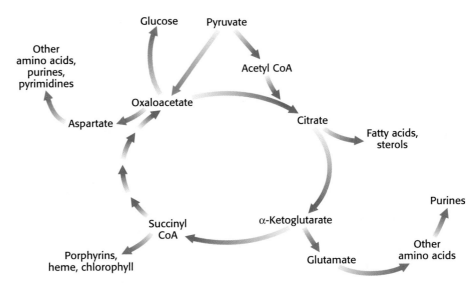

Figure 17.20 Biosynthetic roles of the citric acid cycle. Intermediates are drawn off for biosyntheses (shown by red arrows) when the energy needs of the cell are met. Intermediates are replenished by the formation of oxaloacetate from pyruvate.

17.4 The Citric Acid Cycle Is a Source of Biosynthetic Precursors

Thus far, discussion has focused on the citric acid cycle as the *major degradative pathway for the generation of ATP.* As a major metabolic hub of the cell, the citric acid cycle also *provides intermediates for biosyntheses* (Figure 17.20). For example, most of the carbon atoms in porphyrins come from *succinyl CoA.* Many of the amino acids are derived from *α-ketoglutarate* and *oxaloacetate.* These biosynthetic processes will be considered in subsequent chapters.

The citric acid cycle must be capable of being rapidly replenished

The important point now is that *citric acid cycle intermediates must be replenished if any are drawn off for biosyntheses.* Suppose that much oxaloacetate is converted into amino acids for protein synthesis and, subsequently, the energy needs of the cell rise. The citric acid cycle will operate to a reduced extent unless new oxaloacetate is formed, because acetyl CoA cannot enter the cycle unless it condenses with oxaloacetate. Even though oxaloacetate is recycled, a minimal level must be maintained to allow the cycle to function.

How is oxaloacetate replenished? Mammals lack the enzymes for the net conversion of acetyl CoA into oxaloacetate or any other citric acid cycle intermediate. Rather, oxaloacetate is formed by the carboxylation of pyruvate, in a reaction catalyzed by the biotin-dependent enzyme *pyruvate carboxylase* (Figure 17.21).

$$\text{Pyruvate} + CO_2 + \text{ATP} + H_2O \rightarrow \text{oxaloacetate} + \text{ADP} + P_i + 2\,H^+$$

Recall that this enzyme plays a crucial role in gluconeogenesis (Section 16.3). It is active only in the presence of acetyl CoA, which signifies the need for more oxaloacetate. If the energy charge is high, oxaloacetate is converted into glucose. If the energy charge is low, oxaloacetate replenishes the citric acid cycle. The synthesis of oxaloacetate by the carboxylation of pyruvate is an example of an *anaplerotic reaction* (*anaplerotic* is of Greek origin, meaning to "fill up"), a reaction that leads to the net synthesis, or

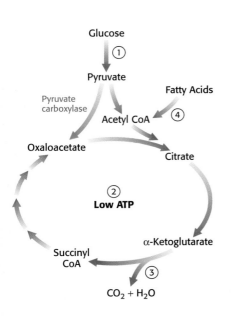

Active pathways

① Glycolysis, Ch. 16
② Citric acid cycle, Ch. 17
③ Oxidative phosphorylation, Ch. 18
④ Fatty acid oxidation, Ch. 22

Figure 17.21 PATHWAY INTEGRATION: Pathways active during exercise after a night's rest. The rate of the citric acid cycle increases during exercise, requiring the replenishment of oxaloacetate and acetyl CoA. Oxaloacetate is replenished by its formation from pyruvate. Acetyl CoA may be produced from the metabolism of both pyruvate and fatty acids.

replenishment, of pathway components. Note that because the citric acid cycle is a cycle, it can be replenished by the generation of any of the intermediates.

The disruption of pyruvate metabolism is the cause of beriberi and poisoning by mercury and arsenic

Beriberi, a neurologic and cardiovascular disorder, is caused by a dietary deficiency of thiamine (also called *vitamin B₁*). The disease has been and continues to be a serious health problem in the Far East because rice, the major food, has a rather low content of thiamine. This deficiency is partly ameliorated if the whole rice grain is soaked in water before milling; some of the thiamine in the husk then leaches into the rice kernel. The problem is exacerbated if the rice is polished (that is, converted from brown to white rice), because only the outer layer contains significant amounts of thiamine. Beriberi is also occasionally seen in alcoholics who are severely malnourished and thus thiamine deficient. The disease is characterized by neurologic and cardiac symptoms. Damage to the peripheral nervous system is expressed as pain in the limbs, weakness of the musculature, and distorted skin sensation. The heart may be enlarged and the cardiac output inadequate.

Which biochemical processes might be affected by a deficiency of thiamine? Thiamine is the precursor of the cofactor thiamine pyrophosphate. *This cofactor is the prosthetic group of three important enzymes: pyruvate dehydrogenase, α-ketoglutarate dehydrogenase, and transketolase.* Transketolase functions in the pentose phosphate pathway, which will be considered in Chapter 20. *The common feature of enzymatic reactions utilizing TPP is the transfer of an activated aldehyde unit.* In beriberi, the levels of pyruvate and α-ketoglutarate in the blood are higher than normal. The increase in the level of pyruvate in the blood is especially pronounced after the ingestion of glucose. A related finding is that the activities of the pyruvate and α-ketoglutarate dehydrogenase complexes in vivo are abnormally low. The low transketolase activity of red blood cells in beriberi is an easily measured and reliable diagnostic indicator of the disease.

Why does TPP deficiency lead primarily to neurological disorders? The nervous system relies essentially on glucose as its only fuel. The product of glycolysis, pyruvate, can enter the citric acid cycle only through the pyruvate dehydrogenase complex. With that enzyme deactivated, the nervous system has no source of fuel. In contrast, most other tissues can use fats as a source of fuel for the citric acid cycle.

Symptoms similar to those of beriberi appear in organisms exposed to mercury or arsenite (AsO_3^{3-}). Both materials have a high affinity for neighboring sulfhydryls, such as those in the reduced dihydrolipoyl groups of the E₃ component of the pyruvate dehydrogenase complex (Figure 17.22). The binding of mercury or arsenite to the dihydrolipoyl groups inhibits the complex and leads to central nervous system pathologies. The proverbial phrase "mad as a hatter" refers to the strange behavior of poisoned hat makers who used mercury nitrate to soften and shape animal furs. This form of mercury is absorbed through the skin. Similar symptoms afflicted the early photographers, who used vaporized mercury to create daguerreotypes.

Treatment for these poisons is the administration of sulfhydryl reagents with adjacent sulfhydryl groups to compete with the dihydrolipoyl residues for binding with the metal ion. The reagent–metal complex is then excreted in the urine. Indeed, 2,3-dimercaptopropanol (see Figure 17.22) was developed after World War I as an antidote to lewisite, an arsenic-based chemical weapon. This compound was initially called BAL, for British anti-lewisite.

> **Beriberi**
>
> A vitamin-deficiency disease first described in 1630 by Jacob Bonitus, a Dutch physician working in Java:
>
> "A certain very troublesome affliction, which attacks men, is called by the inhabitants Beriberi (which means sheep). I believe those, whom this same disease attacks, with their knees shaking and the legs raised up, walk like sheep. It is a kind of paralysis, or rather Tremor: for it penetrates the motion and sensation of the hands and feet indeed sometimes of the whole body."

[The Granger Collection.]

Figure 17.22 Arsenite poisoning. Arsenite inhibits the pyruvate dehydrogenase complex by inactivating the dihydrolipoamide component of the transacetylase. Some sulfhydryl reagents, such as 2,3-dimercaptoethanol, relieve the inhibition by forming a complex with the arsenite that can be excreted.

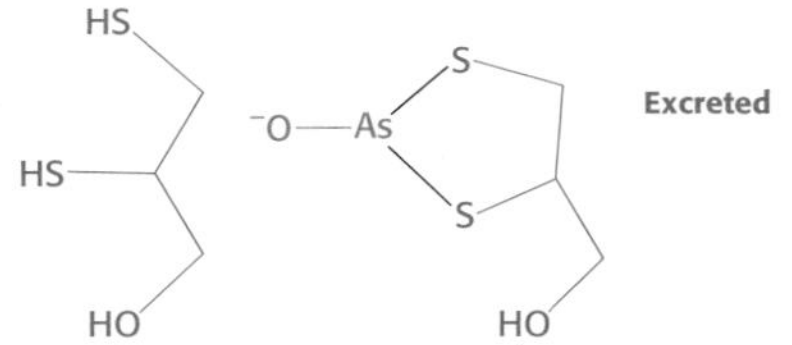

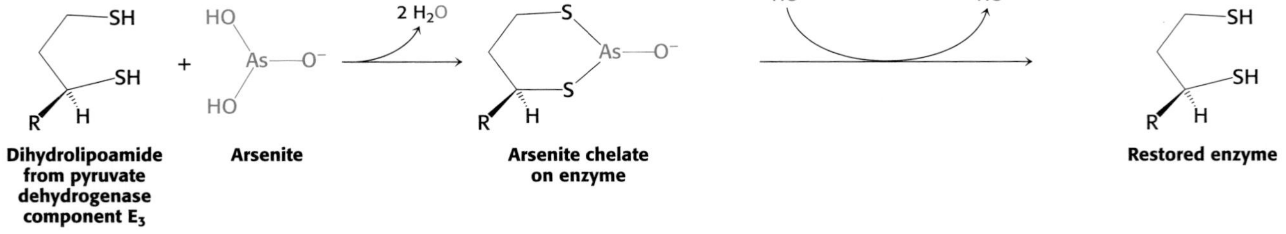

The manuscript proposing the citric acid cycle was submitted for publication to *Nature* but was rejected in June 1937. That same year it was published in *Enzymologia.* Dr. Krebs proudly displayed the rejection letter throughout his career as encouragement for young scientists.

"The editor of NATURE presents his compliments to Dr. H. A. Krebs and regrets that as he has already sufficient letters to fill the correspondence columns of NATURE for seven or eight weeks, it is undesirable to accept further letters at the present time on account of the time delay which must occur in their publication.

If Dr. Krebs does not mind much delay the editor is prepared to keep the letter until the congestion is relieved in the hope of making use of it.

He returns it now, in case Dr. Krebs prefers to submit it for early publication to another periodical."

The citric acid cycle may have evolved from preexisting pathways

How did the citric acid cycle come into being? Although definitive answers are elusive, informed speculation is possible. We can perhaps begin to comprehend how evolution might work at the level of biochemical pathways.

The citric acid cycle was most likely assembled from preexisting reaction pathways. As noted earlier, many of the intermediates formed in the citric acid cycle are used in metabolic pathways for amino acids and porphyrins. Thus, compounds such as pyruvate, α-ketoglutarate, and oxaloacetate were likely present early in evolution for biosynthetic purposes. The oxidative decarboxylation of these α-ketoacids is quite favorable thermodynamically and can be used to drive the synthesis of both acyl CoA derivatives and NADH. These reactions almost certainly formed the core of processes that preceded the citric acid cycle evolutionarily. Interestingly, α-ketoglutarate can be directly converted into oxaloacetate by transamination of the respective amino acids by aspartate aminotransferase, another key biosynthetic enzyme. Thus, cycles comprising smaller numbers of intermediates used for a variety of biochemical purposes could have existed before the present form evolved.

17.5 The Glyoxylate Cycle Enables Plants and Bacteria to Grow on Acetate

Acetyl CoA that enters the citric acid cycle has but one fate: oxidation to CO_2 and H_2O. Most organisms thus cannot convert acetyl CoA into glucose, because although oxaloacetate, a key precursor to glucose, is formed in the citric acid cycle, the two decarboxylations that take place before the regeneration of oxaloacetate preclude the *net* conversion of acetyl CoA into glucose.

In plants and in some microorganisms, there is a metabolic pathway that allows the conversion of acetyl CoA generated from fats stores into glucose. This reaction sequence, called the *glyoxylate cycle,* is similar to the citric acid cycle but bypasses the two decarboxylation steps of the cycle. Another important difference is that two molecules of acetyl CoA enter per turn of the glyoxylate cycle, compared with one in the citric acid cycle.

The glyoxylate cycle (Figure 17.23), like the citric acid cycle, begins with the condensation of acetyl CoA and oxaloacetate to form citrate, which is then isomerized to isocitrate. Instead of being decarboxylated, as in the citric acid cycle, isocitrate is cleaved by *isocitrate lyase* into succinate and

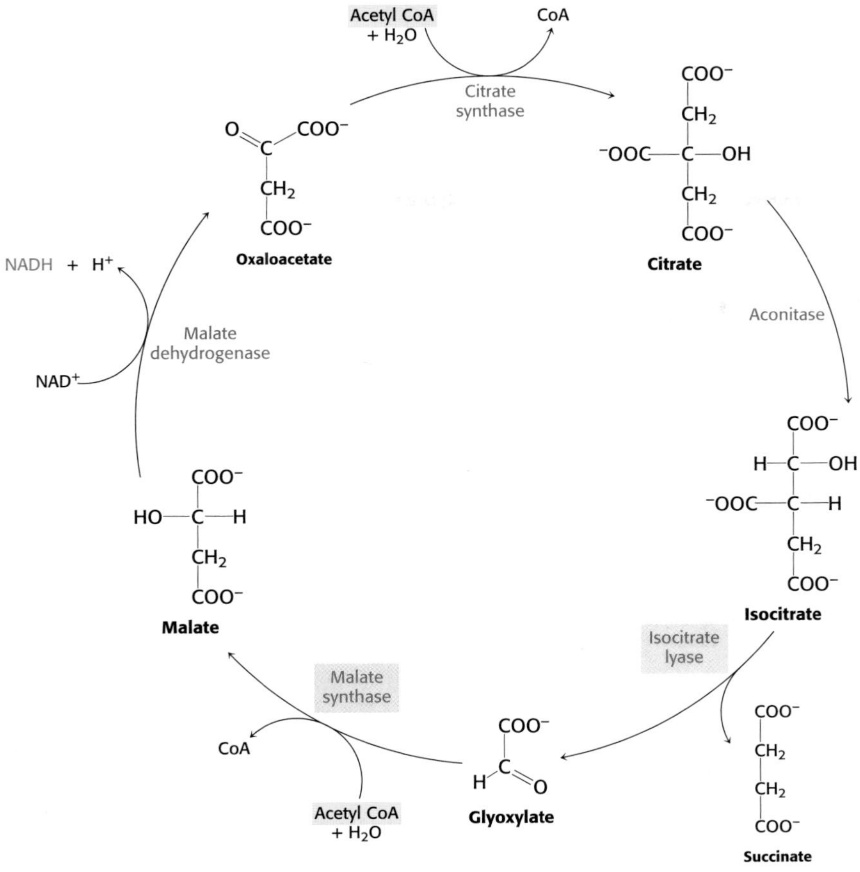

Figure 17.23 The glyoxylate pathway. The glyoxylate cycle allows plants and some microorganisms to grow on acetate because the cycle bypasses the decarboxylation steps of the citric acid cycle. The reactions of this cycle are the same as those of the citric acid cycle except for the ones catalyzed by isocitrate lyase and malate synthase, which are boxed in blue.

glyoxylate. The ensuing steps regenerate oxaloacetate from glyoxylate. First, acetyl CoA condenses with glyoxylate to form malate in a reaction catalyzed by *malate synthase,* and then malate is oxidized to oxaloacetate, as in the citric acid cycle. The sum of these reactions is

$$2 \, \text{Acetyl CoA} + \text{NAD}^+ + 2 \, \text{H}_2\text{O} \longrightarrow$$
$$\text{succinate} + 2 \, \text{CoASH} + \text{NADH} + 2 \, \text{H}^+$$

In plants, these reactions take place in organelles called *glyoxysomes.* This cycle is especially prominent in oil-rich seeds, such as those from sunflowers, cucumbers, and castor beans. Succinate, released midcycle, can be converted into carbohydrates by a combination of the citric acid cycle and gluconeogenesis. The carbohydrates power seedling growth until the cell can begin photosynthesis. Thus, organisms with the glyoxylate cycle gain a metabolic versatility because they can use acetyl CoA as a precursor of glucose and other biomolecules.

Summary

The citric acid cycle is the final common pathway for the oxidation of fuel molecules. It also serves as a source of building blocks for biosyntheses.

17.1 Pyruvate Dehydrogenase Links Glycolysis to the Citric Acid Cycle
Most fuel molecules enter the cycle as acetyl CoA. The link between glycolysis and the citric acid cycle is the oxidative decarboxylation of pyruvate to form acetyl CoA. In eukaryotes, this reaction and those of

the cycle take place inside mitochondria, in contrast with glycolysis, which takes place in the cytoplasm.

17.2 The Citric Acid Cycle Oxidizes Two-Carbon Units

The cycle starts with the condensation of oxaloacetate (C_4) and acetyl CoA (C_2) to give citrate (C_6), which is isomerized to isocitrate (C_6). Oxidative decarboxylation of this intermediate gives α-ketoglutarate (C_5). The second molecule of carbon dioxide comes off in the next reaction, in which α-ketoglutarate is oxidatively decarboxylated to succinyl CoA (C_4). The thioester bond of succinyl CoA is cleaved by orthophosphate to yield succinate, and an ATP is concomitantly generated. Succinate is oxidized to fumarate (C_4), which is then hydrated to form malate (C_4). Finally, malate is oxidized to regenerate oxaloacetate (C_4). Thus, two carbon atoms from acetyl CoA enter the cycle, and two carbon atoms leave the cycle as CO_2 in the successive decarboxylations catalyzed by isocitrate dehydrogenase and α-ketoglutarate dehydrogenase. In the four oxidation–reduction reactions in the cycle, three pairs of electrons are transferred to NAD^+ and one pair to FAD. These reduced electron carriers are subsequently oxidized by the electron-transport chain to generate approximately 9 molecules of ATP. In addition, 1 molecule of a compound having a high phosphoryl-transfer potential is directly formed in the citric acid cycle. Hence, a total of 10 molecules of compounds having high phosphoryl-transfer potential are generated for each two-carbon fragment that is completely oxidized to H_2O and CO_2.

17.3 Entry to the Citric Acid Cycle and Metabolism Through It Are Controlled

The citric acid cycle operates only under aerobic conditions because it requires a supply of NAD^+ and FAD. The irreversible formation of acetyl CoA from pyruvate is an important regulatory point for the entry of glucose-derived pyruvate into the citric acid cycle. The activity of the pyruvate dehydrogenase complex is stringently controlled by reversible phosphorylation. The electron acceptors are regenerated when NADH and $FADH_2$ transfer their electrons to O_2 through the electron-transport chain, with the concomitant production of ATP. Consequently, the rate of the citric acid cycle depends on the need for ATP. In eukaryotes, the regulation of two enzymes in the cycle also is important for control. A high energy charge diminishes the activities of isocitrate dehydrogenase and α-ketoglutarate dehydrogenase. These mechanisms complement each other in reducing the rate of formation of acetyl CoA when the energy charge of the cell is high and when biosynthetic intermediates are abundant.

17.4 The Citric Acid Cycle Is a Source of Biosynthetic Precursors

When the cell has adequate energy available, the citric acid cycle can also provide a source of building blocks for a host of important biomolecules, such as nucleotide bases, proteins, and heme groups. This use depletes the cycle of intermediates. When the cycle again needs to metabolize fuel, anaplerotic reactions replenish the cycle intermediates.

17.5 The Glyoxylate Cycle Enables Plants and Bacteria to Grow on Acetate

The glyoxylate cycle enhances the metabolic versatility of many plants and bacteria. This cycle, which uses some of the reactions of the citric acid cycle, enables these organisms to subsist on acetate because it bypasses the two decarboxylation steps of the citric acid cycle.

Key Terms

citric acid (tricarboxylic acid, TCA; Krebs) cycle (p. 497)

acetyl CoA (p. 497)

oxidative phosphorylation (p. 498)

pyruvate dehydrogenase complex (p. 499)

flavoprotein (p. 502)

citrate synthase (p. 504)

iron–sulfur (nonheme iron) protein (p. 506)

isocitrate dehydrogenase (p. 506)

α-ketoglutarate dehydrogenase (p. 507)

metabolon (p. 512)

anaplerotic reaction (p. 516)

beriberi (p. 517)

glyoxylate cycle (p. 518)

isocitrate lyase (p. 518)

malate synthase (p. 519)

glyoxysome (p. 519)

Problems

1. *Naming names.* What are the five enzymes (including regulatory enzymes) that constitute the pyruvate dehydrogenase complex? Which reactions do they catalyze?

2. *Coenzymes.* What coenzymes are required by the pyruvate dehydrogenase complex? What are their roles?

3. *More coenzymes.* Distinguish between catalytic coenzymes and stoichiometric coenzymes in the pyruvate dehydrogenase complex.

4. *Joined at the hip.* List some of the advantages of organizing the enzymes that catalyze the formation of acetyl CoA from pyruvate into a single large complex.

5. *Flow of carbon atoms.* What is the fate of the radioactive label when each of the following compounds is added to a cell extract containing the enzymes and cofactors of the glycolytic pathway, the citric acid cycle, and the pyruvate dehydrogenase complex? (The ^{14}C label is printed in red.)

(a)

(b)

(c)

(d)

(e) Glucose 6-phosphate labeled at C-1.

6. $C_2 + C_2 \rightarrow C_4$.

(a) Which enzymes are required to get *net synthesis* of oxaloacetate from acetyl CoA?

(b) Write a balanced equation for the net synthesis.

(c) Do mammalian cells contain the requisite enzymes?

7. *Driving force.* What is the $\Delta G^{\circ\prime}$ for the complete oxidation of the acetyl unit of acetyl CoA by the citric acid cycle?

8. *Acting catalytically.* The citric acid cycle itself, which is composed of enzymatically catalyzed steps, can be thought of essentially as a supramolecular enzyme. Explain.

9. *A potent inhibitor.* Thiamine thiazolone pyrophosphate binds to pyruvate dehydrogenase about 20,000 times as strongly as does thiamine pyrophosphate, and it competitively inhibits the enzyme. Why?

TPP

Thiazolone analog of TPP

10. *Lactic acidosis.* Patients in shock often suffer from lactic acidosis owing to a deficiency of O_2. Why does a lack of O_2 lead to lactic acid accumulation? One treatment for shock is to administer dichloroacetate, which inhibits the kinase associated with the pyruvate dehydrogenase complex. What is the biochemical rationale for this treatment?

11. *Energy rich.* What are the thioesters in the reaction catalyzed by PDH complex?

12. *Alternative fates.* Compare the regulation of the pyruvate dehydrogenase complex in muscle and in liver.

13. *Mutations.* (a) Predict the effect of a mutation that enhances the activity of the kinase associated with the PDH complex. (b) Predict the effect of a mutation that reduces the activity of the phosphatase associated with the PDH complex.

14. *Flaking paint, green wallpaper.* Clare Boothe Luce, ambassador to Italy in the 1950s (and Connecticut congressperson, playwright, editor of *Vanity Fair*, and the wife of Henry Luce, founder of *Time* magazine and *Sports Illustrated*) became ill when she was staying at the ambassadorial residence in Rome. The paint on the dining room ceiling, an arsenic-based paint, was flaking; the wallpaper of her bedroom in the ambassadorial residence was colored a mellow green owing to the presence of cupric arsenite in the pigment. Suggest a possible cause of Ambassador Luce's illness.

15. *A hoax, perhaps?* The citric acid cycle is part of aerobic respiration, but no O_2 is required for the cycle. Explain this paradox.

16. *Coupling reactions.* The oxidation of malate by NAD^+ to form oxaloacetate is a highly endergonic reaction under standard conditions [$\Delta G^{\circ\prime} = 29$ kJ mol^{-1} (7 kcal mol^{-1})]. The reaction proceeds readily under physiological conditions.

(a) Why?
(b) Assuming an [NAD^+]/[NADH] ratio of 8 and a pH of 7, what is the lowest [malate]/[oxaloacetate] ratio at which oxaloacetate can be formed from malate?

17. *Synthesizing α-ketoglutarate.* It is possible, with the use of the reactions and enzymes considered in this chapter, to convert pyruvate into α-ketoglutarate without depleting any of the citric acid cycle components. Write a balanced reaction scheme for this conversion, showing cofactors and identifying the required enzymes.

18. *Seven o'clock roadblock.* Malonate is a competitive inhibitor of succinate dehydrogenase. How will the concentrations of citric acid cycle intermediates change immediately after the addition of malonate? Why is malonate not a substrate for succinate dehydrogenase?

$$
\begin{array}{c}
COO^- \\
| \\
CH_2 \\
| \\
COO^-
\end{array}
$$
Malonate

19. *No signal, no activity.* Why is acetyl CoA an especially appropriate activator for pyruvate carboxylase?

20. *Power differentials.* As we will see in the next chapter, when NADH reacts with oxygen 2.5 ATP are generated. When $FADH_2$ reduces oxygen only 1.5 ATP are generated. Why then does succinate dehydrogenase produce $FADH_2$ and not NADH when succinate is reduced to fumarate?

21. *Back to Orgo.* Before any oxidation can occur in the citric acid cycle, citrate must be isomerized into isocitrate. Why is this the case?

22. *A nod is as good as a wink to a blind horse.* Explain why a GTP molecule, or another nucleoside triphosphate, is energetically equivalent to an ATP molecule in metabolism.

23. *One from two.* The synthesis of citrate from acetyl CoA and oxaloacetate is a biosynthetic reaction. What is the energy source that drives formation of citrate?

Chapter Integration Problems

24. *Fats into glucose?* Fats are usually metabolized into acetyl CoA and then further processed through the citric acid cycle. In Chapter 16, we saw that glucose can be synthesized from oxaloacetate, a citric acid cycle intermediate. Why, then, after a long bout of exercise depletes our carbohydrate stores, do we need to replenish those stores by eating carbohydrates? Why do we not simply replace them by converting fats into carbohydrates?

25. *Alternative fuels.* As we will see (Chapter 22), fatty acid breakdown generates a large amount of acetyl CoA. What will be the effect of fatty acid breakdown on pyruvate dehydrogenase complex activity? On glycolysis?

Mechanism Problems

26. *Theme and variation.* Propose a reaction mechanism for the condensation of acetyl CoA and glyoxylate in the glyoxylate cycle of plants and bacteria.

27. *Symmetry problems.* In experiments carried out in 1941 to investigate the citric acid cycle, oxaloacetate labeled with ^{14}C in the carboxyl carbon atom farthest from the keto group was introduced to an active preparation of mitochondria.

$$
\begin{array}{c}
O \quad \quad COO^- \\
\backslash \quad / \\
C \\
| \\
CH_2 \\
| \\
COO^-
\end{array}
$$
Oxaloacetate

Analysis of the α-ketoglutarate formed showed that none of the radioactive label had been lost. Decarboxylation of α-ketoglutarate then yielded succinate devoid of radioactivity. All the label was in the released CO_2. Why were the early investigators of the citric acid cycle surprised that *all* the label emerged in the CO_2?

28. *Symmetric molecules reacting asymmetrically.* The interpretation of the experiments described in Problem 27 was that citrate (or any other symmetric compound) cannot be an intermediate in the formation of α-ketoglutarate, because of the asymmetric fate of the label. This view seemed compelling until Alexander Ogston incisively pointed out in 1948 that "it is possible that *an asymmetric enzyme which attacks a symmetrical compound can distinguish between its identical groups* [italics added]." For simplicity, consider a molecule in which two hydrogen atoms, a group X, and a different group Y are bonded to a tetrahedral carbon atom as a model for citrate. Explain how a symmetric molecule can react with an enzyme in an asymmetric way.

Data Interpretation Problem

29. *A little goes a long way.* As will become clearer in Chapter 18, the activity of the citric acid cycle can be monitored by measuring the amount of O_2 consumed. The greater the rate of O_2 consumption, the faster the rate of the cycle. Hans Krebs used this assay to investigate the cycle in 1937. He used as his experimental system minced pigeon-breast muscle, which is rich in mitochondria. In one set of experiments, Krebs measured the O_2 consumption in the presence of carbohydrate only and in the presence of

carbohydrate and citrate. The results are shown in the following table.

Effect of citrate on oxygen consumption by minced pigeon-breast muscle

	Micromoles of oxygen consumed	
Time (min)	Carbohydrate only	Carbohydrate plus 3 μmol of citrate
10	26	28
60	43	62
90	46	77
150	49	85

(a) How much O_2 would be absorbed if the added citrate were completely oxidized to H_2O and CO_2?

(b) On the basis of your answer to part *a*, what do the results given in the table suggest?

30. *Arsenite poisoning.* The effect of arsenite on the experimental system of Problem 29 was then examined. Experimental data (not presented here) showed that the amount of citrate present did not change in the course of the experiment in the absence of arsenite. However, if arsenite was added to the system, different results were obtained, as shown in the following table.

Disappearance of citric acid in pigeon-breast muscle in the presence of arsenite

Micromoles of citrate added	Micromoles of citrate found after 40 minutes	Micromoles of citrate used
22	00.6	21
44	20.0	24
90	56.0	34

(a) What is the effect of arsenite on the disappearance of citrate?

(b) How is the action of arsenite altered by the addition of more citrate?

(c) What do these data suggest about the site of action of arsenite?

31. *Isocitrate lyase and tuberculosis.* The bacterium *Mycobacterium tuberculosis*, the cause of tuberculosis, can invade the lungs and persist in a latent state for years. During this time, the bacteria reside in granulomas— nodular scars containing bacteria and host-cell debris in the center and surrounded by immune cells. The granulomas are lipid-rich, oxygen-poor environments. How these bacteria manage to persist is something of a mystery. The results of recent research suggest that the glyoxylate cycle is required for the persistence. The following data show the amount of bacteria [presented as colony-forming units (cfu)] in mice lungs in the weeks after an infection.

In graph A, the black circles represent the results for wild-type bacteria and the red circles represent the results for bacteria from which the gene for isocitrate lyase was deleted.

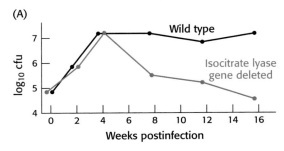

(a) What is the effect of the absence of isocitrate lyase?

The techniques described in Chapter 5 were used to reinsert the gene encoding isocitrate lyase into bacteria from which it had previously been deleted.

In graph B, black circles represent bacteria into which the gene was reinserted and red circles represent bacteria in which the gene was still missing.

(b) Do these results support those obtained in part *a*?

(c) What is the purpose of the experiment in part *b*?

(d) Why do these bacteria perish in the absence of the glyoxylate cycle?

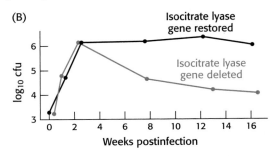

[Data after McKinney et al., *Nature* 406(2000):735–738.]

Oxidative Phosphorylation

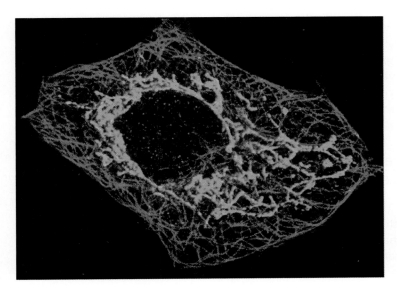

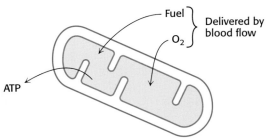

Mitochondria, stained green, form a network inside a fibroblast cell (left). Mitochondria oxidize carbon fuels to form cellular energy in the form of ATP. [(Left) Courtesy of Michael P. Yaffee, Department of Biology, University of California at San Diego.]

The amount of ATP that human beings require to go about their lives is staggering. A sedentary male of 70 kg (154 lbs) requires about 8400 kJ (2000 kcal) for a day's worth of activity. To provide this much energy requires 83 kg of ATP. However, human beings possess only about 250 g of ATP at any given moment. The disparity between the amount of ATP that we have and the amount that we require is compensated by recycling ADP back to ATP. Each ATP molecule is recycled approximately 300 times per day. This recycling takes place primarily through *oxidative phosphorylation.*

We begin our study of oxidative phosphorylation by examining the oxidation–reduction reactions that allow the flow of electrons from NADH and FADH$_2$ to oxygen. The electron flow takes place in four large protein complexes that are embedded in the inner mitochondrial membrane, together called the *respiratory chain* or the *electron-transport chain.*

$$NADH + \tfrac{1}{2}O_2 + H^+ \longrightarrow H_2O + NAD^+$$
$$\Delta G^{\circ\prime} = -220.1 \text{ kJ mol}^{-1} (-52.6 \text{ kcal mol}^{-1})$$

The overall reaction is exergonic. Importantly, three of the complexes of the electron-transport chain use the energy released by the electron flow to pump protons from the mitochondrial matrix into the cytoplasm. In essence, energy is transformed. The resulting unequal distribution of protons generates a pH gradient and a transmembrane electrical potential that creates a *proton-motive force.* ATP is synthesized when protons flow back to the mitochondrial matrix through an enzyme complex.

$$ADP + P_i + H^+ \longrightarrow ATP + H_2O$$
$$\Delta G^{\circ\prime} = +30.5 \text{ kJ mol}^{-1} (+7.3 \text{ kcal mol}^{-1})$$

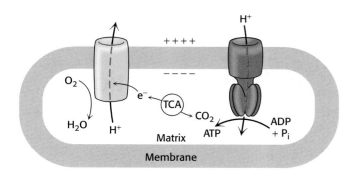

Figure 18.1 Overview of oxidative phosphorylation. Oxidation and ATP synthesis are coupled by transmembrane proton fluxes. Electrons flow from NADH and FADH$_2$ through four protein complexes to reduce oxygen to water. Three of the complexes pump protons from the mitochondrial matrix to the exterior of the mitochondria. The protons return to the matrix by flowing through another protein complex, ATP synthase, powering the synthesis of ATP.

Respiration

An ATP-generating process in which an inorganic compound (such as molecular oxygen) serves as the ultimate electron acceptor. The electron donor can be either an organic compound or an inorganic one.

Thus, *the oxidation of fuels and the phosphorylation of ADP are coupled by a proton gradient across the inner mitochondrial membrane* (Figure 18.1).

Collectively, the generation of high-transfer-potential electrons by the citric acid cycle, their flow through the respiratory chain, and the accompanying synthesis of ATP is called *respiration* or *cellular respiration*.

18.1 Eukaryotic Oxidative Phosphorylation Takes Place in Mitochondria

Recall that the biochemical purpose of the citric acid cycle, which takes place in mitochondria, is to generate high-energy electrons. It is fitting, therefore, that oxidative phosphorylation, which will convert the energy of these electrons into ATP, also takes place in mitochondria. Mitochondria are oval-shaped organelles, typically about 2 μm in length and 0.5 μm in diameter, about the size of a bacterium. Eugene Kennedy and Albert Lehninger discovered more than a half-century ago that *mitochondria contain the respiratory assembly, the enzymes of the citric acid cycle, and the enzymes of fatty acid oxidation.*

Mitochondria are bounded by a double membrane

Electron microscopic studies by George Palade and Fritjof Sjöstrand revealed that mitochondria have two membrane systems: an *outer membrane* and an extensive, highly folded *inner membrane*. The inner membrane is folded into a series of internal ridges called *cristae*. Hence, there are two compartments in mitochondria: (1) the *intermembrane space* between the outer and the inner membranes and (2) the *matrix*, which is bounded by the inner membrane (Figure 18.2). The mitochondrial matrix is the site of most of the reactions of the citric acid cycle and fatty acid oxidation. In contrast, oxidative phosphorylation takes place in the inner mitochondrial membrane. The increase in surface area of the inner mitochondrial membrane provided by the cristae creates more sites for oxidative phosphorylation than would be the case with a simple, unfolded membrane. Humans contain an estimated 14,000 m^2 of inner mitochondrial membrane, which is the approximate equivalent of three football fields in the United States.

The outer membrane is quite permeable to most small molecules and ions because it contains many copies of *mitochondrial porin*, a 30- to 35-kd pore-forming protein also known as VDAC, for *voltage-dependent anion channel*. VDAC, the most prevalent protein in the outer mitochondrial membrane, plays a role in the regulated flux of metabolites—usually anionic species such as phosphate, chloride, organic anions, and the adenine nucleotides—across the outer membrane. In contrast, the inner membrane is impermeable to nearly all ions and polar molecules. A large family of

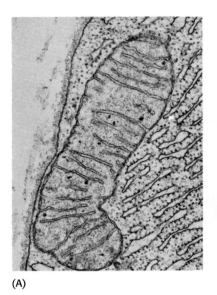

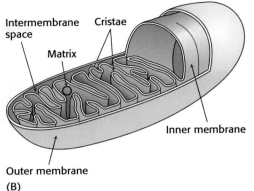

(A)   (B)

Figure 18.2 Electron micrograph (A) and diagram (B) of a mitochondrion. [(A) Courtesy of George Palade. (B) From Wolfe, *Biology of the Cell*, 2e, © 1981 Brooks/ Cole, a part of Cengage Learning, Inc. Reproduced by permission www. cengage.com/ permission 3.]

transporters shuttles metabolites such as ATP, pyruvate, and citrate across the inner mitochondrial membrane. The two faces of this membrane will be referred to as the *matrix side* and the *cytoplasmic side* (the latter because it is freely accessible to most small molecules in the cytoplasm). They are also called the N and P sides, respectively, because the membrane potential is negative on the matrix side and positive on the cytoplasmic side.

In prokaryotes, the electron-driven proton pumps and ATP-synthesizing complex are located in the cytoplasmic membrane, the inner of two membranes. The outer membrane of bacteria, like that of mitochondria, is permeable to most small metabolites because of the presence of porins.

Mitochondria are the result of an endosymbiotic event

Mitochondria are semiautonomous organelles that live in an endosymbiotic relation with the host cell. These organelles contain their own DNA, which encodes a variety of different proteins and RNAs. Mitochondrial DNA is usually portrayed as being circular, but recent research suggests that the mitochondrial DNA of many organisms may be linear. The genomes of mitochondria range broadly in size across species. The mitochondrial genome of the protist *Plasmodium falciparum* consists of fewer than 6000 base pairs (bp), whereas those of some land plants comprise more than 200,000 bp (Figure 18.3). Human mitochondrial DNA comprises 16,569 bp and encodes 13 respiratory-chain proteins as well as the small and large ribosomal RNAs and enough tRNAs to translate all codons. However, mitochondria also contain many proteins encoded by nuclear DNA. Cells that contain mitochondria depend on these organelles for oxidative phosphorylation, and the mitochondria in turn depend on the cell for their very existence. How did this intimate symbiotic relation come to exist?

An *endosymbiotic event* is thought to have occurred whereby a free-living organism capable of oxidative phosphorylation was engulfed by another cell. The double-membrane, circular DNA (with exceptions) and the mitochondrial-specific transcription and translation machinery all point to this conclusion. Thanks to the rapid accumulation of sequence data for mitochondrial and bacterial genomes, speculation on the origin of the "original" mitochondrion with some authority is now possible. The most mitochondrial-like bacterial genome is that of *Rickettsia prowazekii*, the cause of louse-borne typhus. The genome for this organism is more than

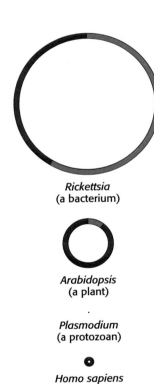

Figure 18.3 Sizes of mitochondrial genomes. The sizes of three mitochondrial genomes compared with the genome of *Rickettsia*, a relative of the presumed ancestor of all mitochondria. For genomes of more than 60 kbp, the DNA coding region for genes with known function is shown in red.

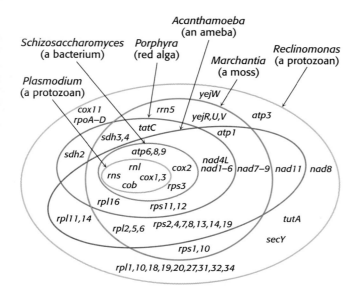

Figure 18.4 Overlapping gene complements of mitochondria. The genes present within each oval are those present within the organism represented by the oval. Only rRNA- and protein-coding genes are shown. The genome of *Reclinomonas* contains all the protein-coding genes found in all the sequenced mitochondrial genomes. [After M. W. Gray, G. Burger, and B. F. Lang. *Science* 283:1476–1481, 1999.]

1 million base pairs in size and contains 834 protein-encoding genes. Sequence data suggest that all extant mitochondria are derived from an ancestor of *R. prowazekii* as the result of a single endosymbiotic event.

The evidence that modern mitochondria result from a single event comes from examination of the most bacteria-like mitochondrial genome, that of the protozoan *Reclinomonas americana*. Its genome contains 97 genes, of which 62 specify proteins. The genes encoding these proteins include all of the protein-coding genes found in all of the sequenced mitochondrial genomes (Figure 18.4). Yet, this genome encodes less than 2% of the protein-coding genes in the bacterium *E. coli*. In other words, a small fraction of bacterial genes—2%—are found in all examined mitochondria. How is it possible that all mitochondria have the same 2% of the bacterial genome? It seems unlikely that mitochondrial genomes resulting from several endosymbiotic events could have been independently reduced to the same set of genes found in *R. americana*. Thus, the simplest explanation is that the endosymbiotic event took place just once and all existing mitochondria are descendants of that ancestor.

Note that transient engulfment of prokaryotic cells by larger cells is not uncommon in the microbial world. In regard to mitochondria, such a transient relation became permanent as the bacterial cell lost DNA, making it incapable of independent living, and the host cell became dependent on the ATP generated by its tenant.

18.2 Oxidative Phosphorylation Depends on Electron Transfer

In Chapter 17, the primary function of the citric acid cycle was identified as the generation of NADH and $FADH_2$ by the oxidation of acetyl CoA. In oxidative phosphorylation, electrons from NADH and $FADH_2$ are used to reduce molecular oxygen to water. The highly exergonic reduction of molecular oxygen by NADH and $FADH_2$ is accomplished by a number of electron-transfer reactions, which take place in a set of membrane proteins known as the *electron-transport chain*.

The electron-transfer potential of an electron is measured as redox potential

In oxidative phosphorylation, the *electron-transfer potential* of NADH or $FADH_2$ is converted into the *phosphoryl-transfer potential* of ATP. We need quantitative expressions for these forms of free energy. The measure of phosphoryl-transfer potential is already familiar to us: it is given by $\Delta G^{\circ\prime}$ for the hydrolysis of the activated phosphoryl compound. The corresponding expression for the electron-transfer potential is E_0', the *reduction potential* (also called the *redox potential* or *oxidation–reduction potential*).

The reduction potential is an electrochemical concept. Consider a substance that can exist in an oxidized form X and a reduced form X^-. Such a pair is called a *redox couple* and is designated $X : X^-$. The reduction potential of this couple can be determined by measuring the electromotive force generated by an apparatus called a *sample half-cell* connected to a *standard reference half-cell* (Figure 18.5). The sample half-cell consists of an electrode

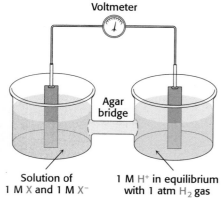

Figure 18.5 Measurement of redox potential. Apparatus for the measurement of the standard oxidation–reduction potential of a redox couple. Electrons, but not X or X^-, can flow through the agar bridge.

immersed in a solution of 1 M oxidant (X) and 1 M reductant (X^-). The standard reference half-cell consists of an electrode immersed in a 1 M H^+ solution that is in equilibrium with H_2 gas at 1 atmosphere (1 atm) of pressure. The electrodes are connected to a voltmeter, and an agar bridge allows ions to move from one half-cell to the other, establishing electrical continuity between the half-cells. Electrons then flow from one half-cell to the other through the wire connecting the two half-cells to the voltmeter. If the reaction proceeds in the direction

$$X^- + H^+ \rightarrow X + \frac{1}{2} H_2$$

the reactions in the half-cells (referred to as *half-reactions* or *couples*) must be

$$X^- \rightarrow X + e^- \qquad H^+ + e^- \rightarrow \frac{1}{2} H_2$$

Thus, electrons flow from the sample half-cell to the standard reference half-cell, and the sample-cell electrode is taken to be negative with respect to the standard-cell electrode. *The reduction potential of the $X:X^-$ couple is the observed voltage at the start of the experiment* (when X, X^-, and H^+ are 1 M with 1 atm of H_2). *The reduction potential of the $H^+:H_2$ couple is defined to be 0 volts.* In oxidation–reduction reactions, the donor of electrons, in this case X, is called the reductant or reducing agent, whereas the acceptor of electrons, H^+ here, is called the oxidant.

The meaning of the reduction potential is now evident. A negative reduction potential means that the oxidized form of a substance has lower affinity for electrons than does H_2, as in the preceding example. A positive reduction potential means that the oxidized form of a substance has higher affinity for electrons than does H_2. These comparisons refer to standard conditions—namely, 1 M oxidant, 1 M reductant, 1 M H^+, and 1 atm H_2. Thus, *a strong reducing agent (such as NADH) is poised to donate electrons and has a negative reduction potential, whereas a strong oxidizing agent (such as O_2) is ready to accept electrons and has a positive reduction potential.*

The reduction potentials of many biologically important redox couples are known (Table 18.1). Table 18.1 is like those presented in chemistry

Table 18.1 Standard reduction potentials of some reactions

Oxidant	Reductant	n	E'_0 (V)
Succinate + CO_2	α-Ketoglutarate	2	−0.67
Acetate	Acetaldehyde	2	−0.60
Ferredoxin (oxidized)	Ferredoxin (reduced)	1	−0.43
$2 H^+$	H_2	2	−0.42
NAD^+	NADH + H^+	2	−0.32
$NADP^+$	NADPH + H^+	2	−0.32
Lipoate (oxidized)	Lipoate (reduced)	2	−0.29
Glutathione (oxidized)	Glutathione (reduced)	2	−0.23
FAD	$FADH_2$	2	−0.22
Acetaldehyde	Ethanol	2	−0.20
Pyruvate	Lactate	2	−0.19
Fumarate	Succinate	2	+0.03
Cytochrome b (+3)	Cytochrome b (+2)	1	+0.07
Dehydroascorbate	Ascorbate	2	+0.08
Ubiquinone (oxidized)	Ubiquinone (reduced)	2	+0.10
Cytochrome c (+3)	Cytochrome c (+2)	1	+0.22
Fe (+3)	Fe (+2)	1	+0.77
$\frac{1}{2} O_2 + 2 H^+$	H_2O	2	+0.82

Note: E'_0 is the standard oxidation–reduction potential (pH 7, 25°C) and n is the number of electrons transferred. E'_0 refers to the partial reaction written as Oxidant + $e^- \rightarrow$ reductant

textbooks, except that a hydrogen ion concentration of 10^{-7} M (pH 7) instead of 1 M (pH 0) is the standard state adopted by biochemists. This difference is denoted by the prime in E_0'. Recall that the prime in $\Delta G^{\circ\prime}$ denotes a standard free-energy change at pH 7.

The standard free-energy change $\Delta G^{\circ\prime}$ is related to the change in reduction potential $\Delta E_0'$ by

$$\Delta G^{\circ\prime} = -nF\Delta E_0'$$

in which n is the number of electrons transferred, F is a proportionality constant called the *faraday* [96.48 kJ mol^{-1} V^{-1} (23.06 kcal mol^{-1} V^{-1})], $\Delta E_0'$ is in volts, and $\Delta G^{\circ\prime}$ is in kilojoules or kilocalories per mole.

The free-energy change of an oxidation–reduction reaction can be readily calculated from the reduction potentials of the reactants. For example, consider the reduction of pyruvate by NADH, catalyzed by lactate dehydrogenase. Recall that this reaction maintains redox balance in lactic acid fermentation (see Figure 16.11).

$$\text{Pyruvate} + \text{NADH} + \text{H}^+ \rightleftharpoons \text{lactate} + \text{NAD}^+ \qquad \text{(A)}$$

The reduction potential of the NAD$^+$: NADH couple, or half-reaction, is -0.32 V, whereas that of the pyruvate : lactate couple is -0.19 V. By convention, reduction potentials (as in Table 18.1) refer to partial reactions written as reductions: oxidant $+\, e^- \rightarrow$ reductant. Hence,

$$\text{Pyruvate} + 2\,\text{H}^+ + 2\,e^- \rightarrow \text{lactate} \qquad E_0' = -0.19\,\text{V} \qquad \text{(B)}$$
$$\text{NAD}^+ + \text{H}^+ + 2\,e^- \rightarrow \text{NADH} \qquad E_0' = -0.32\,\text{V} \qquad \text{(C)}$$

To obtain reaction A from reactions B and C, we need to reverse the direction of reaction C so that NADH appears on the left side of the arrow. In doing so, the sign of E_0' must be changed.

$$\text{Pyruvate} + 2\,\text{H}^+ + 2\,e^- \rightarrow \text{lactate} \qquad E_0' = -0.19\,\text{V} \qquad \text{(B)}$$
$$\text{NADH} \rightarrow \text{NAD}^+ + \text{H}^+ + 2\,e^- \qquad E_0' = +0.32\,\text{V} \qquad \text{(D)}$$

For reaction B, the free energy can be calculated with $n = 2$.

$$\begin{aligned}\Delta G^{\circ\prime} &= -2 \times 96.48\,\text{kJ mol}^{-1}\,\text{V}^{-1} \times -0.19\,\text{V} \\ &= +36.7\,\text{kJ mol}^{-1}\ (+8.8\,\text{kcal mol}^{-1})\end{aligned}$$

Likewise, for reaction D,

$$\begin{aligned}\Delta G^{\circ\prime} &= -2 \times 96.48\,\text{kJ mol}^{-1}\,\text{V}^{-1} \times +0.32\,\text{V} \\ &= -61.8\,\text{kJ mol}^{-1}\ (-14.8\,\text{kcal mol}^{-1})\end{aligned}$$

Thus, the free energy for reaction A is given by

$$\begin{aligned}\Delta G^{\circ\prime} &= \Delta G^{\circ\prime}\ (\text{for reaction B}) + \Delta G^{\circ\prime}\ (\text{for reaction D}) \\ &= +36.7\,\text{kJ mol}^{-1} + (-61.8\,\text{kJ mol}^{-1}) \\ &= -25.1\,\text{kJ mol}^{-1}\ (-6.0\,\text{kcal mol}^{-1})\end{aligned}$$

A 1.14-volt potential difference between NADH and molecular oxygen drives electron transport through the chain and favors the formation of a proton gradient

The driving force of oxidative phosphorylation is the electron-transfer potential of NADH or FADH$_2$ relative to that of O$_2$. How much energy is released by the reduction of O$_2$ with NADH? Let us calculate $\Delta G^{\circ\prime}$ for this reaction. The pertinent half-reactions are

$$\frac{1}{2} O_2 + 2\,H^+ + 2\,e^- \rightarrow H_2O \qquad E_0' = +0.82\,V \qquad (A)$$
$$NAD^+ + H^+ + 2\,e^- \rightarrow NADH \qquad E_0' = -0.32\,V \qquad (B)$$

The combination of the two half-reactions, as it proceeds in the electron-transport chain, yields

$$\frac{1}{2} O_2 + NADH + H^+ \rightarrow H_2O + NAD^+ \qquad (C)$$

The standard free energy for this reaction is then given by

$$\begin{aligned}\Delta G^{\circ\prime} &= (-2 \times 96.48\,\text{kJ mol}^{-1}\,V^{-1} \times +0.82\,V) - \\ &\quad (-2 \times 96.48\,\text{kJ mol}^{-1}\,V^{-1} \times 0.32\,V) \\ &= -158.2\,\text{kJ mol}^{-1} - 61.9\,\text{kJ mol}^{-1} \\ &= -220.1\,\text{kJ mol}^{-1}\,(-52.6\,\text{kcal mol}^{-1})\end{aligned}$$

This release of free energy is substantial. Recall that $\Delta G^{\circ\prime}$ for the hydrolysis of ATP is -30.5 kJ mol^{-1} (-7.3 kcal mol^{-1}). The released energy is initially used to generate a proton gradient that is then used for the synthesis of ATP and the transport of metabolites across the mitochondrial membrane.

How can the energy associated with a proton gradient be quantified? Recall that the free-energy change for a species moving from one side of a membrane where it is at concentration c_1 to the other side where it is at a concentration c_2 is given by

$$\Delta G = RT \ln(c_2/c_1) + ZF\Delta V$$

in which Z is the electrical charge of the transported species and ΔV is the potential in volts across the membrane (Section 13.1). Under typical conditions for the inner mitochondrial membrane, the pH outside is 1.4 units lower than inside [corresponding to $\ln(c_2/c_1)$ of 1.4] and the membrane potential is 0.14 V, the outside being positive. Because $Z = +1$ for protons, the free-energy change is $(8.32 \times 10^{-3}$ kJ mol^{-1} K$^{-1} \times 310$ K $\times 1.4) + (+1 \times 96.48$ kJ mol^{-1} V$^{-1} \times 0.14$ V$) = 21.8$ kJ mol^{-1} (5.2 kcal mol^{-1}). Thus, each proton that is transported out of the matrix to the cytoplasmic side corresponds to 21.8 kJ mol^{-1} of free energy.

18.3 The Respiratory Chain Consists of Four Complexes: Three Proton Pumps and a Physical Link to the Citric Acid Cycle

Electrons are transferred from NADH to O_2 through a chain of three large protein complexes called *NADH-Q oxidoreductase, Q-cytochrome c oxidoreductase,* and *cytochrome c oxidase* (Figure 18.6 and Table 18.2). *Electron flow within these transmembrane complexes leads to the transport of protons across the inner mitochondrial membrane.* A fourth large protein complex, called *succinate-Q reductase,* contains the succinate dehydrogenase that generates FADH$_2$ in the citric acid cycle. Electrons from this FADH$_2$ enter the electron-transport chain at Q-cytochrome oxidoreductase. Succinate-Q reductase, in contrast with the other complexes, does not pump protons. NADH-Q oxidoreductase, succinate-Q reductase, Q-cytochrome c oxidoreductase, and cytochrome c oxidase are also called *Complex I, II, III,* and *IV,* respectively. Complexes I, II, and III appear to be associated in a supramolecular complex termed the *respirasome*. As we have seen before, such supramolecular complexes facilitate the rapid transfer of substrate and prevent the release of reaction intermediates.

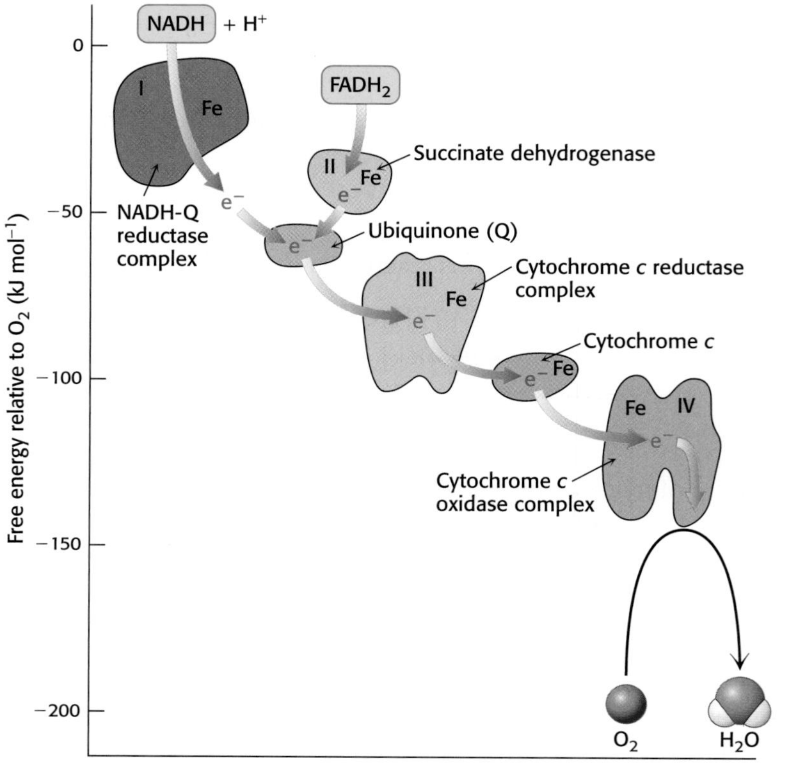

Figure 18.6 Components of the electron-transport chain. Electrons flow down an energy gradient from NADH to O_2. The flow is catalyzed by four protein complexes. Iron is a component of Complexes I, III, IV and cytochrome c. [After D. Sadava et al., *Life*, 8th ed. (Sinauer, 2008), p. 150.]

Two special electron carriers ferry the electrons from one complex to the next. The first is *coenzyme Q* (Q), also known as *ubiquinone* because it is a *ubi*quitous *quinone* in biological systems. Ubiquinone is a hydrophobic quinone that diffuses rapidly within the inner mitochondrial membrane. Electrons are carried from NADH-Q oxidoreductase to Q-cytochrome c oxidoreductase, the second complex of the chain, by the reduced form of Q. Electrons from the $FADH_2$ generated by the citric acid cycle are transferred first to ubiquinone and then to the Q-cytochrome c oxidoreductase complex.

Coenzyme Q is a quinone derivative with a long tail consisting of five-carbon isoprene units that account for its hydrophobic nature. The number of isoprene units in the tail depends on the species. The most common mammalian form contains 10 isoprene units (coenzyme Q_{10}). For simplicity,

Table 18.2 Components of the mitochondrial electron-transport chain

Enzyme complex	Mass (kd)	Subunits	Prosthetic group	Oxidant or reductant		
				Matrix side	Membrane core	Cytoplasmic side
NADH-Q oxidoreductase	>900	46	FMN Fe-S	NADH	Q	
Succinate-Q reductase	140	4	FAD Fe-S	Succinate	Q	
Q-cytochrome c oxidoreductase	250	11	Heme b_H Heme b_L Heme c_1 Fe-S		Q	Cytochrome c
Cytochrome c oxidase	160	13	Heme a Heme a_3 Cu_A and Cu_B			Cytochrome c

Sources: J. W. DePierre and L. Ernster. *Annu. Rev. Biochem.* 46:215, 1977; Y. Hatefi. *Annu Rev. Biochem.* 54:1015, 1985; and J. E. Walker. *Q. Rev. Biophys.* 25:253, 1992.

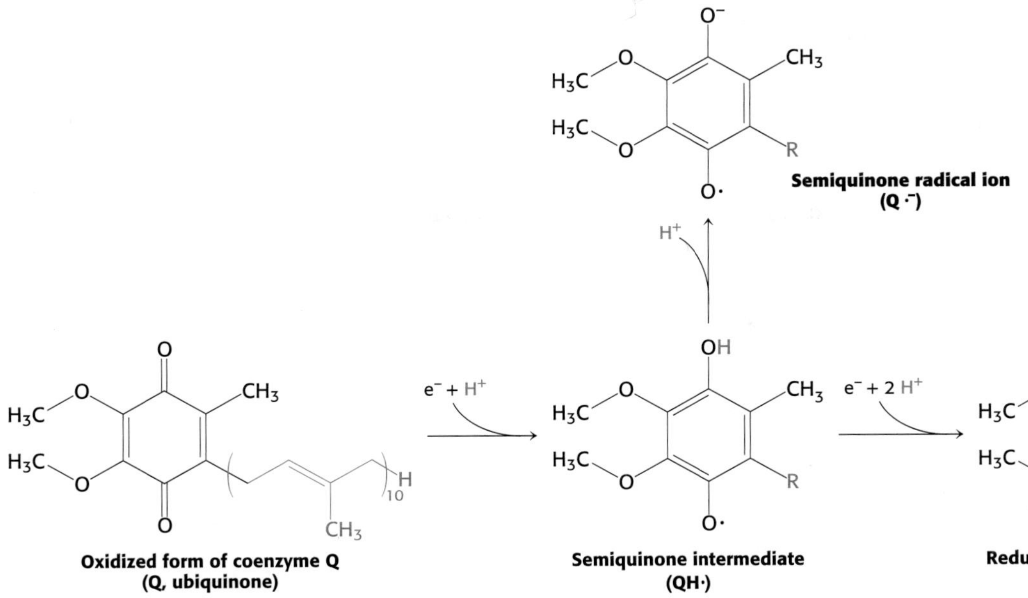

Figure 18.7 Oxidation states of quinones. The reduction of ubiquinone (Q) to ubiquinol (QH₂) proceeds through a semiquinone intermediate (QH·).

the subscript will be omitted from this abbreviation because all varieties function in an identical manner. Quinones can exist in three oxidation states. In the fully oxidized state (Q), coenzyme Q has two keto groups (Figure 18.7). The addition of one electron and one proton results in the semiquinone form (QH·). The semiquinone can lose a proton to form a semiquinone radical anion (Q·$^-$). The addition of a second electron and proton to the semiquinone generates ubiquinol (QH₂), the fully reduced form of coenzyme Q, which holds its protons more tightly. Thus, *for quinones, electron-transfer reactions are coupled to proton binding and release*, a property that is key to transmembrane proton transport. Because ubiquinone is soluble in the membrane, a pool of Q and QH₂—the Q *pool*—is thought to exist in the inner mitochondrial membrane.

In contrast with Q, the second special electron carrier is a protein. Cytochrome *c*, a small soluble protein, shuttles electrons from Q-cytochrome *c* oxidoreductase to cytochrome *c* oxidase, the final component in the chain and the one that catalyzes the reduction of O_2.

The high-potential electrons of NADH enter the respiratory chain at NADH-Q oxidoreductase

The electrons of NADH enter the chain at *NADH-Q oxidoreductase* (also called *Complex I* and *NADH dehydrogenase*), an enormous enzyme (>900 kd) consisting of approximately 46 polypeptide chains. This proton pump, like that of the other two in the respiratory chain, is encoded by genes residing in both the mitochondria and the nucleus. NADH-Q oxidoreductase is L-shaped, with a horizontal arm lying in the membrane and a vertical arm that projects into the matrix.

The reaction catalyzed by this enzyme appears to be

$$NADH + Q + 5\,H^+_{matrix} \rightarrow NAD^+ + QH_2 + 4\,H^+_{cytoplasm}$$

The initial step is the binding of NADH and the transfer of its two high-potential electrons to the *flavin mononucleotide* (FMN) prosthetic group of this complex to give the reduced form, FMNH₂ (Figure 18.8). The electron acceptor of FMN, the isoalloxazine ring, is identical with that of FAD.

Electrons are then transferred from FMNH₂ to a series of *iron–sulfur clusters*, the second type of prosthetic group in NADH-Q oxidoreductase.

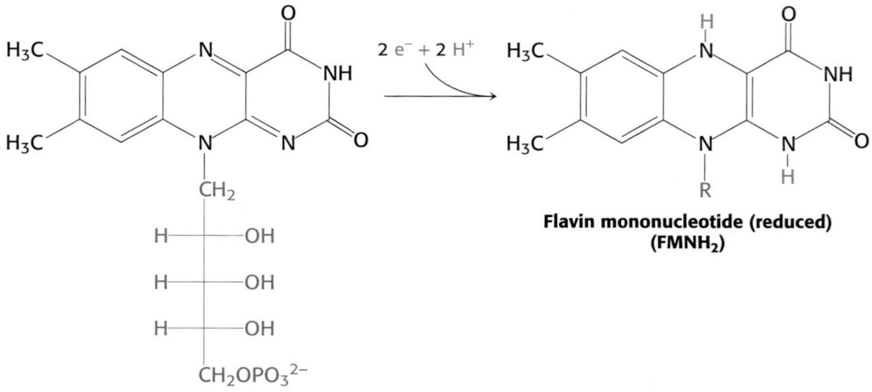

$2 e^- + 2 H^+$

Flavin mononucleotide (oxidized)
(FMN)

Flavin mononucleotide (reduced)
(FMNH$_2$)

Figure 18.8 Oxidation states of flavins.

Fe-S clusters in *iron–sulfur proteins* (also called *nonheme iron proteins*) play a critical role in a wide range of reduction reactions in biological systems. Several types of Fe-S clusters are known (Figure 18.9). In the simplest kind, a single iron ion is tetrahedrally coordinated to the sulfhydryl groups of four cysteine residues of the protein. A second kind, denoted by 2Fe-2S, contains two iron ions, two inorganic sulfides, and usually four cysteine residues. A third type, designated 4Fe-4S, contains four iron ions, four inorganic sulfides, and four cysteine residues. NADH-Q oxidoreductase contains both 2Fe-2S and 4Fe-4S clusters. Iron ions in these Fe-S complexes cycle between Fe^{2+} (reduced) and Fe^{3+} (oxidized) states. Unlike quinones and flavins, iron–sulfur clusters generally undergo oxidation–reduction reactions without releasing or binding protons.

All of the redox reactions take place in the extramembranous part of NADH-Q oxidoreductase. Although the details of electron transfer through this complex remain the subject of ongoing investigation, NADH clearly binds to a site in the extramembranous domain. NADH transfers its two electrons to FMN. These electrons flow through a series of Fe-S centers and then to coenzyme Q. *The flow of two electrons from NADH to coenzyme Q through NADH-Q oxidoreductase leads to the pumping of four hydrogen ions out of the matrix of the mitochondrion. In accepting two electrons, Q takes up two protons from the matrix as it is reduced to QH$_2$* (Figure 18.10). The QH$_2$ leaves the enzyme for the hydrophobic interior of the membrane.

It is important to note that the citric acid cycle is not the only source of mitochondrial NADH. As we will see in Chapter 22, fatty acid degradation,

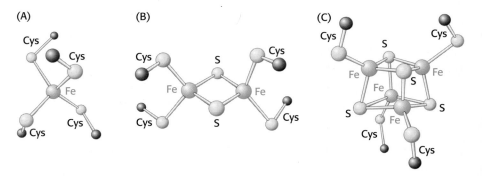

Figure 18.9 Iron–sulfur clusters. (A) A single iron ion bound by four cysteine residues. (B) 2Fe-2S cluster with iron ions bridged by sulfide ions. (C) 4Fe-4S cluster. Each of these clusters can undergo oxidation–reduction reactions.

which also takes place in mitochondria, is another crucial source of NADH for the electron-transport chain. Moreover, cytoplasmically generated NADH can be transported into mitochondria for use by the electron-transport chain (Section 18.5).

Ubiquinol is the entry point for electrons from FADH$_2$ of flavoproteins

FADH$_2$ enters the electron-transport chain at the second protein complex of the chain. Recall that FADH$_2$ is formed in the citric acid cycle, in the oxidation of succinate to fumarate by succinate dehydrogenase (Section 17.2). Succinate dehydrogenase, a citric acid cycle enzyme, is part of the *succinate-Q reductase complex (Complex II)*, an integral membrane protein of the inner mitochondrial membrane. FADH$_2$ does not leave the complex. Rather, its electrons are transferred to Fe-S centers and then finally to Q to form QH$_2$, which then is ready to transfer electrons further down the electron-transport chain. The succinate-Q reductase complex, in contrast with NADH-Q oxidoreductase, does not pump protons from one side of the membrane to the other. Consequently, less ATP is formed from the oxidation of FADH$_2$ than from NADH.

Two other enzymes that we will encounter later, *glycerol phosphate dehydrogenase* (p. 551) and *fatty acyl CoA dehydrogenase* (Section 22.2), likewise transfer their high-potential electrons from FADH$_2$ to Q to form ubiquinol (QH$_2$), the reduced state of ubiquinone. These enzymes oxidize glycerol and fats, respectively, providing electrons for oxidative phosphorylation. These enzymes also do not pump protons.

Electrons flow from ubiquinol to cytochrome *c* through Q-cytochrome *c* oxidoreductase

What is the fate of ubiquinol generated by Complexes I and II? The electrons from QH$_2$ are passed on to cytochrome *c* by the second of the three proton pumps in the respiratory chain, *Q-cytochrome* c *oxidoreductase* (also known as *Complex III* and as *cytochrome reductase*). The function of Q-cytochrome *c* oxidoreductase is to catalyze the transfer of electrons from QH$_2$ to oxidized *cytochrome* c (Cyt *c*), a water-soluble protein, and concomitantly pump protons out of the mitochondrial matrix. The flow of a pair of electrons through this complex leads to the effective net transport of 2 H$^+$ to the cytoplasmic side, half the yield obtained with NADH-Q reductase because of a smaller thermodynamic driving force.

$$QH_2 + 2\ Cyt\ c_{ox} + 2\ H^+_{matrix} \rightarrow Q + 2\ Cyt\ c_{red} + 4\ H^+_{cytoplasm}$$

Q-cytochrome *c* oxidoreductase itself contains two types of cytochromes, named *b* and *c$_1$* (Figure 18.11). *A cytochrome is an electron-transferring protein that contains a heme prosthetic group*. The iron ion of a cytochrome alternates between a reduced ferrous (+2) state and an oxidized ferric (+3) state during electron transport. The two cytochrome subunits of Q-cytochrome *c* oxidoreductase contain a total of three hemes: two hemes within cytochrome *b*, termed heme *b$_L$* (L for low affinity) and heme *b$_H$* (H for high affinity), and one heme within cytochrome *c$_1$*. The heme prosthetic group in cytochromes *b*, *c$_1$*, and *c* is iron-protoporphyrin IX, the same heme present in myoglobin and hemoglobin (Section 7.1). These identical hemes have different electron affinities because they are in different

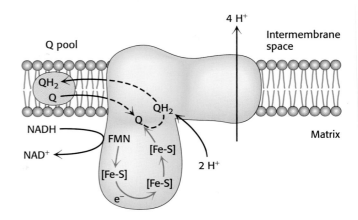

Figure 18.10 Coupled electron–proton transfer reactions through NADH-Q oxidoreductase. Electrons flow in Complex I from NADH through FMN and a series of iron–sulfur clusters to ubiquinone (Q). The electron flow (red arrows) results in the pumping of four protons and the uptake of two protons from the mitochondrial matrix. [Based on U. Brandt et al. *FEBS Letters* 545:9–17, 2003, Fig. 2.]

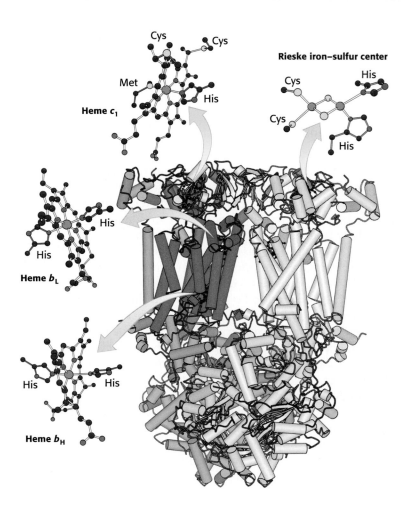

▶ **Figure 18.11 Structure of Q-cytochrome *c* oxidoreductase (cytochrome *bc*₁).** This enzyme is a homodimer with 11 distinct polypeptide chains. *Notice* that the major prosthetic groups, three hemes and a 2Fe-2S cluster, are located either near the cytoplasmic edge of the complex bordering the intermembrane space (top) or in the region embedded in the membrane (α helices represented by tubes). They are well positioned to mediate the electron-transfer reactions between quinones in the membrane and cytochrome *c* in the intermembrane space. [Drawn from 1BCC.pdb.]

polypeptide environments. For example, heme b_L, which is located in a cluster of helices near the cytoplasmic face of the membrane, has lower affinity for an electron than does heme b_H, which is near the matrix side. Q-cytochrome *c* oxidoreductase is also known as cytochrome bc_1 after its cytochrome groups.

In addition to the hemes, the enzyme contains an iron–sulfur protein with a 2Fe-2S center. This center, termed the *Rieske center,* is unusual in that one of the iron ions is coordinated by two histidine residues rather than two cysteine residues. This coordination stabilizes the center in its reduced form, raising its reduction potential so that it can readily accept electrons from QH_2.

The Q cycle funnels electrons from a two-electron carrier to a one-electron carrier and pumps protons

QH_2 passes two electrons to Q-cytochrome *c* oxidoreductase, but the acceptor of electrons in this complex, cytochrome *c*, can accept only one electron. How does the switch from the two-electron carrier ubiquinol to the one-electron carrier cytochrome *c* take place? The mechanism for the coupling of electron transfer from Q to cytochrome *c* to transmembrane proton transport is known as the *Q cycle* (Figure 18.12). Two QH_2 molecules bind to the complex consecutively, each giving up two electrons and two H⁺. *These protons are released to the cytoplasmic side of the membrane.* The first QH_2 to exit the Q pool binds to the first Q binding site (Q_o), and its two electrons travel through the complex to different destinations. One electron flows, first, to the Rieske 2Fe-2S cluster; then, to cytochrome c_1; and, finally, to a

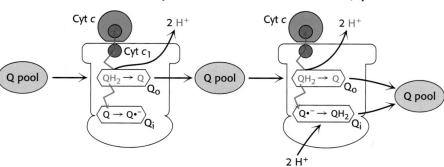

Figure 18.12 Q cycle. The Q cycle takes place in Complex III, which is represented in outline form. In the first half of the cycle, two electrons of a bound QH_2 are transferred, one to cytochrome c and the other to a bound Q in a second binding site to form the semiquinone radical anion $Q\cdot^-$. The newly formed Q dissociates and enters the Q pool. In the second half of the cycle, a second QH_2 also gives up its electrons to complex II, one to a second molecule of cytochrome c and the other to reduce $Q\cdot^-$ to QH_2. This second electron transfer results in the uptake of two protons from the matrix. The path of electron transfer is shown in red.

molecule of oxidized cytochrome c, converting it into its reduced form. The reduced cytochrome c molecule is free to diffuse away from the enzyme to continue down the respiratory chain.

The second electron passes through two heme groups of cytochrome b to an oxidized ubiquinone in a second Q binding site (Q_i). The Q in the second binding site is reduced to a semiquinone radical anion ($Q\cdot^-$) by the electron from the first QH_2. The now fully oxidized Q leaves the first Q site, free to reenter the Q pool.

A second molecule of QH_2 binds to the Q_o site of Q-cytochrome c oxidoreductase and reacts in the same way as the first. One of the electrons is transferred to cytochrome c. The second electron passes through the two heme groups of cytochrome b to partly reduced ubiquinone bound in the Q_i binding site. On the addition of the electron from the second QH_2 molecule, this quinone radical anion takes up two protons from the matrix side to form QH_2. *The removal of these two protons from the matrix contributes to the formation of the proton gradient.* In sum, four protons are released on the cytoplasmic side, and two protons are removed from the mitochondrial matrix.

$$2\,QH_2 + Q + 2\,\text{Cyt}\,c_{ox} + 2\,H^+_{matrix} \longrightarrow$$
$$2\,Q + QH_2 + 2\,\text{Cyt}\,c_{red} + 4\,H^+_{cytoplasm}$$

In one Q cycle, two QH_2 molecules are oxidized to form two Q molecules, and then one Q molecule is reduced to QH_2. The problem of how to efficiently funnel electrons from a two-electron carrier (QH_2) to a one-electron carrier (cytochrome c) is solved by the Q cycle. The cytochrome b component of the reductase is in essence a recycling device that enables both electrons of QH_2 to be used effectively.

Cytochrome c oxidase catalyzes the reduction of molecular oxygen to water

The last of the three proton-pumping assemblies of the respiratory chain is *cytochrome c oxidase (Complex IV)*. Cytochrome c oxidase catalyzes the transfer of electrons from the reduced form of cytochrome c to molecular oxygen, the final acceptor.

$$4\,\text{Cyt}\,c_{red} + 8\,H^+_{matrix} + \longrightarrow 4\,\text{Cyt}\,c_{ox} + 2\,H_2O + 4\,H^+_{cytoplasm}$$

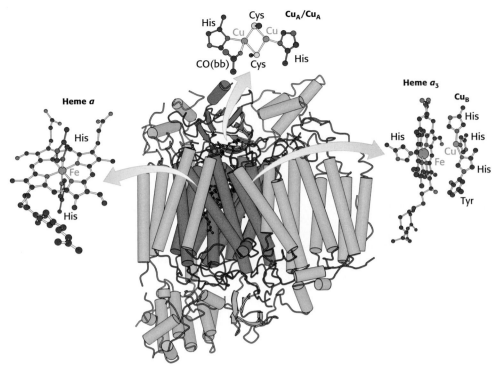

Figure 18.13 Structure of cytochrome c oxidase. This enzyme consists of 13 polypeptide chains. *Notice* that most of the complex, as well as two major prosthetic groups (heme *a* and heme a_3–Cu_B) are embedded in the membrane (α helices represented by vertical tubes). Heme a_3–Cu_B is the site of the reduction of oxygen to water. The Cu_A/Cu_A prosthetic group is positioned near the intermembrane space to better accept electrons from cytochrome c. CO(bb) is a carbonyl group of the peptide backbone. [Drawn from 2OCC.pdb.]

The requirement of oxygen for this reaction is what makes "aerobic" organisms aerobic. To obtain oxygen for this reaction is the reason that human beings must breath. Four electrons are funneled to O_2 to completely reduce it to H_2O, and, concomitantly, protons are pumped from the matrix to the cytoplasmic side of the inner mitochondrial membrane. This reaction is quite thermodynamically favorable. From the reduction potentials in Table 18.1, the standard free-energy change for this reaction is calculated to be $\Delta G^{\circ\prime} = -231.8$ kJ mol^{-1} (-55.4 kcal mol^{-1}). As much of this free energy as possible must be captured in the form of a proton gradient for subsequent use in ATP synthesis.

Bovine cytochrome *c* oxidase is reasonably well understood at the structural level (Figure 18.13). It consists of 13 subunits, 3 of which are encoded by the mitochondrion's own genome. Cytochrome *c* oxidase contains two *heme A* groups and three *copper ions*, arranged as two copper centers, designated A and B. One center, Cu_A/Cu_A, contains two copper ions linked by two bridging cysteine residues. This center initially accepts electrons from reduced cytochrome *c*. The remaining copper ion, Cu_B, is coordinated by three histidine residues, one of which is modified by covalent linkage to a tyrosine residue. The copper centers alternate between the reduced Cu$^+$ (cuprous) form and the oxidized Cu^{2+} (cupric) form as they accept and donate electrons.

There are two heme A molecules, called *heme* a and *heme* a$_3$, in cytochrome *c* oxidase. Heme A differs from the heme in cytochrome *c* and c_1 in three ways: (1) a formyl group replaces a methyl group, (2) a C_{17} hydrocarbon chain replaces one of the vinyl groups, and (3) the heme is not covalently attached to the protein.

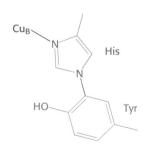

Heme A

Heme a and heme a_3 have distinct redox potentials because they are located in different environments within cytochrome c oxidase. An electron flows from cytochrome c to Cu_A/Cu_A, to heme a to heme a_3 to Cu_B, and finally to O_2. Heme a_3 and Cu_B are directly adjacent. Together, heme a_3 and Cu_B form the active center at which O_2 is reduced to H_2O.

Four molecules of cytochrome c bind consecutively to the enzyme and transfer an electron to reduce one molecule of O_2 to H_2O (Figure 18.14).

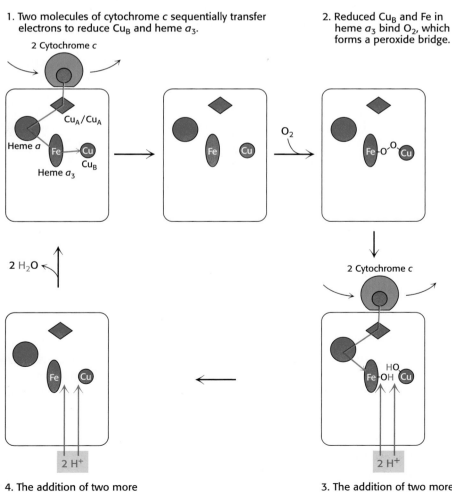

1. Two molecules of cytochrome c sequentially transfer electrons to reduce Cu_B and heme a_3.

2. Reduced Cu_B and Fe in heme a_3 bind O_2, which forms a peroxide bridge.

4. The addition of two more protons leads to the release of water.

3. The addition of two more electrons and two more protons cleaves the peroxide bridge.

Figure 18.14 Cytochrome c oxidase mechanism. The cycle begins and ends with all prosthetic groups in their oxidized forms (shown in blue). Reduced forms are in red. Four cytochrome c molecules donate four electrons, which, in allowing the binding and cleavage of an O_2 molecule, also makes possible the import of four H^+ from the matrix to form two molecules of H_2O, which are released from the enzyme to regenerate the initial state.

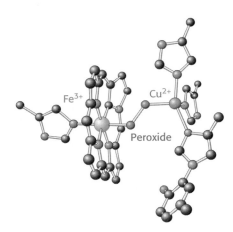

Figure 18.15 Peroxide bridge. The oxygen bound to heme a_3 is reduced to peroxide by the presence of Cu_B.

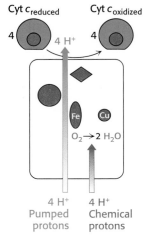

Figure 18.16 Proton transport by cytochrome c oxidase. Four protons are taken up from the matrix side to reduce one molecule of O_2 to two molecules of H_2O. These protons are called "chemical protons" because they participate in a clearly defined reaction with O_2. Four additional "pumped" protons are transported out of the matrix and released on the cytoplasmic side in the course of the reaction. The pumped protons double the efficiency of free-energy storage in the form of a proton gradient for this final step in the electron-transport chain.

1. Electrons from two molecules of reduced cytochrome c flow down an electron-transfer pathway within cytochrome c oxidase, one stopping at Cu_B and the other at heme a_3. With both centers in the reduced state, they together can now bind an oxygen molecule.

2. As molecular oxygen binds, it abstracts an electron from each of the nearby ions in the active center to form a peroxide (O_2^{2-}) bridge between them (Figure 18.15).

3. Two more molecules of cytochrome c bind and release electrons that travel to the active center. The addition of an electron as well as H^+ to each oxygen atom reduces the two ion–oxygen groups to Cu_B^{2+}—OH and Fe^{3+}—OH.

4. Reaction with two more H^+ ions allows the release of two molecules of H_2O and resets the enzyme to its initial, fully oxidized form.

$$4\ \text{Cyt}\ c_{red} + 4\ H^+_{matrix} + O_2 \rightarrow 4\ \text{Cyt}\ c_{ox} + 2\ H_2O$$

The four protons in this reaction come exclusively from the matrix. Thus, the consumption of these four protons contributes directly to the proton gradient. Recall that each proton contributes 21.8 kJ mol^{-1} (5.2 kcal mol^{-1}) to the free energy associated with the proton gradient; so these four protons contribute 87.2 kJ mol^{-1} (20.8 kcal mol^{-1}), an amount substantially less than the free energy available from the reduction of oxygen to water. What is the fate of this missing energy? Remarkably, *cytochrome c oxidase uses this energy to pump four additional protons from the matrix to the cytoplasmic side of the membrane in the course of each reaction cycle for a total of eight protons removed from the matrix* (Figure 18.16). The details of how these protons are transported through the protein is still under study. However, two effects contribute to the mechanism. First, charge neutrality tends to be maintained in the interior of proteins. Thus, the addition of an electron to a site inside a protein tends to favor the binding of H^+ to a nearby site. Second, conformational changes take place, particularly around the heme a_3–Cu_B center, in the course of the reaction cycle. Presumably, in one conformation, protons may enter the protein exclusively from the matrix side, whereas, in another, they may exit exclusively to the cytoplasmic side. Thus, the overall process catalyzed by cytochrome c oxidase is

$$4\ \text{Cyt}\ c_{red} + 8\ H^+_{matrix} + O_2 \rightarrow 4\ \text{Cyt}\ c_{ox} + 2\ H_2O + 4\ H^+_{cytoplasm}$$

Figure 18.17 summarizes the flow of electrons from NADH and FADH$_2$ through the respiratory chain. This series of exergonic reactions is coupled to the pumping of protons from the matrix. As we will see shortly, the energy inherent in the proton gradient will be used to synthesize ATP.

Toxic derivatives of molecular oxygen such as superoxide radical are scavenged by protective enzymes

As discussed earlier, molecular oxygen is an ideal terminal electron acceptor, because its high affinity for electrons provides a large thermodynamic driving force. However, danger lurks in the reduction of O_2. The transfer of four electrons leads to safe products (two molecules of H_2O), but partial reduction generates hazardous compounds. In particular, *the transfer of a single electron to O_2 forms superoxide anion, whereas the transfer of two electrons yields peroxide.*

$$O_2 \xrightarrow{e^-} O_2^{\cdot-} \xrightarrow{e^-} O_2^{2-}$$

Superoxide ion   **Peroxide**

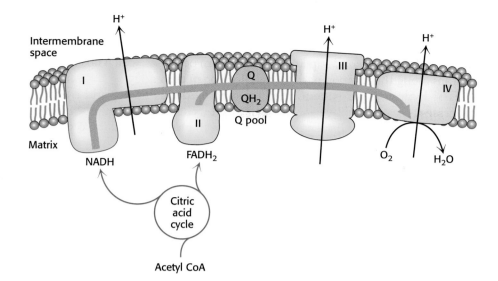

Figure 18.17 The electron-transport chain. High-energy electrons in the form of NADH and FADH$_2$ are generated by the citric acid cycle. These electrons flow through the respiratory chain, which powers proton pumping and results in the reduction of O$_2$.

Both compounds are potentially destructive. The strategy for the safe reduction of O$_2$ is clear: *the catalyst does not release partly reduced intermediates.* Cytochrome *c* oxidase meets this crucial criterion by holding O$_2$ tightly between Fe and Cu ions.

Although cytochrome *c* oxidase and other proteins that reduce O$_2$ are remarkably successful in not releasing intermediates, small amounts of superoxide anion and hydrogen peroxide are unavoidably formed. Superoxide, hydrogen peroxide, and species that can be generated from them such as OH· are collectively referred to as *reactive oxygen species* or *ROS*. Oxidative damage caused by ROS has been implicated in the aging process as well as in a growing list of diseases (Table 18.3).

What are the cellular defense strategies against oxidative damage by ROS? Chief among them is the enzyme *superoxide dismutase*. This enzyme scavenges superoxide radicals by catalyzing the conversion of two of these radicals into hydrogen peroxide and molecular oxygen.

Dismutation
A reaction in which a single reactant is converted into two different products.

$$O_2^{\cdot -} + 2H^+ \underset{}{\overset{\text{Superoxide dismutase}}{\rightleftharpoons}} O_2 + H_2O_2$$

Eukaryotes contain two forms of this enzyme, a manganese-containing version located in mitochondria and a copper- and zinc-dependent cytoplasmic

Table 18.3 Pathological and other conditions that may entail free-radical injury

Atherogenesis
Emphysema; bronchitis
Parkinson disease
Duchenne muscular dystrophy
Cervical cancer
Alcoholic liver disease
Diabetes
Acute renal failure
Down syndrome
Retrolental fibroplasia (conversion of the retina into a fibrous mass in premature infants)
Cerebrovascular disorders
Ischemia; reperfusion injury

Source: After D. B. Marks, A. D. Marks, and C. M. Smith, *Basic Medical Biochemistry: A Clinical Approach* (Williams & Wilkins, 1996), p. 331.

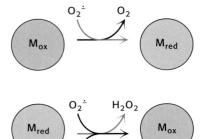

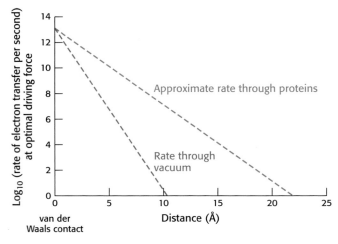

Figure 18.18 Superoxide dismutase mechanism. The oxidized form of superoxide dismutase (M_{ox}) reacts with one superoxide ion to form O_2 and generate the reduced form of the enzyme (M_{red}). The reduced form then reacts with a second superoxide and two protons to form hydrogen peroxide and regenerate the oxidized form of the enzyme.

form. These enzymes perform the dismutation reaction by a similar mechanism (Figure 18.18). The oxidized form of the enzyme is reduced by superoxide to form oxygen. The reduced form of the enzyme, formed in this reaction, then reacts with a second superoxide ion to form peroxide, which takes up two protons along the reaction path to yield hydrogen peroxide.

The hydrogen peroxide formed by superoxide dismutase and by other processes is scavenged by *catalase,* a ubiquitous heme protein that catalyzes the dismutation of hydrogen peroxide into water and molecular oxygen.

$$2\ H_2O_2 \xrightleftharpoons{\text{Catalase}} O_2 + 2\ H_2O$$

Superoxide dismutase and catalase are remarkably efficient, performing their reactions at or near the diffusion-limited rate (Section 8.4). Glutathione peroxidase also plays a role in scavenging H_2O_2 (Section 20.5). Other cellular defenses against oxidative damage include the antioxidant vitamins, vitamins E and C. Because it is lipophilic, vitamin E is especially useful in protecting membranes from lipid peroxidation.

A long-term benefit of exercise may be to increase the amount of superoxide dismutase in the cell. The elevated aerobic metabolism during exercise causes more ROS to be generated. In response, the cell synthesizes more protective enzymes. The net effect is one of protection, because the increase in superoxide dismutase more effectively protects the cell during periods of rest.

Despite the fact that reactive oxygen species are known hazards, recent evidence suggests that, under certain circumstances, the controlled generation of these molecules may be important components of signal-transduction pathways. For instance, growth factors have been shown to increase ROS levels as part of their signaling pathway, and ROS regulate channels and transcription factors. The dual roles of ROS is a excellent example of the wondrous complexity of biochemistry of living systems: even potentially harmful substances can be harnessed to play useful roles.

Electrons can be transferred between groups that are not in contact

How are electrons transferred between electron-carrying groups of the respiratory chain? This question is intriguing because these groups are frequently buried in the interior of a protein in fixed positions and are therefore not directly in contact with one another. Electrons can move through space, even through a vacuum. However, the rate of electron transfer through space falls off rapidly as the electron donor and electron acceptor move apart from each other, decreasing by a factor of 10 for each increase in separation of 0.8 Å. The protein environment provides more-efficient pathways for electron conduction: typically, the rate of electron transfer decreases by a factor of 10 every 1.7 Å (Figure 18.19). For groups in contact, electron-transfer reactions can be quite fast, with rates of approximately $10^{13}\ s^{-1}$. Within proteins in the electron-transport chain, electron-carrying groups are typically separated by 15 Å beyond their van der Waals contact distance. For such separations, we expect electron-transfer rates of approximately $10^4\ s^{-1}$ (i.e., electron transfer in less than 1 ms), assuming that all other factors

Figure 18.19 Distance dependence of electron-transfer rate. The rate of electron transfer decreases as the electron donor and the electron acceptor move apart. In a vacuum, the rate decreases by a factor of 10 for every increase of 0.8 Å. In proteins, the rate decreases more gradually, by a factor of 10 for every increase of 1.7 Å. This rate is only approximate because variations in the structure of the intervening protein medium can affect the rate.

are optimal. Without the mediation of the protein, an electron transfer over this distance would take approximately 1 day.

The case is more complicated when electrons must be transferred between two distinct proteins, such as when cytochrome c accepts electrons from Complex III or passes them on to Complex IV. A series of hydrophobic interactions bring the heme groups of cytochrome c and c_1 to within 4.5 Å of each other, with the iron atoms separated by 17.4 Å. This distance could allow cytochrome c reduction at a rate of $8.3 \times 10^6 \, s^{-1}$.

The conformation of cytochrome c has remained essentially constant for more than a billion years

Cytochrome c is present in all organisms having mitochondrial respiratory chains: plants, animals, and eukaryotic microorganisms. This electron carrier evolved more than 1.5 billion years ago, before the divergence of plants and animals. Its function has been conserved throughout this period, as evidenced by the fact that *the cytochrome* c *of any eukaryotic species reacts in vitro with the cytochrome* c *oxidase of any other species tested thus far.* For example, wheat-germ cytochrome c reacts with human cytochrome c oxidase. Additionally, some prokaryotic cytochromes, such as cytochrome c_2 from the photosynthetic bacterium *Rhodospirillum rubrum* and cytochrome c_{550} from the denitrifying bacterium *Paracoccus denitrificans*, closely resemble cytochrome c from tuna-heart mitochondria (Figure 18.20). This evidence attests to an efficient evolutionary solution to electron transfer bestowed by the structural and functional characteristics of cytochrome c.

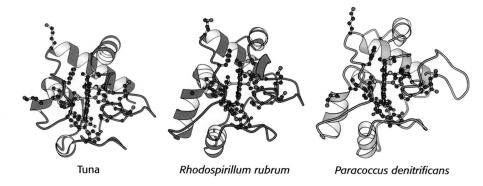

Tuna   *Rhodospirillum rubrum*   *Paracoccus denitrificans*

Figure 18.20 Conservation of the three-dimensional structure of cytochrome *c*. The side chains are shown for the 21 conserved amino acids and the heme. [Drawn from 3CYT.pdb, 3C2C.pdb, and 1SSC.pdb.]

The resemblance among cytochrome c molecules extends to the level of amino acid sequence. Because of the molecule's small size and ubiquity, the amino acid sequences of cytochrome c from more than 80 widely ranging eukaryotic species have been determined by direct protein sequencing by Emil Smith, Emanuel Margoliash, and others. The striking finding is that *21 of 104 residues have been invariant for more than one and a half billion years of evolution.* A phylogenetic tree, constructed from the amino acid sequences of cytochrome c, reveals the evolutionary relationships between many animal species (Figure 18.21).

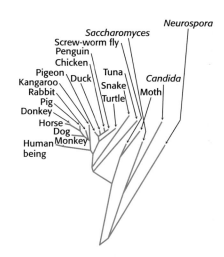

Figure 18.21 Evolutionary tree constructed from sequences of cytochrome *c*. Branch lengths are proportional to the number of amino acid changes that are believed to have occurred. This drawing is an adaptation of the work of Walter M. Fitch and Emanuel Margoliash.

18.4 A Proton Gradient Powers the Synthesis of ATP

Thus far, we have considered the flow of electrons from NADH to O_2, an exergonic process.

$$NADH + \tfrac{1}{2} O_2 + H^+ \rightleftharpoons H_2O + NAD^+$$
$$\Delta G^{\circ\prime} = -220.1 \text{ kJ mol}^{-1} \, (-52.6 \text{ kcal mol}^{-1})$$

Next, we consider how this process is coupled to the synthesis of ATP, an endergonic process.

$$ADP + P_i + H^+ \rightleftharpoons ATP + H_2O$$
$$\Delta G^{\circ\prime} = +30.5 \text{ kJ mol}^{-1}(+7.3 \text{ kcal mol}^{-1})$$

A molecular assembly in the inner mitochondrial membrane carries out the synthesis of ATP. This enzyme complex was originally called the *mitochondrial ATPase* or F_1F_0 *ATPase* because it was discovered through its catalysis of the reverse reaction, the hydrolysis of ATP. *ATP synthase*, its preferred name, emphasizes its actual role in the mitochondrion. It is also called *Complex V*.

How is the oxidation of NADH coupled to the phosphorylation of ADP? Electron transfer was first suggested to lead to the formation of a covalent high-energy intermediate that serves as a compound having a high phosphoryl-transfer potential, analogous to the generation of ATP by the formation of 1,3-bisphosphoglycerate in glycolysis (Section 16.1). An alternative proposal was that electron transfer aids the formation of an activated protein conformation, which then drives ATP synthesis. The search for such intermediates for several decades proved fruitless.

In 1961, Peter Mitchell suggested a radically different mechanism, *the chemiosmotic hypothesis.* He proposed that electron transport and ATP synthesis are coupled by *a proton gradient across the inner mitochondrial membrane.* In his model, the transfer of electrons through the respiratory chain leads to the pumping of protons from the matrix to the cytoplasmic side of the inner mitochondrial membrane. The H^+ concentration becomes lower in the matrix, and an electric field with the matrix side negative is generated (Figure 18.22). Protons then flow back into the matrix to equalize the distribution. Mitchell's idea was that this flow of protons drives the synthesis of ATP by ATP synthase. The energy-rich unequal distribution of protons is called the *proton-motive force*. The proton-motive force can be thought of as being composed of two components: a chemical gradient and a charge gradient. The chemical gradient for protons can be represented as a pH gradient. The charge gradient is created by the positive charge on the unequally distributed protons forming the chemical gradient. Mitchell proposed that both components power the synthesis of ATP.

Proton-motive force (Δp) =
chemical gradient (ΔpH) + charge gradient ($\Delta\psi$)

> Some have argued that, along with the elucidation of the structure of DNA, the discovery that ATP synthesis is powered by a proton gradient is one of the two major advances in biology in the twentieth century. Mitchell's initial postulation of the chemiosmotic theory was not warmly received by all. Efraim Racker, one of the early investigators of ATP synthase, recalls that some thought of Mitchell as a court jester, whose work was of no consequence. Peter Mitchell was awarded the Nobel Prize in chemistry in 1978 for his contributions to understanding oxidative phosphorylation.

Figure 18.22 Chemiosmotic hypothesis. Electron transfer through the respiratory chain leads to the pumping of protons from the matrix to the cytoplasmic side of the inner mitochondrial membrane. The pH gradient and membrane potential constitute a proton-motive force that is used to drive ATP synthesis.

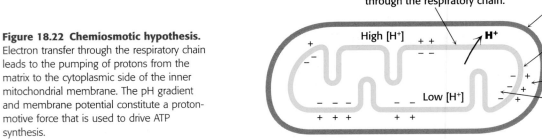

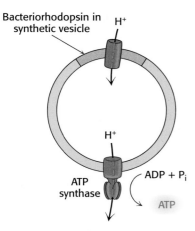

Bacteriorhodopsin in synthetic vesicle

H⁺

H⁺

ATP synthase

ADP + P$_i$

ATP

Figure 18.23 Testing the chemiosmotic hypothesis. ATP is synthesized when reconstituted membrane vesicles containing bacteriorhodopsin (a light-driven proton pump) and ATP synthase are illuminated. The orientation of ATP synthase in this reconstituted membrane is the reverse of that in the mitochondrion.

Mitchell's highly innovative hypothesis that oxidation and phosphorylation are coupled by a proton gradient is now supported by a wealth of evidence. Indeed, electron transport does generate a proton gradient across the inner mitochondrial membrane. The pH outside is 1.4 units lower than inside, and the membrane potential is 0.14 V, the outside being positive. As calculated on page 531, this membrane potential corresponds to a free energy of 21.8 kJ (5.2 kcal) per mole of protons.

An artificial system was created to elegantly demonstrate the basic principle of the chemiosmotic hypothesis. The role of the respiratory chain was played by bacteriorhodopsin, a membrane protein from halobacteria that pumps proteins when illuminated. Synthetic vesicles containing bacteriorhodopsin and mitochondrial ATP synthase purified from beef heart were created (Figure 18.23). When the vesicles were exposed to light, ATP was formed. This key experiment clearly showed that *the respiratory chain and ATP synthase are biochemically separate systems, linked only by a proton-motive force.*

ATP synthase is composed of a proton-conducting unit and a catalytic unit

Two parts of the puzzle of how NADH oxidation is coupled to ATP synthesis are now evident: (1) electron transport generates a proton-motive force; (2) ATP synthesis by ATP synthase can be powered by a proton-motive force. How is the proton-motive force converted into the high phosphoryl-transfer potential of ATP?

Biochemical, electron microscopic, and crystallographic studies of ATP synthase have revealed many details of its structure (Figure 18.24). It is a large, complex enzyme that looks like a ball on a stick. Much of the "stick" part, called the F$_0$ subunit, is embedded in the inner mitochondrial membrane. The 85-Å-diameter ball, called the F$_1$ subunit, protrudes into the mitochondrial matrix. The F$_1$ subunit contains the catalytic activity of the synthase. In fact, isolated F$_1$ subunits display ATPase activity.

The F$_1$ subunit consists of five types of polypeptide chains (α_3, β_3, γ, δ, and ε) with the indicated stoichiometry. The α and β subunits, which make up the bulk of the F$_1$, are arranged alternately in a hexameric ring; they are homologous to one another and are members of the P-loop NTPase family (Section 9.4). Both bind nucleotides but only the β subunits participate directly in catalysis. Beginning just below the α and β subunits is a central stalk consisting of the γ and ε proteins. The γ subunit includes a long helical coiled coil that extends into the center of the $\alpha_3\beta_3$ hexamer. *The γ subunit breaks the symmetry of the $\alpha_3\beta_3$ hexamer: each of the β subunits is distinct by*

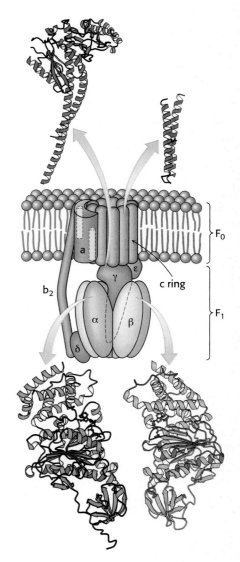

Figure 18.24 Structure of ATP synthase. A schematic structure is shown along with representations of the components for which structures have been determined to high resolution. The P-loop NTPase domains of the α and β subunits are indicated by purple shading. *Notice* that part of the enzyme complex is embedded in the inner mitochondrial membrane, whereas the remainder resides in the matrix. [Drawn from 1E79.pdb and 1COV.pdb.]

virtue of its interaction with a different face of γ. Distinguishing the three β subunits is crucial for understanding the mechanism of ATP synthesis.

The F_0 subunit is a hydrophobic segment that spans the inner mitochondrial membrane. *F_0 contains the proton channel of the complex.* This channel consists of a ring comprising from 10 to 14 **c** subunits that are embedded in the membrane. A single **a** subunit binds to the outside of the ring. The F_0 and F_1 subunits are connected in two ways: by the central γε stalk and by an exterior column. The exterior column consists of one **a** subunit, two **b** subunits, and the δ subunit.

Proton flow through ATP synthase leads to the release of tightly bound ATP: The binding-change mechanism

ATP synthase catalyzes the formation of ATP from ADP and orthophosphate.

$$ADP^{3-} + HPO_4^{2-} + H^+ \rightleftharpoons ATP^{4-} + H_2O$$

The actual substrates are ADP and ATP complexed with Mg^{2+}, as in all known phosphoryl-transfer reactions with these nucleotides. A terminal oxygen atom of ADP attacks the phosphorus atom of P_i to form a pentacovalent intermediate, which then dissociates into ATP and H_2O (Figure 18.25).

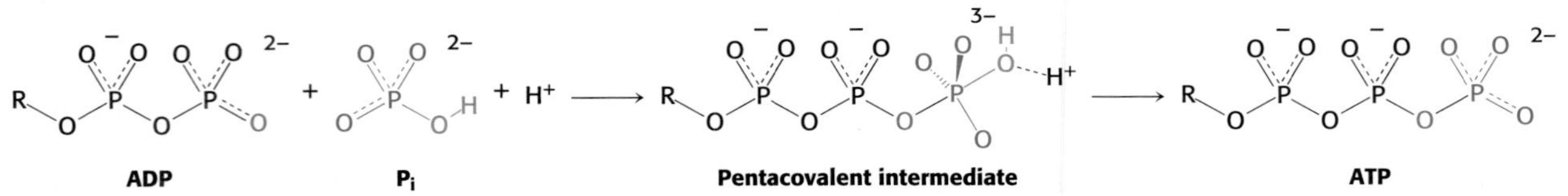

Figure 18.25 ATP-synthesis mechanism. One of the oxygen atoms of ADP attacks the phosphorus atom of P_i to form a pentacovalent intermediate, which then forms ATP and releases a molecule of H_2O.

How does the flow of protons drive the synthesis of ATP? Isotopic-exchange experiments unexpectedly revealed that *enzyme-bound ATP forms readily in the absence of a proton-motive force.* When ADP and P_i were added to ATP synthase in $H_2^{18}O$, ^{18}O became incorporated into P_i through the synthesis of ATP and its subsequent hydrolysis (Figure 18.26). The rate of incorporation of ^{18}O into P_i showed that about equal amounts of bound ATP and ADP are in equilibrium at the catalytic site, even in the absence of a proton gradient. However, ATP does not leave the catalytic site unless protons flow through the enzyme. Thus, *the role of the proton gradient is not to form ATP but to release it from the synthase.*

The fact that three β subunits are components of the F_1 moiety of the ATPase means that there are three active sites on the enzyme, each performing one of three different functions at any instant. The proton-motive force causes the three active sites to sequentially change functions as pro-

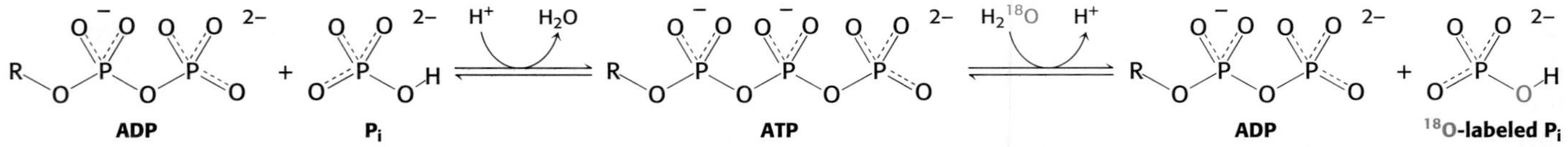

Figure 18.26 ATP forms without a proton-motive force but is not released. The results of isotopic-exchange experiments indicate that enzyme-bound ATP is formed from ADP and P_i in the absence of a proton-motive force.

tons flow through the membrane-embedded component of the enzyme. Indeed, we can think of the enzyme as consisting of a moving part and a stationary part: (1) the moving unit, or *rotor,* consists of the c ring and the γε stalk and (2) the stationary unit, or *stator,* is composed of the remainder of the molecule.

How do the three active sites of ATP synthase respond to the flow of protons? A number of experimental observations suggested a *binding-change mechanism* for proton-driven ATP synthesis. This proposal states that a β subunit can perform each of three sequential steps in the synthesis of ATP by changing conformation. These steps are (1) ADP and P_i binding, (2) ATP synthesis, and (3) ATP release. As already noted, interactions with the γ subunit make the three β subunits unequivalent (Figure 18.27). At any given moment, one β subunit will be in the L, or loose, conformation. This conformation binds ADP and P_i. A second subunit will be in the T, or tight, conformation. This conformation binds ATP with great avidity, so much so that it will convert bound ADP and P_i into ATP. Both the T and L conformations are sufficiently constrained that they cannot release bound nucleotides. The final subunit will be in the O, or open, form. This form has a more open conformation and can bind or release adenine nucleotides.

The rotation of the γ subunit drives the interconversion of these three forms (Figure 18.28). ADP and P_i bound in the subunit in the T form are transiently combining to form ATP. Suppose that the γ subunit is rotated by 120 degrees in a counterclockwise direction (as viewed from the top). This rotation converts the T-form site into an O-form site with the nucleotide bound as ATP. Concomitantly, the L-form site is converted into a T-form site, enabling the transformation of an additional ADP and P_i into ATP. The ATP in the O-form site can now depart from the enzyme to be replaced by ADP and P_i. An additional 120-degree rotation converts this O-form site into an L-form site, trapping these substrates. Each subunit progresses from the T to the O to the L form with no two subunits ever present in the same conformational form. This mechanism suggests that ATP can be synthesized and released by driving the rotation of the γ subunit in the appropriate direction.

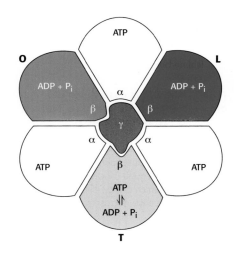

Figure 18.27 ATP synthase nucleotide-binding sites are not equivalent. The γ subunit passes through the center of the $\alpha_3\beta_3$ hexamer and makes the nucleotide-binding sites in the β subunits distinct from one another. *Notice* that each α subunit contains bound ATP, but these nucleotides do not participate in any reactions. The β subunits are colored to distinguish them from one another.

Progressive alteration of the forms of the three active sites of ATP synthase		
Subunit 1	L → T → O → L → T → O......	
Subunit 2	O → L → T → O → L → T......	
Subunit 3	T → O → L → T → O → L......	

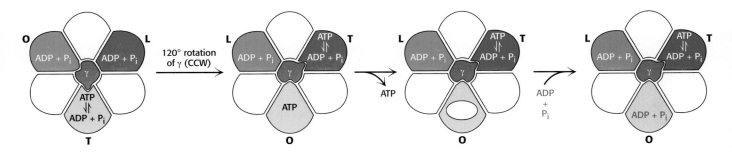

Rotational catalysis is the world's smallest molecular motor

Is it possible to observe the proposed rotation directly? Elegant experiments, using single-molecule techniques (Section 8.6), have demonstrated the rotation through the use of a simple experimental system consisting solely of cloned $\alpha_3\beta_3\gamma$ subunits (Figure 18.29). The β subunits were engineered to contain amino-terminal polyhistidine tags, which have a high affinity for nickel ions (Section 3.1). This property of the tags allowed the $\alpha_3\beta_3$ assembly to be immobilized on a glass surface that had been coated with nickel ions. The γ subunit was linked to a fluorescently labeled actin

Figure 18.28 Binding-change mechanism for ATP synthase. The rotation of the γ subunit interconverts the three β subunits. The subunit in the T (tight) form interconverts ADP and P_i and ATP but does not allow ATP be released. When the γ subunit is rotated by 120 degrees in a counterclockwise (CCW) direction, the T-form subunit is converted into the O form, allowing ATP release. ADP and P_i can then bind to the O-form subunit. An additional 120-degree rotation (not shown) traps these substrates in an L-form subunit.

Figure 18.29 Direct observation of ATP-driven rotation in ATP synthase. The $\alpha_3\beta_3$ hexamer of ATP synthase is fixed to a surface, with the γ subunit projecting upward and linked to a fluorescently labeled actin filament. The addition and subsequent hydrolysis of ATP result in the counterclockwise rotation of the γ subunit, which can be directly seen under a fluorescence microscope.

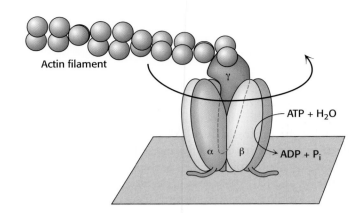

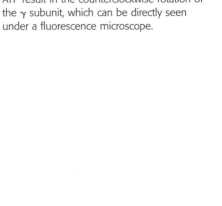

Subunit **c**

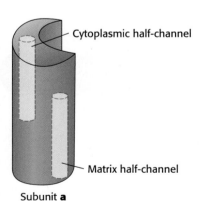

Subunit **a**

Figure 18.30 Components of the proton-conducting unit of ATP synthase. The **c** subunit consists of two α helices that span the membrane. An aspartic acid residue in one of the helices lies on the center of the membrane. The structure of the **a** subunit has not yet been directly observed, but it appears to include two half-channels that allow protons to enter and pass partway but not completely through the membrane.

filament to provide a long segment that could be observed under a fluorescence microscope. Remarkably, the addition of ATP caused the actin filament to rotate unidirectionally in a counterclockwise direction. *The γ subunit was rotating, driven by the hydrolysis of ATP.* Thus, the catalytic activity of an individual molecule could be observed. The counterclockwise rotation is consistent with the predicted mechanism for hydrolysis because the molecule was viewed from below relative to the view shown in Figure 18.29.

More-detailed analysis in the presence of lower concentrations of ATP revealed that the γ subunit rotates in 120-degree increments. Each increment corresponds to the hydrolysis of a single ATP molecule. In addition, from the results obtained by varying the length of the actin filament and measuring the rate of rotation, the enzyme appears to operate near 100% efficiency; that is, essentially all of the energy released by ATP hydrolysis is converted into rotational motion.

Proton flow around the c ring powers ATP synthesis

The direct observation of rotary motion of the γ subunit is strong evidence for the rotational mechanism for ATP synthesis. The last remaining question is: How does proton flow through F_0 drive the rotation of the γ subunit? Howard Berg and George Oster proposed an elegant mechanism that provides a clear answer to this question. The mechanism depends on the structures of the **a** and **c** subunits of F_0 (Figure 18.30). The stationary **a** subunit directly abuts the membrane-spanning ring formed by 10 to 14 **c** subunits. Although the structure of the **a** subunit has not yet been experimentally determined, a variety of evidence is consistent with a structure that includes two hydrophilic half-channels that do not span the membrane (see Figure 18.30). Thus, protons can pass into either of these channels, but they cannot move completely across the membrane. The **a** subunit is positioned such that each half-channel directly interacts with one **c** subunit.

The structure of the **c** subunit was determined both by NMR methods and by x-ray crystallography. Each polypeptide chain forms a pair of α helices that span the membrane. An aspartic acid residue (Asp 61) is found in the middle of one of the helices. The key to proton movement across the membrane is that, in a proton-rich environment, such as the cytoplasmic side of the mitochondrial membrane, a proton will enter a channel and bind the aspartate residue (Figure 18.31). The **c** subunit with the bound proton then rotates through the membrane until the aspartic acid is in a proton-poor environment of the other half-channel, where the proton is released. *The movement of protons through the half-channels from the high proton concentration of the cytoplasm to the low proton concentration of the matrix*

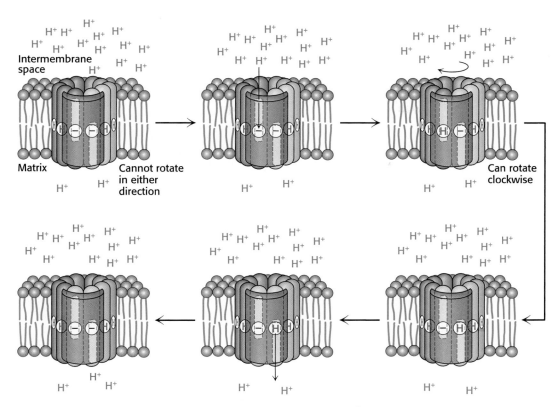

Figure 18.31 Proton motion across the membrane drives rotation of the c ring. A proton enters from the intermembrane space into the cytoplasmic half-channel to neutralize the charge on an aspartate residue in a **c** subunit. With this charge neutralized, the **c** ring can rotate clockwise by one **c** subunit, moving an aspartic acid residue out of the membrane into the matrix half-channel. This proton can move into the matrix, resetting the system to its initial state.

*powers the rotation of the **c** ring.* Its rotation is favored by the ability of the newly protonated (neutralized) aspartic acid residue to occupy the hydrophobic environment of the membrane. Thus, the **c** subunit with the newly protonated aspartic acid moves from contact with the cytoplasmic half-channel into the membrane, and the other **c** subunits move in unison. The **a** unit remains stationary as the **c** ring rotates. Each proton that enters the cytoplasmic half-channel of the **a** unit moves through the membrane by riding around on the rotating **c** ring to exit through the matrix half-channel into the proton-poor environment of the matrix (Figure 18.32).

How does the rotation of the **c** ring lead to the synthesis of ATP? The **c** ring is tightly linked to the γ and ε subunits. Thus, as the **c** ring turns, the γ and ε subunits are turned inside the $\alpha_3\beta_3$ hexamer unit of F_1. The rotation of the γ subunit in turn promotes the synthesis of ATP through the binding-change mechanism. The exterior column formed by the two **b** chains and the δ subunit prevents the $\alpha_3\beta_3$ hexamer from rotating. Recall that the number of **c** subunits in the **c** ring appears to range between 10 and 14. This number is significant because it determines the number of protons that must be transported to generate a molecule of ATP. Each 360-degree rotation of the γ subunit leads to the synthesis and release of three molecules of ATP. Thus, if there are 10 **c** subunits in the ring (as was observed in a crystal structure of yeast mitochondrial ATP synthase), each ATP generated requires the transport of $10/3 = 3.33$ protons. For simplicity, we will assume that three protons must flow into the matrix for each ATP formed, but we must keep in mind that the true value may differ. As we will see, the

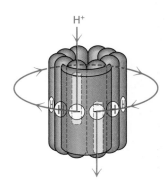

Figure 18.32 Proton path through the membrane. Each proton enters the cytoplasmic half-channel, follows a complete rotation of the **c** ring, and exits through the other half-channel into the matrix.

A little goes a long way

Despite the various molecular machinations and the vast numbers of ATPs synthesized and protons pumped, a resting human being requires surprisingly little power. Approximately 116 watts, the energy output of a typical light bulb, provides enough energy to sustain a resting person.

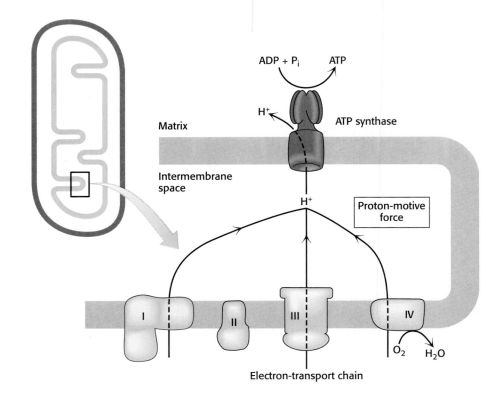

Figure 18.33 Overview of oxidative phosphorylation. The electron-transport chain generates a proton gradient, which is used to synthesize ATP.

electrons from NADH pump enough protons to generate 2.5 molecules of ATP, whereas those from $FADH_2$ yield 1.5 molecules of ATP.

Let us return for a moment to the example with which we began this chapter. If a resting human being requires 85 kg of ATP per day for bodily functions, then 3.3×10^{25} protons must flow through the ATP synthase per day, or 3.3×10^{21} protons per second. Figure 18.33 summarizes the process of oxidative phosphorylation.

ATP synthase and G proteins have several common features

The α and β subunits of ATP synthase are members of the P-loop NTPase family of proteins. In Chapter 14, we learned that the signaling properties of other members of this family, the G proteins, depend on their ability to bind nucleoside triphosphates and diphosphates with great tenacity. They do not exchange nucleotides unless they are stimulated to do so by interaction with other proteins. The binding-change mechanism of ATP synthase is a variation on this theme. The P-loop regions of the β subunits will bind either ADP or ATP (or release ATP), depending on which of three different faces of the γ subunit they interact with. The conformational changes take place in an orderly way, driven by the rotation of the γ subunit.

18.5 Many Shuttles Allow Movement Across Mitochondrial Membranes

The inner mitochondrial membrane must be impermeable to most molecules, yet much exchange has to take place between the cytoplasm and the mitochondria. This exchange is mediated by an array of membrane-spanning transporter proteins (Section 13.4).

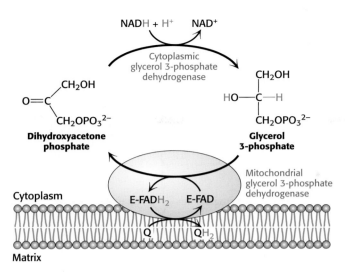

Figure 18.34 Glycerol 3-phosphate shuttle. Electrons from NADH can enter the mitochondrial electron-transport chain by being used to reduce dihydroxyacetone phosphate to glycerol 3-phosphate. Glycerol 3-phosphate is reoxidized by electron transfer to an FAD prosthetic group in a membrane-bound glycerol 3-phosphate dehydrogenase. Subsequent electron transfer to Q to form QH_2 allows these electrons to enter the electron-transport chain.

Electrons from cytoplasmic NADH enter mitochondria by shuttles

One function of the respiratory chain is to regenerate NAD^+ for use in glycolysis. How is cytoplasmic NADH reoxidized to NAD^+ under aerobic conditions? NADH cannot simply pass into mitochondria for oxidation by the respiratory chain, because the inner mitochondrial membrane is impermeable to NADH and NAD^+. The solution is that *electrons from NADH,* rather than NADH itself, are carried across the mitochondrial membrane. One of several means of introducing electrons from NADH into the electron-transport chain is the *glycerol 3-phosphate shuttle* (Figure 18.34). The first step in this shuttle is the transfer of a pair of electrons from NADH to dihydroxyacetone phosphate, a glycolytic intermediate, to form glycerol 3-phosphate. This reaction is catalyzed by a glycerol 3-phosphate dehydrogenase in the cytoplasm. Glycerol 3-phosphate is reoxidized to dihydroxyacetone phosphate on the outer surface of the inner mitochondrial membrane by a membrane-bound isozyme of glycerol 3-phosphate dehydrogenase. An electron pair from glycerol 3-phosphate is transferred to an FAD prosthetic group in this enzyme to form $FADH_2$. This reaction also regenerates dihydroxyacetone phosphate.

The reduced flavin transfers its electrons to the electron carrier Q, which then enters the respiratory chain as QH_2. *When cytoplasmic NADH transported by the glycerol 3-phosphate shuttle is oxidized by the respiratory chain, 1.5 rather than 2.5 molecules of ATP are formed.* The yield is lower because FAD rather than NAD^+ is the electron acceptor in mitochondrial glycerol 3-phosphate dehydrogenase. The use of FAD enables electrons from cytoplasmic NADH to be transported into mitochondria against an NADH concentration gradient. The price of this transport is one molecule of ATP per two electrons. This glycerol 3-phosphate shuttle is especially prominent in muscle and enables it to sustain a very high rate of oxidative phosphorylation. Indeed, some insects lack lactate dehydrogenase and are completely dependent on the glycerol 3-phosphate shuttle for the regeneration of cytoplasmic NAD^+.

NADH + H$^+$ + E−FAD
Cytoplasmic   Mitochondrial

NAD^+ + E−FADH$_2$
Cytoplasmic   Mitochondrial
Glycerol 3-phosphate shuttle

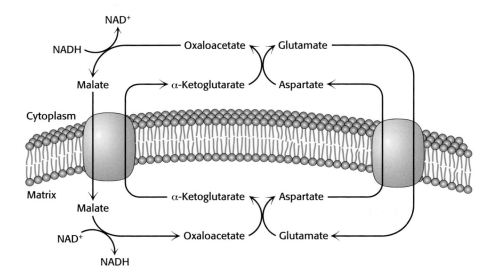

Figure 18.35 Malate–aspartate shuttle.

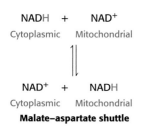

In the heart and liver, electrons from cytoplasmic NADH are brought into mitochondria by the *malate–aspartate shuttle,* which is mediated by two membrane carriers and four enzymes (Figure 18.35). Electrons are transferred from NADH in the cytoplasm to oxaloacetate, forming malate, which traverses the inner mitochondrial membrane in exchange for α-ketoglutarate and is then reoxidized by NAD^+ in the matrix to form NADH in a reaction catalyzed by the citric acid cycle enzyme malate dehydrogenase. The resulting oxaloacetate does not readily cross the inner mitochondrial membrane and so a transamination reaction (Section 23.3) is needed to form aspartate, which can be transported to the cytoplasmic side in exchange for glutamate. Glutamate donates an amino group to oxaloacetate, forming aspartate and α-ketoglutarate. In the cytoplasm, aspartate is then deaminated to form oxaloacetate and the cycle is restarted.

The entry of ADP into mitochondria is coupled to the exit of ATP by ATP-ADP translocase

The major function of oxidative phosphorylation is to generate ATP from ADP. ATP and ADP do not diffuse freely across the inner mitochondrial membrane. How are these highly charged molecules moved across the inner membrane into the cytoplasm? A specific transport protein, *ATP-ADP translocase,* enables these molecules to transverse this permeability barrier. Most important, the flows of ATP and ADP are coupled. *ADP enters the mitochondrial matrix only if ATP exits, and vice versa.* This process is carried out by the translocase, an antiporter:

$$ADP^{3-}_{cytoplasm} + ATP^{4-}_{matrix} \rightarrow ADP^{3-}_{matrix} + ATP^{4-}_{cytoplasm}$$

ATP-ADP translocase is highly abundant, constituting about 15% of the protein in the inner mitochondrial membrane. The abundance is a manifestation of the fact that human beings exchange the equivalent of their weight in ATP each day. The 30-kd translocase contains a single nucleotide-binding site that alternately faces the matrix and the cytoplasmic sides of the membrane (Figure 18.36). ATP and ADP bind to the translocase without Mg^{2+}, and ATP has one more negative charge than that of ADP. Thus, in an actively respiring mitochondrion with a positive membrane potential, ATP transport out of the mitochondrial matrix and ADP transport into the matrix are favored. This ATP–ADP exchange is

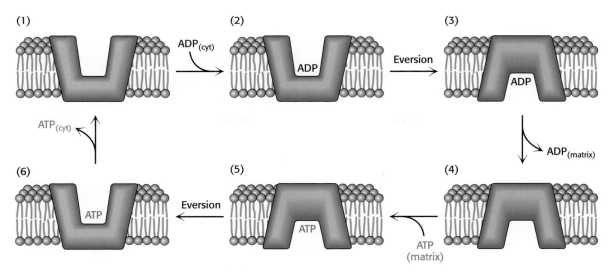

Figure 18.36 Mechanism of mitochondrial ATP-ADP translocase. The translocase catalyzes the coupled entry of ADP into the matrix and the exit of ATP from it. The binding of ADP (1) from the cytoplasm favors eversion of the transporter (2) to release ADP into the matrix (3). Subsequent binding of ATP from the matrix to the everted form (4) favors eversion back to the original conformation (5), releasing ATP into the cytoplasm (6).

energetically expensive; about a quarter of the energy yield from electron transfer by the respiratory chain is consumed to regenerate the membrane potential that is tapped by this exchange process. The inhibition of this process leads to the subsequent inhibition of cellular respiration as well (p. 558).

Mitochondrial transporters for metabolites have a common tripartite structure

Examination of the amino acid sequence of the ATP-ADP translocase revealed that this protein consists of three tandem repeats of a 100-amino-acid module, each of which appears to have two transmembrane segments. This tripartite structure has recently been confirmed by the determination of the three-dimensional structure of this transporter (Figure 18.37). The

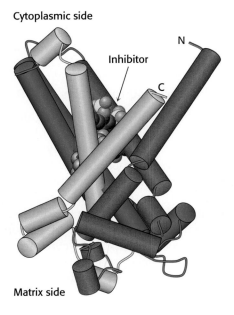

Figure 18.37 Structure of mitochondrial transporters. The structure of the ATP-ADP translocase is shown. *Notice* that this structure comprises three similar units (shown in red, blue, and yellow) that come together to form a binding site, here occupied by an inhibitor of this transporter. Other members of the mitochondrial transporter family adopt similar tripartite structures. [Drawn from 1OKC.pdb.]

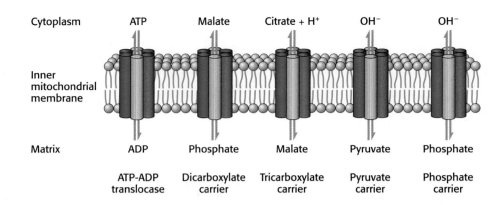

Figure 18.38 Mitochondrial transporters. Transporters (also called carriers) are transmembrane proteins that carry specific ions and charged metabolites across the inner mitochondrial membrane.

transmembrane helices form a tepeelike structure with the nucleotide-binding site (marked by a bound inhibitor) lying in the center. Each of the three repeats adopts a similar structure.

ATP-ADP translocase is but one of many mitochondrial transporters for ions and charged metabolites (Figure 18.38). The *phosphate carrier,* which works in concert with ATP-ADP translocase, mediates the electroneutral exchange of $H_2PO_4^-$ for OH^-. The combined action of these two transporters leads to the exchange of cytoplasmic ADP and P_i for matrix ATP at the cost of the influx of one H^+ (owing to the transport of one OH^- out of the matrix). These two transporters, which provide ATP synthase with its substrates, are associated with the synthase to form a large complex called the *ATP synthasome.*

Other homologous carriers also are present in the inner mitochondrial membrane. The dicarboxylate carrier enables malate, succinate, and fumarate to be exported from the mitochondrial matrix in exchange for P_i. The tricarboxylate carrier exchanges citrate and H^+ for malate. Pyruvate in the cytoplasm enters the mitochondrial membrane in exchange for OH^- by means of the pyruvate carrier. In all, more than 40 such carriers are encoded in the human genome.

18.6 The Regulation of Cellular Respiration Is Governed Primarily by the Need for ATP

Because ATP is the end product of cellular respiration, the ATP needs of the cell are the ultimate determinant of the rate of respiratory pathways and their components.

The complete oxidation of glucose yields about 30 molecules of ATP

We can now estimate how many molecules of ATP are formed when glucose is completely oxidized to CO_2. The number of ATP (or GTP) molecules formed in glycolysis and the citric acid cycle is unequivocally known because it is determined by the stoichiometries of chemical reactions. In contrast, the ATP yield of oxidative phosphorylation is less certain because the stoichiometries of proton pumping, ATP synthesis, and metabolite-transport processes need not be integer numbers or even have fixed values. As stated earlier, the best current estimates for the number of protons pumped out of the matrix by NADH-Q oxidoreductase, Q-cytochrome *c* oxidoreductase, and cytochrome *c* oxidase per electron pair are four, two, and four, respectively. The synthesis of a molecule of ATP is driven by the flow of about three protons through ATP synthase. An additional proton is

Reaction sequence	ATP yield per glucose molecule
Glycolysis: Conversion of glucose into pyruvate (in the cytoplasm)	
Phosphorylation of glucose	−1
Phosphorylation of fructose 6-phosphate	−1
Dephosphorylation of 2 molecules of 1,3-BPG	+2
Dephosphorylation of 2 molecules of phosphoenolpyruvate	+2
2 molecules of NADH are formed in the oxidation of 2 molecules of glyceraldehyde 3-phosphate	
Conversion of pyruvate into acetyl CoA (inside mitochondria)	
2 molecules of NADH are formed	
Citric acid cycle (inside mitochondria)	
2 molecules of adenosine triphosphate are formed from 2 molecules of succinyl CoA	+2
6 molecules of NADH are formed in the oxidation of 2 molecules each of isocitrate, α-ketoglutarate, and malate	
2 molecules of FADH$_2$ are formed in the oxidation of 2 molecules of succinate	
Oxidative phosphorylation (inside mitochondria)	
2 molecules of NADH formed in glycolysis; each yields 1.5 molecules of ATP (assuming transport of NADH by the glycerol 3-phosphate shuttle)	+3
2 molecules of NADH formed in the oxidative decarboxylation of pyruvate; each yields 2.5 molecules of ATP	+5
2 molecules of FADH$_2$ formed in the citric acid cycle; each yields 1.5 molecules of ATP	+3
6 molecules of NADH formed in the citric acid cycle; each yields 2.5 molecules of ATP	+15
Net Yield per Molecule of Glucose	+30

Source: The ATP yield of oxidative phosphorylation is based on values given in P. C. Hinkle, M. A. Kumar, A. Resetar, and D. L. Harris. *Biochemistry* 30:3576, 1991.
Note: The current value of 30 molecules of ATP per molecule of glucose supersedes the earlier value of 36 molecules of ATP. The stoichiometries of proton pumping, ATP synthesis, and metabolite transport should be regarded as estimates. About 2 more molecules of ATP are formed per molecule of glucose oxidized when the malate–aspartate shuttle rather than the glycerol 3-phosphate shuttle is used.

consumed in transporting ATP from the matrix to the cytoplasm. Hence, about 2.5 molecules of cytoplasmic ATP are generated as a result of the flow of a pair of electrons from NADH to O_2. For electrons that enter at the level of Q-cytochrome *c* oxidoreductase, such as those from the oxidation of succinate or cytoplasmic NADH, the yield is about 1.5 molecules of ATP per electron pair. Hence, as tallied in Table 18.4, *about 30 molecules of ATP are formed when glucose is completely oxidized to CO_2;* this value supersedes the traditional estimate of 36 molecules of ATP. Most of the ATP, 26 of 30 molecules formed, is generated by oxidative phosphorylation. Recall that the anaerobic metabolism of glucose yields only 2 molecules of ATP. The efficiency of cellular respiration is manifested in the fact that one of the effects of endurance exercise, a practice that calls for much ATP for an extended period of time, is to increase the number of mitochondria and blood vessels in muscle and thus increase the extent of ATP generation by oxidative phosphorylation.

The rate of oxidative phosphorylation is determined by the need for ATP

How is the rate of the electron-transport chain controlled? Under most physiological conditions, electron transport is tightly coupled to phosphorylation. *Electrons do not usually flow through the electron-transport chain to O_2 unless ADP is simultaneously phosphorylated to ATP.* When ADP concentration rises, as would be the case in active muscle, the rate of oxidative

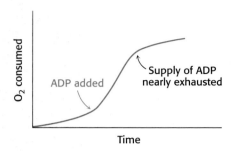

Figure 18.39 Respiratory control. Electrons are transferred to O_2 only if ADP is concomitantly phosphorylated to ATP.

phosphorylation increases to meet the ATP needs of the muscle. The regulation of the rate of oxidative phosphorylation by the ADP level is called *respiratory control* or *acceptor control*. Experiments on isolated mitochondria demonstrate the importance of ADP level (Figure 18.39). The rate of oxygen consumption by mitochondria increases markedly when ADP is added and then returns to its initial value when the added ADP has been converted into ATP.

The level of ADP likewise affects the rate of the citric acid cycle. At low concentrations of ADP, as in a resting muscle, NADH and $FADH_2$ are not consumed by the electron-transport chain. The citric acid cycle slows because there is less NAD^+ and FAD to feed the cycle. As the ADP level rises and oxidative phosphorylation speeds up, NADH and $FADH_2$ are oxidized, and the citric acid cycle becomes more active. *Electrons do not flow from fuel molecules to O_2 unless ATP needs to be synthesized.* We see here another example of the regulatory significance of the energy charge (Figure 18.40).

Figure 18.40 Energy charge regulates the use of fuels. The synthesis of ATP from ADP and P_i controls the flow of electrons from NADH and $FADH_2$ to oxygen. The availability of NAD^+ and FAD in turn control the rate of the citric acid cycle (CAC).

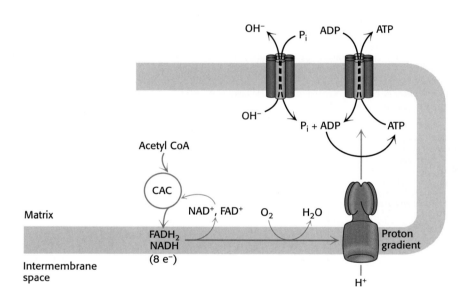

Regulated uncoupling leads to the generation of heat

Some organisms possess the ability to uncouple oxidative phosphorylation from ATP synthesis to generate heat. Such uncoupling is a means to maintain body temperature in hibernating animals, in some newborn animals (including human beings), and in many adult mammals, especially those adapted to cold. The skunk cabbage uses an analogous mechanism to heat its floral spikes in early spring, increasing the evaporation of odoriferous molecules that attract insects to fertilize its flowers. In animals, the uncoupling is in *brown adipose tissue* (BAT), which is specialized tissue for the process of *nonshivering thermogenesis*. In contrast, *white adipose tissue* (WAT), which constitutes the bulk of adipose tissue, plays no role in thermogenesis but serves as an energy source and an endocrine gland (Chapters 26 and 27).

Brown adipose tissue is very rich in mitochondria, often called *brown fat mitochondria*. The tissue appears brown from the combination of the greenish-colored cytochromes in the numerous mitochondria and the red hemoglobin present in the extensive blood supply, which helps to carry the heat through the body. The inner mitochondrial membrane of these mitochondria contains a large amount of *uncoupling protein* (UCP-1), or *thermogenin,* a dimer of 33-kd subunits that resembles ATP-ADP translocase. UCP-1 forms a pathway for the flow of protons from the cytoplasm to the matrix. In essence, *UCP-1 generates heat by short-circuiting the mitochondrial proton battery.* The energy of the proton gradient, normally captured as ATP, is released as heat as the protons flow through UCP-1 to the mitochondrial matrix. This dissipative proton pathway is activated when the core body temperature begins to fall. In response to a temperature drop, the release of hormones leads to the liberation of free fatty acids from triacylglycerols that in turn activate thermogenin (Figure 18.41).

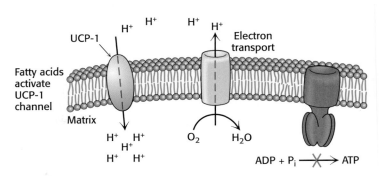

Figure 18.41 Action of an uncoupling protein. Uncoupling protein (UCP-1) generates heat by permitting the influx of protons into the mitochondria without the synthesis of ATP.

We can witness the effects of a lack of nonshivering thermogenesis by examining pig behavior. Pigs are unusual mammals in that they have large litters and are the only ungulates (hoofed animals) that build nests for birth. These behavioral characteristics appear to be the result of a biochemical deficiency. Pigs lack UCP-1 and, hence, brown fat. Piglets must rely on other means of thermogenesis, such as nesting, large litter size, and shivering.

Until recently, adult humans were believed to lack brown fat tissue. However, new studies have established that adults, women especially, have brown adipose tissue in the neck and upper chest regions that is activated by cold (Figure 18.42). Obesity leads to a decrease in brown adipose tissue.

In addition to UCP-1, two other uncoupling proteins have been identified. UCP-2, which is 56% identical in sequence with UCP-1, is found in a wide variety of tissues. UCP-3 (57% identical with UCP-1 and 73% identical with UCP-2) is localized to skeletal muscle and brown fat. This family of uncoupling proteins, especially UCP-2 and UCP-3, may play a role in energy homeostasis. In fact, the genes for UCP-2 and UCP-3 map to regions of the human and mouse chromosomes that have been linked to obesity, supporting the notion that they function as a means of regulating body weight.

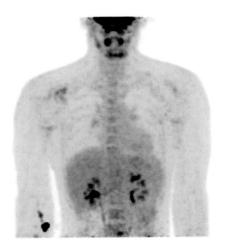
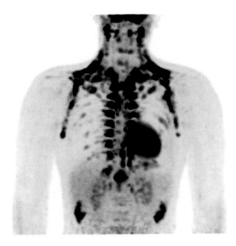

Figure 18.42 Brown adipose tissue is revealed on exposure to cold. The results of PET–CT scanning show the uptake and distribution of ^{18}F-fluorodeoxyglucose (^{18}F-FDG) in adipose tissue. The patterns of ^{18}F-FDG uptake in the same subject are dramatically different under thermoneutral conditions (left) and after exposure to cold (right). [Courtesy of Wouter van Marken Lichtenbelt. Copyright 2009 Massachusetts Medical Society. All rights reserved.]

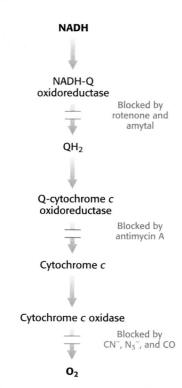

NADH

↓

NADH-Q
oxidoreductase

— Blocked by
rotenone and
amytal

↓

QH_2

↓

Q-cytochrome c
oxidoreductase

— Blocked by
antimycin A

↓

Cytochrome c

↓

Cytochrome c oxidase

— Blocked by
CN^-, N_3^-, and CO

↓

O_2

Figure 18.43 Sites of action of some inhibitors of electron transport.

2,4-Dinitrophenol (DNP)

Oxidative phosphorylation can be inhibited at many stages

Many potent and lethal poisons exert their effect by inhibiting oxidative phosphorylation at one of a number of different locations (Figure 18.43).

1. *Inhibition of the electron-transport chain.* *Rotenone,* which is used as a fish and insect poison, and *amytal,* a barbiturate sedative, block electron transfer in NADH-Q oxidoreductase and thereby prevent the utilization of NADH as a substrate. Rotenone, as an electron-transport-chain inhibitor, may play a role, along with genetic susceptibility, in the development of Parkinson disease. In the presence of rotenone and amytal, electron flow resulting from the oxidation of succinate is unimpaired, because these electrons enter through QH_2, beyond the block. *Antimycin A* interferes with electron flow from cytochrome b_H in Q-cytochrome c oxidoreductase. Furthermore, electron flow in cytochrome c oxidase can be blocked by *cyanide* (CN^-), *azide* (N_3^-), and *carbon monoxide* (CO). Cyanide and azide react with the ferric form of heme a_3, whereas carbon monoxide inhibits the ferrous form. Inhibition of the electron-transport chain also inhibits ATP synthesis because the proton-motive force can no longer be generated.

2. *Inhibition of ATP synthase.* Oligomycin, an antibiotic used as an antifungal agent, and dicyclohexylcarbodiimide (DCC) prevent the influx of protons through ATP synthase. If actively respiring mitochondria are exposed to an inhibitor of ATP synthase, the electron-transport chain ceases to operate. This observation clearly illustrates that electron transport and ATP synthesis are normally tightly coupled.

3. *Uncoupling electron transport from ATP synthesis.* The tight coupling of electron transport and phosphorylation in mitochondria can be uncoupled by 2,4-dinitrophenol (DNP) and certain other acidic aromatic compounds. These substances carry protons across the inner mitochondrial membrane, down their concentration gradient. In the presence of these uncouplers, electron transport from NADH to O_2 proceeds in a normal fashion, but ATP is not formed by mitochondrial ATP synthase, because the proton-motive force across the inner mitochondrial membrane is continuously dissipated. This loss of respiratory control leads to increased oxygen consumption and oxidation of NADH. Indeed, in the accidental ingestion of uncouplers, large amounts of metabolic fuels are consumed, but no energy is captured as ATP. Rather, energy is released as heat. DNP is the active ingredient in some herbicides and fungicides. Remarkably, some people consume DNP as a weight-loss drug, despite the fact that the FDA banned its use in 1938. There are also reports that Soviet soldiers were given DNP to keep them warm during the long Russian winters. Chemical uncouplers are nonphysiological, unregulated counterparts of uncoupling proteins.

4. *Inhibition of ATP export.* ATP-ADP translocase is specifically inhibited by very low concentrations of *atractyloside* (a plant glycoside) or *bongkrekic acid* (an antibiotic from a mold). Atractyloside binds to the translocase when its nucleotide site faces the cytoplasm, whereas bongkrekic acid binds when this site faces the mitochondrial matrix. Oxidative phosphorylation stops soon after either inhibitor is added, showing that ATP-ADP translocase is essential for maintaining adequate amounts of ADP to accept the energy associated with the proton-motive force.

Mitochondrial diseases are being discovered

 The number of diseases that can be attributed to mitochondrial mutations is steadily growing in step with our growing understanding of the biochemistry and genetics of mitochondria. The prevalence of mito-chondrial diseases is estimated to be from 10 to 15 per 100,000 people, roughly equivalent to the prevalence of the muscular dystrophies. The first mitochondrial disease to be understood was *Leber hereditary optic neuropathy* (LHON), a form of blindness that strikes in midlife as a result of mutations in Complex I. Some of these mutations impair NADH utilization, whereas others block electron transfer to Q. Mutations in Complex I are the most frequent cause of mitochondrial diseases. The accumulation of mutations in mitochondrial genes in a span of several decades may contribute to aging, degenerative disorders, and cancer.

A human egg harbors several hundred thousand molecules of mitochondrial DNA, whereas a sperm contributes only a few hundred and thus has little effect on the mitochondrial genotype. Because the maternally inherited mitochondria are present in large numbers and not all of the mitochondria may be affected, the pathologies of mitochondrial mutants can be quite complex. Even within a single family carrying an identical mutation, chance fluctuations in the percentage of mitochondria with the mutation lead to large variations in the nature and severity of the symptoms of the pathological condition as well as the time of onset. As the percentage of defective mitochondria increases, energy-generating capacity diminishes until, at some threshold, the cell can no longer function properly. Defects in cellular respiration are doubly dangerous. Not only does energy transduction decrease, but also the likelihood that reactive oxygen species will be generated increases. Organs that are highly dependent on oxidative phosphorylation, such as the nervous system and the heart, are most vulnerable to mutations in mitochondrial DNA.

Mitochondria play a key role in apoptosis

In the course of development or in cases of significant cell damage, individual cells within multicellular organisms undergo *programmed cell death*, or *apoptosis.* Mitochondria act as control centers regulating this process. Although the details have not yet been established, the outer membrane of damaged mitochondria becomes highly permeable, a process referred to as *mitochondrial outer membrane permeabilization* (MOMP). This permeabilization is instigated by a family of proteins (Bcl family) that were initially discovered because of their role in cancer. One of the most potent activators of apoptosis, cytochrome *c,* exits the mitochondria and interacts with apoptotic peptidase-activating factor 1 (APAF-1), which leads to the formation of the *apoptosome.* The apoptosome recruits and activates a proteolytic enzyme called *caspase* 9, a member of the cysteine protease family (Section 9.1), that in turn activates a cascade of other caspases. Each caspase type destroys a particular target, such as the proteins that maintain cell structure. Another target is a protein that inhibits an enzyme that destroys DNA (an enzyme called caspase-activated DNAse or CAD), freeing CAD to cleave the genetic material. This cascade of proteolytic enzymes has been called "death by a thousand tiny cuts."

Power transmission by proton gradients is a central motif of bioenergetics

The main concept presented in this chapter is that mitochondrial electron transfer and ATP synthesis are linked by a transmembrane proton gradient. ATP synthesis in bacteria and chloroplasts also is driven by proton gradients. In fact, proton gradients power a variety of energy-requiring processes such as the active transport of calcium ions by mitochondria, the

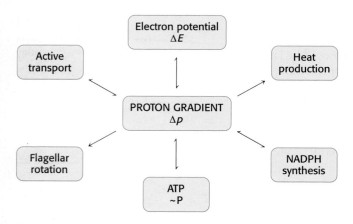

Figure 18.44 The proton gradient is an interconvertible form of free energy.

entry of some amino acids and sugars into bacteria, the rotation of bacterial flagella, and the transfer of electrons from $NADP^+$ to NADPH. Proton gradients can also be used to generate heat, as in hibernation. It is evident that *proton gradients are a central interconvertible currency of free energy in biological systems* (Figure 18.44). Mitchell noted that the proton-motive force is a marvelously simple and effective store of free energy because it requires only a thin, closed lipid membrane between two aqueous phases.

Summary

18.1 Eukaryotic Oxidative Phosphorylation Takes Place in Mitochondria

Mitochondria generate most of the ATP required by aerobic cells through a joint endeavor of the reactions of the citric acid cycle, which take place in the mitochondrial matrix, and oxidative phosphorylation, which takes place in the inner mitochondrial membrane. Mitochondria are descendants of a free-living bacterium that established a symbiotic relation with another cell.

18.2 Oxidative Phosphorylation Depends on Electron Transfer

In oxidative phosphorylation, the synthesis of ATP is coupled to the flow of electrons from NADH or $FADH_2$ to O_2 by a proton gradient across the inner mitochondrial membrane. Electron flow through three asymmetrically oriented transmembrane complexes results in the pumping of protons out of the mitochondrial matrix and the generation of a membrane potential. ATP is synthesized when protons flow back to the matrix through a channel in an ATP-synthesizing complex, called ATP synthase (also known as F_0F_1-ATPase). Oxidative phosphorylation exemplifies a fundamental theme of bioenergetics: the transmission of free energy by proton gradients.

18.3 The Respiratory Chain Consists of Four Complexes: Three Proton Pumps and a Physical Link to the Citric Acid Cycle

The electron carriers in the respiratory assembly of the inner mitochondrial membrane are quinones, flavins, iron–sulfur complexes, heme groups of cytochromes, and copper ions. Electrons from NADH are transferred to the FMN prosthetic group of NADH-Q oxidoreductase (Complex I), the first of four complexes. This oxidoreductase also contains Fe-S centers. The electrons emerge in QH_2, the reduced form of ubiquinone (Q). The citric acid cycle enzyme succinate dehydrogenase is a component of the succinate-Q reductase complex (Complex II), which donates electrons from $FADH_2$ to Q to form QH_2. This highly mobile hydrophobic carrier transfers its electrons to Q-cytochrome c oxidoreductase (Complex III), a complex that contains cytochromes b and c_1 and an Fe-S center. This complex reduces cytochrome c, a water-soluble peripheral membrane protein. Cytochrome c, like Q, is a mobile carrier of electrons, which it then transfers to cytochrome c oxidase (Complex IV). This complex contains cytochromes a and a_3 and three copper ions. A heme iron ion and a copper ion in this oxidase transfer electrons to O_2, the ultimate acceptor, to form H_2O.

18.4 A Proton Gradient Powers the Synthesis of ATP

The flow of electrons through Complexes I, III, and IV leads to the transfer of protons from the matrix side to the cytoplasmic side of the inner mitochondrial membrane. A proton-motive force consisting of a pH gradient (matrix side basic) and a membrane potential (matrix side negative) is generated. The flow of protons back to the matrix side through ATP synthase drives ATP synthesis. The enzyme complex is a molecular motor made of two operational units: a rotating component and a stationary component. The rotation of the γ subunit induces structural changes in the β subunit that result in the synthesis and release of ATP from the enzyme. Proton influx provides the force for the rotation.

The flow of two electrons through NADH-Q oxidoreductase, Q-cytochrome c oxidoreductase, and cytochrome c oxidase generates a gradient sufficient to synthesize 1, 0.5, and 1 molecule of ATP, respectively. Hence, 2.5 molecules of ATP are formed per molecule of NADH oxidized in the mitochondrial matrix, whereas only 1.5 molecules of ATP are made per molecule of $FADH_2$ oxidized, because its electrons enter the chain at QH_2, after the first proton-pumping site.

18.5 Many Shuttles Allow Movement Across Mitochondrial Membranes

Mitochondria employ a host of transporters, or carriers, to move molecules across the inner mitochondrial membrane. The electrons of cytoplasmic NADH are transferred into mitochondria by the glycerol phosphate shuttle to form $FADH_2$ from FAD or by the malate–aspartate shuttle to form mitochondrial NADH. The entry of ADP into the mitochondrial matrix is coupled to the exit of ATP by ATP-ADP translocase, a transporter driven by membrane potential.

18.6 The Regulation of Oxidative Phosphorylation Is Governed Primarily by the Need for ATP

About 30 molecules of ATP are generated when a molecule of glucose is completely oxidized to CO_2 and H_2O. Electron transport is normally tightly coupled to phosphorylation. NADH and $FADH_2$ are oxidized only if ADP is simultaneously phosphorylated to ATP, a form of regulation called acceptor or respiratory control. Proteins have been identified that uncouple electron transport and ATP synthesis for the generation of heat. Uncouplers such as DNP also can disrupt this coupling; they dissipate the proton gradient by carrying protons across the inner mitochondrial membrane.

Key Terms

oxidative phosphorylation (p. 525)

proton-motive force (p. 525)

cellular respiration (p. 526)

electron-transport chain (p. 528)

reduction (redox, oxidation–reduction, E_0') potential (p. 528)

coenzyme Q (Q, ubiquinone) (p. 532)

Q pool (p. 533)

NADH-Q oxidoreductase (Complex I) (p. 533)

flavin mononucleotide (FMN) (p. 533)

iron–sulfur (nonheme iron) protein (p. 534)

succinate-Q reductase (Complex II) (p. 535)

Q-cytochrome c oxidoreductase (Complex III) (p. 535)

cytochrome c (Cyt c) (p. 535)

Rieske center (p. 536)

Q cycle (p. 536)

cytochrome c oxidase (Complex IV) (p. 537)

superoxide dismutase (p. 541)

catalase (p. 542)

ATP synthase (Complex V, F_1F_0 ATPase) (p. 544)

glycerol 3-phosphate shuttle (p. 551)

malate–aspartate shuttle (p. 552)

ATP-ADP translocase (adenine nucleotide translocase, ANT) (p. 552)

respiratory (acceptor) control (p. 556)

uncoupling protein (UCP) (p. 557)

programmed cell death (apoptosis) (p. 559)

mitochondrial outer membrane permeabilization (MOMP) (p. 559)

apoptosome (p. 559)

caspase (p. 559)

Problems

1. *Breathe or ferment?* Compare fermentation and respiration with respect to electron donors and electron acceptors.

2. *Reference states.* The standard oxidation–reduction potential for the reduction of O_2 to H_2O is given as 0.82 V in Table 18.1. However, the value given in textbooks of chemistry is 1.23 V. Account for this difference.

3. *Less energetic electrons.* Why are electrons carried by $FADH_2$ not as energy rich as those carried by NADH? What is the consequence of this difference?

4. *Now prove it.* Calculate the energy released by the reduction of O_2 with $FADH_2$.

5. *Thermodynamic constraint.* Compare the $\Delta G°'$ values for the oxidation of succinate by NAD^+ and by FAD. Use the data given in Table 18.1 to find the E_0' of the NAD^+ $^-$NADH and fumarate-succinate couples, and assume that E_0' for the FAD–$FADH_2$ redox couple is nearly 0.05 V. Why is FAD rather than NAD^+ the electron acceptor in the reaction catalyzed by succinate dehydrogenase?

6. *The benefactor and beneficiary.* Identify the oxidant and the reductant in the following reaction.

$$\text{Pyruvate} + \text{NADH} + \text{H}^+ \rightleftharpoons \text{lactate} + \text{NAD}^+$$

7. *Six of one, half dozen of the other.* How is the redox potential ($\Delta E_0'$) related to the free-energy change of a reaction ($\Delta G°'$)?

8. *Location, location, location.* Iron is a component of many of the electron carriers of the electron-transport chain. How can it participate in a series of coupled redox reactions if the E_0' value is +0.77 V, as seen in Table 18.1?

9. *Line up.* Place the following components of the electron-transport chain in their proper order: (a) cytochrome *c;* (b) Q-cytochrome *c* oxidoreductase; (c) NADH-Q reductase; (d) cytochrome *c* oxidase; (e) ubiquinone.

10. *Match 'em.*

(a) Complex I___   1. Q-cytochrome c oxidoreductase
(b) Complex II___   2. Coenzyme Q
(c) Complex III___   3. Succinate-Q reductase
(d) Complex IV___   4. NADH-Q oxidoreductase
(e) Ubiquinone___   5. Cytochrome *c* oxidase

11. *Structural considerations.* Explain why coenzyme Q is an effective mobile electron carrier in the electron-transport chain.

12. *Inhibitors.* Rotenone inhibits electron flow through NADH-Q oxidoreductase. Antimycin A blocks electron flow between cytochromes *b* and c_1. Cyanide blocks electron flow through cytochrome oxidase to O_2. Predict the relative oxidation–reduction state of each of the following

respiratory-chain components in mitochondria that are treated with each of the inhibitors: NAD^+; NADH-Q oxidoreductase; coenzyme Q; cytochrome c_1; cytochrome *c;* cytochrome *a*.

13. *Rumored to be a favorite of Elvis.* Amytal is a barbiturate sedative that inhibits electron flow through Complex I. How would the addition of amytal to actively respiring mitochondria affect the relative oxidation–reduction states of the components of the electron-transport chain and the citric acid cycle?

14. *Efficiency.* What is the advantage of having Complexes I, III, and IV associated with one another in the form of a respirasome?

15. *ROS, not ROUS.* What are the reactive oxygen species and why are they especially dangerous to cells?

16. *Reclaim resources.* Humans have only about 250 g of ATP, but even a couch potato needs about 83 kg of ATP to open the bag of chips and use the remote. How is this discrepancy between requirements and resources reconciled?

17. *Energy harvest.* What is the yield of ATP when each of the following substrates is completely oxidized to CO_2 by a mammalian cell homogenate? Assume that glycolysis, the citric acid cycle, and oxidative phosphorylation are fully active.

(a) Pyruvate   (d) Phosphoenolpyruvate
(b) Lactate   (e) Galactose
(c) Fructose   (f) Dihydroxyacetone
1,6-bisphosphate   phosphate

18. *Potent poisons.* What is the effect of each of the following inhibitors on electron transport and ATP formation by the respiratory chain?

(a) Azide   (d) DNP
(b) Atractyloside   (e) Carbon monoxide
(c) Rotenone   (f) Antimycin A

19. *A question of coupling.* What is the mechanistic basis for the observation that the inhibitors of ATP synthase also lead to an inhibition of the electron-transport chain?

20. *A Brownian ratchet wrench.* What causes the c subunits of ATP synthase to rotate? What determines the direction of rotation?

21. *Alternative routes.* The most common metabolic sign of mitochondrial disorders is lactic acidosis. Why?

22. *Connections.* How does the inhibition of ATP-ADP translocase affect the citric acid cycle? Glycolysis?

23. *O_2 consumption.* Oxidative phosphorylation in mitochondria is often monitored by measuring oxygen con-

sumption. When oxidative phosphorylation is proceeding rapidly, the mitochondria will rapidly consume oxygen. If there is little oxidative phosphorylation, only small amounts of oxygen will be used. You are given a suspension of isolated mitochondria and directed to add the following compounds in the order from *a* to *h*. With the addition of each compound, all of the previously added compounds remain present. Predict the effect of each addition on oxygen consumption by the isolated mitochondria.

(a) Glucose   (e) Succinate
(b) ADP + P_i (f) Dinitrophenol
(c) Citrate   (g) Rotenone
(d) Oligomycin   (h) Cyanide

24. *P:O ratios.* The number of molecules of inorganic phosphate incorporated into organic form per atom of oxygen consumed, termed the *P:O ratio*, was frequently used as an index of oxidative phosphorylation.

(a) What is the relation of the P:O ratio to the ratio of the number of protons translocated per electron pair $(H^+/2\,e^-)$ and the ratio of the number of protons needed to synthesize ATP and transport it to the cytoplasm (P/H^+)?

(b) What are the P:O ratios for electrons donated by matrix NADH and by succinate?

25. *Cyanide antidote.* The immediate administration of nitrite is a highly effective treatment for cyanide poisoning. What is the basis for the action of this antidote? (Hint: Nitrite oxidizes ferrohemoglobin to ferrihemoglobin.)

26. *Runaway mitochondria 1.* Suppose that the mitochondria of a patient oxidize NADH irrespective of whether ADP is present. The P:O ratio for oxidative phosphorylation by these mitochondria is less than normal. Predict the likely symptoms of this disorder.

27. *Recycling device.* The cytochrome *b* component of Q-cytochrome *c* oxidoreductase enables both electrons of QH_2 to be effectively utilized in generating a proton-motive force. Cite another recycling device in metabolism that brings a potentially dead end reaction product back into the mainstream.

28. *Crossover point.* The precise site of action of a respiratory-chain inhibitor can be revealed by the *crossover technique.* Britton Chance devised elegant spectroscopic methods for determining the proportions of the oxidized and reduced forms of each carrier. This determination is feasible because the forms have distinctive absorption spectra, as illustrated in the adjoining graph for cytochrome *c.* You are given a new inhibitor and find that its addition to respiring mitochondria causes the carriers between NADH and QH_2 to become more reduced and those between cytochrome *c* and O_2 to become more oxidized. Where does your inhibitor act?

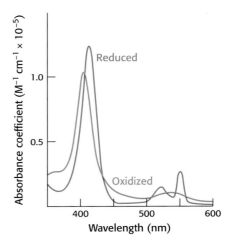

29. *Runaway mitochondria 2.* Years ago, uncouplers were suggested to make wonderful diet drugs. Explain why this idea was proposed and why it was rejected. Why might the producers of antiperspirants be supportive of the idea?

30. *Everything is connected.* If actively respiring mitochondria are exposed to an inhibitor of ATP-ADP translocase, the electron-transport chain ceases to operate. Why?

31. *Identifying the inhibition.* You are asked to determine whether a chemical is an electron-transport-chain inhibitor or an inhibitor of ATP synthase. Design an experiment to make this determination.

32. *To each according to its needs.* It has been noted that the mitochondria of muscle cells often have more cristae than the mitochondria of liver cells. Provide an explanation for this observation.

33. *Opposites attract.* An arginine residue (Arg 210) in the **a** subunit of ATP synthase is near the aspartate residue (Asp 61) in the matrix-side proton channel. How might Arg 210 assist proton flow?

34. *Variable **c** subunits.* Recall that the number of **c** subunits in the **c** ring appears to range between 10 and 14. This number is significant because it determines the number of protons that must be transported to generate a molecule of ATP. Each 360-degree rotation of the γ subunit leads to the synthesis and release of three molecules of ATP. Thus, if there are 10 **c** subunits in the ring (as was observed in a crystal structure of yeast mitochondrial ATP synthase), each ATP generated requires the transport of $10/3 = 3.33$ protons. How many protons are required to form ATP if the ring has 12 **c** subunits? 14?

35. *Counterintuitive.* Under some conditions, mitochondrial ATP synthase has been observed to actually run in reverse. How would that situation affect the proton-motive force?

36. *Etiology? What does that mean?* What does the fact that rotenone appears to increase the susceptibility to Parkinson disease indicate about the etiology of Parkinson disease?

37. *Exaggerating the difference.* Why must ATP-ADP translocase (also called adenine nucleotide translocase or ANT) use Mg^{2+}-free forms of ATP and ADP?

38. *Respiratory control.* The rate of oxygen consumption by mitochondria increases markedly when ADP is added and then returns to its initial value when the added ADP has been converted into ATP (see Figure 18.39). Why does the rate decrease?

39. *Same, but different.* Why is the electroneutral exchange of $H_2PO_4^-$ for OH^- indistinguishable from the electroneutral symport of $H_2PO_4^-$ and H^+?

40. *Multiple uses.* Give an example of the use of the proton-motive force in ways other than for the synthesis of ATP?

Chapter Integration Problems

41. *Just obeying the laws.* Why do isolated F_1 subunits of ATP synthase catalyze ATP hydrolysis?

42. *The right location.* Some cytoplasmic kinases, enzymes that phosphorylate substrates at the expense of ATP, bind to voltage-dependent anion channels. What might the advantage of this binding be?

43. *No exchange.* Mice that completely lack ATP-ADP translocase (ANT^-/ANT^-) can be made by using the knockout technique. Remarkably, these mice are viable but have the following pathological conditions: (1) high serum levels of lactate, alanine, and succinate; (2) little electron transport; and (3) a six- to eightfold increase in the level of mitochondrial H_2O_2 compared with that in normal mice. Provide a possible biochemical explanation for each of these conditions.

44. *Maybe you shouldn't take your vitamins.* Exercise is known to increase insulin sensitivity and to ameliorate type 2 diabetes (Chapter 27). Recent research suggests that taking antioxidant vitamins might mitigate the beneficial effects of exercise with respect to ROS protection.

(a) What are the antioxidant vitamins?
(b) How does exercise protect against ROS?
(c) Explain why vitamins might counteract the effects of exercise.

Data Interpretation Problem

45. *Mitochondrial disease.* A mutation in a mitochondrial gene encoding a component of ATP synthase has been identified. People who have this mutation suffer from muscle weakness, ataxia, and retinitis pigmentosa. A tissue biopsy was performed on each of three patients having this mutation, and submitochondrial particles were isolated that were capable of succinate-sustained ATP synthesis. First, the activity of the ATP synthase was measured on the addition of succinate and the following results were obtained.

ATP synthase activity (nmol of ATP formed min^{-1} mg^{-1})	
Controls	3.0
Patient 1	0.25
Patient 2	0.11
Patient 3	0.17

(a) What was the purpose of the addition of succinate?
(b) What is the effect of the mutation on succinate-coupled ATP synthesis?

Next, the ATPase activity of the enzyme was measured by incubating the submitochondrial particles with ATP in the absence of succinate.

ATP hydrolysis (nmol of ATP hydrolyzed min^{-1} mg^{-1})	
Controls	33
Patient 1	30
Patient 2	25
Patient 3	31

(c) Why was succinate omitted from the reaction?
(d) What is the effect of the mutation on ATP hydrolysis?
(e) What do these results, in conjunction with those obtained in the first experiment, tell you about the nature of the mutation?

Mechanism Problem

46. *Chiral clue.* ATPγS, a slowly hydrolyzed analog of ATP, can be used to probe the mechanism of phosphoryl-transfer reactions. Chiral ATPγS has been synthesized containing ^{18}O in a specific γ position and ordinary ^{16}O elsewhere in the molecule. The hydrolysis of this chiral molecule by ATP synthase in ^{17}O-enriched water yields inorganic $[^{16}O,^{17}O,^{18}O]$thiophosphate having the following absolute configuration. In contrast, the hydrolysis of this chiral ATPγS by a calcium-pumping ATPase from muscle gives thiophosphate of the opposite configuration. What is the simplest interpretation of these data?

CHAPTER 19

The Light Reactions of Photosynthesis

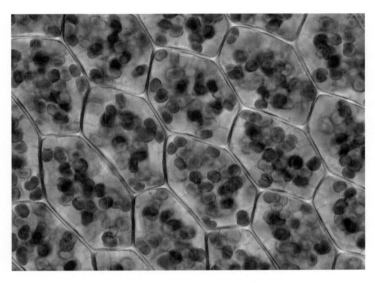

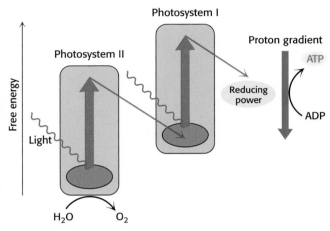

Chloroplasts (left) convert light energy into chemical energy. High-energy electrons in chloroplasts are transported through two photosystems (right). In this transit, which culminates in the generation of reducing power, ATP is synthesized in a manner analogous to mitochondrial ATP synthesis. In contrast with mitochondrial electron transport, however, electrons in chloroplasts are energized by light. [(Left) Created by Kristian Peters/GNU Free Documentation Licencse.]

On our planet are organisms capable of collecting the electromagnetic energy of the visible spectrum and converting it into chemical energy. Green plants are the most obvious of these organisms, though 60% of this conversion is carried out by algae and bacteria. This transformation is perhaps the most important of all of the energy transformations that we will see in our study of biochemistry; without it, life on our planet as we know it simply could not exist.

The process of converting electromagnetic radiation into chemical energy is called *photosynthesis*, which uses light energy to convert carbon dioxide and water into carbohydrates and oxygen.

$$CO_2 + H_2O \xrightarrow{\text{Light}} (CH_2O) + O_2$$

In this equation, CH_2O represents carbohydrate, primarily sucrose and starch. These carbohydrates provide not only the energy to run the biological world, but also the carbon molecules to make a wide array of biomolecules. Photosynthetic organisms are called *autotrophs* (literally, "self-feeders") because they can synthesize chemical fuels such as glucose from carbon dioxide and water by using sunlight as an energy source and then recover some of this energy from the synthesized glucose through the glycolytic

OUTLINE

pathway and aerobic metabolism. Organisms that obtain energy from chemical fuels only are called *heterotrophs,* which ultimately depend on autotrophs for their fuel.

We can think of photosynthesis as comprising two parts: the light reactions and the dark reactions. In the *light reactions,* light energy is transformed into two forms of biochemical energy with which we are already familiar: reducing power and ATP. The products of the light reactions are then used in the dark reactions to drive the reduction of CO_2 and its conversion into glucose and other sugars. The dark reactions are also called the *Calvin cycle* or *light-independent reactions* and will be discussed in Chapter 20.

Photosynthesis converts light energy into chemical energy

The light reactions of photosynthesis closely resemble the events of oxidative phosphorylation. In Chapters 17 and 18, we learned that cellular respiration is the oxidation of glucose to CO_2 with the reduction of O_2 to water, a process that generates ATP. In photosynthesis, this process must be reversed—reducing CO_2 and oxidizing H_2O to synthesize glucose.

$$\text{Energy} + 6\,H_2O + 6\,CO_2 \xrightarrow{\text{Photosynthesis}} C_6H_{12}O_6 + 6\,O_2$$

$$C_6H_{12}O_6 + 6\,O_2 \xrightarrow[\text{respiration}]{\text{Cellular}} 6\,O_2 + 6\,H_2O + \text{energy}$$

Although the processes of respiration and photosynthesis are chemically opposite each other, the biochemical principles governing the two processes are nearly identical. The key to both processes is the generation of high-energy electrons. The citric acid cycle oxidizes carbon fuels to CO_2 to generate high-energy electrons. The flow of these high-energy electrons down an electron-transport chain generates a proton-motive force. This proton-motive force is then transduced by ATP synthase to form ATP. To synthesize glucose from CO_2, high-energy electrons are required for two purposes: (1) to provide reducing power in the form of NADPH to reduce CO_2 and (2) to generate ATP to power the reduction. How can high-energy electrons be generated without using a chemical fuel? *Photosynthesis uses energy from light to boost electrons from a low-energy state to a high-energy state.* In the high-energy, unstable state, nearby molecules can abscond with the excited electrons. These electrons are used to produce reducing power, and they are used indirectly through an electron-transport chain and a proton-motive force across a membrane, which subsequently drives the synthesis of ATP. The reactions that are powered by sunlight are called the *light reactions* (Figure 19.1).

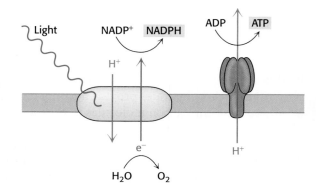

Figure 19.1 The light reactions of photosynthesis. Light is absorbed and the energy is used to drive electrons from water to generate NADPH and to drive protons across a membrane. These protons return through ATP synthase to make ATP.

Photosynthesis in green plants is mediated by two kinds of light reactions. Photosystem I generates reducing power in the form of NADPH but, in the process, becomes electron deficient. Photosystem II oxidizes water and transfers the electrons to replenish the electrons lost by photosystem I. A side product of these reactions is O_2. Electron flow from photosystem II to photosystem I generates the transmembrane proton gradient, augmented by the protons released by the oxidation of water, that drives the synthesis of ATP. In keeping with the similarity of their principles of operation, both processes take place in double-membrane organelles: mitochondria for cellular respiration and chloroplasts for photosynthesis.

19.1 Photosynthesis Takes Place in Chloroplasts

Photosynthesis, the means of converting light into chemical energy, takes place in organelles called *chloroplasts*, typically 5 μm long. Like a mitochondrion, a chloroplast has an outer membrane and an inner membrane, with an intervening intermembrane space (Figure 19.2). The inner membrane surrounds a space called the *stroma*, which is the site of the dark reactions of photosynthesis (Section 20.1). In the stroma are membranous structures called *thylakoids*, which are flattened sacs, or discs. The thylakoid sacs are stacked to form a *granum*. Different grana are linked by regions of thylakoid membrane called *stroma lamellae* (Figure 19.3). The thylakoid membranes separate the thylakoid space from the stroma space. Thus, chloroplasts have three different membranes (*outer, inner,* and *thylakoid membranes*) and three separate spaces (*intermembrane, stroma,* and *thylakoid spaces*). In developing chloroplasts, thylakoids arise from budding of the inner membrane, and so they are analogous to the mitochondrial cristae. Like the mitochondrial cristae, they are the site of coupled oxidation–reduction reactions of the light reactions that generate the proton-motive force.

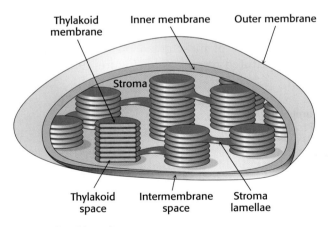

Figure 19.2 Diagram of a chloroplast.

Labels: Thylakoid membrane, Inner membrane, Outer membrane, Stroma, Thylakoid space, Intermembrane space, Stroma lamellae

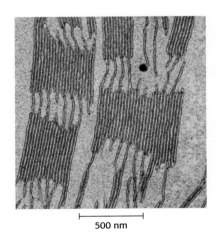

500 nm

Figure 19.3 Electron micrograph of a chloroplast from a spinach leaf. The thylakoid membranes pack together to form grana. [Courtesy of Dr. Kenneth Miller.]

Photosynthetic catastrophe

If photosynthesis were to cease, all higher forms of life would be extinct in about 25 years. A milder version of such a catastrophe ended the Cretaceous period 65.1 million years ago when a large asteroid struck the Yucatan Peninsula of Mexico. Enough dust was sent into the atmosphere that photosynthetic capacity was greatly diminished, which apparently led to the disappearance of the dinosaurs and allowed the mammals to rise to prominence.

The primary events of photosynthesis take place in thylakoid membranes

The thylakoid membranes contain the energy-transforming machinery: light-harvesting proteins, reaction centers, electron-transport chains, and ATP synthase. These membranes contain nearly equal amounts of lipids and proteins. The lipid composition is highly distinctive: about 40% of the total lipids are *galactolipids* and 4% are *sulfolipids*, whereas only 10% are phospholipids. The thylakoid membrane and the inner membrane, like the inner mitochondrial membrane, are impermeable to most molecules and ions. The outer membrane of a chloroplast, like that of a mitochondrion, is highly permeable to small molecules and ions. The stroma contains the soluble enzymes that utilize the NADPH and ATP synthesized by the thylakoids to convert CO_2 into sugar. Plant-leaf cells contain between 1 and 100 chloroplasts, depending on the species, cell type, and growth conditions.

Chloroplasts arose from an endosymbiotic event

Chloroplasts contain their own DNA and the machinery for replicating and expressing it. However, chloroplasts are not autonomous: they also contain many proteins encoded by nuclear DNA. How did the intriguing relation between the cell and its chloroplasts develop? We now believe that, in a manner analogous to the evolution of mitochondria (Section 18.1), chloroplasts are the result of endosymbiotic events in which a photosynthetic microorganism, most likely an ancestor of a cyanobacterium (Figure 19.4), was engulfed by a eukaryotic host. Evidence suggests that chloroplasts in higher plants and green algae are derived from a single endosymbiotic event, whereas those in red and brown algae are derived from at least one additional event.

The chloroplast genome is smaller than that of a cyanobacterium, but the two genomes have key features in common. Both are circular and have a single start site for DNA replication, and the genes of both are arranged in operons—sequences of functionally related genes under common control (Chapter 31). In the course of evolution, many of the genes of the chloroplast ancestor were transferred to the plant cell's nucleus or, in some cases, lost entirely, thus establishing a fully dependent relation.

Figure 19.4 Cyanobacteria. A colony of the photosynthetic filamentous cyanobacterium *Anabaena* shown at 450× magnification. Ancestors of these bacteria are thought to have evolved into present-day chloroplasts. [James W. Richardson/Visuals Unlimited.]

19.2 Light Absorption by Chlorophyll Induces Electron Transfer

The trapping of light energy is the key to photosynthesis. The first event is the absorption of light by a photoreceptor molecule. The principal photoreceptor in the chloroplasts of most green plants is the pigment molecule *chlorophyll* a, a substituted tetrapyrrole (Figure 19.5). The four nitrogen

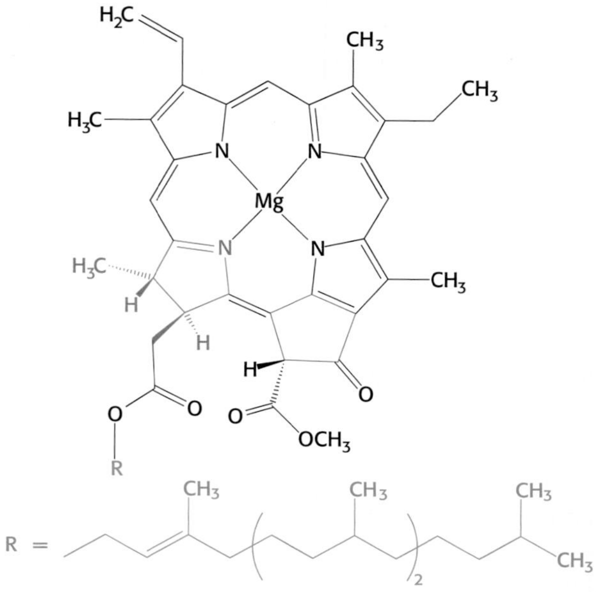

Figure 19.5 Chlorophyll. Like heme, chlorophyll *a* is a cyclic tetrapyrrole. One of the pyrrole rings (shown in red) is reduced, and an additional five-carbon ring (shown in blue) is fused to another pyrrole ring. A phytol chain (shown in green) is connected by an ester linkage. Magnesium ion binds at the center of the structure.

atoms of the pyrroles are coordinated to a magnesium ion. Unlike a porphyrin such as heme, chlorophyll has a reduced pyrrole ring and an additional 5-carbon ring fused to one of the pyrrole rings. Another distinctive feature of chlorophyll is the presence of *phytol*, a highly hydrophobic 20-carbon alcohol, esterified to an acid side chain.

Chlorophylls are very effective photoreceptors because they contain networks of conjugated double bonds—alternating single and double bonds. Such compounds are called conjugated *polyenes*. In polyenes, the electrons are not localized to a particular atomic nucleus and consequently can more readily absorb light energy. Chlorophylls have very strong absorption bands in the visible region of the spectrum, where the solar output reaching Earth is maximal (Figure 19.6). Chlorophyll *a*'s peak molar extinction coefficient (ε), a measure of a compound's ability to absorb light, is higher than 10^5 M^{-1} cm^{-1}, among the highest observed for organic compounds.

What happens when light is absorbed by a pigment molecule such as chlorophyll? The energy from the light excites an electron from its ground energy level to an excited energy level (Figure 19.7). This high-energy electron can have one of two fates. For most compounds that absorb light, the electron simply returns to the ground state and the absorbed energy is converted into heat. However, if a suitable electron acceptor is nearby, the excited electron can move from the initial molecule to the acceptor (Figure 19.8). A positive charge forms on the initial molecule, owing to the loss of an electron, and a negative charge forms on the acceptor, owing to the gain of an electron. Hence, this process is referred to as *photoinduced charge separation*.

In chloroplasts, the sites at which the charge separation takes place within each photosystem is called the *reaction center*. The photosynthetic apparatus is arranged to maximize photoinduced charge separation and minimize an unproductive return of the electron to its ground state. The electron, extracted from its initial site by the absorption of light, now has reducing power: it can reduce other molecules to store the energy originally obtained from light in chemical forms.

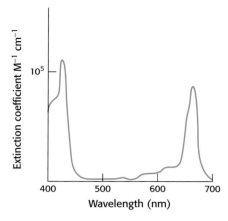

Figure 19.6 Light absorption by chlorophyll *a*. Chlorophyll *a* absorbs visible light efficiently as judged by the extinction coefficient near 10^5 M^{-1} cm^{-1}.

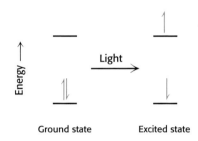

Figure 19.7 Light absorption. The absorption of light leads to the excitation of an electron from its ground state to a higher energy level.

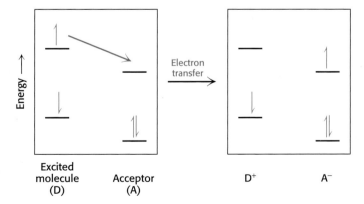

Figure 19.8 Photoinduced charge separation. If a suitable electron acceptor is nearby, an electron that has been moved to a high energy level by light absorption can move from the excited molecule to the acceptor.

A special pair of chlorophylls initiate charge separation

Photosynthetic bacteria such as *Rhodopseudomonas viridis* contain a photosynthetic reaction center that has been revealed at atomic resolution. The

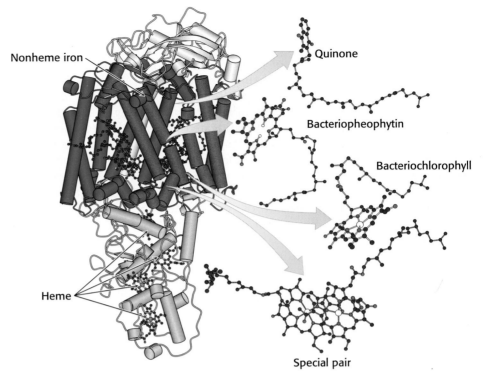

Bacteriochlorophyll *b*
(BChl-*b*)

Bacteriopheophytin
(BPh)

Figure 19.9 Bacterial photosynthetic reaction center. The core of the reaction center from *Rhodopseudomonas viridis* consists of two similar chains: L (red) and M (blue). An H chain (white) and a cytochrome subunit (yellow) complete the structure. *Notice* that the L and M subunits are composed largely of α helices that span the membrane. *Also notice* that a chain of electron-carrying prosthetic groups, beginning with a special pair of bacteriochlorophylls and ending at a bound quinone, runs through the structure from bottom to top in this view. [Drawn from 1PRC.pdb.]

bacterial reaction center consists of four polypeptides: L (31 kd), M (36 kd), and H (28 kd) subunits and C, a *c*-type cytochrome with four *c*-type hemes (Figure 19.9). *Sequence comparisons and low-resolution structural studies have revealed that the bacterial reaction center is homologous to the more complex plant systems.* Thus, many of our observations of the bacterial system will apply to plant systems as well.

The L and M subunits form the structural and functional core of the bacterial photosynthetic reaction center (see Figure 19.9). Each of these homologous subunits contains five transmembrane helices, in contrast with the H subunit, which has just one. The H subunit lies on the cytoplasmic side of the cell membrane, and the cytochrome subunit lies on the exterior face of the cell membrane, called the periplasmic side because it faces the periplasm, the space between the cell membrane and the cell wall. Four bacteriochlorophyll *b* (BChl-*b*) molecules, two bacteriopheophytin *b* (BPh) molecules, two quinones (Q_A and Q_B), and a ferrous ion are associated with the L and M subunits.

Bacteriochlorophylls are photoreceptors similar to chlorophylls, except for the reduction of an additional pyrrole ring and other minor differences that shift their absorption maxima to the near infrared, to wavelengths as long as 1000 nm. *Bacteriopheophytin* is the term for a bacteriochlorophyll that has two protons instead of a magnesium ion at its center.

The reaction begins with light absorption by a pair of BChl-*b* molecules that lie near the periplasmic side of the membrane in the L-M dimer. The

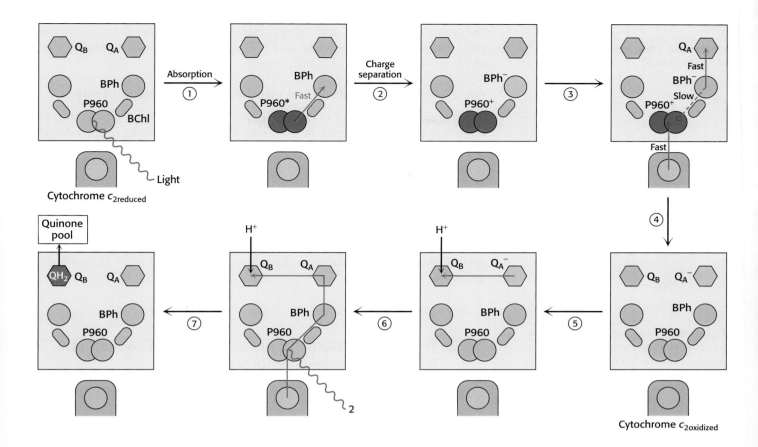

Figure 19.10 Electron chain in the photosynthetic bacterial reaction center. The absorption of light by the special pair (P960) results in the rapid transfer of an electron from this site to a bacteriopheophytin (BPh), creating a photoinduced charge separation (steps 1 and 2). (The asterisk on P960 stands for excited state.) The possible return of the electron from the pheophytin to the oxidized special pair is suppressed by the "hole" in the special pair being refilled with an electron from the cytochrome subunit and the electron from the pheophytin being transferred to a quinone (Q_A) that is farther away from the special pair (steps 3 and 4). Q_A passes the electron to Q_B. The reduction of a quinone (Q_B) on the cytoplasmic side of the membrane results in the uptake of two protons from the cytoplasm (steps 5 and 6). The reduced quinone can move into the quinone pool in the membrane (step 7).

pair of BChl-*b* molecules is called the *special pair* because of its fundamental role in photosynthesis. The special pair absorbs light maximally at 960 nm, and, for this reason, is often called *P960* (P stands for pigment). After absorbing light, the excited special pair ejects an electron, which is transferred through another BChl-*b* to a bacteriopheophytin (Figure 19.10, steps 1 and 2). This initial charge separation yields a positive charge on the special pair ($P960^+$) and a negative charge on BPh. The electron ejection and transfer take place in less than 10 picoseconds (10^{-11} s).

A nearby electron acceptor, a tightly bound quinone (Q_A), quickly grabs the electron away from BPh^- before the electron has a chance to fall back to the P960 special pair. From Q_A, the electron moves to a more loosely associated quinone, Q_B. The absorption of a second photon and the movement of a second electron from the special pair through the bacteriopheophytin to the quinones completes the two-electron reduction of Q_B from Q to QH_2. Because the Q_B-binding site lies near the cytoplasmic side of the membrane, *two protons are taken up from the cytoplasm, contributing to the development of a proton gradient across the cell membrane* (Figure 19.10, steps 5, 6, and 7).

In their high-energy states, $P960^+$ and BPh^- could undergo charge recombination; that is, the electron on BPh^- could move back to neutralize the positive charge on the special pair. Its return to the special pair would waste a valuable high-energy electron and simply convert the absorbed light energy into heat. How is charge recombination prevented? Two factors in the structure of the reaction center work together to suppress charge recombination nearly completely (Figure 19.10, steps 3 and 4). First, the next electron acceptor (Q_A) is less than 10 Å away from BPh^-, and so the electron is rapidly transferred farther away from the special pair. Second, one of

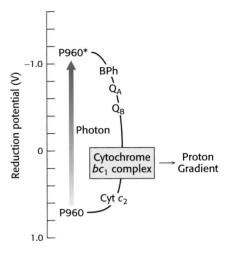

Figure 19.11 Cyclic electron flow in the bacterial reaction center. Excited electrons from the P960 reaction center flow through bacteriopheophytin (BPh), a pair of quinone molecules (Q_A and Q_B), cytochrome bc_1 complex, and finally through cytochrome c_2 to the reaction center. The cytochrome bc_1 complex pumps protons as a result of electron flow, which powers the formation of ATP.

the hemes of the cytochrome subunit is less than 10 Å away from the special pair, and so the positive charge on P960 is neutralized by the transfer of an electron from the reduced cytochrome.

Cyclic electron flow reduces the cytochrome of the reaction center

The cytochrome subunit of the reaction center must regain an electron to complete the cycle. It does so by taking back two electrons from reduced quinone (QH_2). QH_2 first enters the Q pool in the membrane where it is reoxidized to Q by complex bc_1, which is homologous to complex III of the respiratory electron-transport chain. Complex bc_1 transfers the electrons from QH_2 to cytochrome c_2, a water-soluble protein in the periplasm, and in the process pumps protons into the periplasmic space. The electrons now on cytochrome c_2 flow to the cytochrome subunit of the reaction center. The flow of electrons is thus cyclic (Figure 19.11). The proton gradient generated in the course of this cycle drives the generation of ATP through the action of ATP synthase.

19.3 Two Photosystems Generate a Proton Gradient and NADPH in Oxygenic Photosynthesis

Photosynthesis is more complicated in green plants than in photosynthetic bacteria. In green plants, photosynthesis depends on the interplay of two kinds of membrane-bound, light-sensitive complexes—*photosystem I* (PS I) and *photosystem II* (PS II), as shown in Figure 19.12. There are similarities in photosynthesis between green plants and photosynthetic bacteria. Both require light to energize reaction centers consisting of special pairs, called P680 for photosystem I and P700 for photosystem II, and both transfer electrons by using electron-transport chains. However, in plants, electron flow is not cyclic but progresses from photosystem II to photosystem I under most circumstances.

Photosystem I, which responds to light with wavelengths shorter than 700 nm, uses light-derived high-energy electrons to create biosynthetic reducing power in the form of NADPH, a versatile reagent for driving biosynthetic processes. The electrons for creating one molecule of NADPH are taken from two molecules of water by photosystem II, which responds to wavelengths shorter than 680 nm. A molecule of O_2 is generated as a side product of the actions of photosystem II. The electrons travel from photosystem II to photosystem I through cytochrome *bf,* a membrane-bound complex homologous to Complex III in oxidative phosphorylation. Cytochrome *bf* generates a proton gradient across the thylakoid membrane that drives the formation of ATP. Thus, the two photosystems cooperate to produce NADPH and ATP.

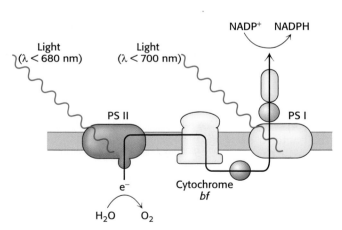

Figure 19.12 Two photosystems. The absorption of photons by two distinct photosystems (PS I and PS II) is required for complete electron flow from water to $NADP^+$.

Photosystem II transfers electrons from water to plastoquinone and generates a proton gradient

Photosystem II, an enormous transmembrane assembly of more than 20 subunits, catalyzes the light-driven transfer of electrons from water to plastoquinone. This electron acceptor closely resembles ubiquinone, a component of the mitochondrial electron-transport chain. Plastoquinone cycles between an oxidized form (Q) and a reduced form (QH$_2$, plastoquinol). The overall reaction catalyzed by photosystem II is

$$2 \, Q + 2 \, H_2O \xrightarrow{\text{Light}} O_2 + 2 \, QH_2$$

The electrons in QH$_2$ are at a higher redox potential than those in H$_2$O. Recall that, in oxidative phosphorylation, electrons flow from ubiquinol to an acceptor, O$_2$, which is at a *lower* potential. Photosystem II drives the reaction in a thermodynamically uphill direction by using the free energy of light.

This reaction is similar to one catalyzed by the bacterial system in that a quinone is converted from its oxidized into its reduced form. Photosystem II is reasonably similar to the bacterial reaction center (Figure 19.13). The core of the photosystem is formed by D1 and D2, a pair of similar 32-kd subunits that span the thylakoid membrane. These subunits are homologous to the L and M chains of the bacterial reaction center. Unlike the bacterial system, photosystem II contains a large number of additional subunits that bind more than 30 chlorophyll molecules altogether and increase the efficiency with which light energy is absorbed and transferred to the reaction center (Section 19.5).

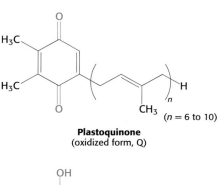

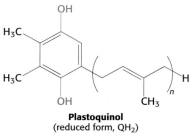

Plastoquinone (oxidized form, Q)
($n = 6$ to 10)

Plastoquinol (reduced form, QH$_2$)

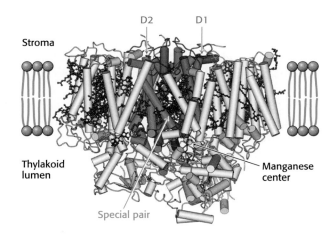

Stroma

D2   D1

Thylakoid lumen

Special pair

Manganese center

Figure 19.13 The structure of photosystem II. The D1 and D2 subunits are shown in red and blue, respectively, and the numerous bound chlorophyll molecules are shown in green. *Notice* that the special pair and the manganese center (the site of oxygen evolution) lie toward the thylakoid-lumen side of the membrane. [Drawn from 1S5L.pdb.]

The photochemistry of photosystem II begins with excitation of a special pair of chlorophyll molecules that are bound by the D1 and D2 subunits (Figure 19.14). Because the chlorophyll *a* molecules of the special pair absorb light at 680 nm, the special pair is often called *P680*. On excitation, P680 rapidly transfers an electron to a nearby pheophytin. From there, the electron is transferred first to a tightly bound plastoquinone at site Q$_A$ and then to a mobile plastoquinone at site Q$_B$. This electron flow is entirely analogous to that in the bacterial system. With the arrival of a second electron and the uptake of two protons, the mobile plastoquinone is reduced to QH$_2$. At this point, the energy of two photons has been safely and efficiently stored in the reducing potential of QH$_2$.

The major difference between the bacterial system and photosystem II is the source of the electrons that are used to neutralize the positive charge formed on the special pair. *P680$^+$, a very strong oxidant, extracts electrons from*

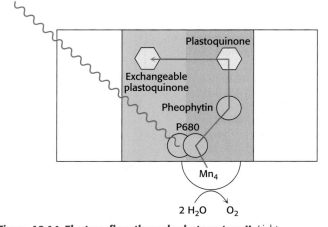

Figure 19.14 Electron flow through photosystem II. Light absorption induces electron transfer from P680 down an electron-transfer pathway to an exchangeable plastoquinone. The positive charge on P680 is neutralized by electron flow from water molecules bound at the manganese center.

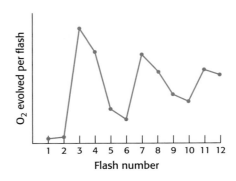

Figure 19.15 Four photons are required to generate one oxygen molecule. When dark-adapted chloroplasts are exposed to a brief flash of light, one electron passes through photosystem II. Monitoring the O_2 released after each flash reveals that four flashes are required to generate each O_2 molecule. The peaks in O_2 release are after the 3rd, 7th, and 11th flashes because the dark-adapted chloroplasts start in the S_1 state—that is, the one-electron reduced state.

Evolution of oxygen is evident by the generation of bubbles in the aquatic plant *Elodea*. [Colin Milkins/Oxford Scientific Films/Photolibrary.]

water molecules bound at the manganese center. The structure of this center includes a calcium ion and four manganese ions. Manganese was apparently evolutionarily selected for this role because of its ability to exist in multiple oxidation states (Mn^{2+}, Mn^{3+}, Mn^{4+}, Mn^{5+}) and to form strong bonds with oxygen-containing species. The *manganese center,* in its reduced form, oxidizes two molecules of water to form a single molecule of oxygen. Each time the absorbance of a photon kicks an electron out of P680, the positively charged special pair extracts an electron from the manganese center (Figure 19.15). However, the electrons do not come directly from the manganese ions. A tyrosine residue (often designated Z) of subunit D1 in photosystem II is the immediate electron donor, forming a tyrosine radical. The tyrosine radical removes electrons from the manganese ions, which in turn remove electrons from H_2O to generate O_2 and H^+. Four photons must be absorbed to extract four electrons from a water molecule (Figure 19.16). The four electrons harvested from water are used to reduce two molecules of Q to QH_2.

Photosystem II spans the thylakoid membrane such that the site of quinone reduction is on the side of the stroma, whereas the manganese center, hence the site of water oxidation, lies in the thylakoid lumen. Thus, the two protons that are taken up with the reduction of Q to QH_2 come from the stroma, and the four protons that are liberated in the course of water oxidation are released into the lumen. This distribution of protons gener-

Figure 19.16 A plausible scheme for oxygen evolution from the manganese center. The deduced core structure of the manganese center including four manganese ions and one calcium ion is shown, although many additional ligands are omitted for clarity. The center is oxidized, one electron at a time, until two bound H_2O molecules are linked to form a molecule of O_2, which is then released from the center. A tyrosine residue (not shown) participates in the coupled proton–electron transfer steps. The structures are designated S_0 to S_4 to indicate the number of electrons that have been removed.

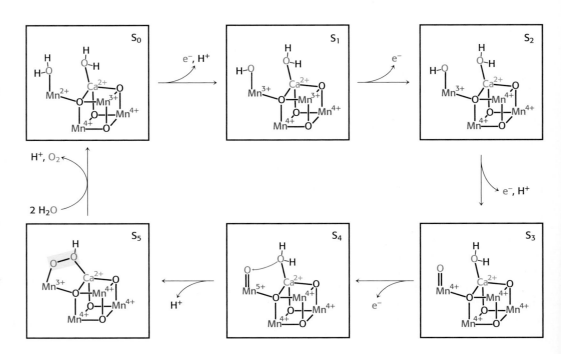

ates a proton gradient across the thylakoid membrane characterized by an excess of protons in the thylakoid lumen compared with the stroma (Figure 19.17).

Cytochrome *bf* links photosystem II to photosystem I

Electrons flow from photosystem II to photosystem I through the *cytochrome* bf complex. This complex catalyzes the transfer of electrons from plastoquinol (QH_2) to plastocyanin (Pc), a small, soluble copper protein in the thylakoid lumen.

$$QH_2 + 2\,Pc(Cu^{2+}) \rightarrow Q + 2\,Pc(Cu^+) + 2\,H^+_{\text{thylakoid lumen}}$$

The two protons from plastoquinol are released into the thylakoid lumen. This reaction is reminiscent of that catalyzed by Complex III in oxidative phosphorylation, and most components of the *cytochrome* bf complex are homologous to those of Complex III. The cytochrome *bf* complex includes four subunits: a 23-kd cytochrome with two *b*-type hemes, a 20-kd Rieske-type Fe-S protein, a 33-kd cytochrome *f* with a *c*-type cytochrome, and a 17-kd chain.

This complex catalyzes the reaction by proceeding through the Q cycle (see Figure 18.12). In the first half of the Q cycle, plastoquinol (QH_2) is oxidized to plastoquinone (Q), one electron at a time. The electrons from plastoquinol flow through the Fe-S protein to convert oxidized plastocyanin (Pc) into its reduced form.

In the second half of the Q cycle, cytochrome *bf* reduces a molecule of plastoquinone from the Q pool to plastoquinol, taking up two protons from one side of the membrane, and then reoxidizes plastoquinol to release these protons on the other side. The enzyme is oriented so that protons are released into the thylakoid lumen and taken up from the stroma, contributing further to the proton gradient across the thylakoid membrane (Figure 19.18).

Photosystem I uses light energy to generate reduced ferredoxin, a powerful reductant

The final stage of the light reactions is catalyzed by photosystem I, a transmembrane complex consisting of about 14 polypeptide chains and multiple associated proteins and cofactors (Figure 19.19). The core of this system is a pair of similar subunits, psaA (83 kd) and psaB (82 kd). These subunits are quite a bit larger than the core subunits of photosystem II and the bacterial

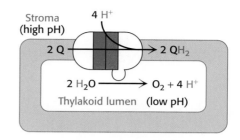

Figure 19.17 Proton-gradient direction. Photosystem II releases protons into the thylakoid lumen and takes them up from the stroma. The result is a pH gradient across the thylakoid membrane with an excess of protons (low pH) inside.

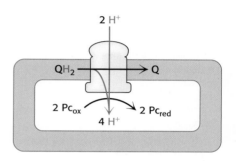

Figure 19.18 Cytochrome *bf* contribution to proton gradient. The cytochrome *bf* complex oxidizes QH_2 to Q through the Q cycle. Four protons are released into the thylakoid lumen in each cycle.

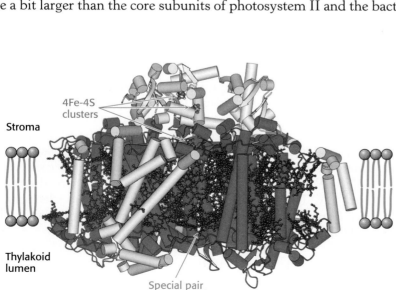

Figure 19.19 The structure of photosystem I. The psaA and psaB subunits are shown in red and blue, respectively. *Notice* the numerous bound chlorophyll molecules, shown in green, including the special pair, as well as the iron–sulfur clusters that facilitate electron transfer from the stroma. [Drawn from 1JB0.pdb.]

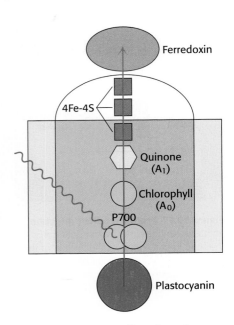

Figure 19.20 Electron flow through photosystem I to ferredoxin. Light absorption induces electron transfer from P700 down an electron-transfer pathway that includes a chlorophyll molecule, a quinone molecule, and three 4Fe-4S clusters to reach ferredoxin. The positive charge left on P700 is neutralized by electron transfer from reduced plastocyanin.

reaction center. Nonetheless, they appear to be homologous; the terminal 40% of each subunit is similar to a corresponding subunit of photosystem II. A special pair of chlorophyll *a* molecules lie at the center of the structure and absorb light maximally at 700 nm. This center, called *P700*, initiates photo-induced charge separation (Figure 19.20). The electron travels from P700 down a pathway through chlorophyll at site A_0 and quinone at site A_1 to a set of 4Fe-4S clusters. The next step is the transfer of the electron to ferre-doxin (Fd), a soluble protein containing a 2Fe-2S cluster coordinated to four cysteine residues (Figure 19.21). Ferredoxin transfers electrons to $NADP^+$. Meanwhile, $P700^+$ captures an electron from reduced plastocyanin to return to P700 so that P700 can be excited again. Thus, the overall reaction catalyzed by photosystem I is a simple one-electron oxidation–reduction reaction.

$$Pc(Cu^+) + Fd_{ox} \xrightarrow{\text{Light}} Pc(Cu^{2+}) + Fd_{red}$$

Given that the reduction potentials for plastocyanin and ferredoxin are $+0.37\,V$ and $-0.45\,V$, respectively, the standard free energy for this reaction is $+79.1\,\text{kJ mol}^{-1}$ ($+18.9\,\text{kcal mol}^{-1}$). This uphill reaction is driven by the absorption of a 700-nm photon, which has an energy of 171 kJ mol^{-1} ($40.9\,\text{kcal mol}^{-1}$).

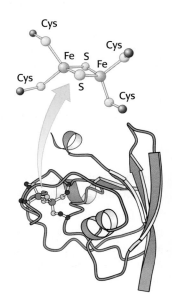

Figure 19.21 Structure of ferredoxin. In plants, ferredoxin contains a 2Fe-2S cluster. This protein accepts electrons from photosystem I and carries them to ferredoxin–NADP reductase. [Drawn from 1FXA.pdb.]

Ferredoxin–NADP⁺ reductase converts NADP⁺ into NADPH

Although reduced ferredoxin is a strong reductant, it is not useful for driving many reactions, in part because ferredoxin carries only one available electron. In contrast, NADPH, a two-electron reductant, is a widely used electron donor in biosynthetic processes, including the reactions of the Calvin cycle (Chapter 20). How is reduced ferredoxin used to drive the reduction of $NADP^+$ to NADPH? This reaction is catalyzed by *ferredoxin–NADP⁺ reductase*, a flavoprotein with an FAD prosthetic group (Figure 19.22A). The bound FAD moiety accepts two electrons and two protons from two molecules of reduced ferredoxin to form $FADH_2$ (Figure 19.22B). The enzyme then transfers a hydride ion (H^-) to $NADP^+$ to form NADPH. This reaction takes place on the stromal side of the membrane. Hence, the uptake of a proton in the reduction of $NADP^+$

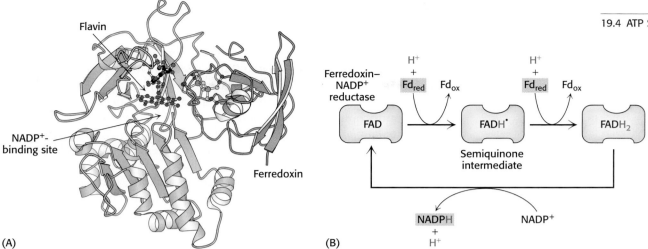

Figure 19.22 Structure and function of ferredoxin–NADP$^+$ reductase. (A) Structure of ferredoxin–NADP$^+$ reductase. This enzyme accepts electrons, one at a time, from ferredoxin (shown in orange). (B) Ferredoxin–NADP$^+$ reductase first accepts two electrons and two protons from two molecules of reduced ferredoxin (Fd) to form FADH$_2$, which then transfers two electrons and a proton to NADP$^+$ to form NADPH. [Drawn from 1EWY.pdb.]

further contributes to the generation of the proton gradient across the thylakoid membrane.

The cooperation between photosystem I and photosystem II creates a flow of electrons from H$_2$O to NADP$^+$. The pathway of electron flow is called the *Z scheme of photosynthesis* because the redox diagram from P680 to P700* looks like the letter Z (Figure 19.23).

19.4 A Proton Gradient Across the Thylakoid Membrane Drives ATP Synthesis

In 1966, André Jagendorf showed that chloroplasts synthesize ATP in the dark when an artificial pH gradient is imposed across the thylakoid membrane. To create this transient pH gradient, he soaked chloroplasts in a pH 4 buffer for several hours and then rapidly mixed them with a pH 8 buffer

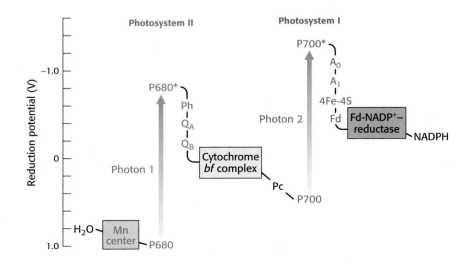

Figure 19.23 Pathway of electron flow from H$_2$O to NADP$^+$ in photosynthesis. This endergonic reaction is made possible by the absorption of light by photosystem II (P680) and photosystem I (P700). Abbreviations: Ph, pheophytin; Q$_A$ and Q$_B$, plastoquinone-binding proteins; Pc, plastocyanin; A$_0$ and A$_1$, acceptors of electrons from P700*; Fd, ferredoxin; Mn, manganese.

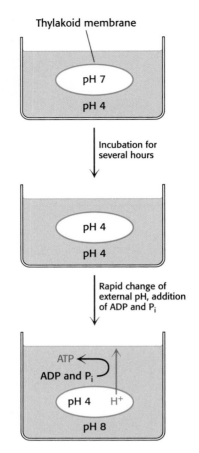

Thylakoid membrane

pH 7

pH 4

Incubation for several hours

pH 4

pH 4

Rapid change of external pH, addition of ADP and P$_i$

ATP

ADP and P$_i$

pH 4   H$^+$

pH 8

Figure 19.24 Jagendorf's demonstration. Chloroplasts synthesize ATP after the imposition of a pH gradient.

containing ADP and P$_i$. The pH of the stroma suddenly increased to 8, whereas the pH of the thylakoid space remained at 4. *A burst of ATP synthesis then accompanied the disappearance of the pH gradient across the thylakoid membrane* (Figure 19.24). This incisive experiment was one of the first to unequivocally support the hypothesis put forth by Peter Mitchell that ATP synthesis is driven by proton-motive force.

The principles of ATP synthesis in chloroplasts are nearly identical with those in mitochondria. *ATP formation is driven by a proton-motive force in both photophosphorylation and oxidative phosphorylation.* We have seen how light induces electron transfer through photosystems II and I and the cytochrome *bf* complex. At various stages in this process, protons are released into the thylakoid lumen or taken up from the stroma, generating a proton gradient. The gradient is maintained because the thylakoid membrane is essentially impermeable to protons. *The thylakoid space becomes markedly acidic, with the pH approaching 4. The light-induced transmembrane proton gradient is about 3.5 pH units.* As discussed in Section 18.4, energy inherent in the proton gradient, called the *proton-motive force* (Δp), is described as the sum of two components: a charge gradient and a chemical gradient. In chloroplasts, nearly all of Δp arises from the pH gradient, whereas, in mitochondria, the contribution from the membrane potential is larger. The reason for this difference is that the thylakoid membrane is quite permeable to Cl$^-$ and Mg^{2+}. The light-induced transfer of H$^+$ into the thylakoid space is accompanied by the transfer of either Cl$^-$ in the same direction or Mg^{2+} (1 Mg^{2+} per 2 H$^+$) in the opposite direction. Consequently, electrical neutrality is maintained and no membrane potential is generated. The influx of Mg^{2+} into the stroma plays a role in the regulation of the Calvin Cycle (Section 20.2). A pH gradient of 3.5 units across the thylakoid membrane corresponds to a proton-motive force of 0.20 V or a ΔG of -20.0 kJ mol^{-1} (-4.8 kcal mol^{-1}).

The ATP synthase of chloroplasts closely resembles those of mitochondria and prokaryotes

The proton-motive force generated by the light reactions is converted into ATP by the *ATP synthase* of chloroplasts, also called the *CF$_1$–CF$_0$ complex* (*C* stands for chloroplast and *F* for factor). CF$_1$–CF$_0$ ATP synthase closely resembles the F$_1$–F$_0$ complex of mitochondria (Section 18.4). CF$_0$ conducts protons across the thylakoid membrane, whereas CF$_1$ catalyzes the formation of ATP from ADP and P$_i$.

CF$_0$ is embedded in the thylakoid membrane. It consists of four different polypeptide chains known as I (17 kd), II (16.5 kd), III (8 kd), and IV (27 kd) having an estimated stoichiometry of $1:2:12:1$. Subunits I and II have sequence similarity to subunit **b** of the mitochondrial F$_0$ subunit, III corresponds to subunit **c** of the mitochondrial complex, and subunit IV is similar in sequence to subunit **a**. CF$_1$, the site of ATP synthesis, has a subunit composition $\alpha_3\beta_3\gamma\delta_\varepsilon$. The β subunits contain the catalytic sites, similarly to the F$_1$ subunit of mitochondrial ATP synthase. Remarkably, the β subunits of ATP synthase in corn chloroplasts are more than 60% identical in amino acid sequence with those of human ATP synthase, despite the passage of approximately 1 billion years since the separation of the plant and animal kingdoms.

Note that the membrane orientation of CF$_1$–CF$_0$ is reversed compared with that of the mitochondrial ATP synthase (Figure 19.25). However, the functional orientation of the two synthases is identical: protons flow from the lumen through the enzyme to the stroma or matrix where ATP is synthesized. Because CF$_1$ is on the stromal surface of the thylakoid

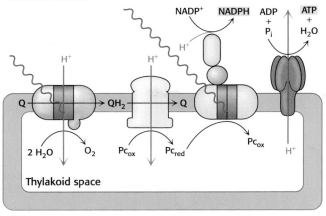

OXIDATIVE PHOSPHORYLATION

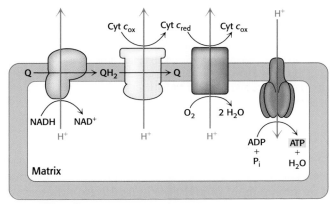

Figure 19.25 Comparison of photosynthesis and oxidative phosphorylation. The light-induced electron transfer in photosynthesis drives protons into the thylakoid lumen. The excess protons flow out of the lumen through ATP synthase to generate ATP in the stroma. In oxidative phosphorylation, electron flow down the electron-transport chain pumps protons out of the mitochondrial matrix. Excess protons from the intermembrane space flow into the matrix through ATP synthase to generate ATP in the matrix.

membrane, the newly synthesized ATP is released directly into the stromal space. Likewise, NADPH formed by photosystem I is released into the stromal space. Thus, *ATP and NADPH, the products of the light reactions of photosynthesis, are appropriately positioned for the subsequent dark reactions, in which CO_2 is converted into carbohydrate.*

Cyclic electron flow through photosystem I leads to the production of ATP instead of NADPH

On occasion, when the ratio of $NADPH$ to $NADP^+$ is very high as might be the case if there was another source of electrons to form NADPH (Section 20.3), $NADP^+$ may be unavailable to accept electrons from reduced ferredoxin. In this case, electrons arising from P700, the reaction center of photosystem I, may take an alternative pathway that does not end at NADPH. The electron in reduced ferredoxin is transferred to the cytochrome *bf* complex rather than to $NADP^+$. This electron then flows back through the cytochrome *bf* complex to reduce plastocyanin, which can then be reoxidized by $P700^+$ to complete a cycle. The net outcome of this cyclic flow of electrons is the pumping of protons by the cytochrome *bf*

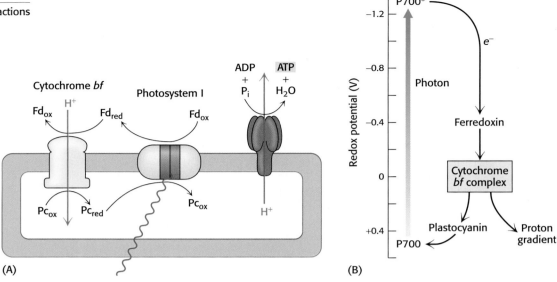

Figure 19.26 Cyclic photophosphorylation. (A) In this pathway, electrons from reduced ferredoxin are transferred to cytochrome *bf* rather than to ferredoxin–NADP$^+$ reductase. The flow of electrons through cytochrome *bf* pumps protons into the thylakoid lumen. These protons flow through ATP synthase to generate ATP. Neither NADPH nor O_2 is generated by this pathway. (B) A scheme showing the energetic basis for cyclic photophosphorylation. Abbreviations: Fd, ferredoxin; Pc, plastocyanin.

complex. The resulting proton gradient then drives the synthesis of ATP. In this process, called *cyclic photophosphorylation, ATP is generated without the concomitant formation of NADPH* (Figure 19.26). Photosystem II does not participate in cyclic photophosphorylation, and so O_2 is not formed from H_2O.

The absorption of eight photons yields one O_2, two NADPH, and three ATP molecules

We can now estimate the overall stoichiometry for the light reactions. The absorption of four photons by photosystem II generates one molecule of O_2 and releases 4 protons into the thylakoid lumen. The two molecules of plastoquinol are oxidized by the Q cycle of the cytochrome *bf* complex to release 8 protons into the lumen. Finally, the electrons from four molecules of reduced plastocyanin are driven to ferredoxin by the absorption of four additional photons. The four molecules of reduced ferredoxin generate two molecules of NADPH. Thus, the overall reaction is

$$2\,H_2O + 2\,NADP^+ + 10\,H^+_{stroma} \rightarrow O_2 + 2\,NADPH + 12\,H^+_{lumen}$$

The 12 protons released in the lumen can then flow through ATP synthase. Given that there are apparently 12 subunit III components in CF_0, we expect that 12 protons must pass through CF_0 to complete one full rotation of CF_1. A single rotation generates three molecules of ATP. Given the ratio of 3 ATP for 12 protons, the overall reaction is

$$2\,H_2O + 2\,NADP^+ + 10\,H^+_{stroma} \longrightarrow O_2 + 2\,NADPH + 12\,H^+_{lumen}$$

$$3\,ADP^{3-} + 3\,P_i^{2-} + 3\,H^+ + 12\,H^+_{lumen} \longrightarrow 3\,ATP^{4-} + 3\,H_2O + 12\,H^+_{stroma}$$

$$\overline{2\,NADP^+ + 3\,ADP^{3-} + 3\,P_i^{2-} + H^+ \longrightarrow O_2 + 2\,NADPH + 3\,ATP^{4-} + H_2O}$$

Thus, eight photons are required to yield three molecules of ATP (2.7 photons/ATP).

Cyclic photophosphorylation is a somewhat more productive way to synthesize ATP. The absorption of four photons by photosystem I leads to the release of 8 protons into the lumen by the cytochrome *bf* system. These protons flow through ATP synthase to yield two molecules of ATP. Thus, each two absorbed photons yield one molecule of ATP. No NADPH is produced.

19.5 Accessory Pigments Funnel Energy into Reaction Centers

A light-harvesting system that relied only on the chlorophyll *a* molecules of the special pair would be rather inefficient for two reasons. First, chlorophyll *a* molecules absorb light only at specific wavelengths (see Figure 19.6). A large gap is present in the middle of the visible region between approximately 450 and 650 nm. This gap falls right at the peak of the solar spectrum, and so failure to collect this light would constitute a considerable lost opportunity. Second, even on a cloudless day, many photons that can be absorbed by chlorophyll *a* pass through the chloroplast without being absorbed, because the density of chlorophyll *a* molecules in a reaction center is not very great. Accessory pigments, both additional chlorophylls and other classes of molecules, are closely associated with reaction centers. *These pigments absorb light and funnel the energy to the reaction center for conversion into chemical forms.* Accessory pigments prevent the reaction center from sitting idle.

Resonance energy transfer allows energy to move from the site of initial absorbance to the reaction center

How is energy funneled from an associated pigment to a reaction center? The absorption of a photon does not always lead to electron excitation and transfer. More commonly, excitation energy is transferred from one molecule to a nearby molecule through electromagnetic interactions through space (Figure 19.27). The rate of this process, called *resonance energy transfer*, depends strongly on the distance between the energy-donor and the energy-acceptor molecules; an increase in the distance between the donor and the acceptor by a factor of two typically results in a decrease in the energy-transfer rate by a factor of $2^6 = 64$. For reasons of conservation of energy, energy transfer must be from a donor in the excited state to an acceptor of equal or lower energy. *The excited state of the special pair of*

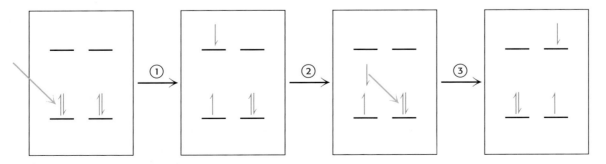

Figure 19.27 Resonance energy transfer. (1) An electron can accept energy from electron magnetic radiation of appropriate wavelength and jump to a higher energy state. (2) When the excited electron falls back to its lower energy state, the absorbed energy is released. (3) The released energy can be absorbed by an electron in a nearby molecule, and this electron jumps to a high energy state.

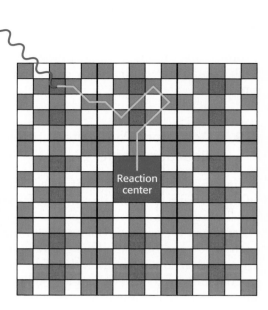

Figure 19.28 Energy transfer from accessory pigments to reaction centers. Light energy absorbed by accessory chlorophyll molecules or other pigments can be transferred to reaction centers, where it drives photoinduced charge separation. The green squares represent accessory chlorophyll molecules and the red squares represent carotenoid molecules; the white squares designate protein.

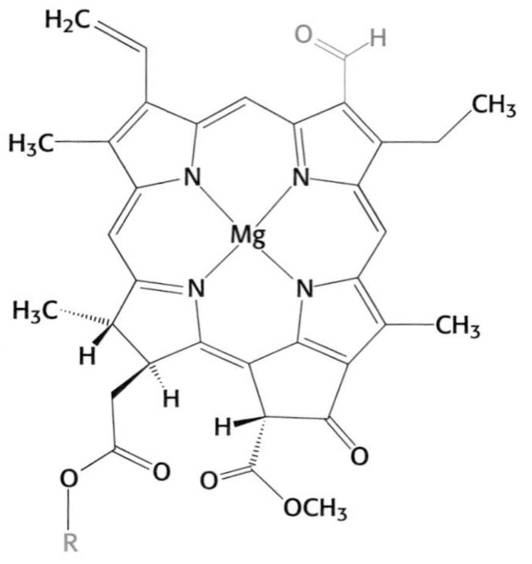

Chlorophyll b

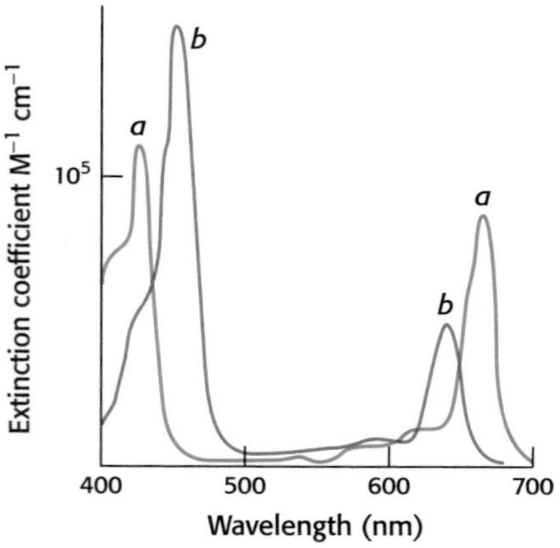

Figure 19.29 Absorption spectra of chlorophylls *a* and *b*.

chlorophyll molecules is lower in energy than that of single chlorophyll molecules, allowing reaction centers to trap the energy transferred from other molecules (Figure 19.28).

Light-harvesting complexes contain additional chlorophylls and carotenoids

Chlorophyll b and *carotenoids* are important light-harvesting molecules that funnel energy to the reaction center. Chlorophyll *b* differs from chlorophyll *a* in having a formyl group in place of a methyl group. This small difference shifts its two major absorption peaks toward the center of the visible region. In particular, chlorophyll *b* efficiently absorbs light with wavelengths between 450 and 500 nm (Figure 19.29).

Carotenoids are extended polyenes that absorb light between 400 and 500 nm. The carotenoids are responsible for most of the yellow and red colors of fruits and flowers, and they provide the brilliance of fall, when the chlorophyll molecules degrade, revealing the carotenoids.

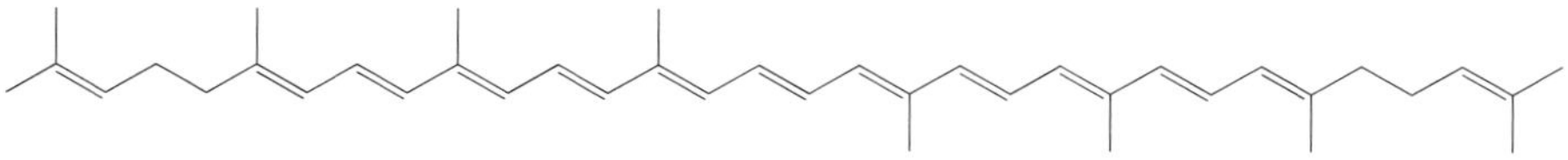

Lycopene

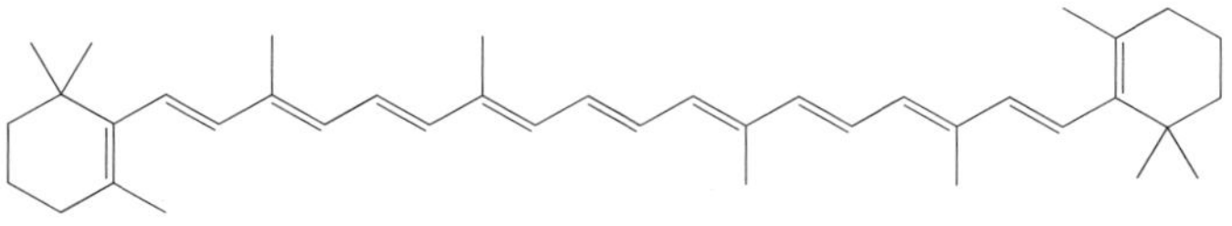

β-Carotene

In addition to their role in transferring energy to reaction centers, the carotenoids serve a safeguarding function. Carotenoids suppress damaging photochemical reactions, particularly those including oxygen that can be induced by bright sunlight. This protection may be especially important in the fall when the primary pigment chlorophyll is being degraded and thus not able to absorb light energy. Plants lacking carotenoids are quickly killed on exposure to light and oxygen.

The accessory pigments are arranged in numerous *light-harvesting complexes* that completely surround the reaction center. The 26-kd subunit of light-harvesting complex II (LHC-II) is the most abundant membrane protein in chloroplasts. This subunit binds seven chlorophyll *a* molecules, six chlorophyll *b* molecules, and two carotenoid molecules. Similar light-harvesting assemblies exist in photosynthetic bacteria (Figure 19.30).

The components of photosynthesis are highly organized

The complexity of photosynthesis, seen already in the elaborate interplay of complex components, extends even to the placement of the components in the thylakoid membranes. *Thylakoid membranes of most plants are differentiated into stacked* (appressed) *and unstacked* (nonappressed) *regions* (see Figures 19.2 and 19.3). Stacking increases the amount of thylakoid membrane in a given chloroplast volume. Both regions surround a common internal thylakoid space, but only unstacked regions make direct contact with the chloroplast stroma. Stacked and unstacked regions differ in the nature of their photosynthetic assemblies (Figure 19.31). Photosystem I and ATP synthase are located almost exclusively in unstacked regions, whereas photosystem II is present mostly in stacked regions. The cytochrome *bf* complex is found in both regions. Indeed, this complex rapidly moves back and forth between the stacked and the unstacked regions. Plastoquinone and plastocyanin are the mobile carriers of electrons between assemblies located in different regions of the thylakoid membrane. A common internal thylakoid space enables protons liberated by photosystem II in stacked membranes to be utilized by ATP synthase molecules that are located far away in unstacked membranes.

What is the functional significance of this lateral differentiation of the thylakoid membrane system? The positioning of photosystem I in the unstacked membranes also gives it direct access to the stroma for the reduction of $NADP^+$. ATP synthase, too, is located in the unstacked region to provide space for its large CF_1 globule and to give access to ADP. In contrast, the tight quarters of the appressed region pose no problem for

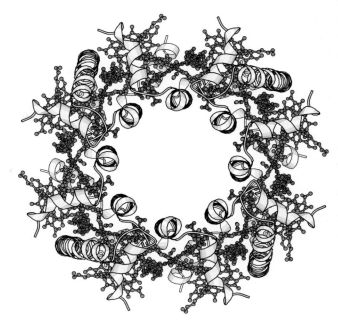

Figure 19.30 Structure of a bacterial light-harvesting complex. Eight polypeptides, each of which binds three chlorophyll molecules (green) and a carotenoid molecule (red), surround a central cavity that contains the reaction center (not shown). *Notice* the high concentration of accessory pigments that surround the reaction center. [Drawn from 1LGH.pdb.]

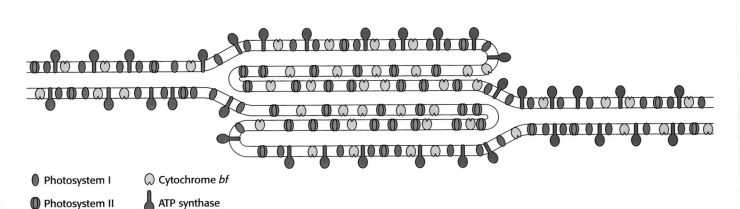

Photosystem I   Cytochrome *bf*

Photosystem II   ATP synthase

Figure 19.31 Location of photosynthesis components. Photosynthetic assemblies are differentially distributed in the stacked (appressed) and unstacked (nonappressed) regions of thylakoid membranes. [After a drawing kindly provided by Dr. Jan M. Anderson and Dr. Bertil Andersson.]

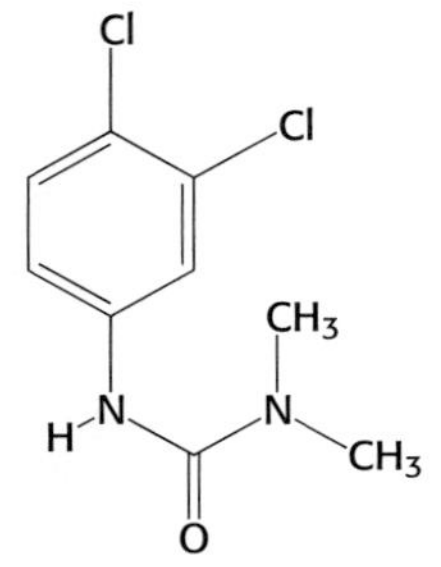

Diuron

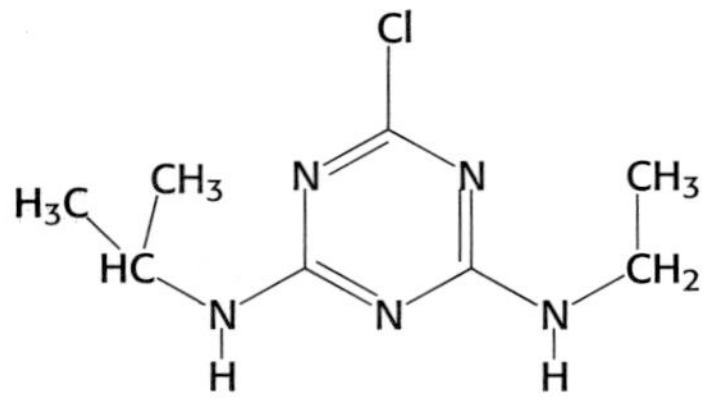

Atrazine

photosystem II, which interacts with a small polar electron donor (H_2O) and a highly lipid soluble electron carrier (plastoquinone).

Many herbicides inhibit the light reactions of photosynthesis

Many commercial herbicides kill weeds by interfering with the action of photosystem II or photosystem I. Inhibitors of photosystem II block electron flow, whereas inhibitors of photosystem I divert electrons from the terminal part of this photosystem. Photosystem II inhibitors include urea derivatives such as *diuron* and triazine derivatives such as *atrazine*. These chemicals bind to the Q_B site of the D1 subunit of photosystem II and block the formation of plastoquinol (QH_2).

Paraquat (1,1′-dimethyl-4-4′-bipyridinium) is an inhibitor of photosystem I. Paraquat, a dication, can accept electrons from photosystem I to become a radical. This radical reacts with O_2 to produce reactive oxygen species such as superoxide (O_2^-) and hydroxyl radical ($OH\cdot$). Such reactive oxygen species react with double bonds in membrane lipids, damaging the membrane.

19.6 The Ability to Convert Light into Chemical Energy Is Ancient

The ability to convert light energy into chemical energy is a tremendous evolutionary advantage. Geological evidence suggests that oxygenic photosynthesis became important approximately 2 billion years ago. Anoxygenic photosynthetic systems arose much earlier in the 3.5-billion-year history of life on Earth (Table 19.1). The photosynthetic system of the nonsulfur purple bacterium *Rhodopseudomonas viridis* has most features common to oxygenic photosynthetic systems and clearly predates them. Green sulfur bacteria such as *Chlorobium thiosulfatophilum* carry out a reaction that also seems to have appeared before oxygenic photosynthesis and is even more similar to oxygenic photosynthesis than *R. viridis* is. Reduced sulfur species such as H_2S are electron donors in the overall photosynthetic reaction:

$$CO_2 + 2\,H_2S \xrightarrow{\text{Light}} (CH_2O) + 2\,S + H_2O$$

Nonetheless, photosynthesis did not evolve immediately at the origin of life. No photosynthetic organisms have been discovered in the domain of Archaea, implying that photosynthesis evolved in the domain of Bacteria after Archaea and Bacteria diverged from a common ancestor. All domains of life do have electron-transport chains in common, however. As we have seen, components such as the ubiquinone–cytochrome *c* oxidoreductase and cytochrome *bf* family are present in both respiratory and photosynthetic electron-transport chains. These components were the foundations on which light-energy-capturing systems evolved.

Table 19.1   Major groups of photosynthetic prokaryotes

Bacteria	Photosynthetic electron donor	O_2 use
Green sulfur	H_2, H_2S, S	Anoxygenic
Green nonsulfur	Variety of amino acids and organic acids	Anoxygenic
Purple sulfur	H_2, H_2S, S	Anoxygenic
Purple nonsulfur	Usually organic molecules	Anoxygenic
Cyanobacteria	H_2O	Oxygenic

Summary

19.1 Photosynthesis Takes Place in Chloroplasts

The proteins that participate in the light reactions of photosynthesis are located in the thylakoid membranes of chloroplasts. The light reactions result in (1) the creation of reducing power for the production of NADPH, (2) the generation of a transmembrane proton gradient for the formation of ATP, and (3) the production of O_2.

19.2 Light Absorption by Chlorophyll Induces Electron Transfer

Chlorophyll molecules—tetrapyrroles with a central magnesium ion—absorb light quite efficiently because they are polyenes. An electron excited to a high-energy state by the absorption of a photon can move to nearby electron acceptors. In photosynthesis, an excited electron leaves a pair of associated chlorophyll molecules known as the special pair. The functional core of photosynthesis, a reaction center, from a photosynthetic bacterium has been studied in great detail. In this system, the electron moves from the special pair (containing bacteriochlorophyll) to a bacteriopheophytin (a bacteriochlorophyll lacking the central magnesium ion) to quinones. The reduction of quinones leads to the generation of a proton gradient, which drives ATP synthesis in a manner analogous to that of oxidative phosphorylation.

19.3 Two Photosystems Generate a Proton Gradient and NADPH in Oxygenic Photosynthesis

Photosynthesis in green plants is mediated by two linked photosystems. In photosystem II, the excitation of a special pair of chlorophyll molecules called P680 leads to electron transfer to plastoquinone in a manner analogous to that of the bacterial reaction center. The electrons are replenished by the extraction of electrons from a water molecule at a center containing four manganese ions. One molecule of O_2 is generated at this center for each four electrons transferred. The plastoquinol produced at photosystem II is reoxidized by the cytochrome bf complex, which transfers the electrons to plastocyanin, a soluble copper protein. From plastocyanin, the electrons enter photosystem I. In photosystem I, the excitation of special pair P700 releases electrons that flow to ferredoxin, a powerful reductant. Ferredoxin–NADP$^+$ reductase, a flavoprotein located on the stromal side of the membrane, then catalyzes the formation of NADPH. A proton gradient is generated as electrons pass through photosystem II, through the cytochrome bf complex, and through ferredoxin–NADP$^+$ reductase.

19.4 A Proton Gradient Across the Thylakoid Membrane Drives ATP Synthesis

The proton gradient across the thylakoid membrane creates a proton-motive force, used by ATP synthase to form ATP. The ATP synthase of chloroplasts (also called CF_0–CF_1) closely resembles the ATP-synthesizing assemblies of bacteria and mitochondria (F_0–F_1). If the NADPH:NADP$^+$ ratio is high, electrons transferred to ferredoxin by photosystem I can reenter the cytochrome bf complex. This process, called cyclic photophosphorylation, leads to the generation of a proton gradient by the cytochrome bf complex without the formation of NADPH or O_2.

19.5 Accessory Pigments Funnel Energy into Reaction Centers

Light-harvesting complexes that surround the reaction centers contain additional molecules of chlorophyll a, as well as carotenoids and chlorophyll b molecules, which absorb light in the center of the visible spectrum. These accessory pigments increase the efficiency of light capture by absorbing light and transferring the energy to reaction centers through resonance energy transfer.

19.6 The Ability to Convert Light into Chemical Energy Is Ancient

The photosystems have structural features in common that suggest a common evolutionary origin. Similarities in organization and molecular structure to those of oxidative phosphorylation suggest that the photosynthetic apparatus evolved from an early energy-transduction system.

Key Terms

light reactions (p. 566)

chloroplast (p. 567)

stroma (p. 567)

thylakoid (p. 567)

granum (p. 567)

chlorophyll *a* (p. 568)

photoinduced charge separation (p. 569)

reaction center (p. 569)

special pair (p. 571)

P960 (p. 571)

photosystem I (PS I) (p. 572)

photosystem II (PS II) (p. 572)

P680 (p. 573)

manganese center (p. 574)

cytochrome *bf* (p. 575)

P700 (p. 576)

Z scheme of photosynthesis (p. 577)

proton-motive force (p. 578)

ATP synthase (CF_1–CF_0 complex) (p. 578)

cyclic photophosphorylation (p. 580)

carotenoid (p. 582)

light-harvesting complex (p. 583)

Problems

1. *Complementary powers.* Photosystem I produces a powerful reductant, whereas photosystem II produces a powerful oxidant. Identify the reductant and oxidant and describe their roles.

2. *If a little is good.* What is the advantage of having an extensive set of thylakoid membranes in the chloroplasts?

3. *Cooperation.* Explain how light-harvesting complexes enhance the efficiency of photosynthesis.

4. *One thing leads to another.* What is the ultimate electron acceptor in photosynthesis? The ultimate electron donor? What powers the electron flow between the donor and the acceptor?

5. *Neutralization compensation.* In chloroplasts, a greater pH gradient across the thylakoid membrane is required to power the synthesis of ATP than is required across the mitochondrial inner membrane. Explain this difference.

6. *Environmentally appropriate.* Chlorophyll is a hydrophobic molecule. Why is this property crucial for the function of chlorophyll?

7. *Proton origins.* What are the various sources of protons that contribute to the generation of a proton gradient in chloroplasts?

8. *Efficiency matters.* What fraction of the energy of 700-nm light absorbed by photosystem I is trapped as high-energy electrons?

9. *That's not right.* Explain the defect or defects in the hypothetical scheme for the light reactions of photosynthesis depicted here.

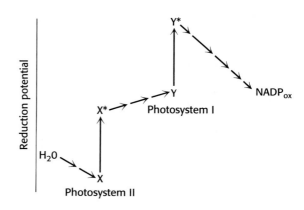

10. *Electron transfer.* Calculate the $\Delta E_0'$ and $\Delta G^{\circ\prime}$ for the reduction of $NADP^+$ by ferredoxin. Use data given in Table 18.1.

11. *To boldly go.* (a) It can be argued that, if life were to exist elsewhere in the universe, it would require some process like photosynthesis. Why is this argument reasonable? (b) If the *Enterprise* were to land on a distant plant and find no measurable oxygen in the atmosphere, could the crew conclude that photosynthesis is not taking place?

12. *Weed killer 1.* Dichlorophenyldimethylurea (DCMU), a herbicide, interferes with photophosphorylation and O_2 evolution. However, it does not block O_2 evolution in the presence of an artificial electron acceptor such as ferricyanide. Propose a site for the inhibitory action of DCMU.

13. *Weed killer 2.* Predict the effect of the herbicide dichlorophenyldimethylurea (DCMU) on a plant's ability to perform cyclic photophosphorylation.

14. *Infrared harvest.* Consider the relation between the energy of a photon and its wavelength.

(a) Some bacteria are able to harvest 1000-nm light. What is the energy (in kilojoules or kilocalories) of a mole (also called an einstein) of 1000-nm photons?

(b) What is the maximum increase in redox potential that can be induced by a 1000-nm photon?

(c) What is the minimum number of 1000-nm photons needed to form ATP from ADP and P_i? Assume a ΔG of 50 kJ mol^{-1} (12 kcal mol^{-1}) for the phosphorylation reaction.

15. *Missing acceptors.* Suppose that a bacterial reaction center containing only the special pair and the quinones has been prepared. Given the separation of 22 Å between the special pair and the closest quinone, estimate the rate of electron transfer between the excited special pair and this quinone.

16. *Close approach.* Suppose that energy transfer between two chlorophyll *a* molecules separated by 10 Å takes place in 10 picoseconds. Suppose that this distance is increased to 20 Å with all other factors remaining the same. How long would energy transfer take?

Chapter Integration Problems

17. *Functional equivalents.* What structural feature of mitochondria corresponds to the thylakoid membranes?

18. *Compare and contrast.* Compare and contrast oxidative phosphorylation and photosynthesis.

19. *Energy accounts.* On page 580, the balance sheet for the cost of the photosynthetically powered synthesis of glucose is presented. Eighteen molecules of ATP are required. Yet, when glucose undergoes combustion in cellular respiration, 30 molecules of ATP are produced. Account for the difference.

20. *Looking for a place to rest.* Albert Szent-Györgyi, Nobel Prize–winning biochemist, once said something to the effect: Life is nothing more than an electron looking for a place to rest. Explain how this pithy statement applies to photosynthesis and cellular respiration.

Mechanism Problem

21. *Hill reaction.* In 1939, Robert Hill discovered that chloroplasts evolve O_2 when they are illuminated in the presence of an artificial electron acceptor such as ferricyanide $[Fe^{3+}(CN)_6]^{3-}$. Ferricyanide is reduced to ferrocyanide $[Fe^{2+}(CN)_6]^{4-}$ in this process. No NADPH or reduced plastocyanin is produced. Propose a mechanism for the Hill reaction.

Data Interpretation and Chapter Integration Problem

22. *The same, but different.* The $\alpha_3\beta_3\gamma$ complex of mitochondrial or chloroplast ATP synthase will function as an ATPase in vitro. The chloroplast enzyme (both synthase and ATPase activity) is sensitive to redox control, whereas the mitochondrial enzyme is not. To determine where the enzymes differ, a segment of the mitochondrial γ subunit was removed and replaced with the equivalent segment from the chloroplast γ subunit. The ATPase activity of the modified enzyme was then measured as a function of redox conditions.

(a) What is the redox regulator of the ATP synthase in vivo? The adjoining graph shows the ATPase activity of modified and control enzymes under various redox conditions.

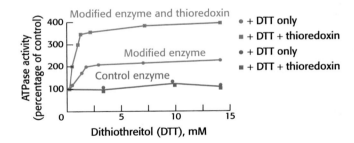

[Data from O. Bald et al. *J. Biol. Chem.* 275:12757–12762, 2000.]

(b) What is the effect of increasing the reducing power of the reaction mixture for the control and the modified enzymes?

(c) What is the effect of the addition of thioredoxin? How do these results differ from those in the presence of DTT alone? Suggest a possible explanation for the difference.

(d) Did the researchers succeed in identifying the region of the γ subunit responsible for redox regulation?

(e) What is the biological rationale of regulation by high concentrations of reducing agents?

(f) What amino acids in the γ subunit are most likely affected by the reducing conditions?

(g) What experiments might confirm your answer to part *e*?

CHAPTER 21

Glycogen Metabolism

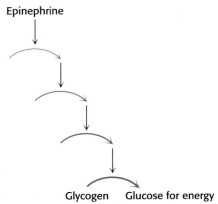

Epinephrine

Glycogen   Glucose for energy

Signaling cascades lead to the mobilization of glycogen to produce glucose, an energy source for runners. [(Left) Steve Krull/Alamy.]

Glucose is an important fuel and, as we will see, a key precursor for the biosynthesis of many molecules. However, glucose cannot be stored, because high concentrations of glucose disrupt the osmotic balance of the cell, which would cause cell damage or death. How can adequate stores of glucose be maintained without damaging the cell? The solution to this problem is to store glucose as a nonosmotically active polymer called glycogen.

Glycogen is a *readily mobilized storage form of glucose*. It is a very large, branched polymer of glucose residues that can be broken down to yield glucose molecules when energy is needed (Figure 21.1). A glycogen molecule has approximately 12 layers of glucose molecules and can be as large as 40 nm. Most of the glucose residues in glycogen are linked by α-1,4-glycosidic bonds (Figure 21.2). Branches at about every tenth residue are created by α-1,6-glycosidic bonds. Recall that α-glycosidic linkages form open helical polymers, whereas β linkages produce nearly straight strands that form structural fibrils, as in cellulose (see Figure 11.14).

Glycogen is not as reduced as fatty acids are and consequently not as energy rich. Why isn't all excess fuel stored as fatty acids rather than as glycogen? The controlled release of glucose from glycogen maintains blood-glucose levels between meals. The circulating blood keeps the brain supplied

OUTLINE

21.1 Glycogen Breakdown Requires the Interplay of Several Enzymes

21.2 Phosphorylase Is Regulated by Allosteric Interactions and Reversible Phosphorylation

21.3 Epinephrine and Glucagon Signal the Need for Glycogen Breakdown

21.4 Glycogen Is Synthesized and Degraded by Different Pathways

21.5 Glycogen Breakdown and Synthesis Are Reciprocally Regulated

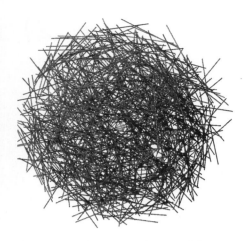

Figure 21.1 Glycogen. At the core of the glycogen molecule is the protein glycogenin (p. 628). The nonreducing ends of the glycogen molecule form the surface of the glycogen granule. Degradation takes place at this surface. [After R. Melendez et al. *Biophys. J.* 77:1327–1332, 1999.]

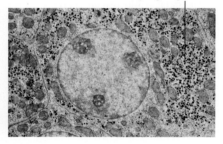

Glycogen granules

Figure 21.3 Electron micrograph of a liver cell. The dense particles in the cytoplasm are glycogen granules. [Courtesy of Dr. George Palade.]

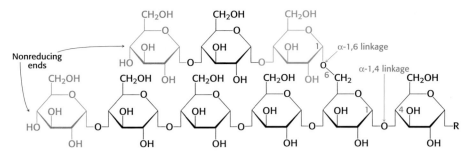

Figure 21.2 Glycogen structure. In this structure of two outer branches of a glycogen molecule, the residues at the nonreducing ends are shown in red and the residue that starts a branch is shown in green. The rest of the glycogen molecule is represented by R.

with glucose, which is virtually the only fuel used by the brain, except during prolonged starvation. Moreover, the readily mobilized glucose from glycogen is a good source of energy for sudden, strenuous activity. Unlike fatty acids, the released glucose can provide energy in the absence of oxygen and can thus supply energy for anaerobic activity.

Although most tissues have some glycogen, the two major sites of glycogen storage are the liver and skeletal muscle. The concentration of glycogen is higher in the liver than in muscle (10% versus 2% by weight), but more glycogen is stored in skeletal muscle overall because of muscle's much greater mass. Glycogen is present in the cytoplasm, with the molecule appearing as granules (Figure 21.3). In the liver, glycogen synthesis and degradation are regulated to maintain blood-glucose levels as required to meet the needs of the organism as a whole. In contrast, in muscle, these processes are regulated to meet the energy needs of the muscle itself.

Glycogen metabolism is the regulated release and storage of glucose

Glycogen degradation and synthesis are simple biochemical processes. Glycogen degradation consists of three steps: (1) the release of glucose 1-phosphate from glycogen, (2) the remodeling of the glycogen substrate to permit further degradation, and (3) the conversion of glucose 1-phosphate into glucose 6-phosphate for further metabolism. The glucose 6-phosphate

Figure 21.4 Fates of glucose 6-phosphate. Glucose 6-phosphate derived from glycogen can (1) be used as a fuel for anaerobic or aerobic metabolism as in, for instance, muscle; (2) be converted into free glucose in the liver and subsequently released into the blood; (3) be processed by the pentose phosphate pathway to generate NADPH or ribose in a variety of tissues.

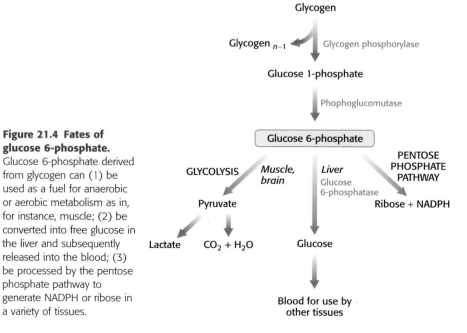

derived from the breakdown of glycogen has three possible fates (Figure 21.4): (1) it is the initial substrate for glycolysis, (2) it can be converted into free glucose for release into the bloodstream, and (3) it can be processed by the pentose phosphate pathway to yield NADPH and ribose derivatives. The conversion of glycogen into free glucose takes place mainly in the liver.

Glycogen synthesis, which takes place when glucose is abundant, requires an activated form of glucose, uridine diphosphate glucose (UDP-glucose), formed by the reaction of UTP and glucose 1-phosphate. As is the case for glycogen degradation, the glycogen molecule must be remodeled for continued synthesis.

The regulation of glycogen degradation and synthesis is complex. Several enzymes taking part in glycogen metabolism allosterically respond to metabolites that signal the energy needs of the cell. *Through these allosteric responses, enzyme activity is adjusted to meet the needs of the cell.* In addition, hormones may initiate signal cascades that lead to the reversible phosphorylation of enzymes, which alters their catalytic rates. *Regulation by hormones adjusts glycogen metabolism to meet the needs of the entire organism.*

21.1 Glycogen Breakdown Requires the Interplay of Several Enzymes

The efficient breakdown of glycogen to provide glucose 6-phosphate for further metabolism requires four enzyme activities: one to degrade glycogen, two to remodel glycogen so that it can be a substrate for degradation, and one to convert the product of glycogen breakdown into a form suitable for further metabolism. We will examine each of these activities in turn.

Phosphorylase catalyzes the phosphorolytic cleavage of glycogen to release glucose 1-phosphate

Glycogen phosphorylase, the key enzyme in glycogen breakdown, cleaves its substrate by the addition of orthophosphate (P_i) to yield *glucose 1-phosphate.* The cleavage of a bond by the addition of orthophosphate is referred to as *phosphorolysis.*

$$\text{Glycogen} + P_i \rightleftharpoons \text{glucose 1-phophase} + \text{glycogen}$$
$$(n \text{ residues}) \qquad\qquad\qquad (n-1 \text{ residues})$$

Phosphorylase catalyzes the sequential removal of glucosyl residues from the nonreducing ends of the glycogen molecule (the ends with a free OH group on carbon 4). Orthophosphate splits the glycosidic linkage between C-1 of the terminal residue and C-4 of the adjacent one. Specifically, it cleaves the bond between the C-1 carbon atom and the glycosidic oxygen atom, and the α configuration at C-1 is retained.

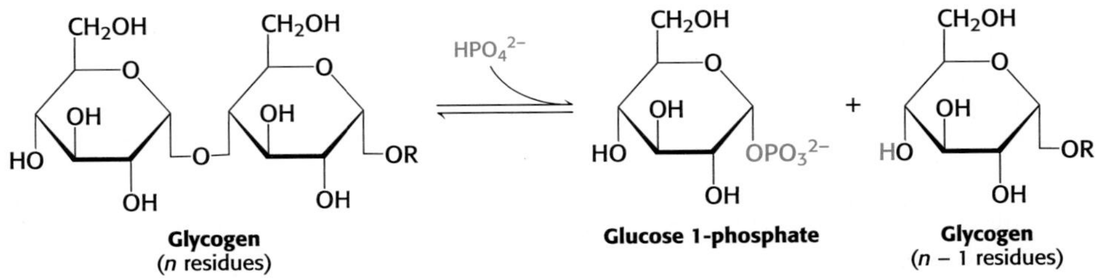

Glycogen
(*n* residues)

Glucose 1-phosphate

Glycogen
(*n* − 1 residues)

Glucose 1-phosphate released from glycogen can be readily converted into glucose 6-phosphate, an important metabolic intermediate, by the enzyme phosphoglucomutase.

The reaction catalyzed by phosphorylase is readily reversible in vitro. At pH 6.8, the equilibrium ratio of orthophosphate to glucose 1-phosphate is 3.6. The value of $\Delta G^{\circ\prime}$ for this reaction is small because a glycosidic bond is replaced by a phosphoryl ester bond that has a nearly equal transfer potential. However, phosphorolysis proceeds far in the direction of glycogen breakdown in vivo because the [P_i]/[glucose 1-phosphate] ratio is usually greater than 100, substantially favoring phosphorolysis. We see here an example of how the cell can alter the free-energy change to favor a reaction's occurrence by altering the ratio of substrate and product.

The phosphorolytic cleavage of glycogen is energetically advantageous because the released sugar is already phosphorylated. In contrast, a hydrolytic cleavage would yield glucose, which would then have to be phosphorylated at the expense of a molecule of ATP to enter the glycolytic pathway. An additional advantage of phosphorolytic cleavage for muscle cells is that no transporters exist for glucose 1-phosphate, which is negatively charged under physiological conditions, and so it cannot be transported out of the cell.

Mechanism: Pyridoxal phosphate participates in the phosphorolytic cleavage of glycogen

The special challenge faced by phosphorylase is to cleave glycogen phosphorolytically rather than hydrolytically to save the ATP required to phosphorylate free glucose. Thus, water must be excluded from the active site. Phosphorylase is a dimer of two identical 97-kd subunits. Each subunit is compactly folded into an *amino-terminal domain* (480 residues) containing a *glycogen-binding site* and a *carboxyl-terminal domain* (360 residues; Figure 21.5). The catalytic site in each subunit is located in a deep crevice formed by residues from both domains. What is the mechanistic basis of the phosphorolytic cleavage of glycogen?

Figure 21.5 Structure of glycogen phosphorylase. This enzyme forms a homodimer: one subunit is shown in white and the other in yellow. Each catalytic site includes a pyridoxal phosphate (PLP) group, linked to lysine 680 of the enzyme. The binding site for the phosphate (P_i) substrate is shown. *Notice* that the catalytic site lies between the C-terminal domain and the glycogen-binding site. A narrow crevice, which binds four or five glucose units of glycogen, connects the two sites. The separation of the sites allows the catalytic site to phosphorolyze several glucose units before the enzyme must rebind the glycogen substrate. [Drawn from 1NOI.pdb.]

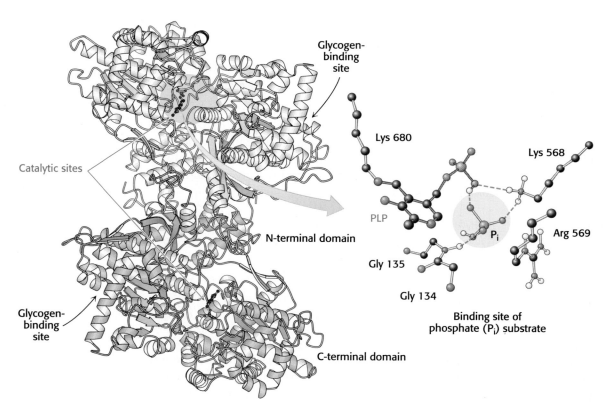

Several clues suggest a mechanism by which phosphorylase achieves the exclusion of water. First, both the glycogen substrate and the glucose 1-phosphate product have an α configuration at C-1. A direct attack by phosphate on C-1 of a sugar would invert the configuration at this carbon atom because the reaction would proceed through a pentacovalent transition state. The fact that the glucose 1-phosphate formed has an α rather than a β configuration suggests that an even number of steps (most simply, two) is required. The most likely explanation for these results is that a *carbonium ion intermediate* is formed from the glucose residue.

A second clue to the catalytic mechanism of phosphorylase is its requirement for the coenzyme *pyridoxal phosphate* (PLP), a derivative of pyridoxine (vitamin B_6, Section 15.4). The aldehyde group of this coenzyme forms a Schiff-base linkage with a specific lysine side chain of the enzyme (Figure 21.6). Structural studies indicate that the reacting orthophosphate group takes a position between the 5′-phosphate group of PLP and the glycogen substrate (Figure 21.7). *The 5′-phosphate group of PLP acts in tandem with orthophosphate by serving as a proton donor and then as a proton acceptor (i.e., as a general acid–base catalyst).* Orthophosphate (in the HPO_4^{2-} form) donates a proton to the oxygen atom attached to carbon 4 of the departing glycogen chain and simultaneously acquires a proton from PLP. The carbocation (carbonium ion) intermediate formed in this step is then attacked by orthophosphate to form α-glucose 1-phosphate, with the concomitant return of a hydrogen atom to pyridoxal phosphate. The special role of pyridoxal phosphate in the reaction is necessary because water is excluded from the active site.

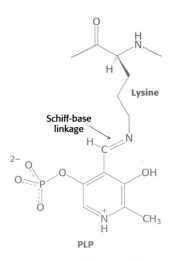

Figure 21.6 PLP–Schiff-base linkage. A pyridoxal phosphate (PLP) group (red) forms a Schiff base with a lysine residue (blue) at the active site of phosphorylase.

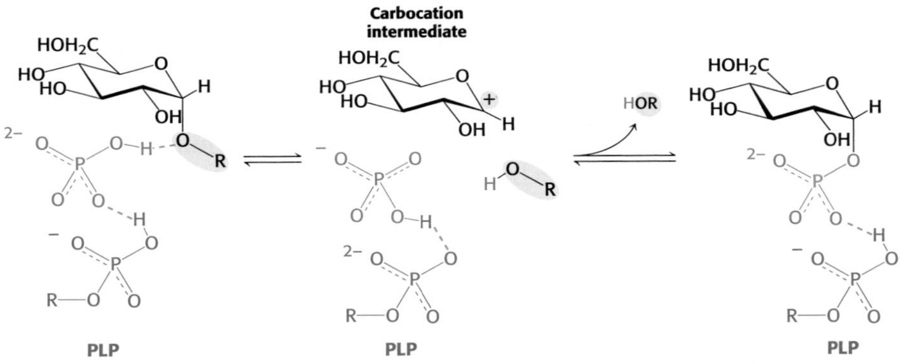

Figure 21.7 Phosphorylase mechanism. A bound HPO_4^{2-} group (red) favors the cleavage of the glycosidic bond by donating a proton to the departing glucose (black). This reaction results in the formation of a carbocation and is favored by the transfer of a proton from the protonated phosphate group of the bound pyridoxal phosphate (PLP) group (blue). The carbocation and the orthophosphate combine to form glucose 1-phosphate.

The glycogen-binding site is 30 Å away from the catalytic site (see Figure 21.5), but it is connected to the catalytic site by a narrow crevice able to accommodate four or five glucose units. The large separation between the binding site and the catalytic site enables the enzyme to phosphorolyze many residues without having to dissociate and reassociate after each catalytic cycle. An enzyme that can catalyze many reactions without having to dissociate and reassociate after each catalytic step is said to be *processive*—a property of enzymes that synthesize and degrade large polymers. We will see such enzymes again when we consider DNA and RNA synthesis.

A debranching enzyme also is needed for the breakdown of glycogen

Glycogen phosphorylase acting alone degrades glycogen to a limited extent. The enzyme can break α-1,4-glycosidic bonds on glycogen branches but soon encounters an obstacle. The α-1,6-glycosidic bonds at the branch points are not susceptible to cleavage by phosphorylase. Indeed, phosphorylase stops cleaving α-1,4 linkages when it reaches a terminal residue four residues away from a branch point. Because about 1 in 10 residues is branched, cleavage by the phosphorylase alone would come to a halt after the release of six glucose molecules per branch.

How can the remainder of the glycogen molecule be mobilized for use as a fuel? Two additional enzymes, a *transferase* and *α-1,6-glucosidase*, remodel the glycogen for continued degradation by the phosphorylase (Figure 21.8). *The transferase shifts a block of three glucosyl residues from one outer branch to another.* This transfer exposes a single glucose residue joined by an α-1,6-glycosidic linkage. α-1,6-Glucosidase, also known as the debranching enzyme, hydrolyzes the α-1,6-glycosidic bond.

Glycogen
(n residues)   **Glucose**   **Glycogen**
(n − 1 residues)

A free glucose molecule is released and then phosphorylated by the glycolytic enzyme hexokinase. Thus, the transferase and α-1,6-glucosidase convert the branched structure into a linear one, which paves the way for further cleavage by phosphorylase. In eukaryotes, the transferase and the α-1,6-glucosidase activities are present in a single 160-kd polypeptide chain, providing yet another example of a bifunctional enzyme (see Figure 16.29).

Phosphoglucomutase converts glucose 1-phosphate into glucose 6-phosphate

Glucose 1-phosphate formed in the phosphorolytic cleavage of glycogen must be converted into glucose 6-phosphate to enter the metabolic mainstream. This shift of a phosphoryl group is catalyzed by *phosphoglucomutase*. Recall that this enzyme is also used in galactose metabolism (Section 16.1). To effect this shift, the enzyme exchanges a phosphoryl group with the substrate (Figure 21.9). The catalytic site of an active mutase molecule contains a phosphorylated serine residue. The phosphoryl group is transferred from the serine residue to the C-6 hydroxyl group of glucose 1-phosphate to form glucose 1,6-bisphosphate. The C-1 phosphoryl group of this intermediate is then shuttled to the same serine residue, resulting in the formation of glucose 6-phosphate and the regeneration of the phosphoenzyme.

These reactions are like those of *phosphoglycerate mutase*, a glycolytic enzyme (Section 16.1). The role of glucose 1,6-bisphosphate in the interconversion of the phosphoglucoses is like that of 2,3-bisphosphoglycerate (2,3-BPG) in the interconversion of 2-phosphoglycerate and 3-phosphoglycerate in glycolysis. A phosphoenzyme intermediate participates in both reactions.

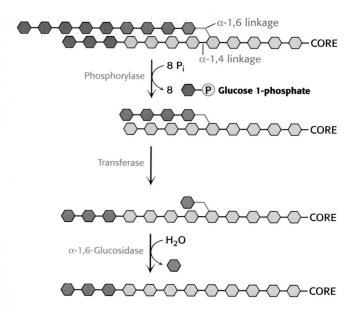

Figure 21.8 Glycogen remodeling. First, α-1,4-glycosidic bonds on each branch are cleaved by phosphorylase, leaving four residues along each branch. The transferase shifts a block of three glucosyl residues from one outer branch to the other. In this reaction, the α-1,4-glycosidic link between the blue and the green residues is broken and a new α-1,4 link between the blue and the yellow residues is formed. The green residue is then removed by α-1,6-glucosidase, leaving a linear chain with all α-1,4 linkages, suitable for further cleavage by phosphorylase.

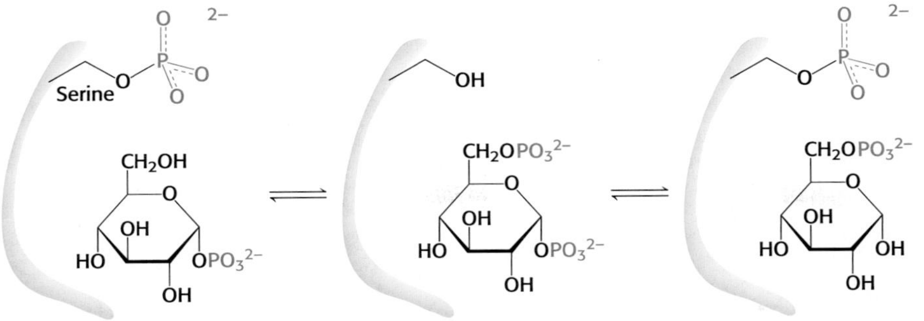

Figure 21.9 Reaction catalyzed by phosphoglucomutase. A phosphoryl group is transferred from the enzyme to the substrate, and a different phosphoryl group is transferred back to restore the enzyme to its initial state.

The liver contains glucose 6-phosphatase, a hydrolytic enzyme absent from muscle

A major function of the liver is to maintain a nearly constant level of glucose in the blood. The liver releases glucose into the blood during muscular activity and between meals. The released glucose is taken up primarily by the brain and skeletal muscle. In contrast with unmodified glucose, however, the phosphorylated glucose produced by glycogen breakdown is not transported out of cells. The liver contains a hydrolytic enzyme, *glucose 6-phosphatase* that enables glucose to leave that organ. This enzyme cleaves the phosphoryl group to form free glucose and orthophosphate. This glucose 6-phosphatase is the same enzyme that releases free glucose at the conclusion of gluconeogenesis. It is located on the lumenal side of the smooth endoplasmic reticulum membrane. Recall that glucose 6-phosphate is transported into the endoplasmic reticulum; glucose and orthophosphate formed by hydrolysis are then shuttled back into the cytoplasm (Section 16.1).

$$\text{Glucose 6-phosphate} + H_2O \longrightarrow \text{glucose} + P_i$$

Glucose 6-phosphatase is absent from most other tissues. Muscle tissues retain glucose 6-phosphate for the generation of ATP. In contrast, glucose is not a major fuel for the liver.

21.2 Phosphorylase Is Regulated by Allosteric Interactions and Reversible Phosphorylation

Glycogen metabolism is precisely controlled by multiple interlocking mechanisms. The focus of this control is the enzyme glycogen phosphorylase. *Phosphorylase is regulated by several allosteric effectors that signal the energy state of the cell as well as by reversible phosphorylation, which is responsive to hormones such as insulin, epinephrine, and glucagon.* We will examine the differences in the control of glycogen metabolism in two tissues: skeletal muscle and liver. These differences are due to the fact that *the muscle uses glucose to produce energy for itself, whereas the liver maintains glucose homeostasis of the organism as a whole.*

Muscle phosphorylase is regulated by the intracellular energy charge

The dimeric skeletal-muscle phosphorylase exists in two interconvertible forms: a *usually active* phosphorylase *a* and a *usually inactive* phosphorylase *b* (Figure 21.10). Each of these two forms exists in equilibrium between an active relaxed (R) state and a much less active tense (T) state, but the equilibrium for phosphorylase *a* favors the active R state, whereas the equilibrium for phosphorylase *b* favors the less-active T state (Figure 21.11). The

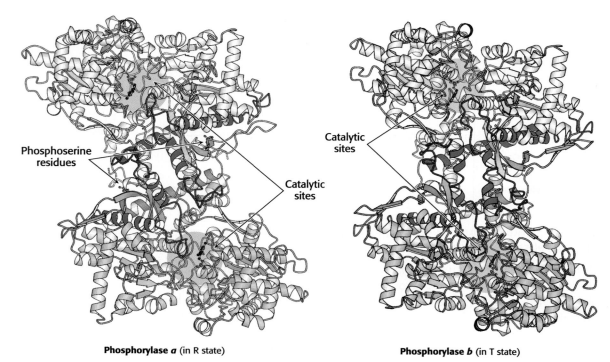

Phosphorylase *a* (in R state)

Phosphorylase *b* (in T state)

▶ **Figure 21.10 Structures of phosphorylase *a* and phosphorylase *b*.** Phosphorylase *a* is phosphorylated on serine 14 of each subunit. This modification favors the structure of the more-active R state. One subunit is shown in white, with helices and loops important for regulation shown in blue and red. The other subunit is shown in yellow, with the regulatory structures shown in orange and green. Phosphorylase *b* is not phosphorylated and exists predominantly in the T state. *Notice* that the catalytic sites are partly occluded in the T state. [Drawn from 1GPA.pdb and 1NOJ.pdb.]

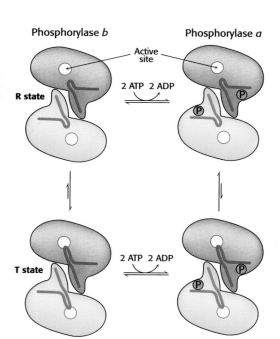

Figure 21.11 Phosphorylase regulation. Both phosphorylase *b* and phosphorylase *a* exist as equilibria between an active R state and a less-active T state. Phosphorylase *b* is usually inactive because the equilibrium favors the T state. Phosphorylase *a* is usually active because the equilibrium favors the R state. Regulatory structures are shown in blue and green.

default state of muscle phosphorylase is the *b* form, owing to the fact that, for muscle, phosphorylase needs to be active during muscle contraction. Muscle phosphorylase *b* is activated by the presence of high concentrations of AMP, which binds to a nucleotide-binding site and stabilizes the conformation of phosphorylase *b* in the active R state (Figure 21.12). Thus, when a muscle contracts and ATP is converted into AMP, the phosphorylase is signaled to degrade glycogen. ATP acts as a negative allosteric effector by competing with AMP. Thus, *the transition of phosphorylase* b *between the active R state and the less-active T state is controlled by the energy charge of the muscle cell.* Glucose 6-phosphate also binds to and stabilizes the less-

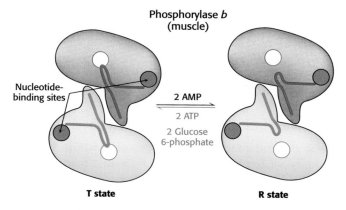

Figure 21.12 Allosteric regulation of muscle phosphorylase. A low energy charge, represented by high concentrations of AMP, favors the transition to the R state.

active state of phosphorylase *b,* an example of feedback inhibition. Under most physiological conditions, *phosphorylase* b *is inactive because of the inhibitory effects of ATP and glucose 6-phosphate.* In contrast, *phosphorylase a is fully active,* regardless of the levels of AMP, ATP, and glucose 6-phosphate. In resting muscle, nearly all the enzyme is in the inactive *b* form.

Phosphorylase *b* is converted into phosphorylase *a* by the phosphorylation of a single serine residue (serine 14) in each subunit. This conversion is initiated by hormones. Fear or the excitement of exercise will cause levels of the hormone epinephrine to increase. The increase in hormone levels and the electrical stimulation of muscle result in phosphorylation of the enzyme to the phosphorylase *a* form. The regulatory enzyme *phosphorylase kinase* catalyzes this covalent modification.

Comparison of the structures of phosphorylase *a* in the R state and phosphorylase *b* in the T state reveals that subtle structural changes at the subunit interfaces are transmitted to the active sites (see Figure 21.10). The transition from the T state (the prevalent state of phosphorylase *b*) to the R state (the prevalent state of phosphorylase *a*) entails a 10-degree rotation around the twofold axis of the dimer. Most importantly, this transition is associated with structural changes in α helices that move a loop out of the active site of each subunit. Thus, the T state is less active because the catalytic site is partly blocked. In the R state, the catalytic site is more accessible and a binding site for orthophosphate is well organized.

Liver phosphorylase produces glucose for use by other tissues

The role of glycogen degradation in the liver is to form glucose for *export to other tissues* when the blood-glucose level is low. Consequently, we can think of the default state of liver phosphorylase as being the *a* form: glucose is to be generated unless the enzyme is signaled otherwise. The liver phosphorylase *a* form thus exhibits the most responsive R ↔ T transition (Figure 21.13). The binding of glucose shifts the *a* form from the active R state to the less-active T state. In essence, the enzyme reverts to the low-activity T state only when it detects the presence of sufficient glucose. If glucose is present in the diet, there is no need to degrade glycogen. As we will see later, the presence of glucose also facilitates the *a*-to-*b* transition.

The regulation of liver phosphorylase differs from that of muscle phosphorylase. In muscle, the default state is the *b* form: there is no need to generate glucose unless energy is required. As discussed previously, AMP shifts the muscle *b* form from the T to the R state. Unlike the enzyme in muscle, the liver phosphorylase is insensitive to regulation by AMP because the liver does not undergo the dramatic changes in energy charge seen in a contracting muscle. We see here a clear example of the use of isozymic forms of the same enzyme to establish the tissue-specific biochemical properties of muscle and the liver. In human beings, liver phosphorylase and muscle phosphorylase are approximately 90% identical in amino acid sequence, yet the 10% difference results in subtle but important shifts in the stability of various forms of the enzyme.

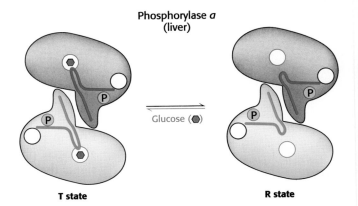

**Phosphorylase *a*
(liver)**

T state   R state

Figure 21.13 Allosteric regulation of liver phosphorylase. The binding of glucose to phosphorylase *a* shifts the equilibrium to the T state and inactivates the enzyme. Thus, glycogen is not mobilized when glucose is already abundant.

Phosphorylase kinase is activated by phosphorylation and calcium ions

Phosphorylase kinase activates phosphorylase *b* by attaching a phosphoryl group. The subunit composition of phosphorylase kinase in skeletal muscle

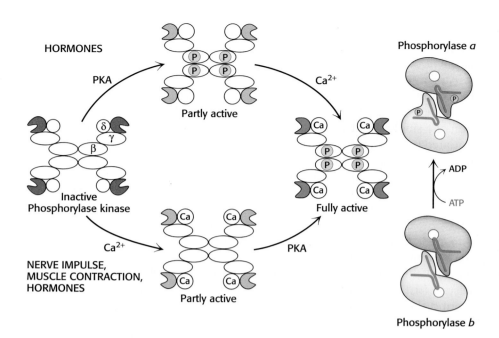

Figure 21.14 Activation of phosphorylase kinase. Phosphorylase kinase, an $(\alpha\beta\gamma\delta)_4$ assembly, is activated by hormones that lead to the phosphorylation of the β subunit and by Ca^{2+} binding to the δ subunit. Both types of stimulation are required for maximal enzyme activity. When active, the enzyme converts phosphorylase b into phosphorylase a.

is $(\alpha\beta\gamma\delta)_4$, and the mass of this very large protein is 1200 kd. The catalytic activity resides in the γ subunit, whereas the other subunits serve regulatory functions. This kinase is under dual control: it is activated both by phosphorylation by phosphorylase kinase A (PKA) and by increases in Ca^{2+} levels (Figure 21.14). Like its own substrate, phosphorylase kinase is activated by phosphorylation: the kinase is converted from *a low-activity form into a high-activity one by phosphorylation of its β subunit*. The activation of phosphorylase kinase is one step in a signal-transduction cascade initiated by hormones.

Phosphorylase kinase can also be partly activated by Ca^{2+} levels of the order of 1 μM. Its δ subunit is *calmodulin*, a calcium sensor that stimulates many enzymes in eukaryotes. This mode of activation of the kinase is especially noteworthy in muscle, where contraction is triggered by the release of Ca^{2+} from the sarcoplasmic reticulum. Phosphorylase kinase attains maximal activity only after both phosphorylation of the β subunit and activation of the δ subunit by Ca^{2+} binding.

21.3 Epinephrine and Glucagon Signal the Need for Glycogen Breakdown

Protein kinase A activates phosphorylase kinase, which in turn activates glycogen phosphorylase. What activates protein kinase A? What is the signal that ultimately triggers an increase in glycogen breakdown?

G proteins transmit the signal for the initiation of glycogen breakdown

Several hormones greatly affect glycogen metabolism. Glucagon and epinephrine trigger the breakdown of glycogen. Muscular activity or its anticipation leads to the release of *epinephrine (adrenaline)*, a catecholamine derived from tyrosine, from the adrenal medulla. Epinephrine markedly stimulates glycogen breakdown in muscle and, to a lesser extent, in the liver. The liver is more responsive to *glucagon*, a polypeptide hormone secreted by the α cells of the pancreas when the blood-sugar level is low. Physiologically, glucagon signifies the starved state (Figure 21.15).

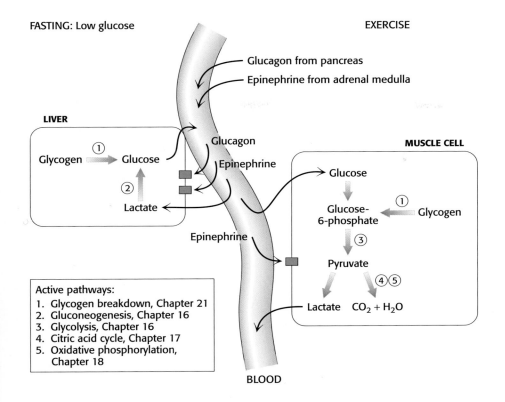

Figure 21.15 PATHWAY INTEGRATION: Hormonal control of glycogen breakdown. Glucagon stimulates liver-glycogen breakdown when blood glucose is low. Epinephrine enhances glycogen breakdown in muscle and the liver to provide fuel for muscle contraction.

How do hormones trigger the breakdown of glycogen? They initiate a cyclic AMP signal-transduction cascade, already discussed in Section 16.1 (Figure 21.16).

1. The signal molecules epinephrine and glucagon bind to specific seven-transmembrane (7TM) receptors in the plasma membranes of target cells (Section 14.1). Epinephrine binds to the β-adrenergic receptor in muscle,

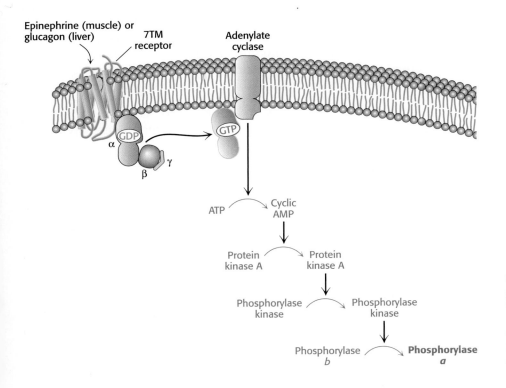

Figure 21.16 Regulatory cascade for glycogen breakdown. Glycogen degradation is stimulated by hormone binding to 7TM receptors. Hormone binding initiates a G-protein-dependent signal-transduction pathway that results in the phosphorylation and activation of glycogen phosphorylase.

whereas glucagon binds to the glucagon receptor in the liver. These binding events activate the G_s protein. *A specific external signal has been transmitted into the cell through structural changes,* first in the receptor and then in the G protein.

$$^+H_3N–His–Ser–Glu–Gly–Thr–Phe–Thr–Ser–Asp–Tyr–$$
$$\text{5} \qquad \text{10}$$

$$–Ser–Lys–Tyr–Leu–Asp–Ser–Arg–Arg–Ala–Gln–$$
$$\text{15} \qquad \text{20}$$

$$–Asp–Phe–Val–Gln–Trp–Leu–Met–Asn–Thr–COO^-$$
$$\text{25} \qquad \text{29}$$

Epinephrine   **Glucagon**

2. The GTP-bound subunit of G_s activates the transmembrane protein adenylate cyclase. This enzyme catalyzes the formation of the second messenger cyclic AMP from ATP.

3. The elevated cytoplasmic level of cyclic AMP activates *protein kinase A* (Section 10.3). The binding of cyclic AMP to inhibitory regulatory subunits triggers their dissociation from the catalytic subunits. The free catalytic subunits are now active.

4. Protein kinase A phosphorylates phosphorylase kinase first on β subunit and then on the α subunit, which subsequently activates glycogen phosphorylase.

The cyclic AMP cascade highly amplifies the effects of hormones. The binding of a small number of hormone molecules to cell-surface receptors leads to the release of a very large number of sugar units. Indeed, much of the stored glycogen would be mobilized within seconds were it not for a counterregulatory system.

The signal-transduction processes in the liver are more complex than those in muscle. Epinephrine can also elicit glycogen degradation in the liver. However, in addition to binding to the β-adrenergic receptor, it binds to the 7TM α-adrenergic receptor, which then initiates the *phosphoinositide cascade* (Section 14.2) that induces the release of Ca^{2+} from endoplasmic reticulum stores. Recall that the δ subunit of phosphorylase kinase is the Ca^{2+} sensor calmodulin. The binding of Ca^{2+} to calmodulin leads to a partial activation of phosphorylase kinase. Stimulation by both glucagon and epinephrine leads to maximal mobilization of liver glycogen.

Glycogen breakdown must be rapidly turned off when necessary

There must be a way to shut down the high-gain system of glycogen breakdown quickly to prevent the wasteful depletion of glycogen after energy needs have been met. When glucose needs have been satisfied, phosphorylase kinase and glycogen phosphorylase are dephosphorylated and inactivated. Simultaneously, glycogen synthesis is activated.

The signal-transduction pathway leading to the activation of glycogen phosphorylase is shut down automatically when the initiating hormone is no longer present. The inherent GTPase activity of the G protein converts the bound GTP into inactive GDP, and phosphodiesterases always present in the cell convert cyclic AMP into AMP. Protein phosphatase 1 (PP1) removes the phosphoryl groups from phosphorylase kinase, thereby inactivating the enzyme. Finally, protein phosphatase 1 also removes the phosphoryl group from glycogen phosphorylase, converting the enzyme into the usually inactive *b* form.

The regulation of glycogen phosphorylase became more sophisticated as the enzyme evolved

Analyses of the primary structures of glycogen phosphorylase from human beings, rats, *Dictyostelium* (slime mold), yeast, potatoes, and *E. coli* have enabled inferences to be made about the evolution of this important enzyme. The 16 residues that come into contact with glucose at the active site are identical in nearly all the enzymes. There is more variation but still substantial conservation of the 15 residues at the pyridoxal phosphate-binding site. Likewise, the glycogen-binding site is well conserved in all the enzymes. The high degree of similarity among these three sites shows that the catalytic mechanism has been maintained throughout evolution.

Differences arise, however, when we compare the regulatory sites. The simplest type of regulation would be feedback inhibition by glucose 6-phosphate. Indeed, the glucose 6-phosphate regulatory site is highly conserved among most of the phosphorylases. The crucial amino acid residues that participate in regulation by phosphorylation and nucleotide binding are well conserved only in the mammalian enzymes. Thus, this level of regulation was a later evolutionary acquisition.

21.4 Glycogen Is Synthesized and Degraded by Different Pathways

As with glycolysis and gluconeogenesis, biosynthetic and degradative pathways rarely operate by precisely the same reactions in the forward and reverse directions. Glycogen metabolism provided the first known example of this important principle. *Separate pathways afford much greater flexibility, both in energetics and in control.*

In 1957, Luis Leloir and his coworkers showed that glycogen is synthesized by a pathway that utilizes *uridine diphosphate glucose* (UDP-glucose) rather than glucose 1-phosphate as the activated glucose donor.

$$\text{Synthesis: Glycogen}_n + \text{UDP-glucose} \longrightarrow \text{glycogen}_{n+1} + \text{UDP}$$
$$\text{Degradation: Glycogen}_{n+1} + P_i \longrightarrow \text{glycogen}_n + \text{glucose 1-phosphate}$$

UDP-glucose is an activated form of glucose

UDP-glucose, the glucose donor in the biosynthesis of glycogen, is an *activated form of glucose,* just as ATP and acetyl CoA are activated forms of orthophosphate and acetate, respectively. The C-1 carbon atom of the glucosyl unit of UDP-glucose is activated because its hydroxyl group is esterified to the diphosphate moiety of UDP.

UDP-glucose is synthesized from glucose 1-phosphate and uridine triphosphate (UTP) in a reaction catalyzed by *UDP-glucose pyrophosphorylase.* This reaction liberates the outer two phosphoryl residues of UTP as pyrophosphate.

Uridine diphosphate glucose (UDP-glucose)

Glucose 1-phosphate **UTP** **UDP-glucose**

This reaction is readily reversible. However, pyrophosphate is rapidly hydrolyzed in vivo to orthophosphate by an inorganic pyrophosphatase. The essentially irreversible hydrolysis of pyrophosphate drives the synthesis of UDP-glucose.

$$\text{Glucose 1-phosphate} + \text{UTP} \rightleftharpoons \text{UDP-glucose} + \text{PP}_i$$
$$\text{PP}_i + \text{H}_2\text{O} \longrightarrow 2\,\text{P}_i$$

$$\overline{\text{Glucose 1-phosphate} + \text{UTP} + \text{H}_2\text{O} \longrightarrow \text{UDP-glucose} + 2\,\text{P}_i}$$

The synthesis of UDP-glucose exemplifies another recurring theme in biochemistry: *many biosynthetic reactions are driven by the hydrolysis of pyrophosphate.*

Glycogen synthase catalyzes the transfer of glucose from UDP-glucose to a growing chain

New glucosyl units are added to the nonreducing terminal residues of glycogen. The activated glucosyl unit of UDP-glucose is transferred to the hydroxyl group at C-4 of a terminal residue to form an α-1,4-glycosidic linkage. UDP is displaced by the terminal hydroxyl group of the growing glycogen molecule. This reaction is catalyzed by *glycogen synthase, the key regulatory enzyme in glycogen synthesis.*

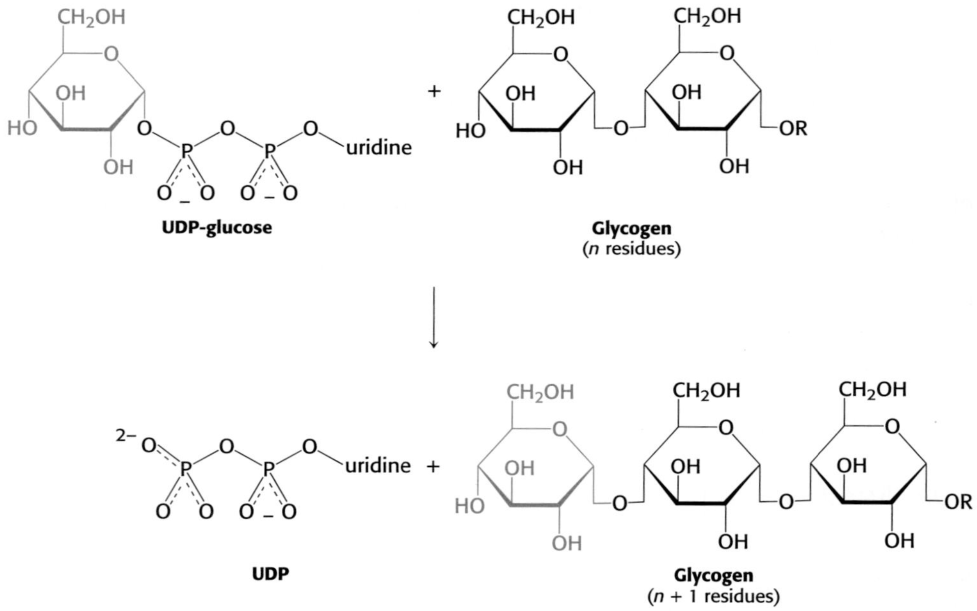

Glycogen synthase can add glucosyl residues only to a polysaccharide chain already containing more than four residues. Thus, glycogen synthesis requires a *primer*. This priming function is carried out by *glycogenin,* a glycosyltransferase (see Figure 11.25) composed of two identical 37-kd subunits. Each subunit of glycogenin catalyzes the addition of eight glucosyl units to the other subunit. These glucosyl units form short α-1,4-glucose polymers, which are covalently attached to the phenolic hydroxyl group of a specific tyrosine residue in each glycogenin subunit. UDP-glucose is the donor in this autoglycosylation. At this point, glycogen synthase takes over to extend the glycogen molecule. Thus, every glycogen molecule has a glycogenin molecule at its core (see Figure 21.1).

Despite no detectable sequence similarity, structural studies have revealed that glycogen synthase is homologous to glycogen phosphorylase. The binding site for UDP-glucose in glycogen synthase corresponds in position to the pyridoxal phosphate in glycogen phosphorylase.

A branching enzyme forms α-1,6 linkages

Glycogen synthase catalyzes only the synthesis of α-1,4 linkages. Another enzyme is required to form the α-1,6 linkages that make glycogen a branched polymer. Branching takes place after a number of glucosyl residues are joined in α-1,4 linkages by glycogen synthase (Figure 21.17). A branch is created by the breaking of an α-1,4 link and the formation of an α-1,6 link: this reaction is different from debranching. A block of residues, typically 7 in number, is transferred to a more interior site. The *branching enzyme* that catalyzes this reaction requires that the block of 7 or so residues must include the nonreducing terminus, and must come from a chain at least 11 residues long. In addition, the new branch point must be at least 4 residues away from a preexisting one.

Branching is important because it increases the solubility of glycogen. Furthermore, branching creates a large number of terminal residues, the sites of action of glycogen phosphorylase and synthase (Figure 21.18). Thus, *branching increases the rate of glycogen synthesis and degradation.*

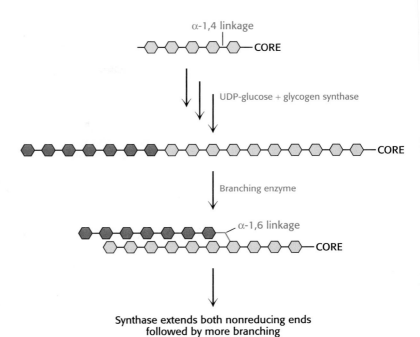

Figure 21.17 Branching reaction. The branching enzyme removes an oligosaccharide of approximately seven residues from the nonreducing end and creates an internal α-1,6 linkage.

Glycogen branching requires a single transferase activity. Glycogen debranching requires two enzyme activities: a transferase and an α-1,6 glucosidase. Sequence analysis suggests that the two transferases and, perhaps, the α-1,6 glucosidase are members of the same enzyme family, termed the *α-amylase family*. An enzyme of this family catalyzes a reaction by forming a covalent intermediate attached to a conserved aspartate residue. Thus, the branching enzyme appears to transfer a chain of glucose molecules from an α-1,4 linkage to an aspartate residue on the enzyme and then from this site to a more interior location on the glycogen molecule to form an α-1,6 linkage.

Glycogen synthase is the key regulatory enzyme in glycogen synthesis

The activity of glycogen synthase, like that of phosphorylase, is regulated by covalent modification. Glycogen synthase is phosphorylated at multiple sites by several protein kinases, notably protein kinase A and *glycogen synthase kinase* (GSK). The resulting alteration of the charges in the protein lead to its inactivation. *Phosphorylation has opposite effects on the enzymatic activities of glycogen synthase and phosphorylase.* Phosphorylation converts the active *a* form of the synthase into a usually inactive *b* form. The phosphorylated *b* form is active only if a high level of the allosteric activator glucose 6-phosphate is present, whereas the *a* form is active whether or not glucose 6-phosphate is present.

Glycogen is an efficient storage form of glucose

What is the cost of converting glucose 6-phosphate into glycogen and back into glucose 6-phosphate? The pertinent reactions have already been described, except for reaction 5, which is the regeneration of UTP. ATP phosphorylates UDP in a reaction catalyzed by *nucleoside diphosphokinase*.

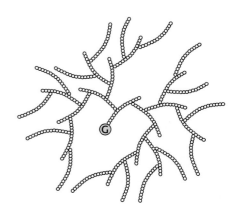

Figure 21.18 Cross section of a glycogen molecule. The component labeled G is glycogenin.

$$\text{Glucose 6-phosphate} \longrightarrow \text{glucose 1-phosphate} \tag{1}$$

$$\text{Glucose 1-phosphate} + \text{UTP} \longrightarrow \text{UDP-glucose} + \text{PP}_i \tag{2}$$

$$\text{PP}_i + \text{H}_2\text{O} \longrightarrow 2\,\text{P}_i \tag{3}$$

$$\text{UDP-glucose} + \text{glycogen}_n \longrightarrow \text{glycogen}_{n+1} + \text{UDP} \tag{4}$$

$$\text{UDP} + \text{ATP} \longrightarrow \text{UTP} + \text{ADP} \tag{5}$$

$$\text{Sum: Glucose 6-phosphate} + \text{ATP} + \text{glycogen}_n + \text{H}_2\text{O} \longrightarrow$$
$$\text{glycogen}_{n+1} + \text{ADP} + 2\,\text{P}_i$$

Thus, 1 molecule of ATP is hydrolyzed to incorporate glucose 6-phosphate into glycogen. The energy yield from the breakdown of glycogen is highly efficient. About 90% of the residues are phosphorolytically cleaved to glucose 1-phosphate, which is converted at no cost into glucose 6-phosphate. The other 10% are branch residues, which are hydrolytically cleaved. One molecule of ATP is then used to phosphorylate each of these glucose molecules to glucose 6-phosphate. The complete oxidation of glucose 6-phosphate yields about 31 molecules of ATP, and storage consumes slightly more than 1 molecule of ATP per molecule of glucose 6-phosphate; so *the overall efficiency of storage is nearly 97%.*

21.5 Glycogen Breakdown and Synthesis Are Reciprocally Regulated

An important control mechanism prevents glycogen from being synthesized at the same time as it is being broken down. *The same glucagon- and epinephrine-triggered cAMP cascades that initiate glycogen breakdown in the liver and muscle, respectively, also shut off glycogen synthesis. Glucagon and*

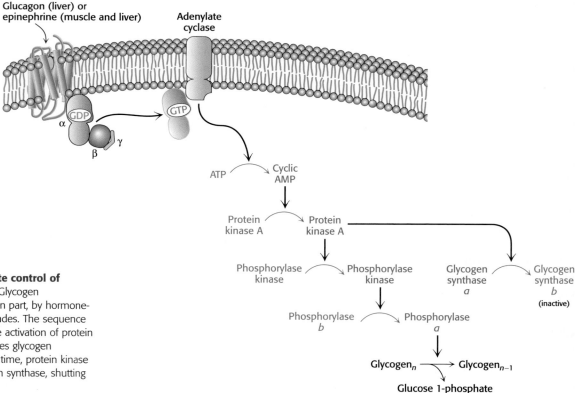

Figure 21.19 Coordinate control of glycogen metabolism. Glycogen metabolism is regulated, in part, by hormone-triggered cyclic AMP cascades. The sequence of reactions leading to the activation of protein kinase A ultimately activates glycogen degradation. At the same time, protein kinase A also inactivates glycogen synthase, shutting down glycogen synthesis.

epinephrine control both glycogen breakdown and glycogen synthesis through protein kinase A (Figure 21.19). Recall that protein kinase A adds a phosphoryl group to phosphorylase kinase, activating that enzyme and initiating glycogen breakdown. Likewise, protein kinase A adds a phosphoryl group to glycogen synthase, but this phosphorylation leads to a *decrease* in enzymatic activity. Other kinases, such as glycogen synthase kinase, help to inactivate the synthase. In this way, glycogen breakdown and synthesis are reciprocally regulated. How is the enzymatic activity reversed so that glycogen breakdown halts and glycogen synthesis begins?

Protein phosphatase 1 reverses the regulatory effects of kinases on glycogen metabolism

After a bout of exercise, muscle must shift from a glycogen-degrading mode to one of glycogen replenishment. A first step in this metabolic task is to shut down the phosphorylated proteins that stimulate glycogen breakdown. This task is accomplished by *protein phosphatases* that catalyze the hydrolysis of phosphorylated serine and threonine residues in proteins. *Protein phosphatase 1 plays key roles in regulating glycogen metabolism* (Figure 21.20). PP1 inactivates phosphorylase *a* and phosphorylase kinase by dephosphorylating them. PP1 decreases the rate of glycogen breakdown; it reverses the effects of the phosphorylation cascade. Moreover, *PP1 also removes phosphoryl groups from glycogen synthase* b *to convert it into the much more active glycogen synthase* a *form*. Here, PP1 also accelerates glycogen synthesis. PP1 is yet another molecular device for coordinating carbohydrate storage.

The catalytic subunit of PP1 is a 37-kd single-domain protein. This subunit is usually bound to one of a family of regulatory subunits with masses of approximately 120 kd; in skeletal muscle and heart, the most prevalent regulatory subunit is called G_M, whereas, in the liver, the most

AFTER A MEAL OR REST

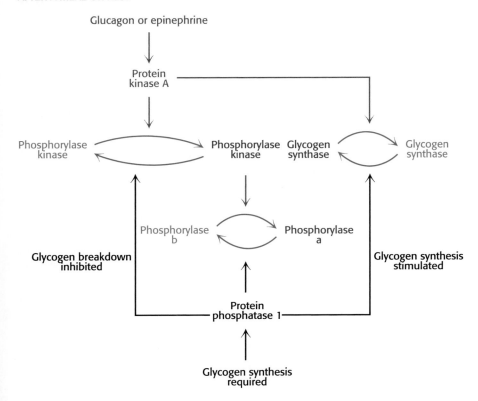

Figure 21.20 Regulation of glycogen synthesis by protein phosphatase 1. Protein phosphatase 1 stimulates glycogen synthesis while inhibiting glycogen breakdown.

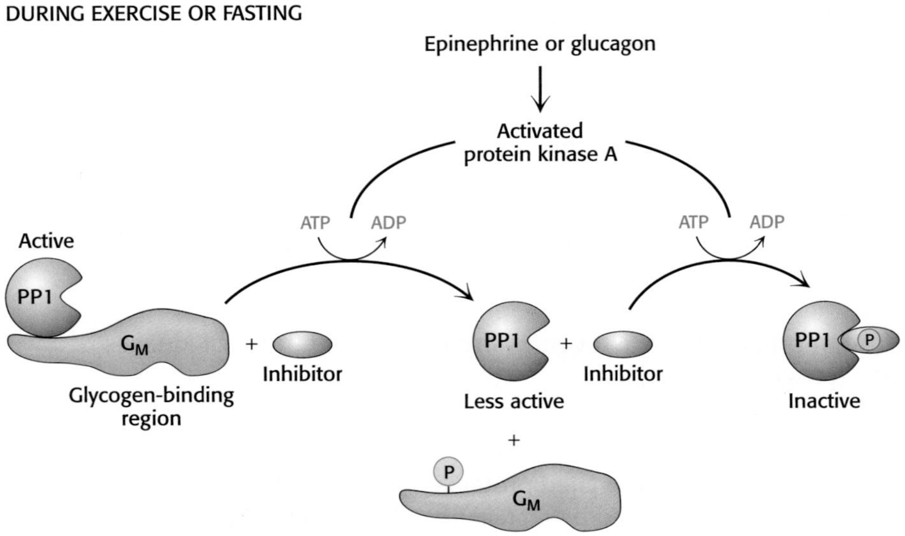

Figure 21.21 Regulation of protein phosphatase 1 (PP1) in muscle takes place in two steps. Phosphorylation of G_M by protein kinase A dissociates the catalytic subunit from its substrates in the glycogen particle. Phosphorylation of the inhibitor subunit by protein kinase A inactivates the catalytic unit of PP1.

prevalent subunit is G_L. These regulatory subunits have modular structures with domains that participate in interactions with glycogen, with the catalytic subunit, and with target enzymes. Thus, *these regulatory subunits act as scaffolds, bringing together the phosphatase and its substrates in the context of a glycogen particle.*

The phosphatase activity of PP1 must be reduced when glycogen degradation is called for (Figure 21.21). In such cases, epinephrine or glucagon has activated the cAMP cascade and protein kinase A is active. Protein kinase A reduces the activity of PP1 by two mechanisms. First, in muscle, G_M is phosphorylated in the domain responsible for binding the catalytic subunit. The catalytic subunit is released from glycogen and from its substrates and dephosphoryation is greatly reduced. Second, almost all tissues contain small proteins that, when phosphorylated, bind to the catalytic subunit of PP1 and inhibit it. Thus, when glycogen degradation is switched on by cAMP, the accompanying phosphorylation of these inhibitors keeps phosphorylase in its active *a* form and glycogen synthase in its inactive *b* form.

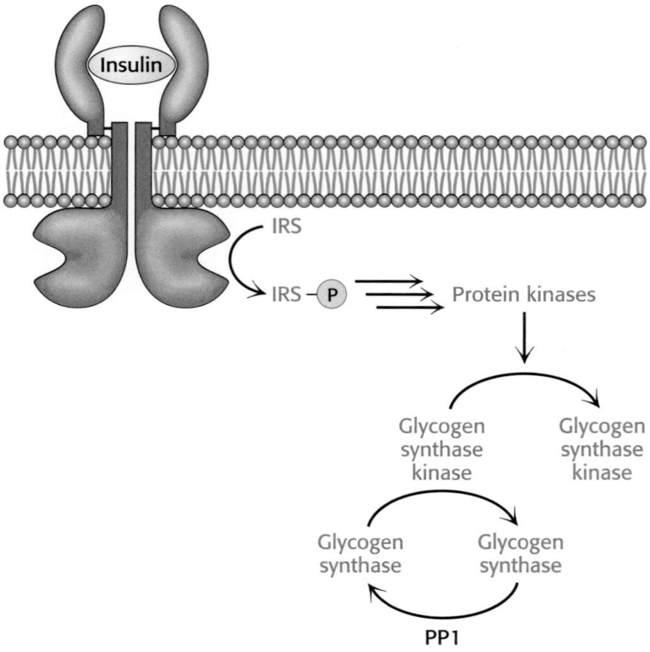

Insulin stimulates glycogen synthesis by inactivating glycogen synthase kinase

After exercise, people often consume carbohydrate-rich foods to restock their glycogen stores. How is glycogen synthesis stimulated? When blood-glucose levels are high, *insulin stimulates the synthesis of glycogen by inactivating glycogen synthase kinase*, the enzyme that maintains glycogen synthase in its phosphorylated, inactive state (Figure 21.22). The first step in the action of insulin is its binding to a receptor tyrosine kinase in the plasma membrane (Section 14.2). The binding of insulin activates the tyrosine kinase activity of the receptor so that it phosphorylates insulin-receptor substrates (IRSs). These phosphorylated proteins trigger signal-transduction pathways that eventually lead to the activation of protein kinases that phosphorylate and inactivate glycogen synthase kinase. The inactive kinase can no longer maintain

Figure 21.22 Insulin inactivates glycogen synthase kinase. Insulin triggers a cascade that leads to the phosphorylation and inactivation of glycogen synthase kinase and prevents the phosphorylation of glycogen synthase. Protein phosphatase 1 (PP1) removes the phosphates from glycogen synthase, thereby activating the enzyme and allowing glycogen synthesis. IRS, insulin-receptor substrate.

glycogen synthase in its phosphorylated, inactive state. Protein phosphatase 1 dephosphorylates glycogen synthase, activating it, and restoring glycogen reserves. Recall that insulin also generates an increase in the amount of glucose in the cell by increasing the number of glucose transports in the membrane. The net effect of insulin is thus the replenishment of glycogen stores.

Glycogen metabolism in the liver regulates the blood-glucose level

After a meal rich in carbohydrates, blood-glucose levels rise, and glycogen synthesis is stepped up in the liver. Although insulin is the primary signal for glycogen synthesis, another is the concentration of glucose in the blood, which normally ranges from about 80 to 120 mg per 100 ml (4.4–6.7 mM). The liver senses the concentration of glucose in the blood and takes up or releases glucose accordingly. The amount of liver phosphorylase *a* decreases rapidly when glucose is infused (Figure 21.23). After a lag period, the amount of glycogen synthase *a* increases, which results in glycogen synthesis. In fact, *phosphorylase a is the glucose sensor in liver cells.* Phosphorylase *a* and PP1 are localized to the glycogen particle by interactions with the G_L subunit of PP1. The binding of glucose to phosphorylase *a* shifts its allosteric equilibrium from the active R form to the inactive T form. This conformational change *renders the phosphoryl group on serine 14 a substrate for protein phosphatase 1.* PP1 binds tightly to phosphorylase *a* only when the phosphorylase is in the R state but is inactive when bound. When glucose induces the transition to the T form, PP1 and the phosphorylase dissociate from each other and the glycogen particle, and PP1 becomes active. Recall that the R $\leftrightarrow$ T transition of muscle phosphorylase *a* is unaffected by glucose and is thus unaffected by the rise in blood-glucose levels (Section 21.2). Efforts are underway to develop drugs that disrupt the interaction of liver phosphorylase with the G_L subunit as a treatment for type 2 diabetes (Section 27.2). Type 2 diabetes is characterized by excess blood glucose. Hence, disrupting the association of phosphorylase with the G_L would render it a substrate for PP1, and glucose release into the blood would be inhibited.

How does glucose activate glycogen synthase? The conversion of *a* into *b* is accompanied by the *release of PP1, which is then free to activate glycogen synthase* and *dephosphorylate glycogen phosphorylase* (Figure 21.24). The

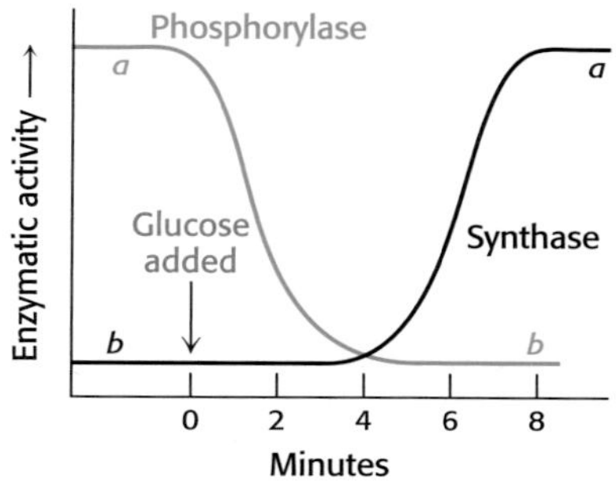

Figure 21.23 Blood glucose regulates liver-glycogen metabolism. The infusion of glucose into the bloodstream leads to the inactivation of phosphorylase, followed by the activation of glycogen synthase, in the liver. [After W. Stalmans, H. De Wulf, L. Hue, and H.-G. Hers. *Eur. J. Biochem.* 41:117–134, 1974.]

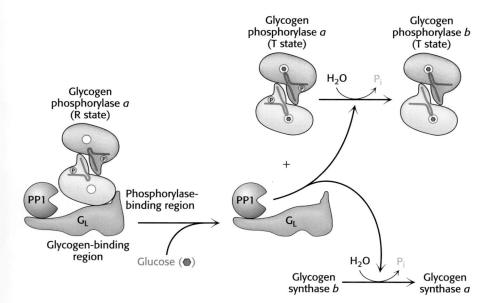

Figure 21.24 Glucose regulation of liver-glycogen metabolism. Glucose binds to and inhibits glycogen phosphorylase *a* in the liver, facilitating the formation of the T state of phosphorylase *a*. The T state of phosphorylase *a* does not bind protein phosphate 1 (PP1), leading to the dissociation and activation of PP1 from glycogen phosphorylase *a*. The free PP1 dephosphorylates glycogen phosphorylase *a* and glycogen synthase *b*, leading to the inactivation of glycogen breakdown and the activation of glycogen synthesis.

removal of the phosphoryl group of inactive glycogen synthase *b* converts it into the active *a* form. Initially, there are about 10 phosphorylase *a* molecules per molecule of phosphatase. Hence, *the activity of glycogen synthase begins to increase only after most of phosphorylase a is converted into b.* The lag between the decrease in glycogen degradation and the increase in glycogen synthesis prevents the two pathways from operating simultaneously. This remarkable glucose-sensing system depends on three key elements: (1) communication between the allosteric site for glucose and the serine phosphate, (2) the use of PP1 to inactivate phosphorylase and activate glycogen synthase, and (3) the binding of the phosphatase to phosphorylase *a* to prevent the premature activation of glycogen synthase.

A biochemical understanding of glycogen-storage diseases is possible

Edgar von Gierke described the first glycogen-storage disease in 1929. A patient with this disease has a huge abdomen caused by a massive enlargement of the liver. There is a pronounced hypoglycemia between meals. Furthermore, the blood-glucose level does not rise on administration of epinephrine and glucagon. An infant with this glycogen-storage disease may have convulsions because of the low blood-glucose level.

The enzymatic defect in von Gierke disease was elucidated in 1952 by Carl and Gerty Cori. They found that *glucose 6-phosphatase is missing from the liver of a patient with this disease.* This finding was the first demonstration of an inherited deficiency of a liver enzyme. The glycogen in the liver is normal in structure but is present in abnormally large amounts. The absence of glucose 6-phosphatase in the liver causes hypoglycemia because glucose cannot be formed from glucose 6-phosphate. This phosphorylated sugar does not leave the liver, because it cannot cross the plasma membrane. The presence of excess glucose 6-phosphate triggers an increase in glycolysis in the liver, leading to a high level of lactate and pyruvate in the blood. Patients who have von Gierke disease also have an increased dependence on fat metabolism. This disease can also be produced by a mutation in the gene

Table 21.1 Glycogen-storage diseases

Type	Defective enzyme	Organ affected	Glycogen in the affected organ	Clinical features
I Von Gierke	Glucose 6-phosphatase or transport system	Liver and kidney	Increased amount; normal structure.	Massive enlargement of the liver. Failure to thrive. Severe hypoglycemia, ketosis, hyperuricemia, hyperlipemia.
II Pompe	α-1,4-Glucosidase (lysosomal)	All organs	Massive increase in amount; normal structure.	Cardiorespiratory failure causes death, usually before age 2.
III Cori	Amylo-1,6-glucosidase (debranching enzyme)	Muscle and liver	Increased amount; short outer branches.	Like type I, but milder course.
IV Andersen	Branching enzyme (α-1,4 ⟶ α-1,6)	Liver and spleen	Normal amount; very long outer branches.	Progressive cirrhosis of the liver. Liver failure causes death, usually before age 2.
V McArdle	Phosphorylase	Muscle	Moderately increased amount; normal structure.	Limited ability to perform strenuous exercise because of painful muscle cramps. Otherwise patient is normal and well developed.
VI Hers	Phosphorylase	Liver	Increased amount.	Like type I, but milder course.
VII	Phosphofructokinase	Muscle	Increased amount; normal structure.	Like type V.
VIII	Phosphorylase kinase	Liver	Increased amount; normal structure.	Mild liver enlargement. Mild hypoglycemia.

Note: Types I through VII are inherited as autosomal recessives. Type VIII is sex linked.

that encodes the *glucose 6-phosphate transporter*. Recall that glucose 6-phosphate must be transported into the lumen of the endoplasmic reticulum to be hydrolyzed by phosphatase. Mutations in the other three essential proteins of this system can likewise lead to von Gierke disease.

Seven other glycogen-storage diseases have been characterized (Table 21.1). In Pompe disease (type II), lysosomes become engorged with glycogen because they lack α-1,4-glucosidase, a hydrolytic enzyme confined to these organelles (Figure 21.25). Carl and Gerty Cori also elucidated the biochemical defect in another glycogen-storage disease (type III), which cannot be distinguished from von Gierke disease (type I) by physical examination alone. In type III disease, the structure of liver and muscle glycogen is abnormal and the amount is markedly increased. Most striking, the outer branches of the glycogen are very short. *Patients having this type lack the debranching enzyme (α-1,6-glucosidase)*, and so only the outermost branches of glycogen can be effectively utilized. Thus, only a small fraction of this abnormal glycogen is functionally active as an accessible store of glucose.

A defect in glycogen metabolism confined to muscle is found in McArdle disease (type V). *Muscle phosphorylase activity is absent*, and a patient's capacity to perform strenuous exercise is limited because of painful muscle cramps. The patient is otherwise normal and well developed. Thus, effective utilization of muscle glycogen is not essential for life. Phosphorus-31 nuclear magnetic resonance studies of these patients have been very informative. The pH of skeletal-muscle cells of normal people drops during strenuous exercise because of the production of lactate. In contrast, the muscle cells of patients with McArdle disease become more alkaline during exercise because of the breakdown of creatine phosphate (Section 15.2). Lactate does not accumulate in these patients, because the glycolytic rate of their muscle is much lower than normal; their glycogen cannot be mobilized. NMR studies have also shown that the painful cramps in this disease are correlated with high levels of ADP (Figure 21.26). NMR spectroscopy is a valuable, noninvasive technique for assessing dietary and exercise therapy for this disease.

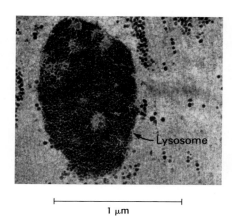

Figure 21.25 Glycogen-engorged lysosome. This electron micrograph shows skeletal muscle from an infant with type II glycogen-storage disease (Pompe disease). The lysosomes are filled with glycogen because of a deficiency in α-1,4-glucosidase, a hydrolytic enzyme confined to lysosomes. The amount of glycogen in the cytoplasm is normal. [From H.-G. Hers and F. Van Hoof, Eds., *Lysosomes and Storage Diseases* (Academic Press, 1973), p. 205.]

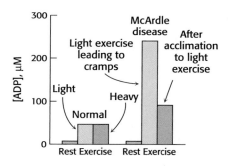

Figure 21.26 NMR study of human arm muscle. The level of ADP during exercise increases much more in a patient with McArdle glycogen-storage disease (type V) than in normal controls. [After G. K. Radda. *Biochem. Soc. Trans.* 14:517–525, 1986.]

Summary

Glycogen, a readily mobilized fuel store, is a branched polymer of glucose residues. Most of the glucose units in glycogen are linked by α-1,4-glycosidic bonds. At about every tenth residue, a branch is created by an α-1,6-glycosidic bond. Glycogen is present in large amounts in muscle cells and in liver cells, where it is stored in the cytoplasm in the form of hydrated granules.

21.1 Glycogen Breakdown Requires the Interplay of Several Enzymes

Most of the glycogen molecule is degraded to glucose 1-phosphate by the action of glycogen phosphorylase, the key enzyme in glycogen breakdown. The glycosidic linkage between C-1 of a terminal residue and C-4 of the adjacent one is split by orthophosphate to give glucose 1-phosphate, which can be reversibly converted into glucose 6-phosphate. Branch points are degraded by the concerted action of an oligosaccharide transferase and an α-1,6-glucosidase.

21.2 Phosphorylase Is Regulated by Allosteric Interactions and Reversible Phosphorylation

Phosphorylase *b*, which is usually inactive, is converted into active phosphorylase *a* by the phosphorylation of a single serine residue in each subunit. This reaction is catalyzed by phosphorylase kinase. The *b* form in muscle can also be activated by the binding of AMP, an effect counteracted by ATP and glucose 6-phosphate. The *a* form in the liver is inhibited by glucose. The AMP-binding sites and phosphorylation sites are located at the subunit interface. In muscle, phosphorylase is activated to generate glucose for use inside the cell as a fuel for contractile activity. In contrast, liver phosphorylase is activated to liberate glucose for export to other organs, such as skeletal muscle and the brain.

21.3 Epinephrine and Glucagon Signal the Need for Glycogen Breakdown
Epinephrine and glucagon stimulate glycogen breakdown through specific 7TM receptors. Muscle is the primary target of epinephrine, whereas the liver is responsive to glucagon. Both signal molecules initiate a kinase cascade that leads to the activation of glycogen phosphorylase.

21.4 Glycogen Is Synthesized and Degraded by Different Pathways
The pathway for glycogen synthesis differs from that for glycogen breakdown. UDP-glucose, the activated intermediate in glycogen synthesis, is formed from glucose 1-phosphate and UTP. Glycogen synthase catalyzes the transfer of glucose from UDP-glucose to the C-4 hydroxyl group of a terminal residue in the growing glycogen molecule. Synthesis is primed by glycogenin, an autoglycosylating protein that contains a covalently attached oligosaccharide unit on a specific tyrosine residue. A branching enzyme converts some of the α-1,4 linkages into α-1,6 linkages to increase the number of ends so that glycogen can be made and degraded more rapidly.

21.5 Glycogen Breakdown and Synthesis Are Reciprocally Regulated
Glycogen synthesis and degradation are coordinated by several amplifying reaction cascades. Epinephrine and glucagon stimulate glycogen breakdown and inhibit its synthesis by increasing the cytoplasmic level of cyclic AMP, which activates protein kinase A. Protein kinase A activates glycogen breakdown by attaching a phosphate to phosphorylase kinase and inhibits glycogen synthesis by phosphorylating glycogen synthase.

The glycogen-mobilizing actions of protein kinase A are reversed by protein phosphatase 1, which is regulated by several hormones. Epinephrine inhibits this phosphatase by blocking its attachment to glycogen molecules and by turning on an inhibitor. Insulin, in contrast, triggers a cascade that phosphorylates and inactivates glycogen synthase kinase, one of the enzymes that inhibits glycogen synthase. Hence, glycogen synthesis is decreased by epinephrine and increased by insulin. Glycogen synthase and phosphorylase are also regulated by noncovalent allosteric interactions. In fact, phosphorylase is a key part of the glucose-sensing system of liver cells. Glycogen metabolism exemplifies the power and precision of reversible phosphorylation in regulating biological processes.

Key Terms

glycogen phosphorylase (p. 617)

phosphorolysis (p. 617)

pyridoxal phosphate (PLP) (p. 619)

phosphorylase kinase (p. 623)

calmodulin (p. 624)

epinephrine (adrenaline) (p. 624)

glucagon (p. 624)

protein kinase A (PKA) (p. 626)

uridine diphosphate glucose (UDP-glucose) (p. 627)

glycogen synthase (p. 628)

glycogenin (p. 628)

protein phosphatase 1 (PP1) (p. 631)

insulin (p. 632)

Problems

1. *Choice is good.* Glycogen is not as reduced as fatty acids are and consequently not as energy rich. Why do animals store any energy as glycogen? Why not convert all excess fuel into fatty acids?

2. *If a little is good, a lot is better.* α-Amylose is an unbranched glucose polymer. Why would this polymer not be as effective a storage form of glucose as glycogen?

3. *Telltale products.* A sample of glycogen from a patient with liver disease is incubated with orthophosphate, phosphorylase, the transferase, and the debranching enzyme (α-1,6-glucosidase). The ratio of glucose 1-phosphate to glucose formed in this mixture is 100. What is the most likely enzymatic deficiency in this patient?

4. *Dare to be different.* Compare the allosteric regulation of phosphorylase in the liver and in muscle, and explain the significance of the difference.

5. *A thumb on the balance.* The reaction catalyzed by phosphorylase is readily reversible in vitro. At pH 6.8, the equilibrium ratio of orthophosphate to glucose 1-phosphate is 3.6. The value of $\Delta G^{\circ\prime}$ for this reaction is small because a glycosidic bond is replaced by a phosphoryl ester bond that has a nearly equal transfer potential. However, phosphorolysis proceeds far in the direction of glycogen breakdown in vivo. Suggest one means by which the reaction can be made irreversible in vivo.

6. *Excessive storage.* Suggest an explanation for the fact that the amount of glycogen in type I glycogen-storage disease (von Gierke disease) is increased.

7. *Recouping an essential phosphoryl.* The phosphoryl group on phosphoglucomutase is slowly lost by hydrolysis. Propose a mechanism that utilizes a known catalytic intermediate for restoring this essential phosphoryl group. How might this phosphoryl donor be formed?

8. *Not all absences are equal.* Hers disease results from an absence of liver glycogen phosphorylase and may result in serious illness. In McArdle disease, muscle glycogen phosphorylase is absent. Although exercise is difficult for patients suffering from McArdle disease, the disease is rarely life threatening. Account for the different manifestations of the absence of glycogen phosphorylase in the two tissues. What does the existence of these two different diseases indicate about the genetic nature of the phosphorylase?

9. *Hydrophobia.* Why is water excluded from the active site of phosphorylase? Predict the effect of a mutation that allows water molecules to enter.

10. *Removing all traces.* In human liver extracts, the catalytic activity of glycogenin was detectable only after treatment with α-amylase (p. 629). Why was α-amylase necessary to reveal the glycogenin activity?

11. *Two in one.* A single polypeptide chain houses the transferase and debranching enzyme. Cite a potential advantage of this arrangement.

12. *How did they do that?* A strain of mice has been developed that lack the enzyme phosphorylase kinase. Yet, after strenuous exercise, the glycogen stores of a mouse of this strain are depleted. Explain how this depletion is possible.

13. *An appropriate inhibitor.* What is the rationale for the inhibition of muscle glycogen phosphorylase by glucose 6-phosphate when glucose 1-phosphate is the product of the phosphorylase reaction?

14. *Passing along the information.* Outline the signal-transduction cascade for glycogen degradation in muscle.

15. *Slammin' on the breaks.* There must be a way to shut down glycogen breakdown quickly to prevent the wasteful depletion of glycogen after energy needs have been met. What mechanisms are employed to turn off glycogen breakdown?

16. *Diametrically opposed.* Phosphorylation has opposite effects on glycogen synthesis and breakdown. What is the advantage of its having opposing effects?

17. *Feeling depleted.* Glycogen depletion resulting from intense, extensive exercise can lead to exhaustion and the inability to continue exercising. Some people also experience dizziness, an inability to concentrate, and a loss of muscle control. Account for these symptoms.

18. *Everyone had a job to do.* What accounts for the fact that liver phosphorylase is a glucose sensor, whereas muscle phosphorylase is not?

19. *If you insist.* Why does activation of the phosphorylated *b* form of glycogen synthase by high concentrations of glucose 6-phosphate make good biochemical sense?

20. *An ATP saved is an ATP earned.* The complete oxidation of glucose 6-phosphate derived from free glucose yields 30 molecules ATP, whereas the complete oxidation of glucose 6-phosphate derived from glycogen yields 31 molecules of ATP. Account for this difference.

21. *Dual roles.* Phosphoglucomutase is crucial for glycogen breakdown as well as for glycogen synthesis. Explain the role of this enzyme in each of the two processes.

22. *Working at cross-purposes.* Write a balanced equation showing the effect of simultaneous activation of glycogen phosphorylase and glycogen synthase. Include the reactions catalyzed by phosphoglucomutase and UDP-glucose pyrophosphorylase.

23. *Achieving immortality.* Glycogen synthase requires a primer. A primer was formerly thought to be provided when the existing glycogen granules are divided between the daughter cells produced by cell division. In other words, parts of the original glycogen molecule were simply passed from generation to generation. Would this strategy have been successful in passing glycogen stores from generation to generation? How are new glycogen molecules now known to be synthesized?

24. *Synthesis signal.* How does insulin stimulate glycogen synthesis?

Mechanism Problem

25. *Family resemblance.* Propose mechanisms for the two enzymes catalyzing steps in glycogen debranching on the basis of their potential membership in the α-amylase family.

Chapter Integration Problems

26. *Carbohydrate conversion.* Write a balanced equation for the formation of glycogen from galactose.

27. *Working together.* What enzymes are required for the liver to release glucose into the blood when an organism is asleep and fasting?

28. *A shattering experience.* Crystals of phosphorylase *a* grown in the presence of glucose shatter when a substrate such as glucose 1-phosphate is added. Why?

29. *I know I've seen that face before.* UDP-glucose is the activated form of glucose used in glycogen synthesis. However, we have previously met other similar activated forms of carbohydrate in our consideration of metabolism. Where else have we seen UDP-carbohydrate?

30. *Same symptoms, different cause.* Suggest another mutation in glucose metabolism that causes symptoms similar to those of von Gierke disease.

Data Interpretation Problems

31. *Glycogen isolation 1.* The liver is a major storage site for glycogen. Purified from two samples of human liver, glycogen was either treated or not treated with α-amylase and subsequently analyzed by SDS-PAGE and western blotting with the use of antibodies to glycogenin. The results are presented in the adjoining illustration.

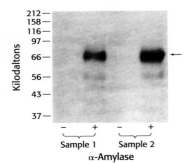

Glycogen isolation 1. [Courtesy of Dr. Peter J. Roach, Indiana University School of Medicine.]

(a) Why are no proteins visible in the lanes without amylase treatment?

(b) What is the effect of treating the samples with α-amylase? Explain the results.

(c) List other proteins that you might expect to be associated with glycogen. Why are other proteins not visible?

32. *Glycogen isolation 2.* The gene for glycogenin was transfected into a cell line that normally stores only small amounts of glycogen. The cells were then manipulated according to the following protocol, and glycogen was isolated and analyzed by SDS-PAGE and western blotting by using an antibody to glycogenin with and without α-amylase treatment. The results are presented in the adjoining illustration.

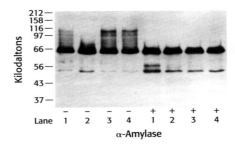

Glycogen isolation 2. [Courtesy of Dr. Peter J. Roach, Indiana University School of Medicine.]

The protocol: Cells cultured in growth medium and 25 mM glucose (lane 1) were switched to medium containing no glucose for 24 hours (lane 2). Glucose-starved cells were refed with medium containing 25 mM glucose for 1 hour (lane 3) or 3 hours (lane 4). Samples (12 μg of protein) were either treated or not treated with α-amylase, as indicated, before being loaded on the gel.

(a) Why did the western analysis produce a "smear"—that is, the high-molecular-weight staining in lane 1(−)?

(b) What is the significance of the decrease in high-molecular-weight staining in lane 2(−)?

(c) What is the significance of the difference between lanes 2(−) and 3(−)?

(d) Suggest a plausible reason why there is essentially no difference between lanes 3(−) and 4(−)?

(e) Why are the bands at 66 kd the same in the lanes treated with amylase, despite the fact that the cells were treated differently?

CHAPTER 22

Fatty Acid Metabolism

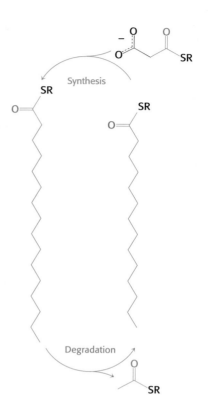

Fats provide efficient means for storing energy for later use. (Right) The processes of fatty acid synthesis (preparation for energy storage) and fatty acid degradation (preparation for energy use) are, in many ways, the reverse of each other. (Above) Studies of mice are revealing the interplay between these pathways and the biochemical bases of appetite and weight control. [Photograph © Jackson/Visuals Unlimited.]

We turn now from the metabolism of carbohydrates to that of fatty acids. A fatty acid contains a long hydrocarbon chain and a terminal carboxylate group. Fatty acids have four major physiological roles. First, *fatty acids are fuel molecules.* They are stored as *triacylglycerols* (also called *neutral fats* or *triglycerides*), which are uncharged esters of fatty acids with glycerol. Triacylglycerols are stored in adipose tissue, composed of cells called adipocytes (Figure 22.1). Fatty acids mobilized from triacylglycerols are oxidized to meet the energy needs of a cell or organism. During rest or moderate exercise, such as walking, fatty acids are our primary source of energy. Second, *fatty acids are building blocks of phospholipids and glycolipids.* These amphipathic molecules are important components of biological membranes, as discussed in Chapter 12. Third, many proteins are modified by the *covalent attachment of fatty acids, which targets the proteins to membrane locations.* Fourth, *fatty acid derivatives serve as hormones and intracellular messengers.* In this chapter, we focus on the degradation and synthesis of fatty acids.

A triacylglycerol

OUTLINE

Fatty acid degradation and synthesis mirror each other in their chemical reactions

Fatty acid degradation and synthesis consist of four steps that are the reverse of each other in their basic chemistry. Degradation is an oxidative process that converts a fatty acid into a set of activated acetyl units (acetyl CoA) that can be processed by the citric acid cycle (Figure 22.2). An activated fatty acid is oxidized to introduce a double bond; the double bond is hydrated to introduce a hydroxyl group; the alcohol is oxidized to a ketone; and, finally, the fatty acid is cleaved by coenzyme A to yield acetyl CoA and a fatty acid chain two carbons shorter. If the fatty acid has an even number of carbon atoms and is saturated, the process is simply repeated until the fatty acid is completely converted into acetyl CoA units.

Fatty acid synthesis is essentially the reverse of this process. The process starts with the individual units to be assembled—in this case with an activated acyl group (most simply, an acetyl unit) and a malonyl unit (see Figure 22.2). The malonyl unit condenses with the acetyl unit to form a four-carbon fragment. To produce the required hydrocarbon chain, the carbonyl group is reduced to a methylene group in three steps: a reduction,

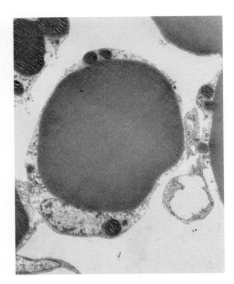

Figure 22.1 Electron micrograph of an adipocyte. A small band of cytoplasm surrounds the large deposit of triacylglycerols. [Biophoto Associates/Photo Researchers.]

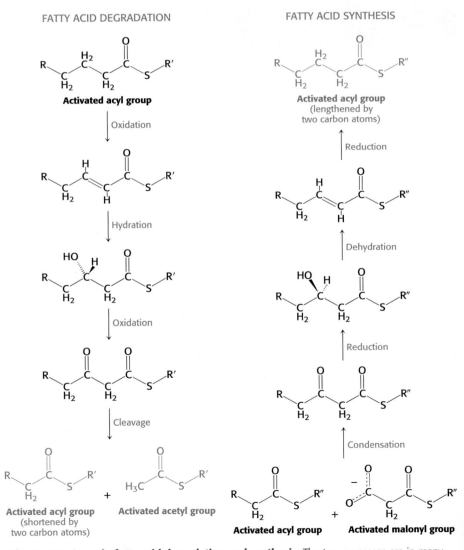

Figure 22.2 Steps in fatty acid degradation and synthesis. The two processes are in many ways mirror images of each other.

a dehydration, and another reduction, exactly the opposite of degradation. The product of the reduction is butyryl CoA. Another activated malonyl group condenses with the butyryl unit, and the process is repeated until a C_{16} or shorter fatty acid is synthesized.

22.1 Triacylglycerols Are Highly Concentrated Energy Stores

Triacylglycerols are highly concentrated stores of metabolic energy because they are *reduced* and *anhydrous*. The yield from the complete oxidation of fatty acids is about 38 kJ g^{-1} (9 kcal g^{-1}), in contrast with about 17 kJ g^{-1} (4 kcal g^{-1}) for carbohydrates and proteins. The basis of this large difference in caloric yield is that fatty acids are much more reduced than carbohydrates or proteins. Furthermore, triacylglycerols are nonpolar, and so they are stored in a nearly anhydrous form, whereas much more polar carbohydrates are more highly hydrated. In fact, 1 g of dry glycogen binds about 2 g of water. Consequently, *a gram of nearly anhydrous fat stores 6.75 times as much energy as a gram of hydrated glycogen,* which is likely the reason that triacylglycerols rather than glycogen were selected in evolution as the major energy reservoir. Consider a typical 70-kg man, who has fuel reserves of 420,000 kJ (100,000 kcal) in triacylglycerols, 100,000 kJ (24,000 kcal) in protein (mostly in muscle), 2500 kJ (600 kcal) in glycogen, and 170 kJ (40 kcal) in glucose. Triacylglycerols constitute about 11 kg of his total body weight. If this amount of energy were stored in glycogen, his total body weight would be 64 kg greater. The glycogen and glucose stores provide enough energy to sustain physiological function for about 24 hours, whereas the triacylglycerol stores allow survival for several weeks.

In mammals, the major site of triacylglycerol accumulation is the cytoplasm of *adipose cells (fat cells)*. This fuel-rich tissue is located throughout the body, notably under the skin (subcutaneous fat) and surrounding the internal organs (visceral fat). Droplets of triacylglycerol coalesce to form a large globule, called a lipid droplet, which may occupy most of the cell volume (see Figure 22.1). The lipid droplet is surrounded by a monolayer of phospholipids and proteins required for triacylglycerol metabolism. Adipose cells are specialized for the synthesis and storage of triacylglycerols and for their mobilization into fuel molecules that are transported to other tissues by the blood. Muscle also stores triacylglycerols for its own energy needs. Indeed, triacylglycerols are evident as the "marbling" of expensive cuts of beef.

The utility of triacylglycerols as an energy source is dramatically illustrated by the abilities of migratory birds, which can fly great distances without eating after having stored energy as triacylglycerols. Examples are the American golden plover and the ruby-throated hummingbird. The golden plover flies from Alaska to the southern tip of South America; a large segment of the flight (3800 km, or 2400 miles) is over open ocean, where the birds cannot feed. The ruby-throated hummingbird can fly nonstop across the Gulf of Mexico. Fatty acids provide the energy source for both these prodigious feats.

Triacylglycerols fuel the long migration flights of the American golden plover (*Pluvialis dominica*). [Gerard Fuehrer/Visuals Unlimited.]

Dietary lipids are digested by pancreatic lipases

Most lipids are ingested in the form of triacylglycerols and must be degraded to fatty acids for absorption across the intestinal epithelium. Intestinal enzymes called *lipases*, secreted by the pancreas, degrade triacylglycerols to free fatty acids and monoacylglycerol (Figure 22.3). Lipids present a special problem because, unlike carbohydrates and proteins, these molecules are

Triacylglycerol **Diacylglycerol** **Monoacylglycerol**

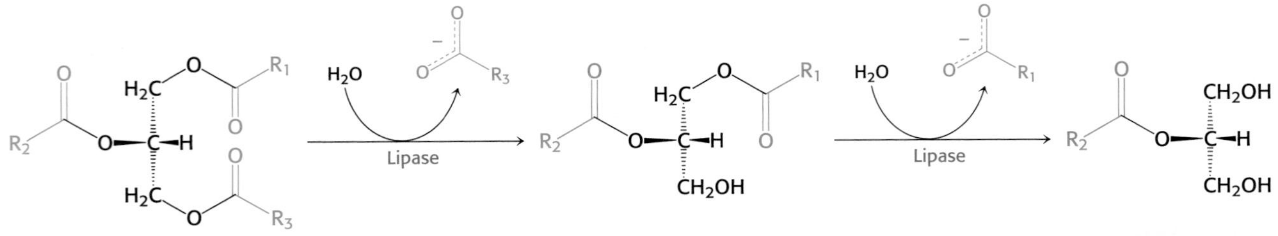

Figure 22.3 Action of pancreatic lipases. Lipases secreted by the pancreas convert triacylglycerols into fatty acids and monoacylglycerol for absorption into the intestine.

Glycocholate

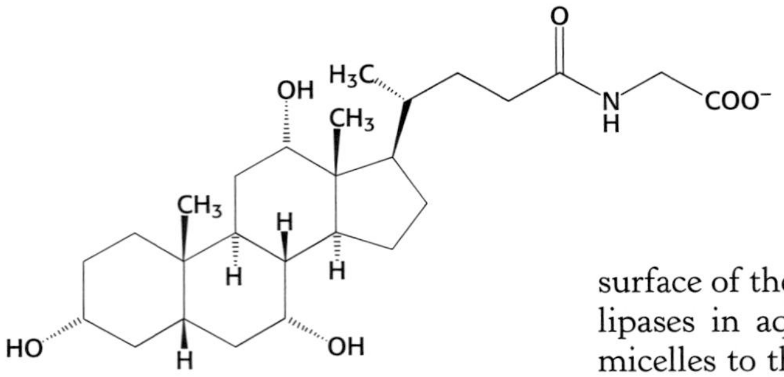

Figure 22.4 Glycocholate. Bile salts, such as glycocholate, facilitate lipid digestion in the intestine.

not soluble in water. How are they made accessible to the lipases, which are in aqueous solution? The solution is to wrap lipids in a soluble container. Triacylglycerols in the intestinal lumen are incorporated into micelles composed of *bile salts* (Figure 22.4), amphipathic molecules synthesized from cholesterol in the liver and secreted from the gall bladder. The ester bond of each lipid is oriented toward the surface of the micelle, rendering the bond more susceptible to digestion by lipases in aqueous solution. The final digestion products are carried in micelles to the intestinal epithelium where they are transported across the plasma membrane (Figure 22.5). If the production of bile salts is inadequate due to liver disease, large amounts of fats (as much as 30 g day^{-1}) are excreted in the feces. This condition is referred to as *steatorrhea,* after stearic acid, a common fatty acid.

Dietary lipids are transported in chylomicrons

In the intestinal mucosal cells, the triacylglycerols are resynthesized from fatty acids and monoacylglycerols and then packaged into lipoprotein transport particles called *chylomicrons,* stable particles approximately 2000 Å (200 nm) in diameter (see Figure 22.5). These particles are composed mainly of triacylglycerols, with apoliprotein B-48 (apo B-48) as the main protein component. Protein constituents of lipoprotein particles are called *apolipoproteins.* Chylomicrons also transport fat-soluble vitamins and cholesterol.

The chylomicrons are released into the lymph system and then into the blood. These particles bind to membrane-bound lipases, primarily at adipose tissue and muscle, where the triacylglycerols are once again degraded into free fatty acids and monoacylglycerol for transport into the tissue. The triacylglycerols are then resynthesized inside the cell and stored. In the muscle, they can be oxidized to provide energy.

Figure 22.5 Chylomicron formation. Free fatty acids and monoacylglycerols are absorbed by intestinal epithelial cells. Triacylglycerols are resynthesized and packaged with other lipids and apolipoprotein B-48 to form chylomicrons, which are then released into the lymph system.

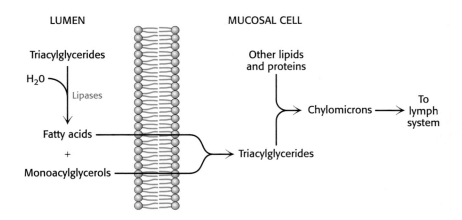

Tissues throughout the body gain access to the lipid energy reserves stored in adipose tissue through three stages of processing. First, the lipids must be mobilized. In this process, triacylglycerols are degraded to fatty acids and glycerol, which are released from the adipose tissue and transported to the energy-requiring tissues. Second, at these tissues, the fatty acids must be activated and transported into mitochondria for degradation. Third, the fatty acids are broken down in a step-by-step fashion into acetyl CoA, which is then processed in the citric acid cycle.

Triacylglycerols are hydrolyzed by hormone-stimulated lipases

Consider someone who has just awakened from a night's sleep and begins a bout of exercise. Glycogen stores will be low, but lipids are readily available. How are these lipid stores mobilized?

Before fats can be used as fuels, the triacylglycerol storage form must be hydrolyzed to yield isolated fatty acids. This reaction is catalyzed by a hormonally controlled lipase. Under the physiological conditions facing an early-morning runner, glucagon and epinephrine will be present. In adipose tissue, these hormones trigger 7 TM receptors that activate adenylate cyclase (Section 14.1). The increased level of cyclic AMP then stimulates protein kinase A, which phosphorylates two key proteins: *perilipin*, a fat-droplet-associated protein, and hormone-sensitive lipase (Figure 22.6). The phosphorylation of perilipin has two crucial effects. First, it restructures the fat droplet so that the triacylglycerols are more accessible to the mobililzation. Second, the phosphorylation of perilipin triggers the release of a coactivator for the adipose triglyceride lipase (ATGL). ATGL initiates the mobilization of triacylglycerols by releasing a fatty acid from triacylglycerol, forming diacylglycerol. Diacylglycerol is converted into a free fatty acid and monoacylglycerol by the hormone-sensitive lipase. Finally, a monoacylglycerol lipase completes the mobilization of fatty acids with the production of a free fatty acid and glycerol. Thus, *epinephrine and glucagon induce lipolysis*. Although their role in muscle is not as firmly established, these hormones probably also regulate the use of triacylglycerol stores in that tissue.

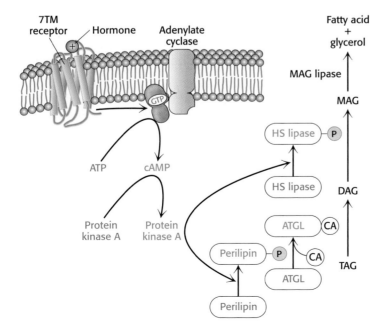

Figure 22.6 Mobilization of triacylglycerols. Triacylglycerols in adipose tissue are converted into free fatty acids in response to hormonal signals. The phosphorylation of perilipin restructures the lipid droplet and releases the coactivator of ATGL. The activation of ATGL by binding with its coactivator initiates the mobilization. Hormone-sensitive lipase releases a fatty acid from diacylglycerol. Monoacylglycerol lipase completes the mobilization process. Abbreviations: 7TM, seven transmembrane receptor; ATGL, adipose triglyceride lipase; CA, coactivator; HS lipase, hormone-sensitive lipase; MAG lipase, monoacylglycerol lipase; DAG, diacylglycerol; TAG, triacylglycerol.

The released fatty acids are not soluble in blood plasma, and so the blood protein albumin binds the fatty acids and serves as a carrier. By these means, free fatty acids are made accessible as a fuel in other tissues. At the tissues, fatty acid transport protein facilitates the transit of the fatty acids across the plasma membrane.

Glycerol formed by lipolysis is absorbed by the liver and phosphorylated. It is then oxidized to dihydroxyacetone phosphate, which is isomerized to glyceraldehyde 3-phosphate. This molecule is an intermediate in both the glycolytic and the gluconeogenic pathways.

Hence, glycerol can be converted into pyruvate or glucose in the liver, which contains the appropriate enzymes (Figure 22.7). The reverse process can take place by the reduction of dihydroxyacetone phosphate to glycerol 3-phosphate. Hydrolysis by a phosphatase then gives glycerol. Thus, glycerol and glycolytic intermediates are readily interconvertible.

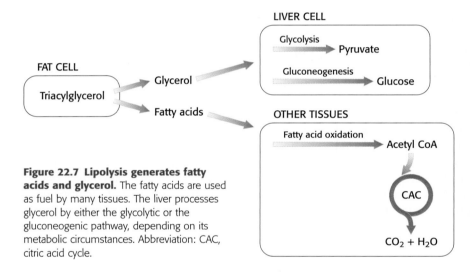

Figure 22.7 Lipolysis generates fatty acids and glycerol. The fatty acids are used as fuel by many tissues. The liver processes glycerol by either the glycolytic or the gluconeogenic pathway, depending on its metabolic circumstances. Abbreviation: CAC, citric acid cycle.

Fatty acids are linked to coenzyme A before they are oxidized

Eugene Kennedy and Albert Lehninger showed in 1949 that fatty acids are oxidized in mitochondria. Subsequent work demonstrated that they are first activated through the formation of a thioester linkage to coenzyme A before they enter the mitochondrial matrix. Adenosine triphosphate drives the formation of the thioester linkage between the carboxyl group of a fatty acid and the sulfhydryl group of coenzyme A. This activation reaction takes place on the outer mitochondrial membrane, where it is catalyzed by *acyl CoA synthetase* (also called *fatty acid thiokinase*).

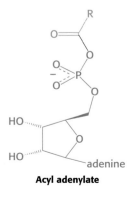

Acyl adenylate

Paul Berg showed that acyl CoA synthetase accomplishes the activation of a fatty acid in two steps. First, the fatty acid reacts with ATP to form an *acyl adenylate*. In this mixed anhydride, the carboxyl group of a fatty acid is bonded to the phosphoryl group of AMP. The other two phosphoryl groups of the ATP substrate are released as pyrophosphate. In the second step, the sulfhydryl group of coenzyme A attacks the acyl adenylate, which is tightly bound to the enzyme, to form acyl CoA and AMP.

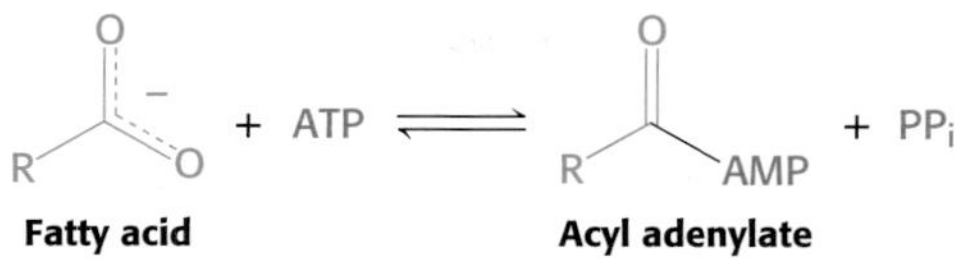

Fatty acid   **Acyl adenylate**   (1)

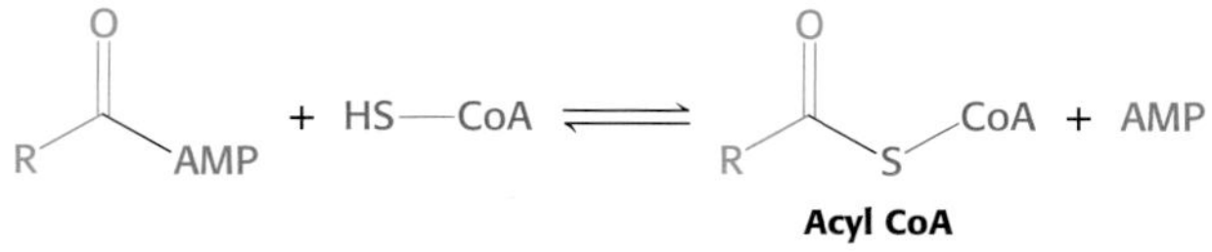

Acyl CoA   (2)

These partial reactions are freely reversible. In fact, the equilibrium constant for the sum of these reactions is close to 1. One high-transfer-potential compound is cleaved (between PP_i and AMP) and one high-transfer-potential compound is formed (the thioester acyl CoA). How is the overall reaction driven forward? The answer is that pyrophosphate is rapidly hydrolyzed by a pyrophosphatase. The complete reaction is

$$RCOO^- + CoA + ATP + H_2O \longrightarrow$$
$$RCO\text{-}CoA + AMP + 2\,P_i + 2\,H^+$$

This reaction is quite favorable because the equivalent of two molecules of ATP is hydrolyzed, whereas only one high-transfer-potential compound is formed. We see here another example of a recurring theme in biochemistry: *many biosynthetic reactions are made irreversible by the hydrolysis of inorganic pyrophosphate.*

Another motif recurs in this activation reaction. The enzyme-bound acyl adenylate intermediate is not unique to the synthesis of acyl CoA. *Acyl adenylates are frequently formed when carboxyl groups are activated in biochemical reactions.* Amino acids are activated for protein synthesis by a similar mechanism (Section 30.2), although the enzymes that catalyze this process are not homologous to acyl CoA synthetase. Thus, *activation by adenylation recurs in part because of convergent evolution.*

Carnitine carries long-chain activated fatty acids into the mitochondrial matrix

Fatty acids are activated on the outer mitochondrial membrane, whereas they are oxidized in the mitochondrial matrix. A special transport mechanism is needed to carry activated long-chain fatty acids across the inner mitochondrial membrane. These fatty acids must be conjugated to *carnitine,* a zwitterionic alcohol. The acyl group is transferred from the sulfur atom of coenzyme A to the hydroxyl group of carnitine to form *acyl carnitine.* This reaction is catalyzed by *carnitine acyltransferase I,* also called *carnitine palmitoyl transferase I* (CPTI), which is bound to the outer mitochondrial membrane.

Acyl CoA   **Carnitine**   **Acyl carnitine**

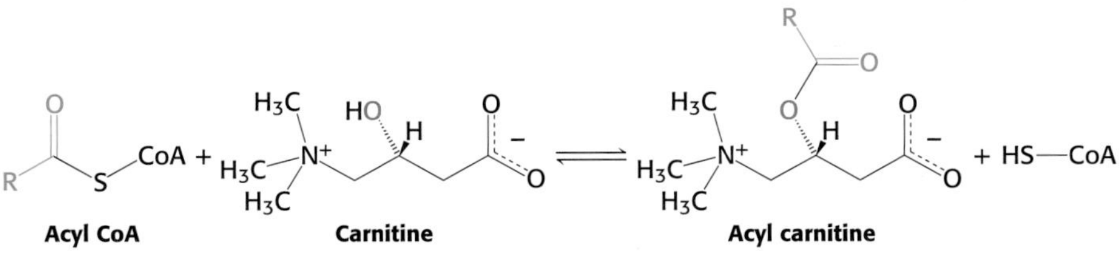

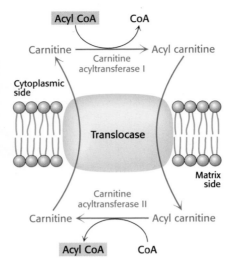

Figure 22.8 Acyl carnitine translocase.
The entry of acyl carnitine into the
mitochondrial matrix is mediated by a
translocase. Carnitine returns to the
cytoplasmic side of the inner mitochondrial
membrane in exchange for acyl carnitine.

Acyl carnitine is then shuttled across the inner mitochondrial membrane by
a translocase (Figure 22.8). The acyl group is transferred back to coenzyme
A on the matrix side of the membrane. This reaction, which is catalyzed by
carnitine acyltransferase II (carnitine palmitoyl transferase II), is simply the
reverse of the reaction that takes place in the cytoplasm. The reaction
is thermodynamically feasible because of the zwitterionic nature of carnitine. The *O*-acyl link in carnitine has a high group-transfer potential,
apparently because, being zwitterions, carnitine and its esters are solvated
differently from most other alcohols and their esters. Finally, the translocase
returns carnitine to the cytoplasmic side in exchange for an incoming acyl
carnitine.

A number of diseases have been traced to a deficiency of carnitine,
the transferase, or the translocase. The symptoms of carnitine deficiency range from mild muscle cramping to severe weakness and even
death. Muscle, kidney, and heart are the tissues primarily impaired. Muscle
weakness during prolonged exercise is a symptom of a deficiency of carnitine acyltransferases because muscle relies on fatty acids as a long-term
source of energy. Medium-chain (C_8–C_{10}) fatty acids are oxidized normally
in these patients because these fatty acids do not require carnitine to enter
the mitochondria. These diseases illustrate that *the impaired flow of a metabolite from one compartment of a cell to another can lead to a pathological
condition.*

Acetyl CoA, NADH, and FADH$_2$ are generated in each round of fatty acid oxidation

A saturated acyl CoA is degraded by a recurring sequence of four reactions:
oxidation by flavin adenine dinucleotide (FAD), hydration, oxidation by
NAD$^+$, and thiolysis by coenzyme A (Figure 22.9). The fatty acid chain is
shortened by two carbon atoms as a result of these reactions, and FADH$_2$,
NADH, and acetyl CoA are generated. Because oxidation takes place at the
β carbon atom, this series of reactions is called the *β-oxidation pathway.*

The first reaction in each round of degradation is the *oxidation* of acyl
CoA by an *acyl CoA dehydrogenase* to give an enoyl CoA with a trans double
bond between C-2 and C-3.

$$\text{Acyl CoA} + \text{E-FAD} \longrightarrow trans\text{-}\Delta^2\text{-enoyl CoA} + \text{E-FADH}_2$$

As in the dehydrogenation of succinate in the citric acid cycle, FAD rather
than NAD$^+$ is the electron acceptor because the ΔG for this reaction is
insufficient to drive the reduction of NAD$^+$. Electrons from the FADH$_2$
prosthetic group of the reduced acyl CoA dehydrogenase are transferred to
a second flavoprotein called *electron-transferring flavoprotein* (ETF). In
turn, ETF donates electrons to *ETF:ubiquinone reductase*, an iron–sulfur
protein. Ubiquinone is thereby reduced to ubiquinol, which delivers its high-
potential electrons to the second proton-pumping site of the respiratory
chain (Section 18.3). Consequently, 1.5 molecules of ATP are generated per
molecule of FADH$_2$ formed in this dehydrogenation step, as in the oxidation of succinate to fumarate.

R—CH$_2$—CH$_2$—R'   E-FAD   ETF-FADH$_2$ Fe-S (oxidized)   Ubiquinol (QH$_2$)
R—CH=CH—R'   E-FADH$_2$ ETF-FAD   Fe-S (reduced)   Ubiquinone (Q)

The next step is the *hydration* of the double bond between C-2 and C-3
by *enoyl CoA hydratase.*

$$trans\text{-}\Delta^2\text{-Enoyl CoA} + \text{H}_2\text{O} \longrightarrow \text{L-3-hydroxyacyl CoA}$$

Table 22.1 Principal reactions in fatty acid oxidation

Step	Reaction	Enzyme
1	Fatty acid + CoA + ATP $\rightleftharpoons$ acyl CoA + AMP + PP$_i$	Acyl CoA synthetase (also called fatty acid thiokinase and fatty acid:CoA ligase)*
2	Carnitine + acyl CoA $\rightleftharpoons$ acyl carnitine + CoA	Carnitine acyltransferase (also called carnitine palmitoyl transferase)
3	Acyl CoA + E-FAD $\longrightarrow$ trans-Δ^2-enoyl CoA + E-FADH$_2$	Acyl CoA dehydrogenases (several isozymes having different chain-length specificity)
4	trans-Δ^2-Enoyl CoA + H$_2$O $\rightleftharpoons$ L-3-hydroxyacyl CoA	Enoyl CoA hydratase (also called crotonase or 3-hydroxyacyl CoA hydrolyase)
5	L-3-Hydroxyacyl CoA + NAD$^+$ $\rightleftharpoons$ 3-ketoacyl CoA + NADH + H$^+$	L-3-Hydroxyacyl CoA dehydrogenase
6	3-Ketoacyl CoA + CoA $\rightleftharpoons$ acetyl CoA + acyl CoA (shortened by C$_2$)	β-Ketothiolase (also called thiolase)

*An AMP-forming ligase.

The hydration of enoyl CoA is stereospecific. Only the L isomer of 3-hydroxyacyl CoA is formed when the trans-Δ^2 double bond is hydrated. The enzyme also hydrates a cis-Δ^2 double bond, but the product then is the D isomer. We shall return to this point shortly in considering how unsaturated fatty acids are oxidized.

The hydration of enoyl CoA is a prelude to the second *oxidation* reaction, which converts the hydroxyl group at C-3 into a keto group and generates NADH. This oxidation is catalyzed by *L-3-hydroxyacyl CoA dehydrogenase*, which is specific for the L isomer of the hydroxyacyl substrate.

L-3-Hydroxyacyl CoA + NAD$^+$ $\rightleftharpoons$ 3-ketoacyl CoA + NADH + H$^+$

The preceding reactions have oxidized the methylene group at C-3 to a keto group. The final step is the *cleavage* of 3-ketoacyl CoA by the thiol group of a second molecule of coenzyme A, which yields acetyl CoA and an acyl CoA shortened by two carbon atoms. This thiolytic cleavage is catalyzed by β-*ketothiolase*.

$$\begin{array}{ccc} \text{3-Ketoacyl CoA + HS-CoA} & \rightleftharpoons & \text{acetyl CoA + acyl CoA} \\ (n \text{ carbons}) & & (n-2 \text{ carbons}) \end{array}$$

Table 22.1 summarizes the reactions in fatty acid oxidation.

The shortened acyl CoA then undergoes another cycle of oxidation, starting with the reaction catalyzed by acyl CoA dehydrogenase (Figure 22.10). Fatty acid chains containing from 12 to 18 carbon atoms are oxidized by the long-chain acyl CoA dehydrogenase. The medium-chain acyl CoA dehydrogenase oxidizes fatty acid chains having from 14 to 4 carbons, whereas the short-chain acyl CoA dehydrogenase acts only on 4- and 6-carbon fatty acid chains. In contrast, β-ketothiolase, hydroxyacyl dehydrogenase, and enoyl CoA hydratase act on fatty acid molecules of almost any length.

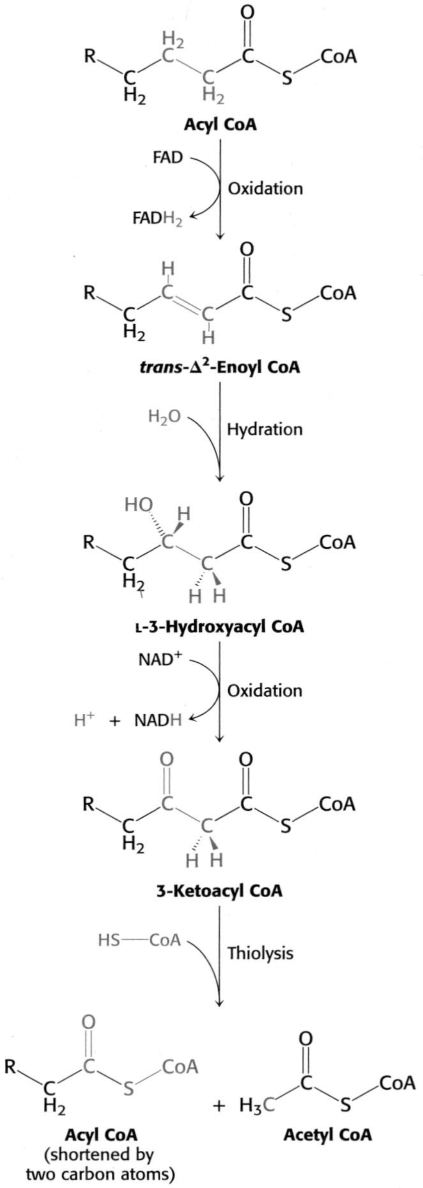

The complete oxidation of palmitate yields 106 molecules of ATP

We can now calculate the energy yield derived from the oxidation of a fatty acid. In each reaction cycle, an acyl CoA is shortened by two carbon atoms, and one molecule each of FADH$_2$, NADH, and acetyl CoA are formed.

$$C_n\text{-acyl CoA} + \text{FAD} + \text{NAD}^+ + \text{H}_2\text{O} + \text{CoA} \longrightarrow$$
$$C_{n-2}\text{-acyl CoA} + \text{FADH}_2 + \text{NADH} + \text{acetyl CoA} + \text{H}^+$$

The degradation of palmitoyl CoA (C$_{16}$-acyl CoA) requires seven reaction cycles. In the seventh cycle, the C$_4$-ketoacyl CoA is thiolyzed to two molecules of acetyl CoA. Hence, the stoichiometry of the oxidation of palmitoyl CoA is

$$\text{Palmitoyl CoA} + 7\,\text{FAD} + 7\,\text{NAD}^+ + 7\,\text{CoA} + 7\,\text{H}_2\text{O} \longrightarrow$$
$$8\,\text{acetyl CoA} + 7\,\text{FADH}_2 + 7\,\text{NADH} + 7\,\text{H}^+$$

Figure 22.9 Reaction sequence for the degradation of fatty acids. Fatty acids are degraded by the repetition of a four-reaction sequence consisting of oxidation, hydration, oxidation, and thiolysis.

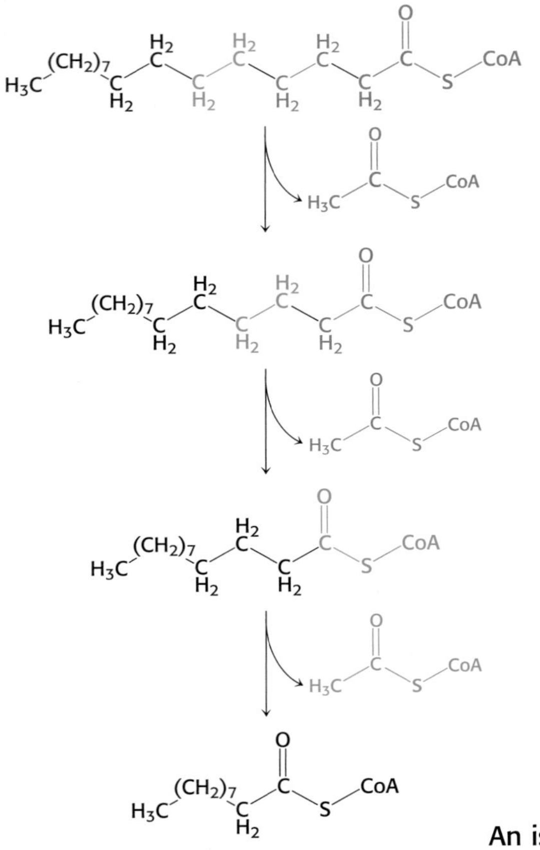

Figure 22.10 First three rounds in the degradation of palmitate. Two-carbon units are sequentially removed from the carboxyl end of the fatty acid.

Palmitoleoyl CoA

cis-Δ³-Enoyl CoA

cis-Δ³-Enoyl CoA isomerase

trans-Δ²-Enoyl CoA

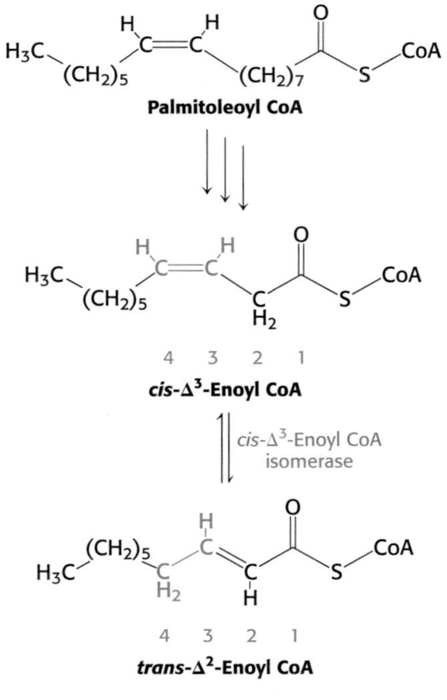

Figure 22.11 The degradation of a monounsaturated fatty acid. *Cis*-Δ³-Enoyl CoA isomerase allows continued β-oxidation of fatty acids with a single double bond.

648

Approximately 2.5 molecules of ATP are generated when the respiratory chain oxidizes each of these NADH molecules, whereas 1.5 molecules of ATP are formed for each $FADH_2$ because their electrons enter the chain at the level of ubiquinol. Recall that the oxidation of acetyl CoA by the citric acid cycle yields 10 molecules of ATP. Hence, the number of ATP molecules formed in the oxidation of palmitoyl CoA is 10.5 from the seven $FADH_2$, 17.5 from the seven NADH, and 80 from the eight acetyl CoA molecules, which gives a total of 108. The equivalent of 2 molecules of ATP is consumed in the activation of palmitate, in which ATP is split into AMP and two molecules of orthophosphate. Thus, *the complete oxidation of a molecule of palmitate yields 106 molecules of ATP.*

22.3 Unsaturated and Odd-Chain Fatty Acids Require Additional Steps for Degradation

The β-oxidation pathway accomplishes the complete degradation of saturated fatty acids having an even number of carbon atoms. Most fatty acids have such structures because of their mode of synthesis (to be addressed later in this chapter). However, not all fatty acids are so simple. The oxidation of fatty acids containing double bonds requires additional steps, as does the oxidation of fatty acids containing an odd number of carbon atoms.

An isomerase and a reductase are required for the oxidation of unsaturated fatty acids

The oxidation of unsaturated fatty acids presents some difficulties, yet many such fatty acids are available in the diet. Most of the reactions are the same as those for saturated fatty acids. In fact, only two additional enzymes—an isomerase and a reductase—are needed to degrade a wide range of unsaturated fatty acids.

Consider the oxidation of palmitoleate (Figure 22.11) This C_{16} unsaturated fatty acid, which has one double bond between C-9 and C-10, is activated and transported across the inner mitochondrial membrane in the same way as saturated fatty acids are. Palmitoleoyl CoA then undergoes three cycles of degradation, which are carried out by the same enzymes as those in the oxidation of saturated fatty acids. However, the *cis*-Δ^3-enoyl CoA formed in the third round is not a substrate for acyl CoA dehydrogenase. The presence of a double bond between C-3 and C-4 prevents the formation of another double bond between C-2 and C-3. This impasse is resolved by a new reaction that shifts the position and configuration of the *cis*-Δ^3 double bond. *cis*-Δ^3-*Enoyl CoA isomerase converts this double bond into a trans*-Δ^2 *double bond.* The double bond is now between C-2 and C-3. The subsequent reactions are those of the saturated fatty acid oxidation pathway, in which the *trans*-Δ^2-enoyl CoA is a regular substrate.

Human beings require polyunsaturated fatty acids, which have multiple double bonds, as important precursors for signal molecules, but excess polyunsaturated fatty acids are degraded by β oxidation. However, another problem arises with the oxidation of polyunsaturated fatty acids. Consider linoleate, a C_{18} polyunsaturated fatty acid with *cis*-Δ^9 and *cis*-Δ^{12} double bonds (Figure 22.12). The *cis*-Δ^3 double bond (between carbons 3 and 4) formed after three rounds of β-oxidation is converted into a *trans*-Δ^2 double bond (between carbons 2 and 3) by the aforementioned isomerase. The acyl CoA produced by another round of β-oxidation contains a *cis*-Δ^4 (between

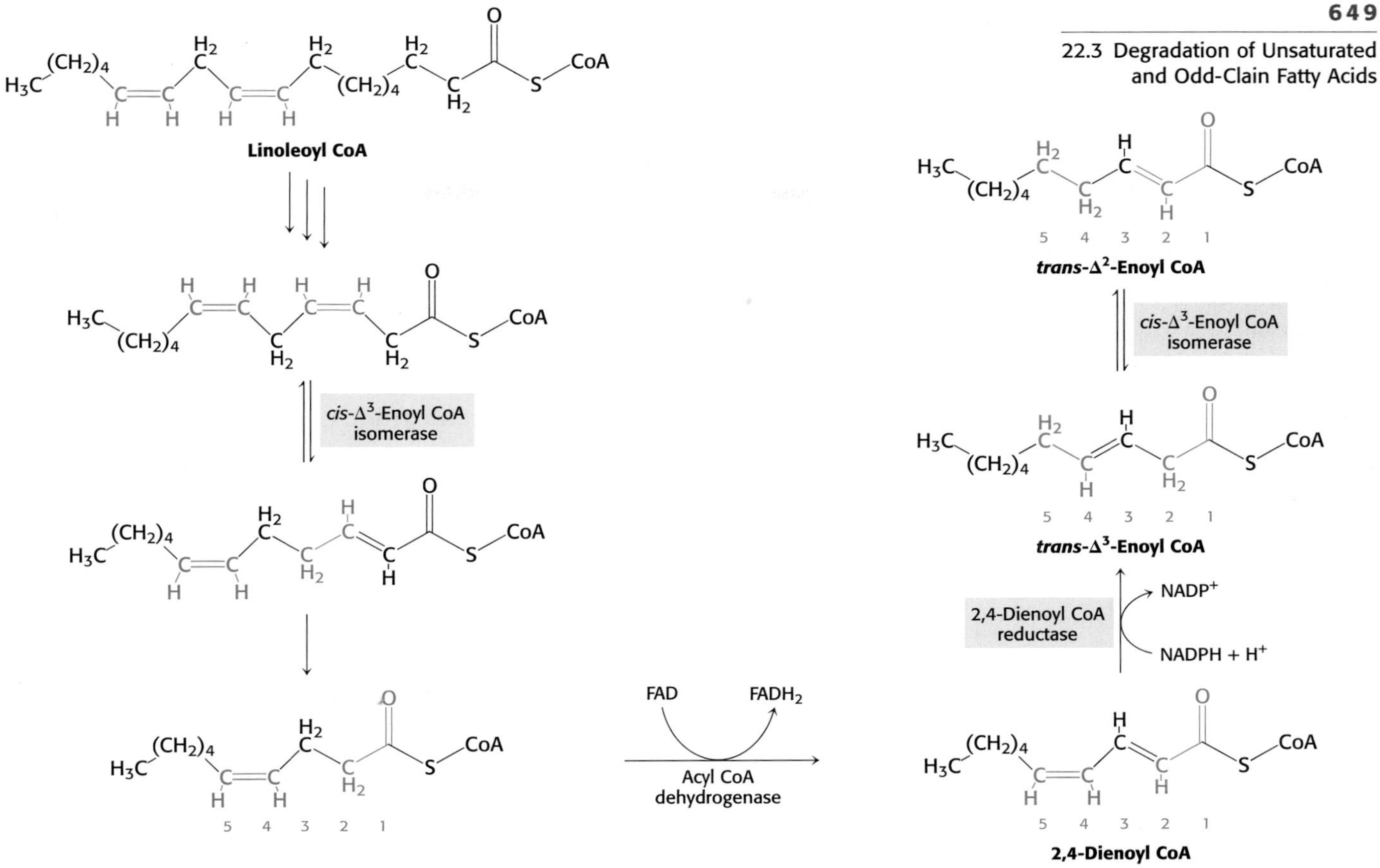

Linoleoyl CoA

cis-Δ³-Enoyl CoA isomerase

Acyl CoA dehydrogenase

FAD → FADH₂

trans-Δ²-Enoyl CoA

cis-Δ³-Enoyl CoA isomerase

trans-Δ³-Enoyl CoA

2,4-Dienoyl CoA reductase

NADP⁺ ← NADPH + H⁺

2,4-Dienoyl CoA

Figure 22.12 Oxidation of linoleoyl CoA. The complete oxidation of the diunsaturated fatty acid linoleate is facilitated by the activity of enoyl CoA isomerase and 2,4-dienoyl CoA reductase.

carbons 4 and 5) double bond. Dehydrogenation of this species by acyl CoA dehydrogenase yields a *2,4-dienoyl intermediate* (double bond between carbons 2 and 3 and carbons 4 and 5), which is not a substrate for the next enzyme in the β-oxidation pathway. This impasse is circumvented by *2,4-dienoyl CoA reductase*, an enzyme that uses NADPH to reduce the 2,4-dienoyl intermediate to *trans*-Δ³-enoyl CoA. *cis*-Δ³-Enoyl CoA isomerase then converts *trans*-Δ³-enoyl CoA into the trans-Δ² form, a customary intermediate in the β-oxidation pathway. These catalytic strategies are elegant and economical. Only two extra enzymes are needed for the oxidation of *any* polyunsaturated fatty acid. *Odd-numbered double bonds are handled by the isomerase, and even-numbered ones by the reductase and the isomerase.*

Odd-chain fatty acids yield propionyl CoA in the final thiolysis step

Fatty acids having an odd number of carbon atoms are minor species. They are oxidized in the same way as fatty acids having an even number, except that propionyl CoA and acetyl CoA, rather than two molecules of acetyl CoA, are produced in the final round of degradation. The activated three-carbon unit in propionyl CoA enters the citric acid cycle after it has been converted into succinyl CoA.

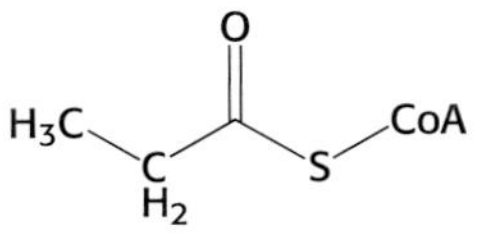

The pathway from propionyl CoA to succinyl CoA is especially interesting because it entails a rearrangement that requires *vitamin B₁₂* (also known as *cobalamin*). Propionyl CoA is carboxylated at the expense of the hydrolysis of a molecule of ATP to yield the D isomer of methylmalonyl CoA (Figure 22.13). This carboxylation reaction is catalyzed by *propionyl*

Propionyl CoA

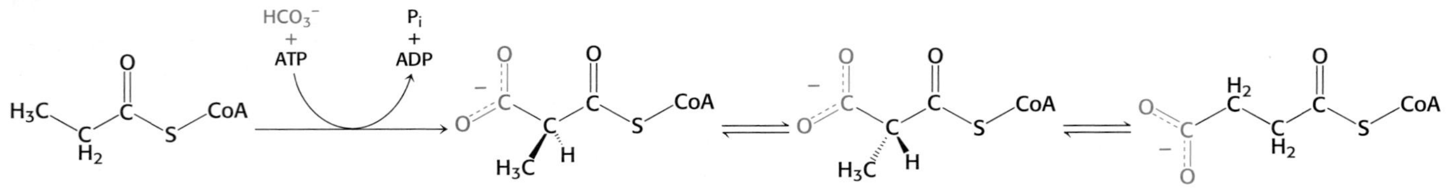

Figure 22.13 Conversion of propionyl CoA into succinyl CoA. Propionyl CoA, generated from fatty acids with an odd number of carbons as well as some amino acids, is converted into the citric acid cycle intermediate succinyl CoA.

Figure 22.14 Structure of coenzyme B$_{12}$. Coenzyme B$_{12}$ is a class of molecules that vary, depending on the component designated X in the left-hand structure. 5′-Deoxyadenosylcobalamin is the form of the coenzyme in methylmalonyl mutase. Substitution of cyano and methyl groups for X creates cyanocobalamin and methylcobalamin, respectively.

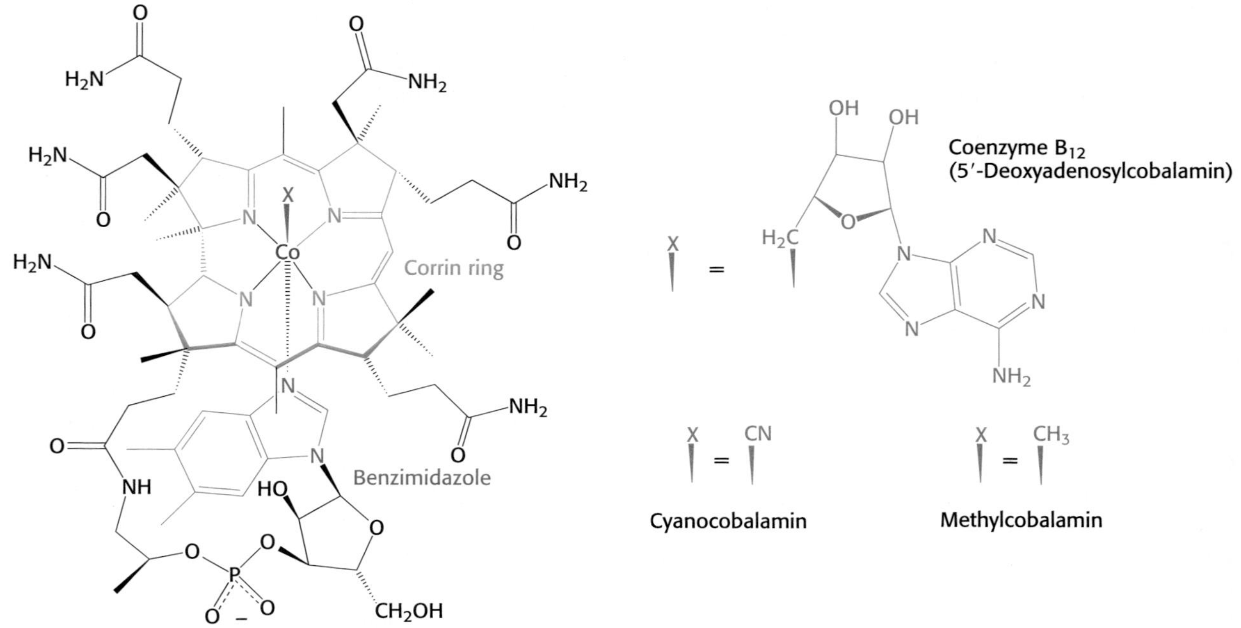

CoA carboxylase, a biotin enzyme that has a catalytic mechanism like that of the homologous enzyme pyruvate carboxylase. The D isomer of methylmalonyl CoA is racemized to the L isomer, the substrate for a mutase that converts it into *succinyl CoA* by an *intramolecular rearrangement.* The —CO—S—CoA group migrates from C-2 to a methyl group in exchange for a hydrogen atom. This very unusual isomerization is catalyzed by *methylmalonyl CoA mutase,* which contains a derivative of cobalamin as its coenzyme.

Vitamin B$_{12}$ contains a corrin ring and a cobalt atom

Cobalamin enzymes, which are present in most organisms, catalyze three types of reactions: (1) *intramolecular rearrangements;* (2) *methylations,* as in the synthesis of methionine; and (3) the *reduction of ribonucleotides to deoxyribonucleotides* (Section 25.3). In mammals, only two reactions are known to require coenzyme B$_{12}$. The conversion of L-methylmalonyl CoA into succinyl CoA is one, and the formation of methionine by the methylation of homocysteine is the other. The latter reaction is especially important because methionine is required for the generation of coenzymes that participate in the synthesis of purines and thymine, which are needed for nucleic acid synthesis.

The core of cobalamin consists of a *corrin ring with a central cobalt atom* (Figure 22.14). The corrin ring, like a porphyrin, has *four pyrrole units.* Two of them are directly bonded to each other, whereas the others are joined by methine bridges, as in porphyrins. The corrin ring is more reduced than that of porphyrins and the substituents are different. A cobalt atom is bonded to the four pyrrole nitrogens. The fifth substituent linked to the cobalt atom is a derivative of *dimethylbenzimidazole* that contains ribose 3-phosphate and aminoisopropanol. One of the nitrogen atoms of dimethylbenzimidazole is linked to the cobalt atom. In coenzyme B_{12}, *the sixth substituent* linked to the cobalt atom is a *5′-deoxyadenosyl unit*. This position can also be occupied by a cyano group, a methyl group, or other ligands. In all of these compounds, the cobalt is in the +3 oxidation state.

Mechanism: Methylmalonyl CoA mutase catalyzes a rearrangement to form succinyl CoA

The rearrangement reactions catalyzed by coenzyme B_{12} are exchanges of two groups attached to adjacent carbon atoms of the substrate (Figure 22.15). A hydrogen atom migrates from one carbon atom to the next, and an R group (such as the —CO—S—CoA group of methylmalonyl CoA) concomitantly moves in the reverse direction. The first step in these intramolecular rearrangements is the cleavage of the carbon–cobalt bond of 5′-deoxyadenosylcobalamin to generate the Co^{2+} form of the coenzyme and a 5′-deoxyadenosyl radical, —$CH_2\cdot$ (Figure 22.16). In this *homolytic cleavage reaction*, one electron of the Co–C bond stays with Co (reducing it from the +3 to the +2 oxidation state), whereas the other electron stays with the carbon atom, generating a free radical. In contrast, nearly all other cleavage reactions in biological systems are *heterolytic*: an electron *pair* is transferred to one of the two atoms that were bonded together.

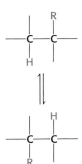

Figure 22.15 Rearrangement reaction catalyzed by cobalamin enzymes. The R group can be an amino group, a hydroxyl group, or a substituted carbon.

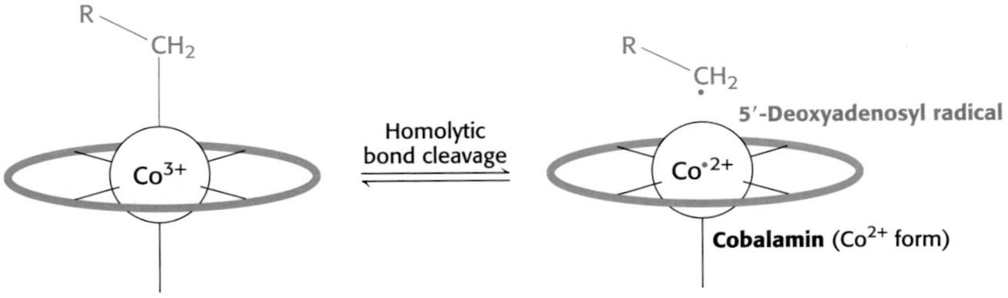

Figure 22.16 Formation of a 5′-deoxyadenosyl radical. The methylmalonyl CoA mutase reaction begins with the homolytic cleavage of the bond joining Co^{3+} of coenzyme B_{12} to a carbon atom of the ribose of the adenosine moiety of the enzyme. The cleavage generates a 5′-deoxyadenosyl radical and leads to the reduction of Co^{3+} to Co^{2+}. The letter R represents the 5′-deoxyadenosyl component of the coenzyme, and the green oval represents the remainder of the coenzyme.

R—CH_2 | Co³⁺ ⇌ (Homolytic bond cleavage) ⇌ R—$CH_2\cdot$ | Co·²⁺ — **5′-Deoxyadenosyl radical** — **Cobalamin (Co²⁺ form)**

What is the role of this very unusual —$CH_2\cdot$ radical? This highly reactive species abstracts a *hydrogen atom* from the substrate to form 5′-deoxyadenosine and a substrate radical (Figure 22.17). This substrate radical spontaneously rearranges: the carbonyl CoA group migrates to the position formerly occupied by H on the neighboring carbon atom to produce a different radical. This product radical abstracts a hydrogen atom from the methyl group of 5′-deoxyadenosine to complete the rearrangement and return the deoxyadenosyl unit to the radical form. *The role of coenzyme B_{12} in such intramolecular migrations is to serve as a source of free radicals for the abstraction of hydrogen atoms.*

Figure 22.17 Formation of succinyl CoA by a rearrangement reaction. A free radical abstracts a hydrogen atom in the rearrangement of methylmalonyl CoA to succinyl CoA.

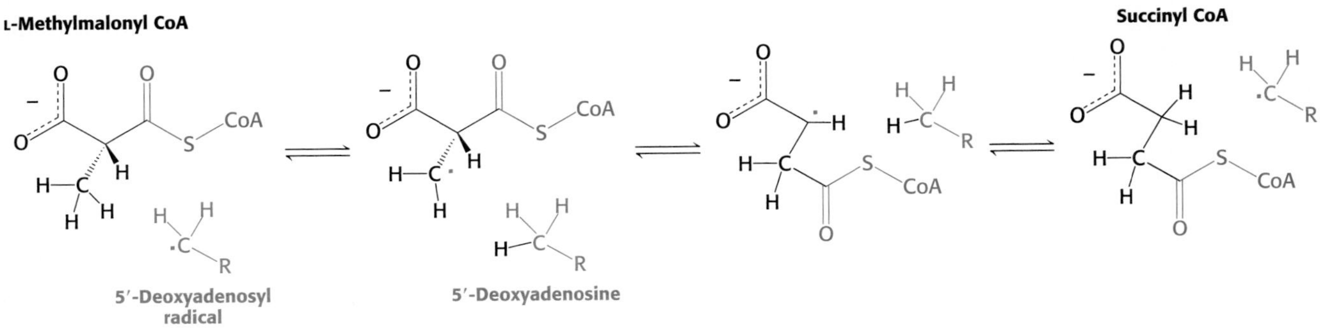

L-Methylmalonyl CoA   **Succinyl CoA**

5′-Deoxyadenosyl radical   5′-Deoxyadenosine

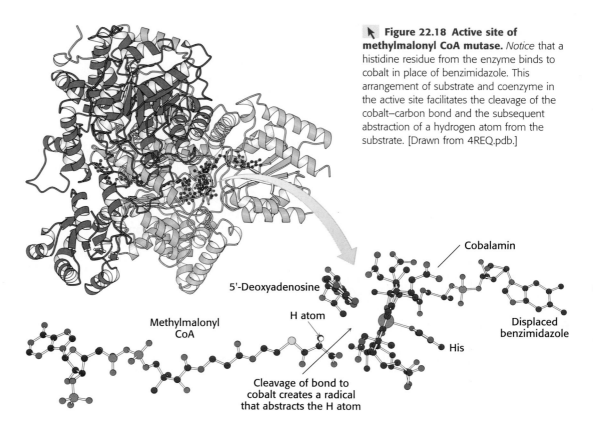

Figure 22.18 Active site of methylmalonyl CoA mutase. *Notice* that a histidine residue from the enzyme binds to cobalt in place of benzimidazole. This arrangement of substrate and coenzyme in the active site facilitates the cleavage of the cobalt–carbon bond and the subsequent abstraction of a hydrogen atom from the substrate. [Drawn from 4REQ.pdb.]

Cobalamin

5'-Deoxyadenosine

Methylmalonyl
CoA

H atom

Displaced
benzimidazole

His

Cleavage of bond to
cobalt creates a radical
that abstracts the H atom

An essential property of coenzyme B_{12} is the weakness of its cobalt–carbon bond, which is readily cleaved to generate a radical. To facilitate the cleavage of this bond, enzymes such as methylmalonyl CoA mutase displace the benzimidazole group from the cobalamin and bind to the cobalt atom through a histidine residue (Figure 22.18). The steric crowding around the cobalt–carbon bond within the corrin ring system contributes to the bond weakness.

Fatty acids are also oxidized in peroxisomes

Although most fatty acid oxidation takes place in mitochondria, some oxidation of fatty acids can take place in cellular organelles called *peroxisomes* (Figure 22.19). These organelles are small membrane-bounded compartments that are present in the cells of most eukaryotes. Fatty acid oxidation in these organelles, which halts at octanoyl CoA, may serve to shorten long chains to make them better substrates of β oxidation in mitochondria. Peroxisomal oxidation differs from β oxidation in the initial dehydrogenation reaction (Figure 22.20). In peroxisomes, acyl CoA dehydrogenase, a flavoprotein, transfers electrons from the substrate to $FADH_2$ and then to O_2 to yield H_2O_2 instead of capturing high-energy electrons as $FADH_2$ for use in the electron-transport chain, as in mitochondrial β oxidation. Peroxisomes contain high concentrations of the enzyme catalase to degrade H_2O_2 into water and O_2. Subsequent steps are identical with those of their mitochondrial counterparts, although they are carried out by different isoforms of the enzymes.

Peroxisomes do not function in patients with Zellweger syndrome. Liver, kidney, and muscle abnormalities usually lead to death by age six. The syndrome is caused by a defect in the import of enzymes into the peroxisomes. Here we see a pathological condition resulting from an inappropriate cellular distribution of enzymes.

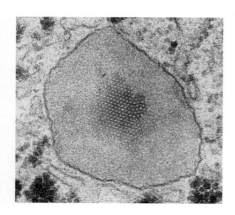

Figure 22.19 Electron micrograph of a peroxisome in a liver cell. A crystal of urate oxidase is present inside the organelle, which is bounded by a single bilayer membrane. The dark granular structures outside the peroxisome are glycogen particles. [Courtesy of Dr. George Palade.]

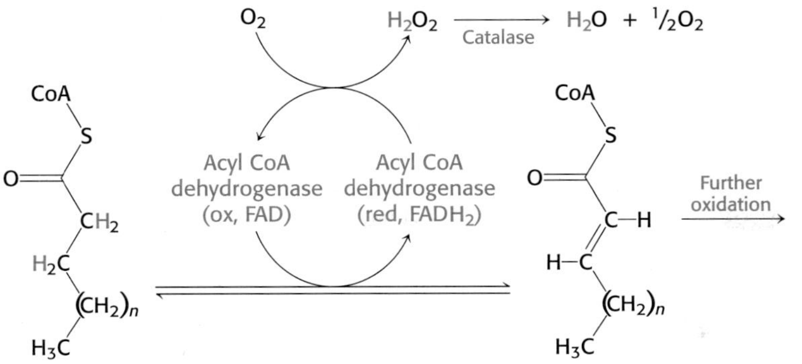

Figure 22.20 Initiation of peroxisomal fatty acid degradation. The first dehydration in the degradation of fatty acids in peroxisomes requires a flavoprotein dehydrogenase that transfers electrons from its $FADH_2$ moiety to O_2 to yield H_2O_2.

Ketone bodies are formed from acetyl CoA when fat breakdown predominates

The acetyl CoA formed in fatty acid oxidation enters the citric acid cycle only if fat and carbohydrate degradation are appropriately balanced. Acetyl CoA must combine with oxaloacetate to gain entry to the citric acid cycle. The availability of oxaloacetate, however, depends on an adequate supply of carbohydrate. Recall that oxaloacetate is normally formed from pyruvate, the product of glucose degradation in glycolysis. If carbohydrate is unavailable or improperly utilized, the concentration of oxaloacetate is lowered and acetyl CoA cannot enter the citric acid cycle. This dependency is the molecular basis of the adage that *fats burn in the flame of carbohydrates.*

In fasting or diabetes, oxaloacetate is consumed to form glucose by the gluconeogenic pathway (Section 16.3) and hence is unavailable for condensation with acetyl CoA. Under these conditions, acetyl CoA is diverted to the formation of acetoacetate and D-3-hydroxybutyrate. Acetoacetate, D-3-hydroxybutyrate, and acetone are often referred to as *ketone bodies.* Abnormally high levels of ketone bodies are present in the blood of untreated diabetics.

Acetoacetate is formed from acetyl CoA in three steps (Figure 22.21). Two molecules of acetyl CoA condense to form acetoacetyl CoA. This reaction, which is catalyzed by thiolase, is the reverse of the thiolysis step in the oxidation of fatty acids. Acetoacetyl CoA then reacts with acetyl CoA and water to give 3-hydroxy-3-methylglutaryl CoA (HMG-CoA) and CoA.

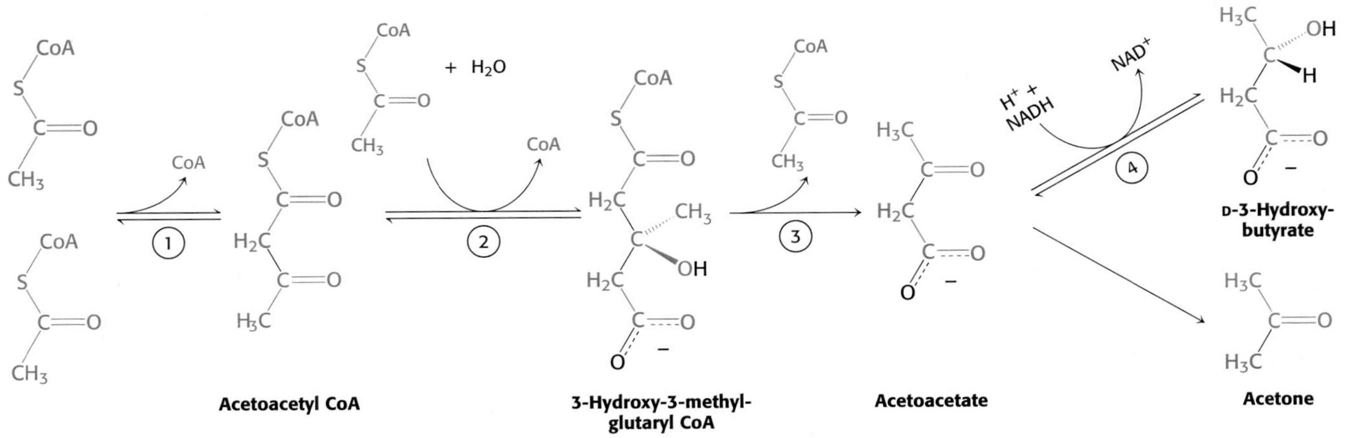

Figure 22.21 Formation of ketone bodies. The ketone bodies—acetoacetate, D-3-hydroxybutyrate, and acetone from acetyl CoA—are formed primarily in the liver. Enzymes catalyzing these reactions are (1) 3-ketothiolase, (2) hydroxymethylglutaryl CoA synthase, (3) hydroxymethylglutaryl CoA cleavage enzyme, and (4) D-3-hydroxybutyrate dehydrogenase. Acetoacetate spontaneously decarboxylates to form acetone.

This condensation resembles the one catalyzed by citrate synthase (Section 17.2). This reaction, which has a favorable equilibrium owing to the hydrolysis of a thioester linkage, compensates for the unfavorable equilibrium in the formation of acetoacetyl CoA. 3-Hydroxy-3-methylglutaryl CoA is then cleaved to acetyl CoA and acetoacetate. The sum of these reactions is

$$2 \text{ Acetyl CoA} + H_2O \longrightarrow \text{acetoacetate} + 2 \text{ CoA} + H^+$$

D-3-Hydroxybutyrate is formed by the reduction of acetoacetate in the mitochondrial matrix by D-3-hydroxybutyrate dehydrogenase. The ratio of hydroxybutyrate to acetoacetate depends on the $NADH/NAD^+$ ratio inside mitochondria.

Because it is a β-ketoacid, acetoacetate also undergoes a slow, spontaneous decarboxylation to acetone. The odor of acetone may be detected in the breath of a person who has a high level of acetoacetate in the blood.

Ketone bodies are a major fuel in some tissues

The major site of the production of acetoacetate and 3-hydroxybutyrate is the liver. These substances diffuse from the liver mitochondria into the blood and are transported to other tissues such as heart and kidney (Figure 22.22). Acetoacetate and 3-hydroxybutyrate are normal fuels of respiration and are quantitatively important as sources of energy. Indeed, heart muscle and the renal cortex use acetoacetate in preference to glucose. In contrast, glucose is the major fuel for the brain and red blood cells in

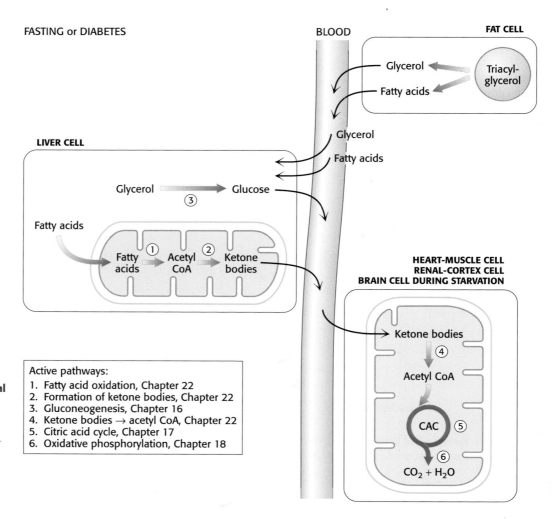

Figure 22.22 PATHWAY INTEGRATION: Liver supplies ketone bodies to the peripheral tissues. During fasting or in untreated diabetics, the liver converts fatty acids into ketone bodies, which are a fuel source for a number of tissues. Ketone-body production is especially important during starvation, when ketone bodies are the predominant fuel.

Active pathways:
1. Fatty acid oxidation, Chapter 22
2. Formation of ketone bodies, Chapter 22
3. Gluconeogenesis, Chapter 16
4. Ketone bodies → acetyl CoA, Chapter 22
5. Citric acid cycle, Chapter 17
6. Oxidative phosphorylation, Chapter 18

well-nourished people on a balanced diet. However, the brain adapts to the utilization of acetoacetate during starvation and diabetes. In prolonged starvation, 75% of the fuel needs of the brain are met by ketone bodies.

Acetoacetate is converted into acetyl CoA in two steps. First, acetoacetate is activated by the transfer of CoA from succinyl CoA in a reaction catalyzed by a specific CoA transferase. Second, acetoacetyl CoA is cleaved by thiolase to yield two molecules of acetyl CoA, which can then enter the citric acid cycle (Figure 22.23). The liver has acetoacetate available to supply to other organs because it lacks this particular CoA transferase. 3-Hydroxybutyrate requires an additional step to yield acetyl CoA. It is first oxidized to produce acetoacetate, which is processed as heretofore described, and NADH for use in oxidative phosphorylation.

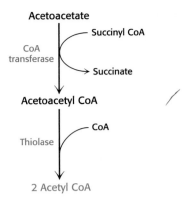

Figure 22.23 Utilization of acetoacetate as a fuel. Acetoacetate can be converted into two molecules of acetyl CoA, which then enter the citric acid cycle.

D-3-Hydroxybutyrate   Acetoacetate

Ketone bodies can be regarded as a water-soluble, transportable form of acetyl units. Fatty acids are released by adipose tissue and converted into acetyl units by the liver, which then exports them as acetoacetate. As might be expected, acetoacetate also has a regulatory role. *High levels of acetoacetate in the blood signify an abundance of acetyl units and lead to a decrease in the rate of lipolysis in adipose tissue.*

High blood levels of ketone bodies, the result of certain pathological conditions, can be life threatening. The most common of these conditions is diabetic ketosis in patients with insulin-dependent diabetes mellitus. These patients are unable to produce insulin. As stated earlier, this hormone, normally released after meals, signals tissues to take up glucose. In addition, it curtails fatty acid mobilization by adipose tissue. The absence of insulin has two major biochemical consequences (Figure 22.24). First, the liver cannot absorb glucose and consequently cannot provide oxaloacetate to process fatty acid-derived acetyl CoA. Second, adipose cells continue to

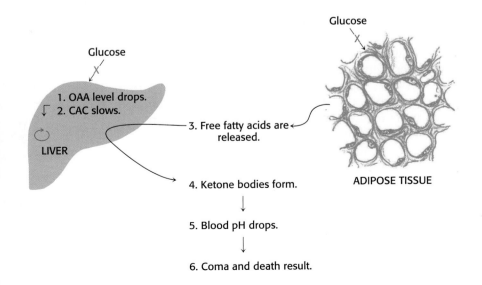

Figure 22.24 Diabetic ketosis results when insulin is absent. In the absence of insulin, fats are released from adipose tissue, and glucose cannot be absorbed by the liver or adipose tissue. The liver degrades the fatty acids by β oxidation but cannot process the acetyl CoA, because of a lack of glucose-derived oxaloacetate (OAA). Excess ketone bodies are formed and released into the blood.

release fatty acids into the bloodstream, which are taken up by the liver and converted into ketone bodies. The liver thus produces large amounts of ketone bodies, which are moderately strong acids. The result is severe acidosis. The decrease in pH impairs tissue function, most importantly in the central nervous system.

Interestingly, diets that promote ketone-body formation, called ketogenic diets, are frequently used as a therapeutic option for children with drug-resistant epilepsy. Ketogenic diets are rich in fats and low in carbohydrates, with adequate amounts of protein. In essence, the body is forced into starvation mode, where fats and ketone bodies become the main fuel source (Section 27.5). How such diets reduce the seizures suffered by the children is currently unknown.

Animals cannot convert fatty acids into glucose

A typical human being has far greater fat stores than glycogen stores. However, glycogen is necessary to fuel very active muscle, as well as the brain, which normally uses only glucose as a fuel. When glycogen stores are low, why can't the body make use of fat stores and convert fatty acids into glucose? Because *animals are unable to effect the net synthesis of glucose from fatty acids*. Specifically, acetyl CoA cannot be converted into pyruvate or oxaloacetate in animals. Recall that the reaction that generates acetyl CoA from pyruvate is irreversible (Section 17.1). The two carbon atoms of the acetyl group of acetyl CoA enter the citric acid cycle, but two carbon atoms leave the cycle in the decarboxylations catalyzed by isocitrate dehydrogenase and α-ketoglutarate dehydrogenase. Consequently, oxaloacetate is regenerated, but it is not formed de novo when the acetyl unit of acetyl CoA is oxidized by the citric acid cycle. In essence, two carbon atoms enter the cycle as an acetyl group, but two carbons leave the cycle as CO_2 before oxaloacetate is generated. Consequently, no net synthesis of oxaloacetate is possible. In contrast, plants have two additional enzymes enabling them to convert the carbon atoms of acetyl CoA into oxaloacetate (Section 17.5).

22.4 Fatty Acids Are Synthesized by Fatty Acid Synthase

Fatty acids are synthesized by a complex of enzymes that together are called *fatty acid synthase*. Because eating a typical Western diet meets our physiological needs for fats and lipids, adult human beings have little need for de novo fatty acid synthesis. However, many tissues, such as liver and adipose tissue, are capable of synthesizing fatty acids, and this synthesis is required under certain physiological conditions. For instance, fatty acid synthesis is necessary during embryonic development and during lactation in mammary glands. Inappropriate fatty acid synthesis in the liver of alcoholics contributes to liver failure.

Acetyl CoA, the end product of fatty acid degradation, is the precursor for virtually all fatty acids. The biochemical challenge is to link the two carbon units together and reduce the carbons to produce palmitate, a C_{16} fatty acid. Palmitate then serves as a precursor for the variety of other fatty acids.

Fatty acids are synthesized and degraded by different pathways

Although fatty acid synthesis is the reversal of the degradative pathway in regard to basic chemical reactions, the synthetic and degradative pathways are different mechanistically, again exemplifying the principle that *synthetic and degradative pathways are almost always distinct*. Some important differences between the pathways are as follows:

1. Synthesis takes place in the *cytoplasm,* in contrast with degradation, which takes place primarily in the mitochondrial matrix.

2. Intermediates in fatty acid synthesis are covalently linked to the sulfhydryl groups of an *acyl carrier protein* (ACP), whereas intermediates in fatty acid breakdown are covalently attached to the sulfhydryl group of coenzyme A.

3. The enzymes of fatty acid synthesis in higher organisms are joined in a *single polypeptide chain* called *fatty acid synthase.* In contrast, the degradative enzymes do not seem to be associated.

4. The growing fatty acid chain is elongated by the *sequential addition of two-carbon units* derived from acetyl CoA. The activated donor of two-carbon units in the elongation step is *malonyl ACP.* The elongation reaction is driven by the release of CO_2.

5. The reductant in fatty acid synthesis is *NADPH,* whereas the oxidants in fatty acid degradation are NAD^+ and *FAD.*

6. Elongation by the fatty acid synthase complex stops on the formation of *palmitate* (C_{16}). Further elongation and the insertion of double bonds are carried out by other enzyme systems.

The formation of malonyl CoA is the committed step in fatty acid synthesis

Fatty acid synthesis starts with the carboxylation of acetyl CoA to *malonyl CoA.* This irreversible reaction is the committed step in fatty acid synthesis.

Acetyl CoA   **Malonyl CoA**

The synthesis of malonyl CoA is catalyzed by *acetyl CoA carboxylase,* which contains a biotin prosthetic group. The carboxyl group of biotin is covalently attached to the ε amino group of a lysine residue, as in pyruvate carboxylase (see Figure 16.24) and propionyl CoA carboxylase (p. 650). As with these other enzymes, a carboxybiotin intermediate is formed at the expense of the hydrolysis of a molecule of ATP. The activated CO_2 group in this intermediate is then transferred to acetyl CoA to form malonyl CoA.

Biotin-enzyme + ATP + HCO_3^- $\rightleftharpoons$
$$CO_2\text{-biotin-enzyme} + ADP + P_i$$

CO_2-biotin-enzyme + acetyl CoA $\longrightarrow$ malonyl CoA + biotin-enzyme

Acetyl CoA carbozylase is also the essential regulatory enzyme for fatty acid metabolism (Section 22.5).

Intermediates in fatty acid synthesis are attached to an acyl carrier protein

The intermediates in fatty acid synthesis are linked to an acyl carrier protein. Specifically, they are linked to the sulfhydryl terminus of a phosphopantetheine group. In the degradation of fatty acids, this unit is present as part of coenzyme A, whereas, in their synthesis, it is attached to a serine

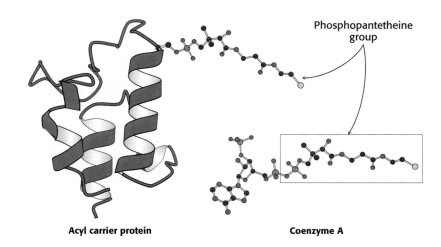

Figure 22.25 Phosphopantetheine. Both acyl carrier protein and coenzyme A include phosphopantetheine as their reactive units.

residue of the acyl carrier protein (Figure 22.25). Thus, ACP, a single polypeptide chain of 77 residues, can be regarded as a giant prosthetic group, a "macro CoA."

Fatty acid synthesis consists of a series of condensation, reduction, dehydration, and reduction reactions

The enzyme system that catalyzes the synthesis of saturated long-chain fatty acids from acetyl CoA, malonyl CoA, and NADPH is called the fatty acid synthase. The synthase is actually a complex of distinct enzymes. The fatty acid synthase complex in bacteria is readily dissociated into individual enzymes when the cells are broken apart. The availability of these isolated enzymes has helped biochemists elucidate the steps in fatty acid synthesis (Table 22.2). In fact, the reactions leading to fatty acid synthesis in higher organisms are very much like those of bacteria.

The elongation phase of fatty acid synthesis starts with the formation of acetyl ACP and malonyl ACP. *Acetyl transacylase* and *malonyl transacylase* catalyze these reactions.

$$\text{Acetyl CoA} + \text{ACP} \rightleftharpoons \text{acetyl ACP} + \text{CoA}$$

$$\text{Malonyl CoA} + \text{ACP} \rightleftharpoons \text{malonyl ACP} + \text{CoA}$$

Malonyl transacylase is highly specific, whereas acetyl transacylase can transfer acyl groups other than the acetyl unit, though at a much slower rate. The synthesis of fatty acids with an odd number of carbon atoms starts with propionyl ACP, which is formed from propionyl CoA by acetyl transacylase.

Acetyl ACP and malonyl ACP react to form acetoacetyl ACP (Figure 22.26). The *β-ketoacyl synthase,* also called the condensing enzyme, catalyzes this condensation reaction.

$$\text{Acetyl ACP} + \text{malonyl ACP} \longrightarrow \text{acetoacetyl ACP} + \text{ACP} + \text{CO}_2$$

Table 22.2 Principal reactions in fatty acid synthesis in bacteria

Step	Reaction	Enzyme
1	Acetyl CoA + HCO_3^- + ATP $\longrightarrow$ malonyl CoA + ADP + P_i + H^+	Acetyl CoA carboxylase
2	Acetyl CoA + ACP $\rightleftharpoons$ acetyl ACP + CoA	Acetyl transacylase
3	Malonyl CoA + ACP $\rightleftharpoons$ malonyl ACP + CoA	Malonyl transacylase
4	Acetyl ACP + malonyl ACP $\longrightarrow$ acetoacetyl ACP + ACP + CO_2	β-Ketoacyl synthase
5	Acetoacetyl ACP + NADPH + H^+ $\rightleftharpoons$ D-3-hydroxybutyryl ACP + $NADP^+$	β-Ketoacyl reductase
6	D-3-Hydroxybutyryl ACP $\rightleftharpoons$ crotonyl ACP + H_2O	3-Hydroxyacyl dehydratase
7	Crotonyl ACP + NADPH + H^+ $\longrightarrow$ butyryl ACP + $NADP^+$	Enoyl reductase

In the condensation reaction, a four-carbon unit is formed from a two-carbon unit and a three-carbon unit, and CO_2 is released. Why is the four-carbon unit not formed from two 2-carbon units—say, two molecules of acetyl ACP? The answer is that the equilibrium for the synthesis of acetoacetyl ACP from two molecules of acetyl ACP is highly unfavorable. In contrast, *the equilibrium is favorable if malonyl ACP is a reactant because its decarboxylation contributes a substantial decrease in free energy.* In effect, ATP drives the condensation reaction, though ATP does not directly participate in the condensation reaction. Instead, ATP is used to carboxylate acetyl CoA to malonyl CoA. The free energy thus stored in malonyl CoA is released in the decarboxylation accompanying the formation of acetoacetyl ACP. Although HCO_3^- is required for fatty acid synthesis, its carbon atom does not appear in the product. Rather, *all the carbon atoms of fatty acids containing an even number of carbon atoms are derived from acetyl CoA.*

The next three steps in fatty acid synthesis reduce the keto group at C-3 to a methylene group (see Figure 22.26). First, acetoacetyl ACP is reduced to D-3-hydroxybutyryl ACP by β-ketoacyl reductase. This reaction differs from the corresponding one in fatty acid degradation in two respects: (1) the D rather than the L isomer is formed; and (2) NADPH is the reducing agent, whereas NAD^+ is the oxidizing agent in β oxidation. This difference exemplifies the general principle that *NADPH is consumed in biosynthetic reactions, whereas NADH is generated in energy-yielding reactions.* Then D-3-hydroxybutyryl ACP is *dehydrated* to form crotonyl ACP, which is a *trans*-Δ^2-enoyl ACP by 3-hydroxyacyl dehydratase. The final step in the cycle *reduces* crotonyl ACP to butyryl ACP. NADPH is again the reductant, whereas FAD is the oxidant in the corresponding reaction in β oxidation. The bacterial enzyme that catalyzes this step, *enoyl reductase,* can be inhibited by *triclosan,* a broad-spectrum antibacterial agent that is added to a variety of products such as toothpaste, soaps, and skin creams. These last three reactions—a reduction, a dehydration, and a second reduction—convert acetoacetyl ACP into butyryl ACP, which completes the first elongation cycle.

In the second round of fatty acid synthesis, butyryl ACP condenses with malonyl ACP to form a C_6-β-ketoacyl ACP. This reaction is like the one in the first round, in which acetyl ACP condenses with malonyl ACP to form a C_4-β-ketoacyl ACP. Reduction, dehydration, and a second reduction convert the C_6-β-ketoacyl ACP into a C_6-acyl ACP, which is ready for a third round of elongation. The elongation cycles continue until C_{16}-acyl ACP is formed. This intermediate is a good substrate for a thioesterase that hydrolyzes C_{16}-acyl ACP to yield palmitate and ACP. *The thioesterase acts as a ruler to determine fatty acid chain length.* The synthesis of longer-chain fatty acids is discussed in Section 22.6.

Fatty acids are synthesized by a multifunctional enzyme complex in animals

Although the basic biochemical reactions in fatty acid synthesis are very similar in *E. coli* and eukaryotes, the structure of the synthase varies considerably. The component enzymes of animal fatty acid synthases, in contrast with those of *E. coli* and plants, are linked in a large polypeptide chain.

The structure of a large part of the mammalian fatty acid synthase has recently been determined, with the acyl carrier protein and thioesterase remaining to be resolved. The enzyme is a dimer of identical 270-kd subunits. Each chain contains all of the active sites required for activity, as well as an acyl carrier protein tethered to the complex (Figure 22.27A). Despite the fact that each chain possesses all of the enzymes required for fatty acid synthesis, the monomers are not active. A dimer is required.

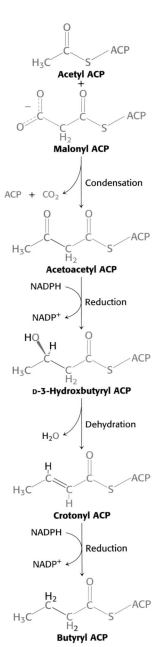

Figure 22.26 The steps of fatty acid synthesis. Fatty acid synthesis begins with the condensation of malonyl ACP and acetyl ACP to form acetoacetyl ACP. Acetoacetyl ACP is then reduced, dehydrated, and reduced again to form butyryl ACP. Another cycle begins with the condensation of butyryl ACP and malonyl ACP. The sequence of reactions is repeated until the final product palmitate is formed.

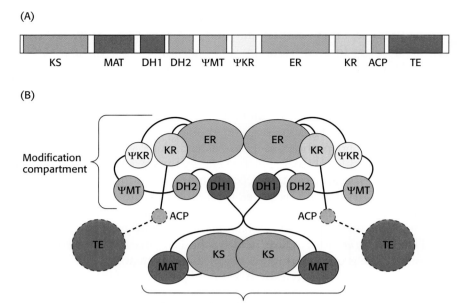

(A)

| KS | MAT | DH1 | DH2 | ΨMT | ΨKR | ER | KR | ACP | TE |

(B)

Modification compartment

Selecting and condensing compartment

Figure 22.27 The structure of the mammalian fatty acid synthase. (A) The arrangement of the catalytic activities present in a single polypeptide chain. (B) A cartoon of the dimer based on an x-ray crystallographic result. The Ψ-MT and Ψ-KR are inactive domains similar to methyl transferase and ketoreductase sequences. Although there are two domains for DH, only one is active. The inactive domains are presented in faded colors. Dotted lines outline domains for which the structure has not yet been determined. Abbreviations: KS, ketosynthase; MAT, malonyl-acetyl transferase; DH, dehydratase; Ψ-MT, methyl transferase (inactive); Ψ-KR, ketoreductase (inactive); ER, enoyl reductase; KR, ketoreductase; ACP, acyl carrier protein; TE, thioesterase.

The two component chains interact such that the enzyme activities are partitioned into two distinct compartments (Figure 22.27B). The selecting and condensing compartment binds the acetyl and malonyl substrates and condenses them to form the growing chain. Interestingly, the mammalian fatty acid synthase has one active site, malonyl-acetyl transacylase, that adds both acetyl CoA and malonyl CoA. In contrast, most other fatty acid synthases have two separate enzyme activities, one for acetyl CoA and one for malonyl CoA. The modification compartment is responsible for the reduction and dehydration activities that result in the saturated fatty acid product.

Let us consider one catalytic cycle of the fatty acid synthase complex (Figure 22.28). An elongation cycle begins when methyl-acetyl transferase (MAT) moves an acetyl unit from coenzyme A to the acyl carrier protein (ACP). β-Keto synthase (β-KS) accepts the acetyl unit, which forms a thioester with a cysteine residue at the β-KS active site. The vacant ACP is reloaded by MAT, this time with a malonyl moiety. Malonyl ACP visits the active site of β-KS where the condensation of the two 2-carbon fragments takes place on the ACP with the concomitant release of CO_2. The selecting and condensing process concludes with the β-ketoacyl product attached to the ACP.

The loaded ACP then sequentially visits the active sites of the modification compartment of the enzyme, where the β-keto group of the substrate is reduced to —OH, dehydrated, and finally reduced to yield the saturated acyl product, still attached to the ACP. With the completion of the modification process, the reduced product is transferred to the β-KS while the ACP accepts another malonyl unit. Condensation takes place and is followed by another modification cycle. The process is repeated until the thioesterase releases the final C_{16} palmitic acid product.

Many eukaryotic multienzyme complexes are multifunctional proteins in which different enzymes are linked covalently. An advantage of this arrangement is that the synthetic activity of different enzymes is coordinated. In addition, intermediates can be efficiently handed from one active site to another without leaving the assembly. Furthermore, a complex of covalently joined enzymes is more stable than one formed by noncovalent attractions. Each of the component enzymes is recognizably homologous to

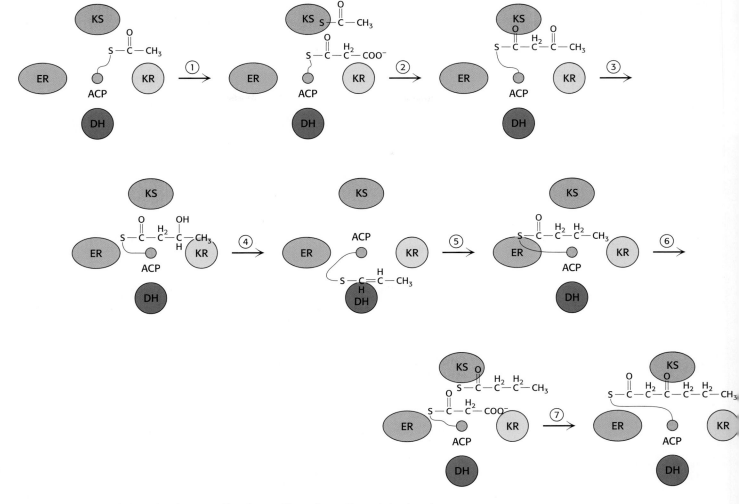

Figure 22.28 A catalytic cycle of mammalian fatty acid synthase. The cycle begins when MAT (not shown) attaches an acetyl unit to ACP. (1) ACP delivers the acetyl unit to KS, and MAT then attaches a malonyl unit to ACP. (2) ACP visits KS again, which condenses the acetyl and malonyl units to form the β-ketoacyl product, attached to the ACP. (3) ACP delivers the β-ketoacyl product to the KR enzyme, which reduces the keto group to an alcohol. (4) The β-hydroxyl product then visits the DH, which introduces a double bond with the loss of water. (5) The enoyl product is delivered to the ER enzyme, where the double bond is reduced. (6) ACP hands the reduced product to KS and is recharged with malonyl CoA by MAT. (7) KS condenses the two molecules on ACP, which is now ready to begin another cycle. See Figure 22.27 for abbreviations.

its bacterial counterpart. Multifunctional enzymes such as fatty acid synthase seem likely to have arisen in eukaryotic evolution by fusion of the individual genes of evolutionary ancestors.

The synthesis of palmitate requires 8 molecules of acetyl CoA, 14 molecules of NADPH, and 7 molecules of ATP

The stoichiometry of the synthesis of palmitate is

$$\text{Acetyl CoA} + 7 \text{ malonyl CoA} + 14 \text{ NADPH} + 20 \text{ H}^+ \longrightarrow$$
$$\text{palmitate} + 7 \text{ CO}_2 + 14 \text{ NADP}^+ + 8 \text{ CoA} + 6 \text{ H}_2\text{O}$$

The equation for the synthesis of the malonyl CoA used in the preceding reaction is

$$7 \text{ Acetyl CoA} + 7 \text{ CO}_2 + 7 \text{ ATP} \longrightarrow$$
$$7 \text{ malonyl CoA} + 7 \text{ ADP} + 7 \text{ P}_i + 14 \text{ H}^+$$

MITOCHONDRION   CYTOPLASM

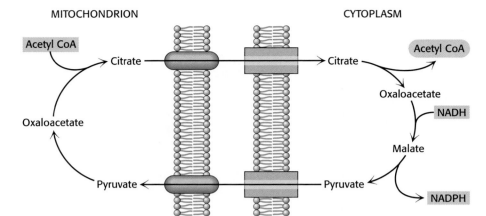

Figure 22.29 Transfer of acetyl CoA to the cytoplasm. Acetyl CoA is transferred from mitochondria to the cytoplasm, and the reducing potential of NADH is concomitantly converted into that of NADPH by this series of reactions.

Hence, the overall stoichiometry for the synthesis of palmitate is

$$8 \text{ Acetyl CoA} + 7 \text{ ATP} + 14 \text{ NADPH} + 6 \text{ H}^+ \longrightarrow$$
$$\text{palmitate} + 14 \text{ NADP}^+ + 8 \text{ CoA} + 6 \text{ H}_2\text{O} + 7 \text{ ADP} + 7 \text{ P}_i$$

Citrate carries acetyl groups from mitochondria to the cytoplasm for fatty acid synthesis

Fatty acids are synthesized in the cytoplasm, whereas acetyl CoA is formed from pyruvate in mitochondria. Hence, acetyl CoA must be transferred from mitochondria to the cytoplasm for fatty acid synthesis. Mitochondria, however, are not readily permeable to acetyl CoA. Recall that carnitine carries only long-chain fatty acids. *The barrier to acetyl CoA is bypassed by citrate, which carries acetyl groups across the inner mitochondrial membrane.* Citrate is formed in the mitochondrial matrix by the condensation of acetyl CoA with oxaloacetate (Figure 22.29). When present at high levels, citrate is transported to the cytoplasm, where it is cleaved by *ATP-citrate lyase.*

$$\text{Citrate} + \text{ATP} + \text{CoA} + \text{H}_2\text{O} \longrightarrow$$
$$\text{acetyl CoA} + \text{ADP} + \text{P}_i + \text{oxaloacetate}$$

Thus, acetyl CoA and oxaloacetate are transferred from mitochondria to the cytoplasm at the expense of the hydrolysis of a molecule of ATP.

Several sources supply NADPH for fatty acid synthesis

Oxaloacetate formed in the transfer of acetyl groups to the cytoplasm must now be returned to the mitochondria. The inner mitochondrial membrane is impermeable to oxaloacetate. Hence, a series of bypass reactions are needed. Most importantly, these reactions generate much of the NADPH needed for fatty acid synthesis. First, oxaloacetate is reduced to malate by NADH. This reaction is catalyzed by a *malate dehydrogenase* in the cytoplasm.

$$\text{Oxaloacetate} + \text{NADH} + \text{H}^+ \rightleftharpoons \text{malate} + \text{NAD}^+$$

Second, malate is oxidatively decarboxylated by an *NADP*$^+$*-linked malate enzyme* (also called *malic enzyme*).

$$\text{Malate} + \text{NADP}^+ \longrightarrow \text{pyruvate} + \text{CO}_2 + \text{NADPH}$$

The pyruvate formed in this reaction readily enters mitochondria, where it is carboxylated to oxaloacetate by pyruvate carboxylase.

Lyases

Enzymes catalyzing the cleavage of C—C, C—O, or C—N bonds by elimination. A double bond is formed in these reactions.

$$\text{Pyruvate} + CO_2 + ATP + H_2O \longrightarrow \text{oxaloacetate} + ADP + P_i + 2\,H^+$$

The sum of these three reactions is

$$NADP^+ + NADH + ATP + H_2O \longrightarrow$$
$$NADPH + NAD^+ + ADP + P_i + H^+$$

Thus, *one molecule of NADPH is generated for each molecule of acetyl CoA that is transferred from mitochondria to the cytoplasm.* Hence, eight molecules of NADPH are formed when eight molecules of acetyl CoA are transferred to the cytoplasm for the synthesis of palmitate. *The additional six molecules of NADPH required for this process come from the pentose phosphate pathway* (Section 20.3).

The accumulation of the precursors for fatty acid synthesis is a wonderful example of the coordinated use of multiple pathways. The citric acid cycle, transport of oxaloacetate from the mitochondria, and pentose phosphate pathway provide the carbon atoms and reducing power, whereas glycolysis and oxidative phosphorylation provide the ATP to meet the needs for fatty acid synthesis (Figure 22.30).

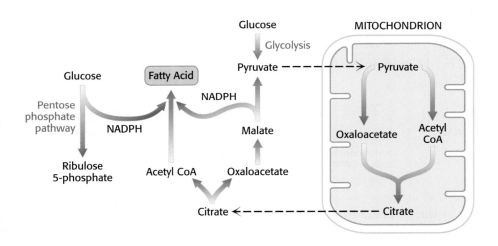

Figure 22.30 PATHWAY INTEGRATION: Fatty acid synthesis. Fatty acid synthesis requires the cooperation of various metabolic pathways located in different cellular compartments.

Fatty acid synthase inhibitors may be useful drugs

Fatty acid synthase is overexpressed in most human cancers and its expression is correlated with tumor malignancy. The fatty acids are not stored as an energy source, but rather are used as precursors for the synthesis of phospholipids, which are then incorporated into membranes in the rapidly growing cancer cells. Researchers intrigued by this observation have tested inhibitors of fatty acid synthase on mice to see if the inhibitors slow tumor growth. These inhibitors do indeed slow tumor growth, apparently by inducing apoptosis. However, another startling observation was made: *mice treated with inhibitors of the condensing enzyme showed remarkable weight loss* because they ate less. Thus, fatty acid synthase inhibitors are exciting candidates both as antitumor and as antiobesity drugs.

22.5 The Elongation and Unsaturation of Fatty Acids Are Accomplished by Accessory Enzyme Systems

The major product of the fatty acid synthase is palmitate. In eukaryotes, longer fatty acids are formed by elongation reactions catalyzed by enzymes on the cytoplasmic face of the *endoplasmic reticulum membrane*. These reactions add two-carbon units sequentially to the carboxyl ends of both saturated and unsaturated fatty acyl CoA substrates. Malonyl CoA is the two-carbon donor in the elongation of fatty acyl CoAs. Again, condensation is driven by the decarboxylation of malonyl CoA.

Membrane-bound enzymes generate unsaturated fatty acids

Endoplasmic reticulum systems also introduce double bonds into long-chain acyl CoAs. For example, in the conversion of stearoyl CoA into oleoyl CoA, a cis-Δ^9 double bond is inserted by an oxidase that employs *molecular oxygen* and *NADH* (or *NADPH*).

$$\text{Stearoyl CoA} + \text{NADH} + \text{H}^+ + \text{O}_2 \longrightarrow$$
$$\text{oleoyl CoA} + \text{NAD}^+ + 2\,\text{H}_2\text{O}$$

This reaction is catalyzed by a complex of three membrane-bound proteins: *NADH-cytochrome b_5 reductase, cytochrome b_5,* and a *desaturase* (Figure 22.31). First, electrons are transferred from NADH to the FAD moiety of NADH-cytochrome b_5 reductase. The heme iron atom of cytochrome b_5 is then reduced to the Fe^{2+} state. The nonheme iron atom of the desaturase is subsequently converted into the Fe^{2+} state, which enables it to interact with O_2 and the saturated fatty acyl CoA substrate. A double bond is formed and two molecules of H_2O are released. Two electrons come from NADH and two from the single bond of the fatty acyl substrate.

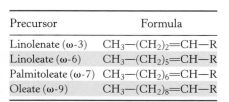

Figure 22.31 Electron-transport chain in the desaturation of fatty acids.

A variety of unsaturated fatty acids can be formed from oleate by a combination of elongation and desaturation reactions. For example, oleate can be elongated to a 20:1 cis-Δ^{11} fatty acid. Alternatively, a second double bond can be inserted to yield an 18:2 cis-Δ^6, Δ^9 fatty acid. Similarly, palmitate (16:0) can be oxidized to palmitoleate (16:1 cis-Δ^9), which can then be elongated to *cis*-vaccenate (18:1 cis-Δ^{11}).

Unsaturated fatty acids in mammals are derived from either palmitoleate (16:1), oleate (18:1), linoleate (18:2), or linolenate (18:3). The number of carbon atoms from the ω end of a derived unsaturated fatty acid to the nearest double bond identifies its precursor.

Mammals lack the enzymes to introduce double bonds at carbon atoms beyond C-9 in the fatty acid chain. Hence, mammals cannot synthesize linoleate (18:2 cis-Δ^9,Δ^{12}) and linolenate (18:3 cis-Δ^9,Δ^{12},Δ^{15}). Linoleate and linolenate are the two essential fatty acids. The term essential means that they must be supplied in the diet because they are required by an organism and cannot be synthesized by the organism itself. Linoleate and linolenate furnished by the diet are the starting points for the synthesis of a variety of other unsaturated fatty acids.

Precursor	Formula
Linolenate (ω-3)	$\text{CH}_3\text{—}(\text{CH}_2)_2\text{=CH—R}$
Linoleate (ω-6)	$\text{CH}_3\text{—}(\text{CH}_2)_5\text{=CH—R}$
Palmitoleate (ω-7)	$\text{CH}_3\text{—}(\text{CH}_2)_6\text{=CH—R}$
Oleate (ω-9)	$\text{CH}_3\text{—}(\text{CH}_2)_8\text{=CH—R}$

Eicosanoid hormones are derived from polyunsaturated fatty acids

Arachidonate, a 20:4 fatty acid derived from linoleate, is the major precursor of several classes of signal molecules: prostaglandins, prostacyclins, thromboxanes, and leukotrienes (Figure 22.32).

A prostaglandin is a 20-carbon fatty acid containing a 5-carbon ring (Figure 22.33). This basic compound is modified by reductases and isomerases to yield nine major classes of prostaglandins, designated PGA through PGI; a subscript denotes the number of carbon–carbon double bonds outside the ring. Prostaglandins with two double bonds, such as PGE_2, are derived from arachidonate; the other two double bonds of this precursor are lost in forming a 5-membered ring. *Prostacyclin* and *thromboxanes* are related compounds that arise from a nascent prostaglandin. They are generated by *prostacyclin synthase* and *thromboxane synthase*, respectively. Alternatively, arachidonate can be converted into *leukotrienes* by the action of *lipoxygenase*. Leukotrienes, first found in leukocytes, contain three conjugated double bonds—hence, the name. Prostaglandins, prostacyclin, thromboxanes, and leukotrienes are called *eicosanoids* (from the Greek *eikosi*, "twenty") because they contain 20 carbon atoms.

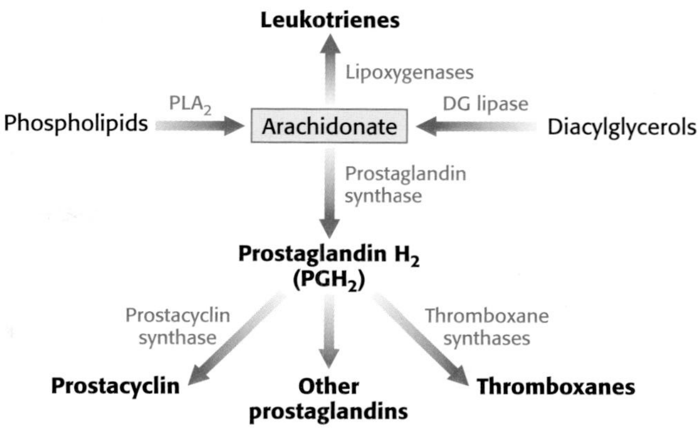

Figure 22.32 Arachidonate is the major precursor of eicosanoid hormones. Prostaglandin synthase catalyzes the first step in a pathway leading to prostaglandins, prostacyclins, and thromboxanes. Lipoxygenase catalyzes the initial step in a pathway leading to leukotrienes.

Prostaglandins and other eicosanoids are *local hormones* because they are short-lived. They alter the activities both of the cells in which they are synthesized and of adjoining cells by binding to 7TM receptors. Their effects may vary from one cell type to another, in contrast with the more-uniform actions of global hormones such as insulin and glucagon. Prostaglandins stimulate inflammation, regulate blood flow to particular organs, control ion transport across membranes, modulate synaptic transmission, and induce sleep.

Recall that aspirin blocks access to the active site of the enzyme that converts arachidonate into prostaglandin H_2 (Section 12.3). Because arachidonate is the precursor of other prostaglandins, prostacyclin, and thromboxanes, blocking this step interferes with many signaling pathways. Aspirin's ability to obstruct these pathways accounts for its wide-ranging effects on inflammation, fever, pain, and blood clotting.

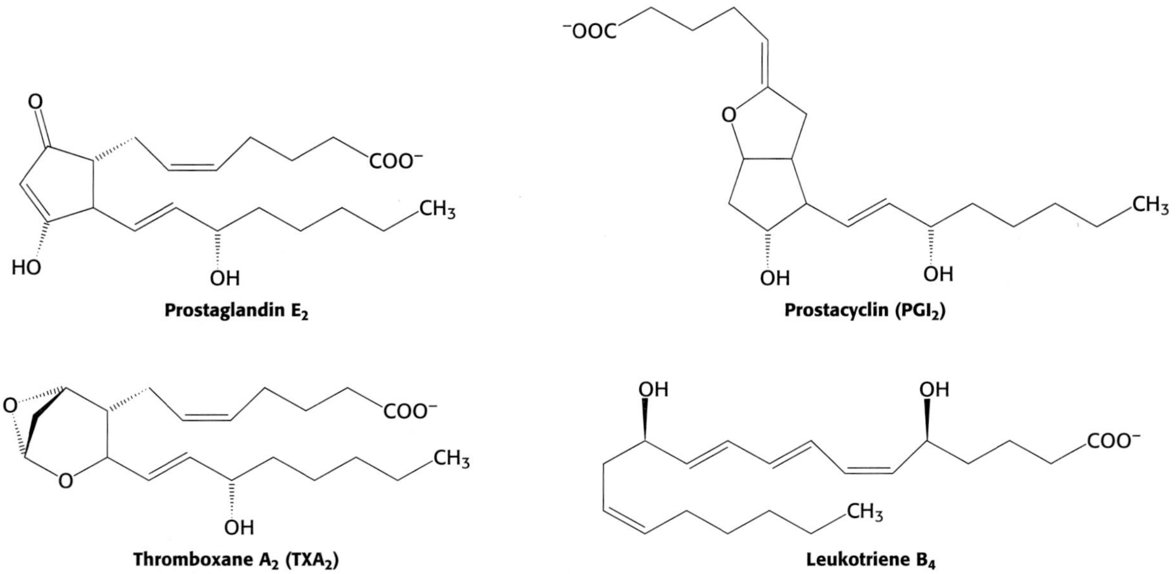

Figure 22.33 Structures of several eicosanoids.

22.6 Acetyl CoA Carboxylase Plays a Key Role in Controlling Fatty Acid Metabolism

Fatty acid metabolism is stringently controlled so that synthesis and degradation are highly responsive to physiological needs. Fatty acid synthesis is maximal when carbohydrates and energy are plentiful and when fatty acids are scarce. *Acetyl CoA carboxylase plays an essential role in regulating fatty acid synthesis and degradation.* Recall that this enzyme catalyzes the committed step in fatty acid synthesis: the production of malonyl CoA (the activated two-carbon donor). This important enzyme is subject to both local and hormonal regulation. We will examine each of these levels of regulation in turn.

Acetyl CoA carboxylase is regulated by conditions in the cell

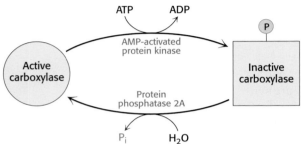

Figure 22.34 Control of acetyl CoA carboxylase. Acetyl CoA carboxylase is inhibited by phosphorylation.

Acetyl CoA carboxylase responds to changes in its immediate environment. *Acetyl CoA carboxylase is switched off by phosphorylation* and activated by dephosphorylation (Figure 22.34). *AMP-dependent protein kinase* (AMPK) converts the carboxylase into an inactive form by modifying three serine residues. AMPK is essentially a fuel gauge; it is activated by AMP and inhibited by ATP. Thus, the carboxylase is inactivated when the energy charge is low. Fats are not synthesized when energy is required.

The carboxylase is also allosterically stimulated by citrate. Citrate acts in an unusual manner on inactive acetyl CoA carboxylase, which exists as isolated inactive dimers. Citrate facilitates the polymerization of the inactive dimers into active filaments (Figure 22.35). Citrate-induced polymerization can partly reverse the inhibition produced by phosphorylation (Figure 22.36). The level of citrate is high when both acetyl CoA and ATP are abundant, signifying that raw materials and energy are available for fatty acid synthesis. The stimulatory effect of citrate on the carboxylase is counteracted by *palmitoyl CoA,* which is abundant when there is an excess of fatty acids. Palmitoyl CoA causes the filaments to disassemble into the inactive subunits. Palmitoyl CoA also inhibits the translocase that transports citrate from mitochondria to the cytoplasm, as well as glucose 6-phosphate dehydrogenase, which generates NADPH in the pentose phosphate pathway.

Acetyl CoA carboxylase also plays a role in the regulation of fatty acid degradation. Malonyl CoA, the product of the carboxylase reaction, is present at a high level when fuel molecules are abundant. *Malonyl CoA inhibits carnitine acyltransferase I, preventing the entry of fatty acyl CoAs into the mitochondrial matrix in times of plenty.* Malonyl CoA is an especially effective inhibitor of carnitine acyltransferase I in heart and muscle, tissues that have little fatty acid synthesis capacity of their own. In these tissues, acetyl CoA carboxylase may be a purely regulatory enzyme.

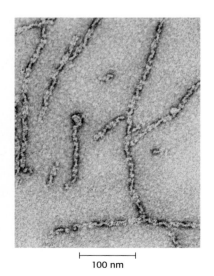

Figure 22.35 Filaments of acetyl CoA carboxylase. The electron micrograph shows the enzymatically active filamentous form of acetyl CoA carboxylase from chicken liver. The inactive form is a dimer of 265-kd subunits. [Courtesy of Dr. M. Daniel Lane.]

Acetyl CoA carboxylase is regulated by a variety of hormones

Acetyl CoA carboxylase is controlled by the hormones glucagon, epinephrine, and insulin, which denote the overall energy status of the organism. *Insulin stimulates fatty acid synthesis by activating the carboxylase, whereas glucagon and epinephrine have the reverse effect.*

Regulation by glucagon and epinephrine.   Consider, again, a person who has just awakened from a night's sleep and begins a bout of exercise. As mentioned, glycogen stores will be low, but lipids are readily available for mobilization.

As stated earlier, the hormones glucagon and epinephrine, present under conditions of fasting and exercise, will stimulate the release of fatty acids from triacylglycerols in fat cells, which will be released into the blood, and probably from muscle cells, where they will be used immediately as fuel. These same hormones will inhibit fatty acid synthesis by inhibiting acetyl CoA carboxylase. Although the exact mechanism by which these hormones exert their effects is not known, the net result is to augment the inhibition by the AMP-dependent kinase. This result makes sound physiological sense: when the energy level of the cell is low, as signified by a high concentration of AMP, and the energy level of the organism is low, as signaled by glucagon, fats should not be synthesized. Epinephrine, which signals the need for immediate energy, enhances this effect. Hence, *these catabolic hormones switch off fatty acid synthesis by keeping the carboxylase in the inactive phosphorylated state.*

Regulation by insulin. Now consider the situation after the exercise has ended and the runner has had a meal. In this case, the hormone insulin inhibits the mobilization of fatty acids and stimulates their accumulation as triacylglycerols by muscle and adipose tissue. Insulin also stimulates fatty acid synthesis by activating acetyl CoA carboxylase. Insulin stimulates the carboxylase by stimulating the activity of a protein phosphatase that dephosphorylates and activates acetyl CoA carboxylase. Thus, the signal molecules glucagon, epinephrine, and insulin act in concert on triacylglycerol metabolism and acetyl CoA carboxylase to carefully regulate the utilization and storage of fatty acids.

Response to diet. *Long-term control is mediated by changes in the rates of synthesis and degradation of the enzymes participating in fatty acid synthesis.* Animals that have fasted and are then fed high-carbohydrate, low-fat diets show marked increases in their amounts of acetyl CoA carboxylase and fatty acid synthase within a few days. This type of regulation is known as *adaptive control.* This regulation, which is mediated both by insulin and glucose, is at the level of gene transcription.

(A)

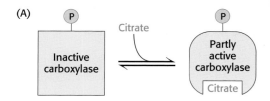

(B)

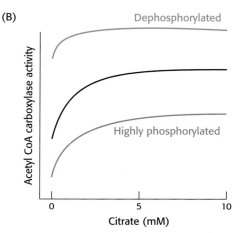

Figure 22.36 Dependence of the catalytic activity of acetyl CoA carboxylase on the concentration of citrate. (A) Citrate can partly activate the phosphorylated carboxylase. (B) The dephosphorylated form of the carboxylase is highly active even when citrate is absent. Citrate partly overcomes the inhibition produced by phosphorylation. [After G. M. Mabrouk, I. M. Helmy, K. G. Thampy, and S. J. Wakil. *J. Biol. Chem.* 265:6330–6338, 1990.]

Summary

22.1 Triacylglycerols Are Highly Concentrated Energy Stores

Fatty acids are physiologically important as (1) fuel molecules, (2) components of phospholipids and glycolipids, (3) hydrophobic modifiers of proteins, and (4) hormones and intracellular messengers. They are stored in adipose tissue as triacylglycerols (neutral fat).

22.2 The Use of Fatty Acids As Fuel Requires Three Stages of Processing

Triacylglycerols can be mobilized by the hydrolytic action of lipases that are under hormonal control. Glucagon and epinephrine stimulate triacylglycerol breakdown by activating the lipase. Insulin, in contrast, inhibits lipolysis. Fatty acids are activated to acyl CoAs, transported across the inner mitochondrial membrane by carnitine, and degraded in the mitochondrial matrix by a recurring sequence of four reactions: oxidation by FAD, hydration, oxidation by NAD^+, and thiolysis by coenzyme A. The $FADH_2$ and NADH formed in the oxidation steps transfer their electrons to O_2 by means of the respiratory chain, whereas the acetyl CoA formed in the thiolysis step normally enters the citric acid cycle by condensing with oxaloacetate. Mammals are unable to convert fatty acids into glucose, because they lack a pathway for the net production of oxaloacetate, pyruvate, or other gluconeogenic intermediates from acetyl CoA.

22.3 Unsaturated and Odd-Chain Fatty Acids Require Additional Steps for Degradation

Fatty acids that contain double bonds or odd numbers of carbon atoms require ancillary steps to be degraded. An isomerase and a reductase are required for the oxidation of unsaturated fatty acids, whereas propionyl CoA derived from chains with odd numbers of carbon atoms requires a vitamin B_{12}-dependent enzyme to be converted into succinyl CoA.

22.4 Fatty Acids Are Synthesized by Fatty Acid Synthase

Fatty acids are synthesized in the cytoplasm by a different pathway from that of β oxidation. Fatty acid synthase is the enzyme complex responsible for fatty acid synthase. Synthesis starts with the carboxylation of acetyl CoA to malonyl CoA, the committed step. This ATP-driven reaction is catalyzed by acetyl CoA carboxylase, a biotin enzyme. The intermediates in fatty acid synthesis are linked to an acyl carrier protein. Acetyl ACP is formed from acetyl CoA, and malonyl ACP is formed from malonyl CoA. Acetyl ACP and malonyl ACP condense to form acetoacetyl ACP, a reaction driven by the release of CO_2 from the activated malonyl unit. A reduction, a dehydration, and a second reduction follow. NADPH is the reductant in these steps. The butyryl ACP formed in this way is ready for a second round of elongation, starting with the addition of a two-carbon unit from malonyl ACP. Seven rounds of elongation yield palmitoyl ACP, which is hydrolyzed to palmitate. In higher organisms, the enzymes catalyzing fatty acid synthesis are covalently linked in a multifunctional enzyme complex. A reaction cycle based on the formation and cleavage of citrate carries acetyl groups from mitochondria to the cytoplasm. NADPH needed for synthesis is generated in the transfer of reducing equivalents from mitochondria by the combined action of cytoplasmic malate dehydrogenase and malic enzyme and by the pentose phosphate pathway.

22.5 The Elongation and Unsaturation of Fatty Acids Are Accomplished by Accessory Enzyme Systems

Fatty acids are elongated and desaturated by enzyme systems in the endoplasmic reticulum membrane. Desaturation requires NADH and O_2 and is carried out by a complex consisting of a flavoprotein, a cytochrome, and a nonheme iron protein. Mammals lack the enzymes to introduce double bonds distal to C-9, and so they require linoleate and linolenate in their diets.

Arachidonate, an essential precursor of prostaglandins and other signal molecules, is derived from linoleate. This 20:4 polyunsaturated fatty acid is the precursor of several classes of signal molecules—prostaglandins, prostacyclins, thromboxanes, and leukotrienes—that act as messengers and local hormones because of their transience. They are called eicosanoids because they contain 20 carbon atoms. Aspirin (acetylsalicylate), an anti-inflammatory and antithrombotic drug, irreversibly blocks the synthesis of these eicosanoids.

22.6 Acetyl CoA Carboxylase Plays a Key Role in Controlling Fatty Acid Metabolism

Fatty acid synthesis and degradation are reciprocally regulated so that both are not simultaneously active. Acetyl CoA carboxylase, the essential control site, is phosphorylated and inactivated by AMP-dependent kinase. The phosphorylation is reversed by a protein phosphatase. Citrate, which signals an abundance of building blocks and energy, partly reverses the inhibition by phosphorylation. Carboxylase activity is stimulated by insulin and inhibited by glucagon and epinephrine. In times of plenty, fatty acyl CoAs do not enter the mitochondrial matrix, because malonyl CoA inhibits carnitine acyltransferase I.

Key Terms

triacylglycerol (neutral fat, triglyceride) (p. 639)

acyl adenylate (p. 645)

carnitine (p. 645)

β-oxidation pathway (p. 646)

vitamin B_{12} (cobalamin) (p. 649)

peroxisome (p. 652)

ketone body (p. 653)

acyl carrier protein (ACP) (p. 657)

fatty acid synthase (p. 657)

malonyl CoA (p. 657)

acetyl CoA carboxylase (p. 657)

arachidonate (p. 664)

prostaglandin (p. 665)

eicosanoid (p. 665)

AMP-dependent protein kinase (AMPK) (p. 666)

Problems

1. *After lipolysis.* Write a balanced equation for the conversion of glycerol into pyruvate. Which enzymes are required in addition to those of the glycolytic pathway?

2. *Forms of energy.* The partial reactions leading to the synthesis of acyl CoA (equations 1 and 2, p. 645) are freely reversible. The equilibrium constant for the sum of these reactions is close to 1, meaning that the energy levels of the reactants and products are about equal, even though a molecule of ATP has been hydrolyzed. Explain why these reactions are readily reversible.

3. *Activation fee.* The reaction for the activation of fatty acids before degradation is

$$R-\overset{\displaystyle O}{\overset{\displaystyle \|}{C}}-O^- + CoA + ATP + H_2O \longrightarrow$$

$$R-\overset{\displaystyle O}{\overset{\displaystyle \|}{C}}-SCoA + AMP + 2\,P_i + 2\,H^+$$

This reaction is quite favorable because the equivalent of two molecules of ATP is hydrolyzed. Explain why, from a biochemical bookkeeping point of view, the equivalent of two molecules of ATP is used despite the fact that the left side of the equation has only one molecule of ATP.

4. *Proper sequence.* Place the following list of reactions or relevant locations in the β oxidation of fatty acids in the proper order.

(a) Reaction with carnitine

(b) Fatty acid in the cytoplasm

(c) Activation of fatty acid by joining to CoA

(d) Hydration

(e) NAD^+-linked oxidation

(f) Thiolysis

(g) Acyl CoA in mitochondrion

(h) FAD-linked oxidation.

5. *Remembrance of reactions past.* We have encountered reactions similar to the oxidation, hydration, and oxidation reactions of fatty acid degradation earlier in our study of biochemistry. What other pathway employs this set of reactions?

6. *A phantom acetyl CoA?* In the equation for fatty acid degradation shown here, only seven molecules of CoA are required to yield eight molecules of acetyl CoA. How is this difference possible?

Palmitoyl CoA + 7 FAD + 7 NAD^+
+ 7 CoASH + 7 $H_2O \longrightarrow$
8 Acetyl CoA + 7 $FADH_2$ + 7 NADH + 7 H^+

7. *Comparing yields.* Compare the ATP yields from palmitic acid and palmitoleic acid.

8. *Counting ATPs 1.* What is the ATP yield for the complete oxidation of C_{17} (heptadecanoic) fatty acid? Assume that the propionyl CoA ultimately yields oxaloacetate in the citric acid cycle.

9. *Sweet temptation.* Stearic acid is a C_{18} fatty acid component of chocolate. Suppose you had a depressing day and decided to settle matters by gorging on chocolate. How much ATP would you derive from the complete oxidation of stearic acid to CO_2?

10. *The best storage form.* Compare the ATP yield from the complete oxidation of glucose, a six-carbon carbohydrate, and hexanoic acid, a six-carbon fatty acid. Hexanoic acid is also called caprioic acid and is responsible for the "aroma" of goats. Why are fats better fuels than carbohydrates?

11. *From fatty acid to ketone body.* Write a balanced equation for the conversion of stearate into acetoacetate.

12. *Generous, but not to a fault.* Liver is the primary site of ketone-body synthesis. However, ketone bodies are not used by the liver but are released for other tissues to use. The liver does gain energy in the process of synthesizing and releasing ketone bodies. Calculate the number of molecules of ATP generated by the liver in the conversion of palmitate, a C_{16} fatty acid, into acetoacetate.

13. *Counting ATPs 2.* How much energy is attained with the complete oxidation of the ketone body D-3-hydroxybutyrate?

14. *Another view.* Why might someone argue that the answer to Problem 13 is wrong?

15. *An accurate adage.* An old biochemistry adage is that *fats burn in the flame of carbohydrates.* What is the molecular basis of this adage?

16. *Refsum disease.* Phytanic acid is a branched-chain fatty acid component of chlorophyll and is a significant component of milk. In susceptible people, phytanic acid can accumulate, leading to neurological problems. This syndrome is called Refsum disease or phytanic acid storage disease.

Phytanic acid

(a) Why does phytanic acid accumulate?

(b) What enzyme activity would you invent to prevent its accumulation?

17. *A hot diet.* Tritium is a radioactive isotope of hydrogen and can be readily detected. A fully tritiated, six-carbon saturated fatty acid is administered to a rat, and a muscle biopsy of the rat is taken by concerned, sensitive, and discrete technical assistants. These assistants carefully isolate all of the acetyl CoA generated from the β oxidation of the radioactive fatty acid and remove the CoA to form acetate. What will be the overall tritium-to-carbon ratio of the isolated acetate?

18. *Finding triacylglycerols in all the wrong places.* Insulin-dependent diabetes is often accompanied by high levels of triacylglycerols in the blood. Suggest a biochemical explanation.

19. *Counterpoint.* Compare and contrast fatty acid oxidation and synthesis with respect to

(a) site of the process.

(b) acyl carrier.

(c) reductants and oxidants.

(d) stereochemistry of the intermediates.

(e) direction of synthesis or degradation.

(f) organization of the enzyme system.

20. *A supple synthesis.* Myristate, a saturated C_{14} fatty acid, is used as an emollient for cosmetics and topical medicinal preparations. Write a balanced equation for the synthesis of myristate.

21. *The cost of cleanliness.* Lauric acid is a 12-carbon fatty acid with no double bonds. The sodium salt of lauric acid (sodium laurate) is a common detergent used in a variety of products, including laundry detergent, shampoo, and toothpaste. How many molecules of ATP and NADPH are required to synthesize lauric acid?

22. *Proper organization.* Arrange the following steps in fatty acid synthesis in their proper order.

(a) Dehydration

(b) Condensation

(c) Release of a C_{16} fatty acid

(d) Reduction of a carbonyl group

(e) Formation of malonyl ACP

23. *No access to assets.* What would be the effect on fatty acid synthesis of a mutation in ATP-citrate lyase that reduces the enzyme's activity? Explain.

24. *The truth and nothing but.* True or False. If false, explain.

(a) Biotin is required for fatty acid synthase activity.

(b) The condensation reaction in fatty acid synthesis is powered by the decarboxylation of malonyl CoA.

(c) Fatty acid synthesis does not depend on ATP.

(d) Palmitate is the end product of fatty acid synthase.

(e) All of the enzyme activities required for fatty acid synthesis in mammals are contained in a single polypeptide chain.

(f) Fatty acid synthase in mammals is active as a monomer.

(g) The fatty acid arachidonate is a precursor for signal molecules.

(h) Acetyl CoA carboxylase is inhibited by citrate.

25. *Odd fat out.* Suggest how fatty acids with odd numbers of carbons are synthesized.

26. *Labels.* Suppose that you had an in vitro fatty acid-synthesizing system that had all of the enzymes and cofactors required for fatty acid synthesis except for acetyl CoA. To this system, you added acetyl CoA that contained radioactive hydrogen (^{3}H, tritium) and carbon 14 (^{14}C) as shown here.

The ratio of ^{3}H/^{14}C is 3. What would the ^{3}H/^{14}C ratio be after the synthesis of palmitic acid (C_{16}) with the use of the radioactive acetyl CoA?

27. *A tight embrace.* Avidin, a glycoprotein found in eggs, has a high affinity for biotin. Avidin can bind biotin and

prevent its use by the body. How might a diet rich in raw eggs affect fatty acid synthesis? What will be the effect on fatty acid synthesis of a diet rich in cooked eggs? Explain.

28. *Alpha or omega?* Only one acetyl CoA molecule is used directly in fatty acid synthesis. Identify the carbon atoms in palmitic acid that were donated by acetyl CoA.

29. *Now you see it, now you don't.* Although HCO_3^- is required for fatty acid synthesis, its carbon atom does not appear in the product. Explain how this omission is possible.

30. *It is all about communication.* Why is citrate an appropriate inhibitor of phosphofructokinase?

31. *Tracing carbon atoms.* Consider a cell extract that actively synthesizes palmitate. Suppose that a fatty acid synthase in this preparation forms one molecule of palmitate in about 5 minutes. A large amount of malonyl CoA labeled with ^{14}C in each carbon atom of its malonyl unit is suddenly added to this system, and fatty acid synthesis is stopped a minute later by altering the pH. The fatty acids are analyzed for radioactivity. Which carbon atom of the palmitate formed by this system is more radioactive—C-1 or C-14?

32. *An unaccepting mutant.* The serine residues in acetyl CoA carboxylase that are the target of the AMP-dependent protein kinase are mutated to alanine. What is a likely consequence of this mutation?

33. *Sources.* For each of the following unsaturated fatty acids, indicate whether the biosynthetic precursor in animals is palmitoleate, oleate, linoleate, or linolenate.

(a) 18:1 cis-Δ^{11} (d) 20:3 cis-Δ^5, Δ^8, Δ^{11}

(b) 18:3 cis-Δ^6, Δ^9, Δ^{12} (e) 22:1 cis-Δ^{13}

(c) 20:2 cis-Δ^{11}, Δ^{14} (f) 22:6 cis-Δ^4, Δ^7, Δ^{10}, Δ^{13}, Δ^{16}, Δ^{19}

34. *Driven by decarboxylation.* What is the role of decarboxylation in fatty acid synthesis? Name another key reaction in a metabolic pathway that employs this mechanistic motif.

35. *Kinase surfeit.* Suppose that a promoter mutation leads to the overproduction of protein kinase A in adipose cells. How might fatty acid metabolism be altered by this mutation?

36. *Blocked assets.* The presence of a fuel molecule in the cytoplasm does not ensure that the fuel molecule can be effectively used. Give two examples of how impaired transport of metabolites between compartments leads to disease.

37. *Elegant inversion.* Peroxisomes have an alternative pathway for oxidizing polyunsaturated fatty acids. They contain a hydratase that converts D-3-hydroxyacyl CoA into *trans*-Δ^2-enoyl CoA. How can this enzyme be used to oxidize CoAs containing a cis double bond at an even-numbered carbon atom (e.g., the cis-Δ^{12} double bond of linoleate)?

38. *Covalent catastrophe.* What is a potential disadvantage of having many catalytic sites together on one very long polypeptide chain?

39. *Missing acyl CoA dehydrogenases.* A number of genetic deficiencies in acyl CoA dehydrogenases have been described. This deficiency presents early in life after a period of fasting. Symptoms include vomiting, lethargy, and sometimes coma. Not only are blood levels of glucose low (hypoglycemia), but starvation-induced ketosis is absent. Provide a biochemical explanation for these last two observations.

40. *Effects of clofibrate.* High blood levels of triacylglycerides are associated with heart attacks and strokes. Clofibrate, a drug that increases the activity of peroxisomes, is sometimes used to treat patients with such a condition. What is the biochemical basis for this treatment?

41. *A different kind of enzyme.* Figure 22.36 shows the response of acetyl CoA carboxylase to varying amounts of citrate. Explain this effect in light of the allosteric effects that citrate has on the enzyme. Predict the effects of increasing concentrations of palmitoyl CoA.

Mechanism Problems

42. *Variation on a theme.* Thiolase is homologous in structure to the condensing enzyme. On the basis of this observation, propose a mechanism for the cleavage of 3-ketoacyl CoA by CoA.

43. *Two plus three to make four.* Propose a reaction mechanism for the condensation of an acetyl unit with a malonyl unit to form an acetoacetyl unit in fatty acid synthesis.

Chapter Integration Problems

44. *Ill-advised diet.* Suppose that, for some bizarre reason, you decided to exist on a diet of whale and seal blubber, exclusively.

(a) How would lack of carbohydrates affect your ability to utilize fats?

(b) What would your breath smell like?

(c) One of your best friends, after trying unsuccessfully to convince you to abandon this diet, makes you promise to consume a healthy dose of odd-chain fatty acids. Does your friend have your best interests at heart? Explain.

45. *Fats to glycogen.* An animal is fed stearic acid that is radioactively labeled with $[^{14}C]$carbon. A liver biopsy reveals the presence of ^{14}C-labeled glycogen. How is this finding possible in light of the fact that animals cannot convert fats into carbohydrates?

Data Interpretation Problem

46. *Mutant enzyme.* Carnitine palmitoyl transferase I (CPTI) catalyzes the conversion of long-chain acyl CoA into acyl carnitine, a prerequisite for transport into mitochondria and subsequent degradation. A mutant enzyme was constructed with a single amino acid change at position 3 of glutamic acid for alanine. Graphs A through C show data from studies performed to identify the effect of the mutation [data from J. Shi, H. Zhu, D. N. Arvidson, and G. J. Woldegiorgis. *J. Biol. Chem.* 274:9421–9426, 1999].

(a) What is the effect of the mutation on enzyme activity when the concentration of carnitine is varied (Graph A)? What are the K_M and V_{max} values for the wild-type and mutant enzymes?

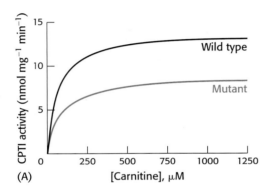

(A)

(b) What is the effect when the experiment is repeated with varying concentrations of palmitoyl CoA (Graph B)? What are the K_M and V_{max} values for the wild-type and mutant enzymes?

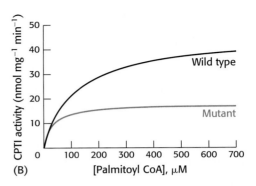

(B)

(c) Graph C shows the inhibitory effect of malonyl CoA on the wild-type and mutant enzymes. Which enzyme is more sensitive to malonyl CoA inhibition?

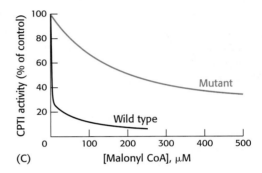

(C)

(d) Suppose that the concentration of palmitoyl CoA = 100 μM, that of carnitine = 100 μM, and that of malonyl CoA = 5 10 μM. Under these conditions, what is the most prominent effect of the mutation on the properties of the enzyme?

(e) What can you conclude about the role of glutamate 3 in carnitine acyltransferase I function?

CHAPTER 27

The Integration of Metabolism

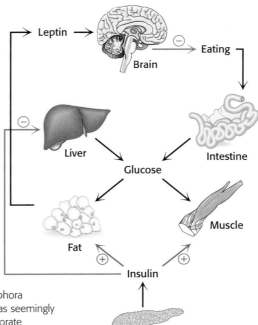

The image at the left shows a detail of runners on a Greek amphora painted in the sixth century B.C. Athletic feats, as well as others as seemingly simple as the maintenance of blood-glucose levels, require elaborate metabolic integration. The representation at the right shows the organs that have essential roles in the metabolic integration that regulates blood-glucose levels during exercise and at rest. Insulin and leptin (secreted by adipocytes) are two of the hormones that modulate the metabolic pathways of organs throughout the body such that adequate energy is available to meet the demands of living. [(Left) Copyright © The Metropolitan Museum of Art/Art Resource, NY.]

We have been examining the biochemistry of metabolism one pathway at a time. We have seen how useful energy is extracted from fuels and used to power biosynthetic reactions and signal-transduction pathways. In the Chapters 28 through 30, we will extend our study of biosynthetic reactions to the synthesis of proteins and nucleic acids. Before we do that, however, in this chapter we will take a step back to examine large-scale biochemical interactions that constitute the physiology of the organisms. In keeping with a central theme of life—energy manipulations—we will look at the regulation of energy at the organismal level, which boils down to an apparently simple but actually quite complex question: At the biochemical level, how does an organism know when to eat and when to refrain from eating? The ability to maintain adequate but not excessive energy stores is called *caloric homeostasis* or *energy homeostasis*.

Next, we will examine a significant perturbation of caloric homeostasis—obesity—and how this physiological condition affects insulin action, frequently resulting in diabetes. We then turn our attention to a biochemical examination of one of the most beneficial activities that humans can engage in—exercise—and see how exercise mitigates the effects of diabetes as well as how different forms of exercise use different sources of fuel.

At the opposite end of the physiological spectrum from obesity and overnutrition are fasting and starvation, and we will examine the biochemical responses to these challenges. The chapter ends with a consideration of another biochemical energy perturbation—excess alcohol consumption.

We have already encountered instances of organismal energy regulation when we considered the actions of insulin and glucagon. Recall that insulin, secreted by the β cells of the pancreas, causes glucose to be removed from the blood and stimulates the synthesis of glycogen and lipids. Glucagon, secreted by the α cells of the pancreas, has effects opposite those of insulin. Glucagon increases the level of blood glucose by stimulating glycogen breakdown and gluconeogenesis. This chapter introduces two hormones that play key roles in caloric homeostasis. Leptin and adiponectin, secreted by the adipose tissue, work in concert with insulin to regulate caloric homeostasis.

27.1 Caloric Homeostasis Is a Means of Regulating Body Weight

By now in our study of biochemistry, we are well aware of the fact that many biochemicals, most notably carbohydrates and lipids, are potential sources of energy. We consume these energy sources as foods, convert the energy into ATP, and use the ATP to power our lives. Like all energy transformations, our energy consumption and expenditure are governed by the laws of thermodynamics. Recall that the Second Law of Thermodynamics states that energy can neither be created nor destroyed. Translated into the practical terms of our diets,

$$\text{Energy consumed} = \text{energy expended} + \text{energy stored}$$

This simple equation has severe physiological and health implications: according to the Second Law of Thermodynamics, if we consume more energy than we expend, we will become overweight or obese. Obesity is generally defined as a body mass index (BMI) of more than 30 kg m^{-2}, whereas overweight is defined as a BMI of more than 25 kg m^{-2} (Figure 27.1). Recall that excess fat is stored in adipocytes as triacylglycerols. The number of adipocytes becomes fixed in adults, and so obesity results in engorged adipocytes. Indeed, the cell may increase as much as 1000-fold in size.

We are all aware that many of us, especially in the developed world, are becoming obese or have already attained that state. In the United States, obesity has become an epidemic, with nearly 30% of adults classified as such. Obesity is identified as a risk factor in a host of pathological conditions including diabetes mellitus, hypertension, and cardiovascular disease (Table 27.1). The cause of obesity is quite simple in most cases: more food is consumed than is needed, and the excess calories are stored as fat. We will consider the biochemical basis of pathologies caused by obesity later in the chapter.

Before we undertake a biochemical analysis of the results of overconsumption, let us consider why the obesity epidemic is occurring in the first place. There are two complementary explanations. The first is a commonly held view that our bodies are programmed to rapidly store excess calories in times of plenty, an evolutionary adaptation from times past when humans

Height in feet and inches (in cm)

Weight in pounds (in kg)	4'8" (142)	4'10" (147)	5'0" (152)	5'2" (157)	5'4" (163)	5'6" (168)	5'8" (173)	5'10" (178)	6'0" (183)	6'2" (188)	6'4" (193)
260 (117.9)	58	54	51	48	45	42	40	37	35	33	32
250 (113.4)	56	52	49	46	43	40	38	36	34	32	30
240 (108.9)	54	50	47	44	41	39	36	34	33	31	29
230 (104.3)	52	48	45	42	39	37	35	33	31	30	28
220 (99.8)	49	46	43	40	38	36	33	32	30	28	27
210 (95.3)	47	44	41	38	36	34	32	30	28	27	26
200 (90.7)	45	42	39	37	34	32	30	29	27	26	24
190 (86.2)	43	40	37	35	33	31	29	27	26	24	23
180 (81.6)	40	38	35	33	31	29	27	26	24	23	22
170 (77.1)	38	36	33	31	29	27	26	24	23	22	21
160 (72.6)	36	33	31	29	27	26	24	23	22	21	19
150 (68.0)	34	31	29	27	26	24	23	22	20	19	18
140 (63.5)	31	29	27	26	24	23	21	20	19	18	17
130 (59.0)	29	27	25	24	22	21	20	19	18	17	16
120 (54.4)	27	25	23	22	21	19	18	17	16	15	15
110 (49.9)	25	23	21	20	19	18	17	16	15	14	13
100 (45.4)	22	21	20	18	17	16	15	14	14	13	12
90 (40.8)	20	19	18	16	15	15	14	13	12	12	11
80 (36.3)	18	17	16	15	14	13	12	11	11	10	10

>30	Obese
25–30	Overweight
18.5–25	Normal
<18.5	Underweight

$$BMI = \frac{weight}{height^2}$$

Figure 27.1 Body mass index (BMI). The BMI value for an individual person is a reliable indicator of obesity for most people. [Data from the Centers for Disease Control.]

were not assured of having ample food, as many of us are today. Consequently, we store calories as if a fast might begin tomorrow, but no such fast arrives. The second possible explanation is that we no longer face the risks of predation. Evidence indicates that predation was a common cause of death for our ancestors. An obese individual would more likely have been culled from a group of our ancestors than would a more nimble, lean individual. As the risk of predation declined, leanness became less beneficial. Regardless of why we may have a propensity to gain weight, this propensity can be negated behaviorally—by eating less and exercising more. However, genetic studies indicate that the tendency toward obesity may be highly heritable.

As disturbing as the obesity epidemic is, an equally intriguing, almost amazing observation is that many people are able to maintain an approximately constant weight throughout adult life. A few simple calculations of a simplified situation illustrates how remarkable this feat is. Consider a 120-pound woman whose weight does not change significantly between

Table 27.1 Health consequences of obesity or being overweight

Coronary heart disease
Type 2 diabetes
Cancers (endometrial, breast, and colon)
Hypertension (high blood pressure)
Dyslipidemia (disruption of lipid metabolism, e.g., high cholesterol and triglycerides)
Stroke
Liver and gallbladder disease
Sleep apnea and respiratory problems
Osteoarthritis (degeneration of cartilage and underlying bone at a joint)
Gynecological problems (abnormal menses, infertility)

Source: Centers for Disease Control and Prevention Web site (www.cdc.gov).

the ages of 25 and 65. Let us say that the woman requires 2000 kcal day^{-1}. Over the 40 years under consideration, she will have consumed

$$40 \text{ years} \times 365 \text{ days year}^{-1} \times 2000 \text{ kcal day}^{-1} = 2.9 \times 10^7 \text{ kcals in 40 years}$$

For simplicity's sake, let us assume that the woman's diet consists predominantly of fatty acids derived from lipids. The energy density of fatty acids is 9 kcal g^{-1}. Thus, over the 40-year span, our subject has ingested

$$2.9 \times 10^7 \text{ kcal}/9 \text{ kcal g}^{-1} = 3.2 \times 10^6 \text{ g} = 3200 \text{ kg of food}$$

which is equivalent to more than 6 tons of food! Yet, remarkably, her weight has remained constant without her having to accurately and constantly calibrate and equalize her energy intake and energy output. Although will power, exercise, and a bathroom scale often play a role in this homeostasis, some biochemical signaling must be taking place to help with her energy regulation. Indeed, it is the case; but, before we consider this regulation, let us be cruel, but not too cruel, to our hypothetical subject and say that her weight increased 10% over the 40-year span, a percentage weight gain that most 65-year-olds would delightfully accept. Thus, at 65, she weighs 132 pounds. On a daily basis, what increase in energy intake—food consumption—would have resulted in a 12-pound weight gain over 40 years? Again, let us consider only fats.

$$12 \text{ pounds} = 5.4 \text{ kg} = 5.4 \times 10^3 \text{ g} = \text{total weight gain}$$

$$5.4 \times 10^3 \text{ g} (40 \text{ years } 365 \text{ days year}^{-1})^{-1} = 0.37 \text{ g day}^{-1}$$

Thus, to gain 12 pounds in 40 years, our subject needed to eat only 0.37 g of food per day more than she needed to meet her biochemical needs. How much food is it? Consider butter, which is essentially pure fat; 0.38 g of butter is approximately one-quarter of a pat. So, the simple excess of the equivalent of one-quarter pat of butter per day will lead to a (modest) weight gain of 12 pounds over 40 years—a startling if depressing fact. However, even just a small sampling of your friends and family shows us that this hypothetical weight gain does not apply to everyone. People vary significantly in the way in which their bodies are able to regulate energy intake; an extra pat of butter a day may not make a difference in the long run to one person, whereas another person may end up with much more than a 10% weight gain over 40 years. All things being equal, Problem 33 illustrates how little excess consumption is required to become obese over the 40-year time period.

27.2 The Brain Plays a Key Role in Caloric Homeostasis

What makes this remarkable balance of energy input and output possible? As you might imagine, the answer is complicated, entailing many biochemical signals as well as a host of behavioral factors. We will focus on a few key biochemical signals, and divide our discussion into two parts: short-term signals that are active during a meal and long-term signals that report on the overall energy status of the body. These signals originate in the gastrointestinal tract, the β cells of the pancreas, and fat cells. The primary target of these signals is the brain, in particular a groups of neurons in a region of the hypothalamus called the arcuate nucleus.

Signals from the gastrointestinal tract induce feelings of satiety

Short-term signals relay feelings of satiety from the gut to various regions of the brain and thus reduce the urge to eat (Figure 27.2). The best-studied short-term signal is cholecystokinin (CCK). *Cholecystokinin* is actually a

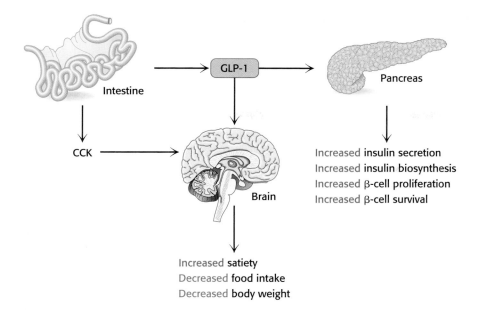

Figure 27.2 Satiation signals.
Cholecystokinin (CCK) and glucagon-like peptide 1 (GLP-1) are signal molecules that induce feelings of satiety in the brain. CCK is secreted by specialized cells of the small intestine in response to a meal and activates satiation pathways in the brain. GLP-1, secreted by L cells in the intestine, also activates satiation pathways in the brain and potentiates insulin action in the pancreas. [After S. C. Wood. *Cell Metab.* 9:489–498, 2009, Fig. 1.]

family of peptide hormones of various lengths (from 8 to 58 amino acids in length, depending on posttranslational processing) secreted into the blood by cells in the duodenum and jejunum regions of the small intestine as a postprandial satiation signal. The CCK binds to the CCK receptor, a G-protein-coupled receptor (p. 406) located in various peripheral neurons that relay signals to the brain. This binding initiates a signal-transduction pathway in the brain that generates a feeling of satiety. CCK also plays an important role in digestion, stimulating the secretion of pancreatic enzymes and bile salts from the gallbladder.

Another important gut signal is *glucagon-like peptide 1* (GLP-1), a hormone of approximately 30 amino acids in length. GLP-1 is secreted by intestinal L cells, hormone-secreting cells located throughout the lining of the gastrointestinal tract, and has a variety of effects, all apparently facilitated by binding to a GLP-1 receptor, another G-protein-coupled receptor. Like CCK, GLP-1 induces feelings of satiety that inhibit further eating. GLP-1 also potentiates glucose-induced insulin secretion by the β cells of the pancreas while inhibiting glucagon secretion. Although we have examined only two short-term signals, many others are believed to exist (Table 27.2). Most of the short-term signals thus far identified are appetite suppressants. Ghrelin, a peptide that is 28 amino acids in length and secreted by the stomach, acts on regions of the hypothalamus to stimulate appetite through its receptor, a G-protein-coupled receptor. Ghrelin secretion increases before a meal and decreases afterward.

Leptin and insulin regulate long-term control over caloric homeostasis

Two key signal molecules regulate energy homeostasis over the time scale of hours or days: *leptin,* which is secreted by the adipocytes, and *insulin,* which is secreted by the β cells of the pancreas. Leptin reports on the status of the triacylglycerol stores, whereas insulin reports on the status of glucose in the blood—in other words, of carbohydrate availability. We will consider leptin first.

Adipose tissue was formerly considered an inert depot of triacylglycerols. However, recent work has shown that adipose tissue is an active endocrine tissue, secreting signal molecules called *adipokines,* such as leptin, that regulate a host of physiological processes. Leptin is secreted by the adipocytes in direct proportion to the amount of fat present. The more fat

Table 27.2 Gastrointestinal peptides that regulate food intake

Appetite-suppressing signals
Cholecystokinin
Glucagon-like peptide 1
Glucagon-like peptide 2
Amylin
Somatostatin
Bombesin
Enterostatin
Apolipoprotein A-IV
Gastric inhibitory peptide

Appetite-enhancing peptides
Ghrelin

Source: After M. H. Stipanuk, Ed., *Biochemical, Physiological, Molecular Aspects of Human Nutrition,* 2d ed. (Saunders/Elsevier, 2006), p. 627, Box 22-1.

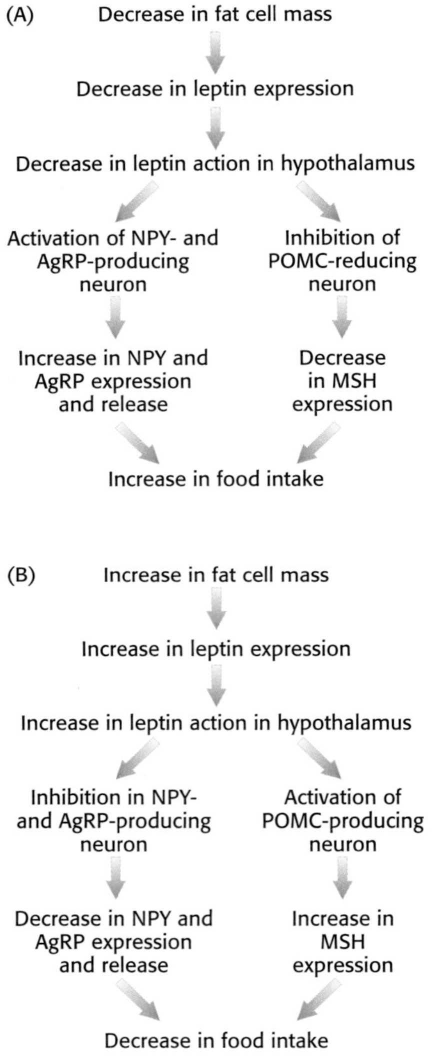

(A)   Decrease in fat cell mass

↓

Decrease in leptin expression

↓

Decrease in leptin action in hypothalamus

↓   ↓

Activation of NPY- and   Inhibition of
AgRP-producing   POMC-reducing
neuron   neuron

↓   ↓

Increase in NPY and   Decrease
AgRP expression   in MSH
and release   expression

↓   ↓

Increase in food intake

(B)   Increase in fat cell mass

↓

Increase in leptin expression

↓

Increase in leptin action in hypothalamus

↓   ↓

Inhibition in NPY-   Activation of
and AgRP-producing   POMC-producing
neuron   neuron

↓   ↓

Decrease in NPY and   Increase in
AgRP expression   MSH
and release   expression

↓   ↓

Decrease in food intake

Figure 27.3 The effects of leptin in the brain. Leptin is an adipokine secreted by adipose tissue in direct relation to fat mass. (A) When leptin levels fall, as in fasting, appetite-enhancing neuropeptides NPY and AgRP are secreted, whereas the secretion of appetite-suppressing signals such as MSH is inhibited. (B) When fat mass increases, leptin inhibits NPY and AgRP secretion while stimulating the release of appetite-suppressing hormone MSH. [After M. H. Stipanuk, *Biochemical, Physiological, & Molecular Aspects of Human Nutrition*, 2d ed. (Saunders-Elsevier, 2006), Fig. 22-2.]

in a body, the more leptin is secreted. Leptin binding to its receptor throughout the body increases the sensitivity of muscle and the liver to insulin, stimulates β oxidation of fatty acids, and decreases triacylglycerol synthesis.

Let us consider the effects of leptin in the brain. Leptin exerts its effect by binding to membrane receptors in various regions of the brain, particularly in the arcuate nucleus of the hypothalamus. There, one population of neurons expresses appetite-stimulating (orexigenic) peptides, called neuropeptide Y (NPY) and agouti-related peptide (AgRP). Leptin inhibits the NPY/AgRP neurons, preventing the release of NPY and AgRP and thus repressing the desire to eat. Fasting, on the other hand, stimulates the production of NPY and AgRP (Figure 27.3) owing to the decrease in leptin levels that results from diminishing adipose tissue.

The second population of neurons containing leptin receptors expresses a large precursor polypeptide, proopiomelanocortin (POMC). In response to leptin binding to its receptor on POMC neurons, POMC is proteolytically processed to yield a variety of signal molecules, one of which, *melanocyte-stimulating hormone* (MSH), is especially important in this context. MSH, originally discovered as a stimulator of melanocytes (cells that synthesize the pigment melanin), activates appetite-suppressing (anorexigenic) neurons and thus inhibits food consumption. Fasting inhibits MSH activity and thus stimulates eating. AgRP inhibits MSH activity by acting as an antagonist, binding to the MSH receptor but failing to activate the receptor (see Figure 27.3). Thus, the net effect of leptin binding to its receptor is the initiation of a complex signal-transduction pathway that ultimately curtails food intake.

Insulin receptors are also present in the hypothalamus, although the mechanism of insulin action in the brain is less clear than that of leptin. Insulin appears to inhibit NPY/AgRP-producing neurons, thus inhibiting food consumption.

Leptin is one of several hormones secreted by adipose tissue

Leptin was the first adipokine discovered because of the dramatic effects of its absence. Researchers discovered a strain of mice called ob/ob mice, which lack leptin and, as a result, are extremely obese. These mice display hyperphagia (overeating), hyperlipidemia (accumulation of triacylglycerides in muscle and liver), and an insensitivity to insulin. Since the discovery of leptin, other adipokines have been detected. For instance, *adiponectin* is another signal molecule produced by the adipocytes that acts in a similar fashion to leptin. Both leptin and adiponectin exert their effects through the key regulatory enzyme, AMP-dependent protein kinase (AMPK). Recall that this enzyme is active when AMP levels are elevated and ATP levels are diminished, and this activation leads to a decrease in anabolism and an increase in catabolism, most notably an increase in fatty acid oxidation. In insulin-resistant obese animals such as the ob/ob mice, leptin levels increase while those of adiponectin decrease.

Adipocytes also produce two hormones, *RBP4* and *resistin*, that promote insulin resistance. Although it is unclear why adipocytes secrete hormones that facilitate insulin resistance, a pathological condition, we can speculate on the answer. These signal molecules may help to fine-tune the actions of leptin and adiponectin or perhaps to act as "brakes" on the action of leptin and adiponectin to prevent hypoglycemia in the fasted state. Some evidence indicates that enlarged adipocytes that result from obesity may secrete higher levels of insulin-antagonizing hormones and thus contribute to insulin resistance.

Leptin resistance may be a contributing factor to obesity

If leptin is produced in proportion to body-fat mass and leptin inhibits eating, why do people become obese? Obese people, in most cases, have both functioning leptin and a high blood concentration of leptin. The failure to respond to the anorexigenic effects of leptin is called *leptin resistance*. What is the basis of leptin resistance?

As for most questions in the exciting area of energy homeostasis, the answer is not well worked out, but recent evidence suggests that a group of proteins called *suppressors of cytokine signaling* (SOCS) may take part. These proteins fine-tune some hormonal systems by inhibiting receptor action. SOCS proteins inhibit receptor signaling by a number of means (Figure 27.4). Consider, for example, the effect of SOCS proteins on the insulin receptor. Recall that insulin stimulates the autophosphorylation of tyrosine residues on the insulin receptor, initiating the insulin-signaling pathway (see Figure 27.5). SOCS proteins bind to phosphorylated tyrosine residues on receptors or other members of the signal-transduction pathway, thereby disrupting signal flow and thus altering the cell's biochemical activity. In other cases, the binding of SOCS proteins to components of the signal-transduction pathway may also enhance proteolytic degradation of these components by the proteasome. Evidence in support of a role for SOCS in leptin resistance comes from mice that have had SOCS selectively deleted from POMC-expressing neurons. These mice display an enhanced sensitivity to leptin and are resistant to weight gain even when fed a high-fat diet. The reason why the activity of SOCS proteins increases, leading to leptin resistance, remains to be determined.

Dieting is used to combat obesity

Given the obesity epidemic that we currently face and its associated disorders, much attention has been focused on determining the most effective

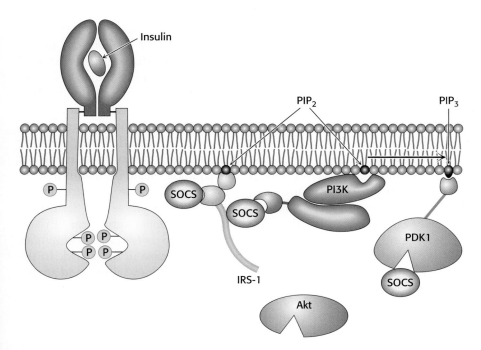

Figure 27.4 Suppressors of cytokine signaling (SOCS) regulate receptor function. SOCS proteins disrupt interactions of components of the insulin-signaling pathway and thereby inhibit the pathway. The binding of a signal component by SOCS results in proteasomal degradation in some cases. (Akt, a protein kinase; IRS-1, insulin-receptor substrate 1; PDK1, PIP_3-dependent protein kinase; PIP_3, phosphatidylinositol 3,4,5-trisphosphate; SOCS, suppressor of cytokine signaling.)

weight-loss diet. In general, two categories of diet try to help us control our caloric intake—low-carbohydrate diets and low-fat diets. Low-carbohydrate diets usually emphasize protein consumption. Although studies of the effects of diets on humans are immensely complex, data are beginning to accumulate suggesting that low-carbohydrate–high-protein diets may be the most effective for losing weight. The exact reasons are not clear, but there are two common hypotheses. First, proteins seem to induce a feeling of satiation more effectively than do fats or carbohydrates. Second, proteins require more energy to digest than do fats or carbohydrates, and the increased energy expenditure contributes to weight loss. For instance, recent studies show that a diet that is 30% protein requires almost 30% more energy to digest than that required by a diet that is 10% protein. The mechanisms by which protein-rich diets enhance energy expenditure and feelings of satiation remain to be determined. Regardless of the type of diet, the adage "Eat less, exercise more" always applies.

27.3 Diabetes Is a Common Metabolic Disease Often Resulting from Obesity

Having taken an overview of the regulation of body weight, we now examine the biochemical results when regulation fails because of behavior, genetics, or a combination of the two. The most common result of such a failure is obesity, a condition in which excess energy is stored as triacylglycerides. Recall that all excess food consumption is ultimately converted into triacylglycerides. Humans maintain about a day's worth of glycogen and, after these stores have been replenished, excess carbohydrates are converted into fats and then into triacylglycerols. Amino acids are not stored at all, and so excess amino acids are ultimately converted into fats also. Thus, regardless of the type of food consumed, excess consumption results in increased fat stores.

We begin our consideration of the effects of disruptions in caloric homeostasis with *diabetes mellitus*, a complex disease characterized by grossly abnormal fuel usage: *glucose is overproduced by the liver and underutilized by other organs.* The incidence of diabetes mellitus (usually referred to simply as *diabetes*) is about 5% of the population. Indeed, diabetes is the most common serious metabolic disease in the world; it affects hundreds of millions. *Type 1 diabetes* is caused by the autoimmune destruction of the insulin-secreting β cells in the pancreas and usually begins before age 20. Type 1 diabetes is also referred to as insulin-dependent diabetes, meaning that the affected person requires the administration of insulin to live. Most diabetics, in contrast, have a normal or even higher level of insulin in their blood, but they are quite unresponsive to the hormone, a characteristic called *insulin resistance*. This form of the disease, known as *type 2 diabetes*, typically arises later in life than does the insulin-dependent form. Type 2 diabetes accounts for approximately 90% of the diabetes cases throughout the world and is the most common metabolic disease in the world. In the United States, it is the leading cause of blindness, kidney failure, and amputation. *Obesity is a significant predisposing factor for the development of type 2 diabetes.*

Diabetes

Named for the excessive urination in the disease. Aretaeus, a Cappadocian physician of the second century A.D., wrote: "The epithet diabetes has been assigned to the disorder, being something like passing of water by a siphon." He perceptively characterized diabetes as "being a melting-down of the flesh and limbs into urine."

Mellitus

From Latin, meaning "sweetened with honey." Refers to the presence of sugar in the urine of patients having the disease. *Mellitus* distinguishes this disease from diabetes *insipidus*, which is caused by impaired renal reabsorption of water.

Insulin initiates a complex signal-transduction pathway in muscle

What is the biochemical basis of insulin resistance? How does insulin resistance lead to failure of the β cells of the pancreas that results in type 2 diabetes? How does obesity contribute to this progression? To answer these questions and begin to unravel the mysteries of metabolic disorders, let us

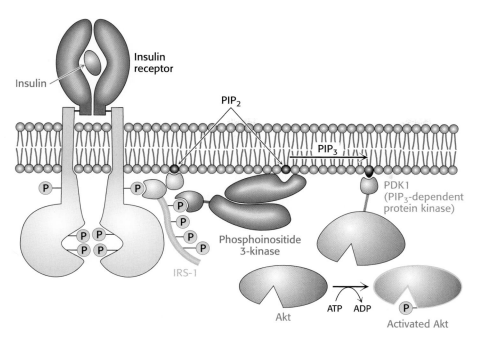

Figure 27.5 Insulin signaling. The binding of insulin results in the cross-phosphorylation and activation of the insulin receptor. Phosphorylated sites on the receptor act as binding sites for insulin-receptor substrates such as IRS-1. The lipid kinase phosphoinositide 3-kinase binds to phosphorylated sites on IRS-1 through its regulatory domain and then converts PIP_2 into PIP_3. Binding to PIP_3 activates PIP_3-dependent protein kinase, which phosphorylates and activates kinases such as Akt1. Activated Akt1 can then diffuse throughout the cell and continue the signal-transduction pathway.

examine the mechanism of action of insulin in muscle, the largest tissue regulated by insulin.

In a normal cell, insulin binds to a receptor, which dimerizes and auto-phosphorylates on tyrosine residues, with each subunit of the dimer phosphorylating its partner. Phosphorylation of the receptor generates binding sites for insulin-receptor substrates (IRSs), such as IRS-1 (Figure 27.5). Subsequent phosphorylation of IRS-1 by the tyrosine kinase activity of the insulin receptor engages the insulin-signaling pathway. Phosphorylated IRS-1 binds to phosphatidylinositol 3-kinase (PI3K) and activates it. PI3K catalyzes the conversion of phosphatidylinositol 4,5-bisphosphate (PIP_2) into phosphatidylinositol 3,4,5-trisphosphate (PIP_3), a second messenger. PIP_3 activates the phosphatidylinositol-dependent protein kinase (PDK), which in turn activates several other kinases, most notably protein kinase B (PKB), also known as Akt. Protein kinase Akt facilitates the translocation of GLUT4-containing vesicles to the cell membrane, which leads to a more robust absorption of glucose from the blood. Moreover, Akt phosphorylates and inhibits glycogen synthase kinase (GSK3). Recall that GSK3 inhibits glycogen synthase (p. 629). Thus, insulin also leads to the activation of glycogen synthase and enhances glycogen synthesis.

Like all signal pathways, the insulin-signaling cascade must be capable of being turned off. Three different processes contribute to the down-regulation of insulin signaling. First, phosphatases deactivate the insulin receptor and destroy a key second messenger. *Tyrosine phosphatase IB* removes phosphoryl groups from the receptor, thus inactivating it. The second messenger PIP_3 is inactivated by the phosphatase *PTEN* (phosphatase and tensin homolog), which dephosphorylates it, forming PIP_2, which itself has no second-messenger properties.

Phosphatidylinositol 3,4,5-trisphosphate (PIP₃)

PTEN →

Phosphatidylinositol 4,5-bisphosphate (PIP₂)

+ P$_i$

Second, the IRS protein can be inactivated by phosphorylation on serine residues by specific Ser/Thr kinases. These kinases are activated by overnutrition and other stress signals and may play a role in the development of insulin resistance. Finally, SOCS proteins, the regulatory proteins discussed earlier, interact with the insulin receptor and IRS-1 and apparently facilitate their proteolytic degradation by the proteasome complex.

Metabolic syndrome often precedes type 2 diabetes

With our knowledge of the key components of energy homeostasis, let us begin our investigation of the biochemical basis of insulin resistance and type 2 diabetes. Obesity is a contributing factor to the development of insulin resistance, which is an early development on the path to type 2 diabetes. Indeed, a cluster of pathologies—including insulin resistance, hyperglycemia, dyslipidemia (high blood levels of triacylglycerols, cholesterol, and low-density lipoproteins)—often develop together. This clustering, called *metabolic syndrome*, is thought to be a predecessor of type 2 diabetes.

A consequence of obesity is that the amount of triacylglycerides consumed exceeds the adipose tissue's storage capacity. As a result, other tissues begin to accumulate fat, most notably liver and muscle (Figure 27.6). For reasons to be presented later in the chapter, this accumulation results in insulin resistance and ultimately in pancreatic failure. We will focus on muscle and the β cells of the pancreas.

Excess fatty acids in muscle modify metabolism

We have seen many times the importance of fats as fuels for cells. In regard to obesity, more fats are present than can be processed by muscle. Although the

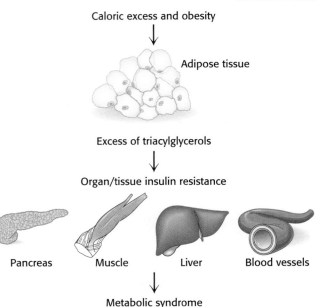

Figure 27.6 The storage capacity of fat tissue can be exceeded in obesity. In caloric excess, the storage capacity of adipocytes can be exceeded with deleterious results. The excess fat accumulates in other tissues, resulting in biochemical malfunction of the tissues. When the pancreas, muscle, liver, and cells lining the blood vessels are affected, metabolic syndrome, a condition that often precedes type 2 diabetes may result. [After S. Fröjdö, H. Vidal, and L. Pirola. *Biochim. Biophys. Acta* 1792:83–92, 2009, Fig. 1.]

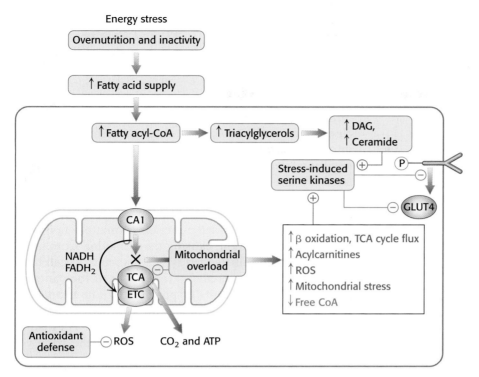

Figure 27.7 Excess fat in peripheral tissues can result in insulin insensitivity. Excess fat accumulation in peripheral tissues, most notably muscle, can disrupt some signal-transduction pathways and inappropriately activate others. In particular, diacylglycerides and ceramide activate stress-induced pathways that interfere with insulin signaling, resulting in insulin resistance. (Abbreviations: DAG, diacylglycerol; TGs, triacylglycerides; ROS, reactive oxygen species; CT1, carnitine acyltransferase 1; GLUT4, glucose transporter; ETC, electron-transport chain.)

rate of β oxidation increases in response to the high concentration of fats, mitochondria are not capable of processing all of the fatty acids by β oxidation; fatty acids accumulate in the mitochondria and eventually spill over into the cytoplasm. Indeed, the inability to process all of the fatty acids results in their reincorporation into triacylglycerols and the accumulation of fat in the cytoplasm. In the cytoplasm, levels of diacylglycerol and ceramide (a component of sphingolipids) also increase. Diacylglycerol is a second messenger that activates protein kinase C (PKC) (p. 409). When active, PKC and other Ser/Thr protein kinases are capable of phosphorylating IRS and reducing the ability of IRS to propagate the insulin signal. Ceramide or its metabolites inhibit glucose uptake and glycogen synthesis, apparently by inhibiting PDK and PKB (p. 799). The result is a diet-induced insulin resistance (Figure 27.7).

Insulin resistance in muscle facilitates pancreatic failure

What is the effect of overnutrition on the pancreas? This question is important because a primary function of the pancreas is to respond to the presence of glucose in the blood by secreting insulin, a process referred to as *glucose-stimulated insulin secretion* (GSIS). Indeed, the β cell is a virtual insulin factory. Proinsulin mRNA constitutes 20% of the total mRNA in the pancreas, whereas 50% of the total protein synthesizes in the pancreas as proinsulin, a precursor of insulin.

Glucose enters the β cells of the pancreas through the glucose transporter GLUT2. Recall that GLUT2 will allow glucose transport only when blood glucose is plentiful, ensuring that insulin is secreted only when glucose is abundant, such as after a meal. The β cell metabolizes glucose to

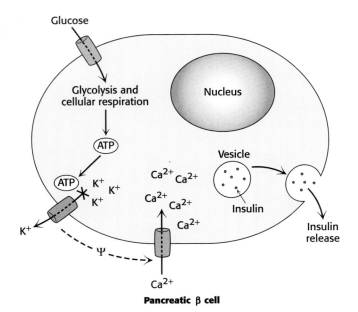

Figure 27.8 Insulin release is regulated by ATP. The metabolism of glucose by glycolysis and cellular respiration increases the concentration of ATP, which causes an ATP-sensitive potassium channel to close. The closure of this channel alters the charge across the membrane (Ψ) and causes a calcium channel to open. The influx of calcium causes insulin-containing granules to fuse with the plasma membrane, releasing insulin into the blood.

CO_2 and H_2O in the process of cellular respiration, generating ATP (Chapters 16, 17, and 18). The resulting increase in the ATP/ADP ratio closes an ATP-sensitive K^+ channel that, when open, allows potassium to flow out of the cell (Figure 27.8). The resulting alteration in the cellular ionic environment opens a Ca^{2+} channel. The influx of Ca^{2+} causes insulin-containing secretory vesicles to fuse with the cell membrane and release insulin into the blood. Thus, the increase in energy charge resulting from the metabolism of glucose has been translated by the membrane proteins into a physiological response—the secretion of insulin and the subsequent removal of glucose from the blood.

What aspect of β-cell function ultimately fails as a result of overnutrition, causing the transition from insulin resistance to full-fledged type 2 diabetes? Recall that, under normal circumstances, the β cells of the pancreas synthesize large amounts of proinsulin. The proinsulin folds in the endoplasmic reticulum, is processed to insulin, and is subsequently packaged into vesicles for secretion. As insulin resistance develops in the muscle, the β cells respond by synthesizing yet more insulin in a futile attempt do drive insulin action. The ability of the endoplasmic reticulum to process all of the proinsulin and insulin becomes compromised, a condition known as *endoplasmic reticulum (ER) stress*, and unfolded or misfolded proteins accumulate. ER stress initiates a signal pathway called the *unfolded protein response (UPR)*, a pathway intended to save the cell. UPR consists of several steps. First, general protein synthesis is inhibited so as to prevent more proteins from entering the ER. Second, chaperone synthesis is stimulated. Recall that chaperones are proteins that assist the folding of other proteins. Third, misfolded proteins are removed from the ER and are subsequently delivered to the proteasome for destruction. Finally, if the described response fails to alleviate the ER stress, apoptosis is triggered, which ultimately leads to cell death and full-fledged type 2 diabetes.

What is the treatment for type 2 diabetes? Most are behavioral in nature. Diabetics are advised to count calories, making sure that energy intake does not exceed energy output; to consume a diet rich in vegetables, fruits, and grains; and to get plenty of aerobic exercise. Note that these guidelines are the same as those for healthy living, even for those not suffering from type 2 diabetes. Treatments specific for type 2 diabetes include the monitoring of blood-glucose levels so that these levels are within the target range (normal is 3.6 to 6.1 mM). For those who are not able to maintain proper glucose levels with the behaviors described herein, drug treatments are required. The administration of insulin may be necessary on pancreatic failure, and treatment with the use of metformin (Glucophage), which activates AMPK, may be effective.

Metabolic derangements in type 1 diabetes result from insulin insufficiency and glucagon excess

We now turn to the more-straightforward type 1 diabetes. In type 1 diabetes, insulin production is insufficient because of autoimmune destruction of the β cells of the pancreas. Consequently, the glucagon/insulin ratio is at higher-than-normal levels. In essence, the diabetic person is in biochemical fasting mode despite a high concentration of blood glucose. Because insulin is deficient, *the entry of glucose into adipose and muscle cells is impaired.* The

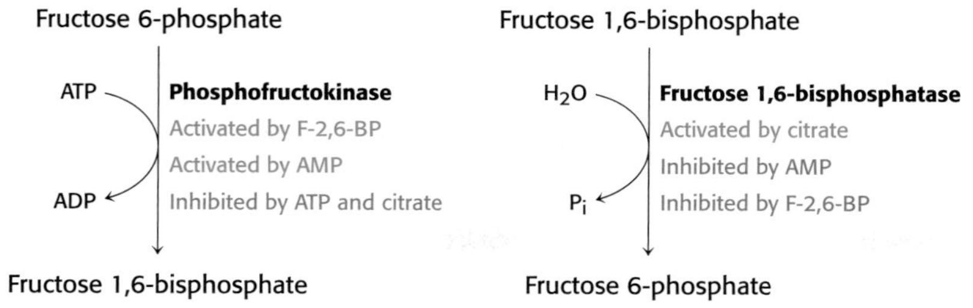

Fructose 6-phosphate   Fructose 1,6-bisphosphate

ATP ⟍ ⎰ **Phosphofructokinase**   H₂O ⟍ ⎰ **Fructose 1,6-bisphosphatase**
      │ Activated by F-2,6-BP   │ Activated by citrate
      │ Activated by AMP   │ Inhibited by AMP
ADP ⟍ ⎱ Inhibited by ATP and citrate   Pᵢ ⟍ ⎱ Inhibited by F-2,6-BP

Fructose 1,6-bisphosphate   Fructose 6-phosphate

Figure 27.9 Regulation of glycolysis and gluconeogenesis. Phosphofructokinase is the key enzyme in the regulation of glycolysis, whereas fructose 1,6-bisphosphatase is the principal enzyme controlling the rate of gluconeogenesis. Note the reciprocal relation between the pathways and the signal molecules.

liver becomes stuck in a gluconeogenic and ketogenic state. The gluconeogenic state is characterized by excessive production of glucose. The excessive level of glucagon relative to that of insulin leads to a decrease in the amount of fructose 2,6-bisphosphate (F-2,6-BP), which stimulates glycolysis and inhibits gluconeogenesis in the liver. Hence, glycolysis is inhibited and gluconeogenesis is stimulated because of the opposite effects of F-2, 6-BP on phosphofructokinase and fructose-1,6-bisphosphatase (Section 16.4; Figure 27.9). Essentially, the cells' response to a lack of insulin amplifies the amount of glucose in the blood. The high glucagon/insulin ratio in diabetes also promotes glycogen breakdown. Hence, *an excessive amount of glucose is produced by the liver and released into the blood.* Glucose is excreted in the urine (hence the name *mellitus*) when its concentration in the blood exceeds the reabsorptive capacity of the renal tubules. Water accompanies the excreted glucose, and so an untreated diabetic in the acute phase of the disease is hungry and thirsty.

Because carbohydrate utilization is impaired, a lack of insulin leads to the uncontrolled breakdown of lipids and proteins, resulting in the ketogenic state. Large amounts of acetyl CoA are then produced by β oxidation. However, much of the acetyl CoA cannot enter the citric acid cycle, because there is insufficient oxaloacetate for the condensation step. Recall that mammals can synthesize oxaloacetate from pyruvate, a product of glycolysis, but not from acetyl CoA; instead, they generate ketone bodies. *A striking feature of diabetes is the shift in fuel usage from carbohydrates to fats; glucose, more abundant than ever, is spurned.* In high concentrations, ketone bodies overwhelm the kidney's capacity to maintain acid–base balance. The untreated diabetic can go into a coma because of a lowered blood-pH level and dehydration. Interestingly, diabetic ketosis is rarely a problem in type 2 diabetes because insulin is active enough to prevent excessive lipolysis in liver and adipose tissue.

What is the treatment for type 1 diabetes? Many of the behaviors applied to type 2 diabetes apply to type 1: watching calories, exercising, and eating a healthy diet. Likewise, blood-glucose levels must be monitored. Insulin treatments are required for survival.

27.4 Exercise Beneficially Alters the Biochemistry of Cells

Exercise, coupled with a healthy diet, is one of the most effective treatments for diabetes as well as a host of other pathological conditions including coronary disease, hypertension, depression, and a variety of cancers. With regard to diabetes, exercise increases the insulin sensitivity of people who are insulin resistant or type 2 diabetics. What is the basis of this beneficial effect?

Mitochondrial biogenesis is stimulated by muscular activity

When muscle is stimulated to contract during exercise by receiving nerve impulses from motor neurons, calcium is released from the sarcoplasmic reticulum. Calcium induces muscle contraction, as will be discussed Chapter 35. Recall that calcium is also a potent second messenger and frequently works in association with the calcium-binding protein calmodulin (p. 410). In its capacity as a second messenger, calcium stimulates various calcium-dependent enzymes, such as calmodulin-dependent protein kinase. The calcium-dependent enzymes, as well as AMPK, subsequently activate particular transcription-factor complexes. As we will see in Chapters 29 and 31, transcription factors are proteins that control gene expression. Two patterns of gene expression, in particular, change in response to regular exercise (Figure 27.10). Regular exercise enhances the production of proteins required for fatty acid metabolism, such as the enzymes of β oxidation. Interestingly, fatty acids themselves function as signal molecules to activate the transcription of enzymes of fatty acid metabolism. Additionally, another set of transcription factors activated by the calcium signal cascade institutes metabolic reprogramming that leads to increased mitochondrial biogenesis. In concert, *the increase in fatty acid oxidizing capability and additional mitochondria allow for the efficient metabolism of fatty acids.* Because an excess of fatty acids results in insulin resistance, as already discussed, efficient metabolism of fatty acids results in *an increase in insulin sensitivity.* Indeed, muscles of well-trained athletes may contain high concentrations of triacylglycerides and still maintain exquisite sensitivity to insulin.

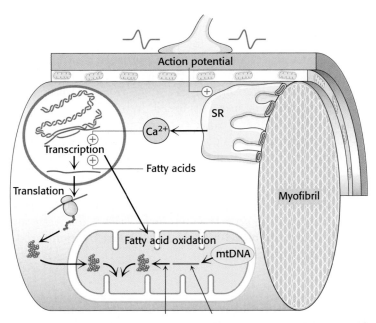

Figure 27.10 Exercise results in mitochondrial biogenesis and enhanced fat metabolism. An action potential causes Ca^{2+} release from the sarcoplasmic reticulum (SR), the muscle-cell equivalent of the endoplasmic reticulum. The Ca^{2+}, in addition to instigating muscle contraction, activates nuclear transcription factors that activate genes that, in conjunction with mitochondrial genes, are responsible for mitochondrial biogenesis. Fatty acids activate a different set of genes that increase the fatty acid oxidation capability of mitochondria. [After D. A. Hood. *J Appl. Physiol.* 90:1137–1157, 2001, Fig. 2.]

Fuel choice during exercise is determined by the intensity and duration of activity

In keeping with our theme of energy use under different physiological conditions, we now examine how fuels are used in different types of exercise. The fuels used in anaerobic exercises—sprinting, for example—differ from those used in aerobic exercises—such as distance running. The selection of fuels during these different forms of exercise illustrates many important facets of energy transduction and metabolic integration. ATP directly powers myosin, the protein immediately responsible for converting chemical energy into movement (Chapter 35). However, the amount of ATP in muscle is small. Hence, the power output and, in turn, the velocity of running depend on the rate of ATP production from other fuels. As shown in Table 27.3, *creatine phosphate* (phosphocreatine) can swiftly transfer its high-potential phosphoryl group to ADP to generate ATP. However, the amount of creatine phosphate, like that of ATP itself, is limited. Creatine phosphate and ATP can power intense muscle contraction for 5 to 6 s. Maximum speed in a sprint can thus be maintained for only 5 to 6 s (see Figure 15.7). Thus, the winner in a 100-meter sprint is the runner who both achieves the highest initial velocity and then slows down the least.

During a ~10-second sprint, the ATP level in muscle drops from 5.2 to 3.7 mM, and that of creatine phosphate decreases from 9.1 to 2.6 mM. Anaerobic glycolysis provides fuel to make up for the loss of ATP and creatine phosphate. *A 100-meter sprint is powered by stored ATP, creatine phosphate, and the anaerobic glycolysis of muscle glycogen.* The conversion of muscle glycogen into lactate can generate a good deal more ATP, but the rate is slower than that of phosphoryl-group transfer from creatine phosphate. Because of anaerobic glycolysis, the blood-lactate level is elevated from 1.6 to 8.3 mM. The release of H^+ from the intensely active muscle concomitantly lowers the blood pH from 7.42 to 7.24. This pace cannot be sustained in a 1000-meter run (~132 s) for two reasons. First, creatine phosphate is consumed within a few seconds. Second, the lactate produced would cause acidosis. Thus, alternative fuel sources are needed.

The complete oxidation of muscle glycogen to CO_2 by aerobic respiration substantially increases the energy yield, but this aerobic process is a good deal slower than anaerobic glycolysis. However, as the distance of a run increases, aerobic respiration, or oxidative phosphorylation, becomes increasingly important. For instance, *part of the ATP consumed in a 1000-meter run must come from oxidative phosphorylation.* Because ATP is produced more slowly by oxidative phosphorylation than by glycolysis (see Table 27.3), the runner's pace is necessarily slower than in

Table 27.3 Fuel sources for muscle contraction

Fuel source	Maximal rate of ATP production (mmol s^{-1})	Total ~P available (mmol)
Muscle ATP		223
Creatine phosphate	73.3	446
Conversion of muscle glycogen into lactate	39.1	6,700
Conversion of muscle glycogen into CO_2	16.7	84,000
Conversion of liver glycogen into CO_2	6.2	19,000
Conversion of adipose-tissue fatty acids into CO_2	6.7	4,000,000

Note: Fuels stored are estimated for a 70-kg person having a muscle mass of 28 kg.
Source: After E. Hultman and R. C. Harris. In *Principles of Exercise Biochemistry,* edited by J. R. Poortmans (Karger, 2004), pp. 78–119.

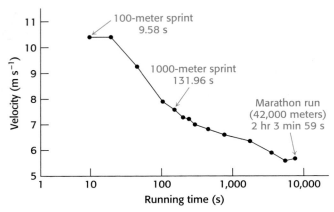

Figure 27.11 Dependency of the velocity of running on the duration of the race. The values shown are world track records. [Data from trackandfieldnews.com.]

a 100-meter sprint. The championship velocity for the 1000-meter run is about 7.6 m s^{-1}, compared with approximately 10.4 m s^{-1} for the 100-meter event (Figure 27.11).

The running of a marathon (26 miles 385 yards, or 42,200 meters) requires a different selection of fuels and is characterized by cooperation between muscle, liver, and adipose tissue. Liver glycogen complements muscle glycogen as an energy store that can be tapped. However, the total body glycogen stores (103 mol of ATP at best) are insufficient to provide the 150 mol of ATP needed for this grueling ~2-hour event. Much larger quantities of ATP can be obtained by the oxidation of fatty acids derived from the breakdown of *fat in adipose tissue*, but the maximal rate of ATP generation is slower yet than that of glycogen oxidation and is more than 10-fold slower than that with creatine phosphate. Thus, *ATP is generated much more slowly from high-capacity stores than from limited ones*, accounting for the different velocities of anaerobic and aerobic events. *ATP generation from fatty acids is essential for distance running.* Fats are rapidly consumed in activities such as distance running, explaining why extended aerobic exercise is beneficial for people who are insulin resistant. However, for an elite marathoner, fats cannot be the sole source of fuel. Studies have shown that, when muscle glycogen has been depleted, the power output of the muscle falls to approximately 50% of maximum. Power output decreases despite the fact that ample supplies of fat are available, suggesting that fats can supply only about 50% of maximal aerobic effort. A marathon would take about 6 hours to run if all the ATP came from fatty acid oxidation, because it is much slower than glycogen oxidation. Elite runners consume about equal amounts of glycogen and fatty acids during a marathon to achieve a mean velocity of 5.5 m s^{-1}, about half the velocity of a 100-meter sprint. How is an optimal mix of these fuels achieved? *A low blood-sugar level leads to a high glucagon/insulin ratio, which in turn mobilizes fatty acids from adipose tissue.* Fatty acids readily enter muscle, where they are degraded by β oxidation to acetyl CoA and then to CO_2. The elevated acetyl CoA level decreases the activity of the pyruvate dehydrogenase complex to block the conversion of pyruvate into acetyl CoA. Hence, fatty acid oxidation decreases the funneling of glucose into the citric acid cycle and oxidative phosphorylation. Glucose is spared so that just enough remains available at the end of the marathon. The simultaneous use of both fuels gives a higher mean velocity than would be attained if glycogen were totally consumed before the start of fatty acid oxidation.

If carbohydrate-rich meals are consumed after glycogen depletion, glycogen stores are rapidly restored. In addition, glycogen synthesis continues during the consumption of carbohydrate-rich meals, increasing glycogen stores far above normal. This phenomenon is called "super compensation" or, more commonly, carbo-loading.

27.5 Food Intake and Starvation Induce Metabolic Changes

Thus far, we have been considering metabolism in the context of excess consumption of calories, as in obesity, or extreme caloric needs, as in exercise. We now look at the opposite physiological condition—lack of calories.

The starved–fed cycle is the physiological response to a fast

We begin with a physiological condition called the *starved–fed cycle*, which we all experience in the hours after an evening meal and through the night's fast. This nightly starved–fed cycle has three stages: the well-fed state after a meal, the early fasting during the night, and the refed state after breakfast. A major goal of the many biochemical alterations in this period is to maintain *glucose homeostasis*—that is, a constant blood-glucose level. Maintaining glucose homeostasis is especially important because glucose is normally the only fuel source for the brain. As discussed earlier, the major defect in diabetes is the inability to perform this vital task. The two primary signals regulating the starved–fed cycle are insulin and glucagon.

1. *The Well-Fed, or Postprandial, State.* After we consume and digest an evening meal, glucose and amino acids are transported from the intestine to the blood. The dietary lipids are packaged into chylomicrons and transported to the blood by the lymphatic system. This fed condition leads to the secretion of insulin, which in cooperation with glucagon, maintains glucose homeostasis. In essence, insulin signals the fed state; it stimulates the storage of fuels and the synthesis of proteins in a variety of ways. Insulin stimulates glycogen synthesis in both muscle and the liver and suppresses gluconeogenesis by the liver. Insulin also accelerates glycolysis in the liver, which in turn increases the synthesis of fatty acids.

The liver helps to limit the amount of glucose in the blood during times of plenty by storing it as glycogen so as to be able to release glucose in times of scarcity. How is the excess blood glucose present after a meal removed? The liver is able to trap large quantities of glucose because it possesses an isozyme of hexokinase called *glucokinase*, which converts glucose into glucose 6-phosphate, which cannot be transported out of the cell. Recall that glucokinase has a high K_M value and is thus active only when blood-glucose levels are high. Furthermore, glucokinase is not inhibited by glucose 6-phosphate as hexokinase is. Consequently, *the liver forms glucose 6-phosphate more rapidly as the blood-glucose level rises. The increase in glucose 6-phosphate coupled with insulin action leads to a buildup of glycogen stores.* The hormonal effects on glycogen synthesis and storage are reinforced by a direct action of glucose itself. *Phosphorylase a is a glucose sensor in addition to being the enzyme that cleaves glycogen.* When the glucose level is high, the binding of glucose to phosphorylase *a* renders the enzyme susceptible to the action of a phosphatase that converts it into phosphorylase *b*, which does not readily degrade glycogen (Section 21.2). Thus, *glucose allosterically shifts the glycogen system from a degradative to a synthetic mode.*

The high insulin level in the fed state also promotes *the entry of glucose into muscle and adipose tissue.* Insulin stimulates the synthesis of glycogen by muscle as well as by the liver. The entry of glucose into adipose tissue provides glycerol 3-phosphate for the synthesis of triacylglycerols. The action of insulin also extends to amino acid and protein metabolism. Insulin promotes the uptake of branched-chain amino acids (valine, leucine, and isoleucine) by muscle. Indeed, insulin has a general stimulating effect on protein synthesis, which favors a building up of muscle protein. In addition, it inhibits the intracellular degradation of proteins.

2. *The Early Fasting, or Postabsorptive, State.* The blood-glucose level begins to drop several hours after a meal, leading to a decrease in insulin secretion and a rise in glucagon secretion; glucagon is secreted by the α cells of the pancreas in response to a *low blood-sugar level in the fasting state.* Just as insulin signals the fed state, glucagon signals the starved state. It serves to mobilize glycogen stores when there is no dietary intake of

glucose. *The main target organ of glucagon is the liver*. Glucagon stimulates glycogen breakdown and inhibits glycogen synthesis by triggering the cyclic AMP cascade leading to the phosphorylation and activation of phosphorylase and the inhibition of glycogen synthase (Section 21.5). Glucagon also inhibits fatty acid synthesis by diminishing the production of pyruvate and by lowering the activity of acetyl CoA carboxylase by maintaining it in a phosphorylated state. In addition, glucagon stimulates gluconeogenesis in the liver and blocks glycolysis by lowering the level of F-2,6-BP (see Figure 27.9).

All known actions of glucagon are mediated by protein kinases that are activated by cyclic AMP. The activation of the cyclic AMP cascade results in a higher level of phosphorylase *a* activity and a lower level of glycogen synthase *a* activity. Glucagon's effect on this cascade is reinforced by the low concentration of glucose in the blood. The diminished binding of glucose to phosphorylase *a* makes the enzyme less susceptible to the hydrolytic action of the phosphatase. Instead, the phosphatase remains bound to phosphorylase *a*, and so the synthase stays in the inactive phosphorylated form. Consequently, there is a rapid mobilization of glycogen.

The large amount of glucose formed by the hydrolysis of glucose 6-phosphate derived from glycogen is then released from the liver into the blood. The entry of glucose into muscle and adipose tissue decreases in response to a low insulin level. The diminished utilization of glucose by muscle and adipose tissue also contributes to the maintenance of the blood-glucose level. The net result of these actions of glucagon is to *markedly increase the release of glucose by the liver*. Both muscle and the liver use fatty acids as fuel when the blood-glucose level drops, saving the glucose for use by the brain and red blood cells. Thus, *the blood-glucose level is kept at or above 4.4 mM (80 mg dl^{-1}) by three major factors: (1) the mobilization of glycogen and the release of glucose by the liver, (2) the release of fatty acids by adipose tissue, and (3) the shift in the fuel used from glucose to fatty acids by muscle and the liver*.

What is the result of the depletion of the liver's glycogen stores? Gluconeogenesis from lactate and alanine continues, but this process merely replaces glucose that had already been converted into lactate and alanine by tissues such as muscle and red blood cells. Moreover, the brain oxidizes glucose completely to CO_2 and H_2O. Thus, for the net synthesis of glucose to take place, another source of carbon is required. Glycerol released from adipose tissue on lipolysis provides some of the carbon atoms, with the remaining carbon atoms coming from the hydrolysis of muscle proteins.

3. *The Refed State*. What are the biochemical responses to a hearty breakfast? Fat is processed exactly as it is processed in the normal fed state. However, it is not the case for glucose. The liver does not initially absorb glucose from the blood, but, instead, leaves it for the other tissues. Moreover, the liver remains in a gluconeogenic mode. Now, however, the newly synthesized glucose is used to replenish the liver's glycogen stores. As the blood-glucose levels continue to rise, the liver completes the replenishment of its glycogen stores and begins to process the remaining excess glucose for fatty acid synthesis.

Metabolic adaptations in prolonged starvation minimize protein degradation

Earlier, we considered the metabolic results of overnutrition, a condition becoming all too common in prosperous nations. Let us now examine the opposite extreme. What are the adaptations if fasting is prolonged to the point of starvation, a circumstance affecting nearly a billion people world-

Table 27.4 Fuel reserves in a typical 70-kg man

Organ	Available energy in kilojoules (kcal)		
	Glucose or glycogen	Triacylglycerols	Mobilizable proteins
Blood	250 (60)	20 (45)	0 (0)
Liver	1700 (400)	2000 (450)	1700 (400)
Brain	30 (8)	0 (0)	0 (0)
Muscle	5000 (1200)	2000 (450)	100,000 (24,000)
Adipose tissue	330 (80)	560,000 (135,000)	170 (40)

Source: After G. F. Cahill, Jr. *Clin. Endocrinol. Metab.* 5(1976):398.

wide? A typical well-nourished 70-kg man has fuel reserves totaling about 670,000 kJ (161,000 kcal; see Table 27.4). The energy need for a 24-hour period ranges from about 6700 kJ (1600 kcal) to 25,000 kJ (6000 kcal), depending on the extent of activity. Thus, stored fuels suffice to meet caloric needs in starvation for 1 to 3 months. However, the carbohydrate reserves are exhausted in only a day.

Even under starvation conditions, the blood-glucose level must be maintained above 2.2 mM (40 mg dl^{-1}). *The first priority of metabolism in starvation is to provide sufficient glucose to the brain and other tissues (such as red blood cells) that are absolutely dependent on this fuel.* However, precursors of glucose are not abundant. Most energy is stored in the fatty acyl moieties of triacylglycerols. However, recall that fatty acids cannot be converted into glucose, because acetyl CoA resulting from fatty acid breakdown cannot be transformed into pyruvate (p. 656). The glycerol moiety of triacylglycerol can be converted into glucose, but only a limited amount is available. The only other potential source of glucose is the carbon skeletons of amino acids derived from the breakdown of proteins. However, proteins are not stored, and so any breakdown will necessitate a loss of function. Thus, *the second priority of metabolism in starvation is to preserve protein, which is accomplished by shifting the fuel being used from glucose to fatty acids and ketone bodies* (Figure 27.12).

The metabolic changes on the first day of starvation are like those after an overnight fast. The low blood-sugar level leads to decreased secretion of insulin and increased secretion of glucagon. *The dominant metabolic processes are the mobilization of triacylglycerols in adipose tissue and gluconeogenesis by the liver. The liver obtains energy for its own needs by oxidizing fatty acids released from adipose tissue.* The concentrations of acetyl CoA and citrate consequently increase, which switches off glycolysis. The uptake of glucose by muscle is markedly diminished because of the low insulin level, whereas fatty acids enter freely. Consequently, *muscle uses no glucose and relies exclusively on fatty acids for fuel.* The β oxidation of fatty acids by muscle halts the conversion of pyruvate into acetyl CoA, because acetyl CoA stimulates the phosphorylation of the pyruvate dehydrogenase complex, which renders it inactive (Section 17.3). Hence, pyruvate, lactate, and alanine are exported to the liver for conversion into glucose. Glycerol derived from the cleavage of triacylglycerols is another raw material for the synthesis of glucose by the liver.

Proteolysis also provides carbon skeletons for gluconeogenesis. During starvation, degraded proteins are not replenished and serve as carbon sources for glucose synthesis. Initial sources of protein are those that turn over rapidly, such as proteins of the intestinal epithelium and the secretions of the pancreas. Proteolysis of muscle protein provides some of the three-carbon precursors of glucose. However, survival for most animals depends on being able to move rapidly, which requires a large muscle mass, and so muscle loss must be minimized.

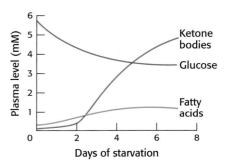

Figure 27.12 Fuel choice during starvation. The plasma levels of fatty acids and ketone bodies increase in starvation, whereas that of glucose decreases.

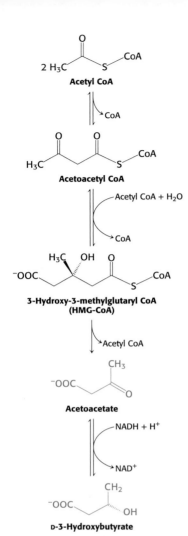

Figure 27.13 Synthesis of ketone bodies by the liver.

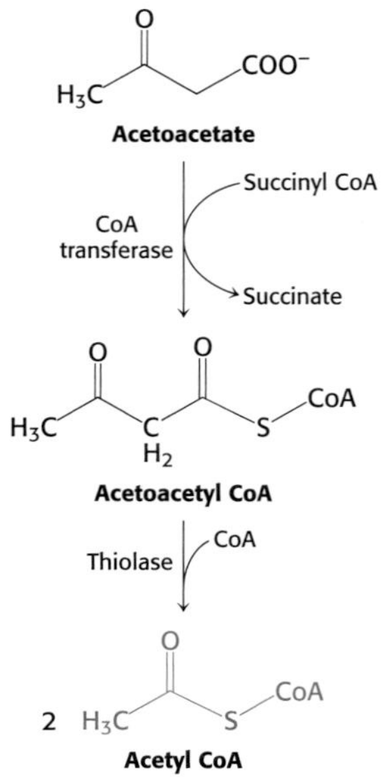

Figure 27.14 Entry of ketone bodies into the citric acid cycle.

Table 27.5 Fuel metabolism in starvation

Fuel exchanges and consumption	Amount formed or consumed in 24 hours (grams)	
	3d day	40th day
Fuel use by the brain		
Glucose	100	40
Ketone bodies	50	100
All other use of glucose	50	40
Fuel mobilization		
Adipose-tissue lipolysis	180	180
Muscle-protein degradation	75	20
Fuel output of the liver		
Glucose	150	80
Ketone bodies	150	150

How is the loss of muscle curtailed? After about 3 days of starvation, the liver forms large amounts of acetoacetate and D-3-hydroxybutyrate (ketone bodies; Figure 27.13). Their synthesis from acetyl CoA increases markedly because the citric acid cycle is unable to oxidize all the acetyl units generated by the degradation of fatty acids. Gluconeogenesis depletes the supply of oxaloacetate, which is essential for the entry of acetyl CoA into the citric acid cycle. Consequently, the liver produces large quantities of ketone bodies, which are released into the blood. At this time, *the brain begins to consume significant amounts of acetoacetate in place of glucose.* After 3 days of starvation, about a quarter of the energy needs of the brain are met by ketone bodies (Table 27.5). The heart also uses ketone bodies as fuel.

After several weeks of starvation, ketone bodies become the major fuel of the brain. Acetoacetate is activated by the transfer of CoA from succinyl CoA to give acetoacetyl CoA (Figure 27.14). Cleavage by thiolase then yields two molecules of acetyl CoA, which enter the citric acid cycle. In essence, *ketone bodies are equivalents of fatty acids that are an accessible fuel source for the brain.* Only 40 g of glucose is then needed per day for the brain, compared with about 120 g in the first day of starvation. *The effective conversion of fatty acids into ketone bodies by the liver and their use by the brain markedly diminishes the need for glucose. Hence, less muscle is degraded than in the first days of starvation.* The breakdown of 20 g of muscle daily compared with 75 g early in starvation is most important for survival. A person's survival time is mainly determined by the size of the triacylglycerol depot.

What happens after depletion of the triacylglycerol stores? The only source of fuel that remains is protein. Protein degradation accelerates, and death inevitably results from a loss of heart, liver, or kidney function.

27.6 Ethanol Alters Energy Metabolism in the Liver

Ethanol has been a part of the human diet for centuries. However, its consumption in excess can result in a number of health problems, most notably liver damage. What is the biochemical basis of these health problems?

Ethanol metabolism leads to an excess of NADH

Ethanol cannot be excreted and must be metabolized, primarily by the liver. This metabolism is accomplished by two pathways. The first pathway comprises two steps. The first step, catalyzed by the enzyme *alcohol dehydrogenase,* takes place in the cytoplasm:

$$\text{CH}_3\text{CH}_2\text{OH} + \text{NAD}^+ \xrightarrow[\text{dehydrogenase}]{\text{Alcohol}} \text{CH}_3\text{CHO} + \text{NADH} + \text{H}^+$$

Ethanol   **Acetaldehyde**

The second step, catalyzed by *aldehyde dehydrogenase,* takes place in mitochondria:

$$\text{CH}_3\text{CHO} + \text{NAD}^+ + \text{H}_2\text{O} \xrightarrow[\text{dehydrogenase}]{\text{Aldehyde}} \text{CH}_3\text{COO}^- + \text{NADH} + \text{H}^+$$

Acetaldehyde   **Acetate**

Note that *ethanol consumption leads to an accumulation of NADH.* This high concentration of NADH inhibits gluconeogenesis by preventing the oxidation of lactate to pyruvate. In fact, the high concentration of NADH will cause the reverse reaction to predominate, and lactate will accumulate. The consequences may be hypoglycemia and lactic acidosis.

The overabundance of NADH also inhibits fatty acid oxidation. The metabolic purpose of fatty acid oxidation is to generate NADH for ATP generation by oxidative phosphorylation, but an alcohol consumer's NADH needs are met by ethanol metabolism. In fact, the excess NADH signals that conditions are right for fatty acid synthesis. Hence, triacylglycerols accumulate in the liver, leading to a condition known as "fatty liver" that is exacerbated in obese persons. The biochemical effects of ethanol consumption can be quite rapid. For instance, fat accumulates in the liver within a few days of moderate alcohol consumption. This accumulation is reversible with a decrease in alcohol intake.

The second pathway for ethanol metabolism is called the ethanol-inducible *microsomal ethanol-oxidizing system* (MEOS). This cytochrome P450-dependent pathway (Section 26.4) generates acetaldehyde and subsequently acetate while oxidizing biosynthetic reducing power, NADPH, to NADP^+. Because it uses oxygen, this pathway generates free radicals that damage tissues. Moreover, because the system consumes NADPH, the antioxidant glutathione cannot be regenerated (Section 20.5), exacerbating the oxidative stress.

What are the effects of the other metabolites of ethanol? Liver mitochondria can convert acetate into acetyl CoA in a reaction requiring ATP. The enzyme is the thiokinase that normally activates short-chain fatty acids.

$$\text{Acetate} + \text{coenzyme A} + \text{ATP} \longrightarrow \text{acetyl CoA} + \text{AMP} + \text{PP}_i$$

$$\text{PP}_i \longrightarrow 2\,\text{P}_i$$

However, further processing of the acetyl CoA by the citric acid cycle is blocked, because NADH inhibits two important citric acid cycle regulatory enzymes—isocitrate dehydrogenase and α-ketoglutarate dehydrogenase. The accumulation of acetyl CoA has several consequences. First, ketone bodies will form and be released into the blood, aggravating the acidic condition already resulting from the high lactate concentration. The processing of the acetate in the liver becomes inefficient, leading to a buildup of acetaldehyde. This very reactive compound forms covalent bonds with many important functional groups in proteins, impairing protein function. If ethanol is consistently consumed at high levels, the acetaldehyde can significantly damage the liver, eventually leading to cell death.

Liver damage from excessive ethanol consumption occurs in three stages. The first stage is the aforementioned development of fatty liver. In the second stage—alcoholic hepatitis—groups of cells die and inflammation results. This stage can itself be fatal. In stage three—cirrhosis—fibrous structure and scar tissue are produced around the dead cells. Cirrhosis impairs many of the liver's biochemical functions. The cirrhotic liver is unable to convert ammonia into urea, and blood levels of ammonia rise. Ammonia is toxic to the nervous system and can cause coma and death. Cirrhosis of the liver arises in about 25% of alcoholics, and about 75% of all cases of liver cirrhosis are the result of alcoholism. Viral hepatitis is a non-alcoholic cause of liver cirrhosis.

Excess ethanol consumption disrupts vitamin metabolism

The adverse effects of ethanol are not limited to the metabolism of ethanol itself. Vitamin A (retinol) is converted into retinoic acid, an important signal molecule for growth and development in vertebrates, by the same dehydrogenases that metabolize ethanol. Consequently, this activation does not take place in the presence of ethanol, which acts as a competitive inhibitor. Moreover, the MEOS system induced by ethanol inactivates retinoic acid. These disruptions in the retinoic acid signaling pathway are believed to be responsible, at least in part, for fetal alcohol syndrome as well as the development of a variety of cancers.

The disruption of vitamin A metabolism is a direct result of the biochemical changes induced by excess ethanol consumption. Other disruptions in metabolism result from another common characteristic of alcoholics—malnutrition. Alcoholics will frequently drink instead of eating. A dramatic neurological disorder, referred to as *Wernicke–Korsakoff syndrome*, results from insufficient intake of the vitamin thiamine. Symptoms include mental confusion, unsteady gait, and lack of fine motor skills. The symptoms of Wernicke–Korsakoff syndrome are similar to those of beriberi (Section 17.4) because both conditions result from a lack of thiamine. Thiamine is converted into the coenzyme thiamine pyrophosphate, a key constituent of the pyruvate dehydrogenase complex. Recall that this complex links glycolysis with the citric acid cycle. Disruptions in the pyruvate dehydrogenase complex are most evident as neurological disorders because the brain is normally dependent on glucose for energy generation.

Alcoholic scurvy is occasionally observed because of an insufficient ingestion of vitamin C. Vitamin C is required for the formation of stable collagen fibers. The symptoms of scurvy include skin lesions and blood-vessel fragility. Most notable are bleeding gums, the loss of teeth, and periodontal infections. Gums are especially sensitive to a lack of vitamin C because the collagen in gums turns over rapidly. What is the biochemical basis for scurvy? Vitamin C is required for the continued activity of prolyl hydroxylase. This enzyme synthesizes

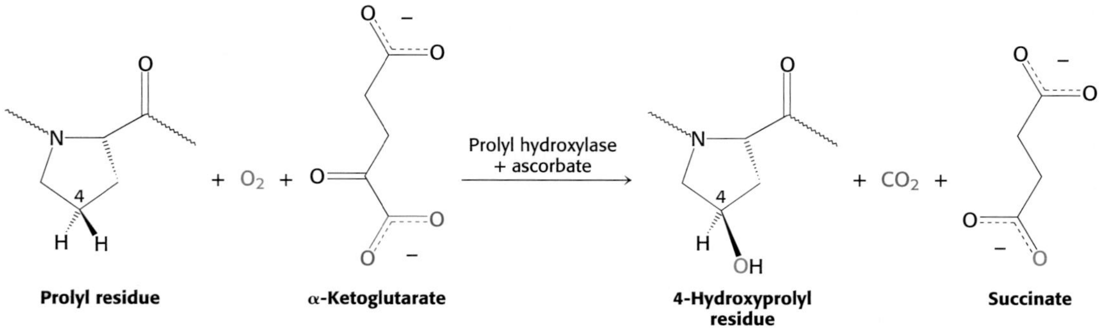

Figure 27.15 Formation of 4-hydroxyproline. Proline is hydroxylated at C-4 by the action of prolyl hydroxylase, an enzyme that activates molecular oxygen.

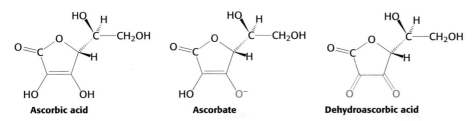

Figure 27.16 Forms of ascorbic acid (vitamin C). Ascorbate is the ionized form of vitamin C, and dehydroascorbic acid is the oxidized form of ascorbate.

4-hydroxyproline, an amino acid that is required in collagen. To form this unusual amino acid, proline residues on the amino side of glycine residues in nascent collagen chains become hydroxylated. One oxygen atom from O_2 becomes attached to C-4 of proline while the other oxygen atom is taken up by α-ketoglutarate, which is converted into succinate (Figure 27.15). This reaction is catalyzed by *prolyl hydroxylase*, a *dioxygenase*, which requires an Fe^{2+} ion to activate O_2. The enzyme also converts α-ketoglutarate into succinate without hydroxylating proline. In this partial reaction, an oxidized iron complex is formed, which inactivates the enzyme. How is the active enzyme regenerated? *Ascorbate (vitamin C)* comes to the rescue by reducing the ferric ion of the inactivated enzyme. In the recovery process, ascorbate is oxidized to dehydroascorbic acid (Figure 27.16). Thus, ascorbate serves here as a specific *antioxidant*. Why does impaired hydroxylation have such devastating consequences? *Collagen synthesized in the absence of ascorbate is less stable than the normal protein.* Hydroxyproline stabilizes the collagen triple helix by forming interstrand hydrogen bonds. The abnormal fibers formed by insufficiently hydroxylated collagen account for the symptoms of scurvy.

Summary

27.1 Caloric Homeostasis Is a Means of Regulating Body Weight

Many people are able to maintain a near-constant body weight throughout adult life. This ability is a demonstration of caloric homeostasis, a physiological condition in which energy needs match energy intake. When energy intake is greater than energy needs, weight gain results. In the developed world, obesity is at epidemic proportions and is implicated as a contributing factor in a host of pathological conditions.

27.2 The Brain Plays a Key Role in Caloric Homeostasis

Various signal molecules act on the brain to control appetite. Short-term signals such as CCK and GLP-1 relay satiety signals to the brain while eating is in progress. Long-term signals include leptin and insulin. Leptin, secreted by adipose tissue in direct proportion to adipose-tissue mass, is an indication of fat stores. Leptin inhibits eating. Insulin also works in the brain, signaling carbohydrate availability.

Leptin acts by binding to a receptor in brain neurons, which initiates signal-transduction pathways that reduce appetite. Obesity can develop in individuals with normal amounts of leptin and the leptin receptor, suggesting that such individuals are leptin resistant. Suppressors of cytokine signaling may inhibit leptin signaling, leading to leptin resistance and obesity.

27.3 Diabetes Is a Common Metabolic Disease Often Resulting from Obesity

Diabetes is the most common metabolic disease in the world. Type 1 diabetes results when insulin is absent due to autoimmune destruction of the β cells of the pancreas. Type 2 diabetes is characterized by normal or higher levels of insulin, but the target tissues of insulin, notably muscle, do not respond to the hormone, a condition called insulin resistance. Obesity is a significant predisposing factor for type 2 diabetes.

In muscle, excess fats accumulate in an obese individual. These fats are processed to second messengers that activate signal-transduction pathways that inhibit insulin signaling, leading to insulin resistance. Insulin resistance in target tissues ultimately leads to pancreatic β-cell failure. The pancreas tries to compensate for a lack of insulin action by synthesizing more insulin, resulting in ER stress and subsequent activation of apoptotic pathways that lead to β-cell death.

Type 1 diabetes is due to metabolic derangements resulting in an insufficiency of insulin and an excess of glucagon relative to a person's needs. The result is an elevated blood-glucose level, the mobilization of triacylglycerols, and excessive ketone-body formation. Accelerated ketone-body formation can lead to acidosis, coma, and death in untreated insulin-dependent diabetics.

27.4 Exercise Beneficially Alters the Biochemistry of Cells

Exercise is a useful prescription for insulin resistance and type 2 diabetes. Muscle activity stimulates mitochondrial biogenesis in a calcium-dependent manner. The increase in the number of mitochondria facilitates fatty acid oxidation in the muscle, resulting in increased insulin sensitivity.

Fuel choice in exercise is determined by the intensity and duration of the bout of exercise. Sprinting and marathon running are powered by different fuels to maximize power output. The 100-meter sprint is powered by stored ATP, creatine phosphate, and anaerobic glycolysis. In contrast, the oxidation of both muscle glycogen and fatty acids derived from adipose tissue is essential in the running of a marathon, a highly aerobic process.

27.5 Food Intake and Starvation Induce Metabolic Changes

Insulin signals the fed state; it stimulates the formation of glycogen and triacylglycerols and the synthesis of proteins. In contrast, glucagon signals a low blood-glucose level; it stimulates glycogen breakdown and gluconeogenesis by the liver and triacylglycerol hydrolysis by adipose tissue. After a meal, the rise in the blood-glucose level leads to an increased secretion of insulin and a decreased secretion of glucagon. Consequently, glycogen is synthesized in muscle and the liver. When the blood-glucose level drops several hours later, glucose is then formed by the degradation of glycogen and by the gluconeogenic pathway, and fatty acids are released by the hydrolysis of triacylglycerols. The liver and muscle then increasingly use fatty acids instead of glucose to meet their own energy needs so that glucose is conserved for use by the brain and the red blood cells.

The metabolic adaptations in starvation serve to minimize protein degradation. Large amounts of ketone bodies are formed by the liver from fatty acids and released into the blood within a few days after the onset of starvation. After several weeks of starvation, ketone bodies become the major fuel of the brain. The diminished need for glucose decreases the rate of muscle breakdown, and so the likelihood of survival is enhanced.

27.6 Ethanol Alters Energy Metabolism in the Liver

The oxidation of ethanol results in an unregulated overproduction of NADH, which has several consequences. A rise in the blood levels of lactic acid and ketone bodies causes a fall in blood pH, or acidosis. The liver is damaged because the excess NADH causes excessive fat formation as well as the generation of acetaldehyde, a reactive molecule. Severe liver damage can result.

Key Terms

caloric homeostasis (energy homeostasis) (p. 791)

cholecystokinin (CCK) (p. 794)

glucagon-like peptide 1 (GLP-1) (p. 795)

leptin (p. 795)

insulin (p. 795)

leptin resistance (p. 797)

type 1 diabetes (p. 798)

insulin resistance (p. 798)

type 2 diabetes (p. 798)

metabolic syndrome (p. 800)

endoplasmic reticulum (ER) stress (p. 802)

unfolded protein response (UPR) (p. 802)

starved–fed cycle (p. 807)

glucose homeostasis (p. 807)

Problems

1. *Depot fat.* Adipose tissue was once only considered a storage site for fat. Why is this view no longer considered correct?

2. *Balancing act.* What is meant by caloric homeostasis?

3. *Dynamic duo.* What are the key hormones responsible for maintaining caloric homeostasis?

4. *Dual roles.* What two biochemical roles does CCK play? GLP-1?

5. *Failure to communicate.* Leptin inhibits eating and is secreted in amounts in direct proportion to body fat. Moreover, obese people have normal amounts of leptin and leptin receptor. Why, then, do people become obese?

6. *Many signals.* Match the characteristic (1–9) with the appropriate hormone (a–f).

1. Secreted by adipose tissue
2. Stimulates liver gluconeogenesis
3. GPCR pathway
4. Satiety signal
5. Enhances insulin secretion
6. Secreted by the pancreas during a fast
7. Secreted after a meal
8. Stimulates glycogen synthesis
9. Missing in type 1 diabetes

(a) leptin
(b) adiponectin
(c) GLP-1
(d) CCK
(e) insulin
(f) glucagon

7. *A key chemical.* What are the sources of glucose 6-phosphate in liver cells?

8. *Neither option is good.* Differentiate between type 1 and type 2 diabetes.

9. *Fighting diabetes.* Leptin is considered an "antidiabetogenic" hormone. Explain.

10. *Metabolic energy and power.* The rate of energy expenditure of a typical 70-kg person at rest is about 70 watts (W), like that of a light bulb.

(a) Express this rate in kilojoules per second and in kilocalories per second.

(b) How many electrons flow through the mitochondrial electron-transport chain per second under these conditions?

(c) Estimate the corresponding rate of ATP production.

(d) The total ATP content of the body is about 50 g. Estimate how often an ATP molecule turns over in a person at rest.

11. *Respiratory quotient (RQ).* This classic metabolic index is defined as the volume of CO_2 released divided by the volume of O_2 consumed.

(a) Calculate the RQ values for the complete oxidation of glucose and of tripalmitoylglycerol.

(b) What do RQ measurements reveal about the contributions of different energy sources during intense exercise? (Assume that protein degradation is negligible.)

12. *Camel's hump.* Compare the H_2O yield from the complete oxidation of 1 g of glucose with that of 1 g of tripalmitoylglycerol. Relate these values to the evolutionary selection of the contents of a camel's hump.

13. *Hungry–nourished.* What is meant by the starved–fed cycle?

14. *Of course, too much is bad for you.* What are the primary means of processing ethanol?

15. *Started out with burgundy, but soon hit the harder stuff.* Describe the three stages of ethanol consumption that lead to liver damage and possibly death.

16. *The wages of sin.* How long does a person have to jog to offset the calories obtained from eating 10 macadamia nuts (75 kJ, or 18 kcal, per nut)? (Assume an incremental power consumption of 400 W.)

17. *Sweet hazard.* Ingesting large amounts of glucose before a marathon might seem to be a good way of increasing the fuel stores. However, experienced runners do not ingest glucose before a race. What is the biochemical reason for their avoidance of this potential fuel? (Hint: Consider the effect of glucose ingestion on the level of insulin.)

18. *Lipodystrophy.* Lipodystrophy is a condition in which an individual lacks adipose tissue. The muscles and liver from such individuals are insulin resistant, and both tissues accumulate large amounts of triacylglycerides (hyperlipidemia). The administration of leptin partly ameliorates this condition. What does it indicate about the relation of adipose tissue to insulin action?

19. *Therapeutic target.* What would be the effect of a mutation in the gene for PTP1B (protein tyrosine phosphatase 1B) that inactivated the enzyme in a person who has type 2 diabetes?

20. *An effect of diabetes.* Insulin-dependent diabetes is often accompanied by hypertriglyceridemia, which is an excess blood level of triacylglycerols in the form of very low density lipoproteins. Suggest a biochemical explanation.

21. *Sharing the wealth.* The hormone glucagon signifies the starved state, yet it inhibits glycolysis in the liver. How does this inhibition of an energy-production pathway benefit the organism?

22. *Compartmentation.* Glycolysis takes place in the cytoplasm, whereas fatty acid degradation takes place in mitochondria. What metabolic pathways depend on the interplay of reactions that take place in both compartments?

23. *Kwashiorkor.* The most common form of malnutrition in children in the world, kwashiorkor, is caused by a diet having ample calories but little protein. The high levels of carbohydrate result in high levels of insulin. What is the effect of high levels of insulin on

(a) lipid utilization?

(b) protein metabolism?

(c) Children suffering from kwashiorkor often have large distended bellies caused by water from the blood leaking into extracellular spaces. Suggest a biochemical basis for this condition.

24. *One for all, all for one.* How is the metabolism of the liver coordinated with that of skeletal muscle during strenuous exercise?

25. *A little help, please?* What is the advantage of converting pyruvate into lactate in skeletal muscle?

26. *Fuel choice.* What is the major fuel for resting muscle? What is the major fuel for muscle under strenuous work conditions?

27. *Hefty reimbursement.* Endurance athletes sometimes follow the exercise-and-diet plan described here: 7 days before an event, do exhaustive exercises so as to all but deplete glycogen stores. For the next 2 to 3 days, consume few carbohydrates and do moderate- to low-intensity exercises. Finally, 3 to 4 days before the event, consume a diet rich in carbohydrates. Explain the benefits of this regime.

28. *Oxygen deficit.* After light exercise, the oxygen consumed in recovery is approximately equal to the oxygen deficit, which is the amount of additional oxygen that would have been consumed had oxygen consumption reached steady state immediately. How is the oxygen consumed in recovery used?

29. *Excess postexercise oxygen consumption.* The oxygen consumed after strenuous exercise stops is significantly greater than the oxygen deficit and is termed *excess postexercise oxygen consumption* (EPOC). Why is so much more oxygen required after intense exercise?

30. *Psychotropic effects.* Ethanol is unusual in that it is freely soluble in both water and lipids. Thus, it has access to all regions of the highly vascularized brain. Although the molecular basis of ethanol action in the brain is not clear, ethanol evidently influences a number of neurotransmitter receptors and ion channels. Suggest a biochemical explanation for the diverse effects of ethanol.

31. *Fiber type.* Skeletal muscle has several distinct fiber types. Type I is used primarily for aerobic activity, whereas type II is specialized for short, intense bursts of activity. How could you distinguish between these types of muscle fiber if you viewed them with an electron microscope?

32. *Tour de France.* Cyclists in the Tour de France (more than 2000 miles in 3 weeks) require about 836,000 kJ (200,000 kcal) of energy, or 41,840 kJ (10,000 kcal) day^{-1} (a resting male requires ~8368 kJ, or 2000 kcal, day^{-1}).

(a) With the assumptions that the energy yield of ATP is about 50.2 kJ (12 kcal) mol^{-1} and that ATP has a molecular weight of 503 g mol^{-1}, how much ATP would be expended by a Tour de France cyclist?

(b) Pure ATP can be purchased at a cost of approximately $150 per gram. How much would it cost to power a cyclist through the Tour de France if the ATP had to be purchased?

33. *Spare tire.* Suppose that our test subject from the beginning of the chapter gained 55 pounds between the ages of 25 and 65, and that her weight at 65 years of age is 175 pounds. Calculate how many excess calories she consumed per day to gain the 55 pounds over 40 years. Assume that our test subject is 5 feet 6 inches tall. What is her BMI? Would she be considered obese at 175 lbs?

34. *Responding to stress.* Why does it make good physiological sense that regular bouts of prolonged exercise will result in mitochondrial biogenesis?

35. *Too much of a good thing.* What is the relation between fatty acid oxidation and insulin resistance in the muscle?

36. *Aneurin? Really?* Why are the symptoms of beriberi similar to those of Wernicke–Korsakoff syndrome?

Data Interpretation Problem

37. *Lactate threshold.* The graph shows the relation between blood-lactate levels, oxygen consumption, and heart rate during exercise of increasing intensity. The values for oxygen consumption and heart rate are indicators of the degree of exertion.

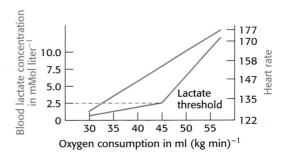

(a) Why is some lactate produced even when exercise is moderate?

(b) Biochemically, what is taking place when the lactate concentration begins to rise rapidly, a point called the lactate threshold?

(c) Endurance athletes will sometimes measure blood-lactate levels during training so that they know their lactate threshold. Then, during events, they will race just at or below their lactate threshold until the late stages of the race. Biochemically, why is this practice wise?

(d) Training can increase the lactate threshold. Explain.

ANSWERS TO PROBLEMS

Chapter 1

1. The hydrogen-bond donors are the NH and NH_2 groups. The hydrogen-bond acceptors are the carbonyl oxygen atoms and those ring nitrogen atoms that are not bonded to hydrogen or to deoxyribose.

2. Interchange the positions of the single and double bonds in the six-membered ring.

3. (a) Electrostatic interactions; (b) van der Waals interactions.

4. Processes *a* and *b*

5. $\Delta S_{system} = -661 \, J \, mol^{-1} \, K^{-1} \, (-158 \, kcal \, mol^{-1} \, K^{-1})$

$\Delta S_{surroundings} = +842 \, J \, mol^{-1} \, K^{-1} \, (+201 \, cal \, mol^{-1} \, K^{-1})$

6. (a) 1.0; (b) 13.0; (c) 1.3; (d) 12.7

7. 2.88

8. 1.96

9. 11.83

10. 447; 0.00050

11. 0.00066 M

12. 6.0

13. 5.53

14. 6.48

15. 7.8

16. 100

17. (a) 1.6; (b) 0.51; (c) 0.16.

18. 0.1 M sodium acetate solution: 6.34; 6.03; 5.70; 4.75. 0.01 M sodium acetate solution: 5.90; 4.75; 3.38; 1.40.

19. 90 mM acetic acid; 160 mM sodium acetate, 0.18 moles acetic acid; 0.32 moles sodium acetate; 10.81 g acetic acid; 26.25 g sodium acetate.

20. 0.50 moles of acetic acid; 0.32 moles of NaOH; 30.03 g of acetic acid; 12.80 g of NaOH.

21. 250 mM; yes; no, it will also contain 90 mM NaCl.

22. 8.63 g Na_2HPO_4; 4.71 g NaH_2PO_4

23. 7.0; this buffer will not be very useful, because the pH value is far from the pK_a value.

24. 1.45 kJ mol^{-1} (0.35 kcal mol^{-1}); 57.9 kJ mol^{-1} (13.8 kcal mol^{-1})

25. There will be approximately 15 million differences.

Chapter 2

1. (A) Proline, Pro, P; (B) tyrosine, Tyr, Y; (C) leucine, Leu, L; (D) lysine, Lys, K.

2. (a) C, B, A; (b) D; (c) D, B; (d) B, D; (e) B.

3. (a) 6; (b) 2; (c) 3; (d) 1; (e) 4; (f) 5.

4. (a) Ala; (b) Tyr; (c) Ser; (d) His.

5. Ser, Glu, Tyr, Thr

6. (a) Alanine-glycine-serine; (b) Alanine; (c and d):

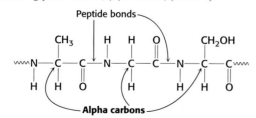

7.

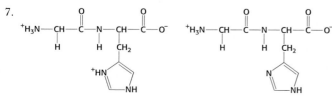

At pH 5.5, the net charge is +1   At pH 7.5, the net charge is 0

8. There are 20 choices for each of the 50 amino acids: 50^{20}, or 5×10^{21}.

9.

Aspartame at pH 7

10. The (nitrogen–α carbon–carbonyl carbon) repeating unit.

11. Side chain is the functional group attached to the α-carbon atom of an amino acid.

12. Amino acid composition refers simply to the amino acids that make up the protein. The order is not specified. Amino acid sequence is the same as the primary structure—the sequence of amino acids from the amino terminal to the carboxyl terminal of the protein. Different proteins may have the same amino acid composition, but amino acid sequence identifies a unique protein.

13. (a) Each strand is 35 kd and hence has about 318 residues (the mean residue mass is 110 daltons). Because the rise per residue in an α helix is 1.5 Å, the length is 477 Å. More precisely, for an α-helical coiled coil, the rise per residue is 1.46 Å; so the length is 464 Å. (b) Eighteen residues in each strand (40 minus 4 divided by 2) are in a β-sheet conformation. Because the rise per residue is 3.5 Å, the length is 63 Å.

14. The methyl group attached to the β-carbon atom of isoleucine sterically interferes with α-helix formation. In leucine, this methyl group is attached to the γ-carbon atom, which is farther from the main chain and hence does not interfere.

15. The first mutation destroys activity because valine occupies more space than alanine does, and so the protein must take a different shape, assuming that this residue lies in the closely packed interior. The second mutation restores activity because of a compensatory reduction of volume; glycine is smaller than isoleucine.

16. The native conformation of insulin is not the thermodynamically most stable form, because it contains two separate chains linked by disulfide bonds. Insulin is formed from proinsulin, a single-chain precursor, that is cleaved to form insulin, a 51-residue molecule, after the disulfide bonds have formed.

17. A segment of the main chain of the protease could hydrogen bond to the main chain of the substrate to form an extended parallel or antiparallel pair of β strands.

18. Glycine has the smallest side chain of any amino acid. Its size is often critical in allowing polypeptide chains to make tight turns or to approach one another closely.

19. Glutamate, aspartate, and the terminal carboxylate can form salt bridges with the guanidinium group of arginine. In addition, this group can be a hydrogen-bond donor to the side chains of glutamine, asparagine, serine, threonine, aspartate, tyrosine, and glutamate and to the main-chain carbonyl group. Histidine can form hydrogen bonds with arginine at pH7.

20. Disulfide bonds in hair are broken by adding a thiol-containing reagent and applying gentle heat. The hair is curled, and an oxidizing agent is added to re-form disulfide bonds to stabilize the desired shape.

21. Some proteins that span biological membranes are "the exceptions that prove the rule" because they have the reverse distribution of hydrophobic and hydrophilic amino acids. For example, consider

porins, proteins found in the outer membranes of many bacteria. Membranes are built largely of hydrophobic chains. Thus, porins are covered on the outside largely with hydrophobic residues that interact with the neighboring hydrophobic chains. In contrast, the center of the protein contains many charged and polar amino acids that surround a water-filled channel running through the middle of the protein. Thus, because porins function in hydrophobic environments, they are "inside out" relative to proteins that function in aqueous solution.

22. The amino acids would be hydrophobic in nature. An α helix is especially suited to crossing a membrane because all of the amide hydrogen atoms and carbonyl oxygen atoms of the peptide backbone take part in intrachain hydrogen bonds, thus stabilizing these polar atoms in a hydrophobic environment.

23. This example demonstrates that the pK_a values are affected by the environment. A given amino acid can have a variety of pK_a values, depending on the chemical environment inside the protein.

24. A possible explanation is that the severity of the symptoms corresponds to the degree of structural disruption. Hence, substitution of alanine for glycine might result in mild symptoms, but substitution of the much larger tryptophan might prevent little or no collagen triple-helix formation.

25. The energy barrier that must be crossed to go from the polymerized state to the hydrolyzed state is large even though the reaction is thermodynamically favorable.

26. Using the Henderson–Hasselbalch equation, we find the ratio of alanine-COOH to alanine-COO$^-$ at pH 7 to be 10^{-4}. The ratio of alanine-NH$_2$ to alanine-NH$_3^+$, determined in the same fashion, is 10^{-1}. Thus, the ratio of neutral alanine to the zwitterionic species is $10^{-4} \times 10^{-1} = 10^{-5}$.

27. The assignment of absolute configuration requires the assignment of priorities to the four groups connected to a tetrahedral carbon atom. For all amino acids except cysteine, the priorities are: (1) amino group; (2) carbonyl group; (3) side chain; (4) hydrogen. For cysteine, because of the sulfur atom in its side chain, the side chain has a greater priority than does the carbonyl group, leading to the assignment of an R rather than S configuration.

28. ELVISISLIVINGINLASVEGAS

29. No, Pro–X would have the characteristics of any other peptide bond. The steric hindrance in X–Pro arises because the R group of Pro is bonded to the amino group. Hence, in X–Pro, the proline R group is near the R group of X, which would not be the case in Pro–X.

30. A, c; B, e; C, d; D, a; E, b.

31. The reason is that the wrong disulfides formed pairs in urea. There are 105 different ways of pairing eight cysteine molecules to form four disulfides; only one of these combinations is enzymatically active. The 104 wrong pairings have been picturesquely termed "scrambled" ribonuclease.

Chapter 3

1. (a) Phenyl isothiocyanate; (b) urea; β-mercaptoethanol to reduce disulfides; (c) chymotrypsin; (d) CNBr; (e) trypsin.

2. Each amino acid residue, except the carboxyl-terminal residue, gives rise to a hydrazide on reacting with hydrazine. The carboxyl-terminal residue can be identified because it yields a free amino acid.

3. The S-aminoethylcysteine side chain resembles that of lysine. The only difference is a sulfur atom in place of a methylene group.

4. A 1 mg ml^{-1} solution of myoglobin (17.8 kd; Table 3.2) corresponds to 5.62×10^{-5} M. The absorbance of a 1-cm path length is 0.84, which corresponds to an I_0/I ratio of 6.96. Hence 14.4% of the incident light is transmitted.

5. The sample was diluted 1000-fold. The concentration after dialysis is thus 0.001 M, or 1 mM. You could reduce the salt concentration by dialyzing your sample, now 1 mM, in more buffer free of (NH$_4$)$_2$SO$_4$.

6. If the salt concentration becomes too high, the salt ions interact with the water molecules. Eventually, there will not be enough water molecules to interact with the protein, and the protein will precipitate. If there is lack of salt in a protein solution, the proteins may interact with one another—the positive charges on one protein with the negative charges on another or several others. Such an aggregate becomes too large to be solublized by water alone. If salt is added, the salt neutralizes the charges on the proteins, preventing protein–protein interactions.

7. Tropomyosin is rod shaped, whereas hemoglobin is approximately spherical.

8. The frictional coefficient, f, and the mass, m, determine s. Specifically, f is proportional to r (see equation 2 on p. 71). Hence, f is proportional to $m^{1/3}$, and so s is proportional to $m^{2/3}$ (see the equation on p. 76). An 80-kd spherical protein undergoes sedimentation 1.59 times as rapidly as a 40-kd spherical protein.

9. The long hydrophobic tail on the SDS molecule (see p. 72) disrupts the hydrophobic interactions in the interior of the protein. The protein unfolds, with the hydrophobic R groups now interacting with SDS rather than with one another.

10. 50 kd.

11. The protein may be modified. For instance, serine, threonine, and tyrosine may have phosphoryl groups attached.

12. A fluorescence-labeled derivative of a bacterial degradation product (e.g., a formylmethionyl peptide) would bind to cells containing the receptor of interest.

13. (a) Trypsin cleaves after arginine (R) and lysine (K), generating AVGWR, VK, and S. Because they differ in size, these products could be separated by molecular exclusion chromatography. (b) Chymotrypsin, which cleaves after large aliphatic or aromatic R groups, generates two peptides of equal size (AVGW) and (RVKS). Separation based on size would not be effective. The peptide RVKS has two positive charges (R and K), whereas the other peptide is neutral. Therefore, the two products could be separated by ion-exchange chromatography.

14. Antibody molecules bound to a solid support can be used for affinity purification of proteins for which a ligand molecule is not known or unavailable.

15. If the product of the enzyme-catalyzed reaction is highly antigenic, it may be possible to obtain antibodies to this particular molecule. These antibodies can be used to detect the presence of product by ELISA, providing an assay format suitable for the purification of this enzyme.

16. An inhibitor of the enzyme being purified might have been present and subsequently removed by a purification step. This removal would lead to an apparent increase in the total amount of enzyme present.

17. Many proteins have similar masses but different sequences and different patterns when digested with trypsin. The set of masses of tryptic peptides forms a detailed "fingerprint" of a protein that is very unlikely to appear at random in other proteins regardless of size. (A conceivable analogy is: "Just as similarly sized fingers will give different individual fingerprints, so also similarly sized proteins will give different digestion patterns with trypsin.")

18. Isoleucine and leucine are isomers and, hence, have identical masses. Peptide sequencing by mass spectrometry as described in this chapter is incapable of distinguishing these residues. Further analytical techniques are required to differentiate these residues.

19. See the table at the top of the facing page.

Purification procedure	Total protein (mg)	Total activity (units)	Specific activity (units mg^{-1})	Purification level	Yield (%)
Crude extract	20,000	4,000,000	200	1	100
(NH$_4$)$_2$SO$_4$ precipitation	5,000	3,000,000	600	3	75
DEAE–cellulose chromatography	1,500	1,000,000	667	3.3	25
Gel-filtration chromatography	500	750,000	1,500	7.5	19
Affinity chromatography	45	675,000	15,000	75	17

20. Protein crystal formation requires the ordered arrangement of identically positioned molecules. Proteins with flexible linkers can introduce disorder into this arrangement and prevent the formation of suitable crystals. A ligand or binding partner may induce an ordered conformation to this linker and could be included in the solution to facilitate crystal growth. Alternatively, the individual domains separated by the linker may be expressed by recombinant methods and their crystal structures solved separately.

21. Treatment with urea will disrupt noncovalent bonds. Thus the original 60-kd protein must be made of two 30-kd subunits. When these subunits are treated with urea and β-mercaptoethanol, a single 15-kd species results, suggesting that disulfide bonds link the 30-kd subunits.

22. (a) Electrostatic repulsion between positively charged ε-amino groups hinders α-helix formation at pH 7. At pH 10, the side chains become deprotonated, allowing α-helix formation.
(b) Poly-L-glutamate is a random coil at pH 7 and becomes α helical below pH 4.5 because the γ-carboxylate groups become protonated.

23. The difference between the predicted and the observed masses for this fragment equals 28.0, exactly the mass shift that would be expected in a formylated peptide. This peptide is likely formylated at its amino terminus, and corresponds to the most N-terminal fragment of the protein.

24. Light was used to direct the synthesis of these peptides. Each amino acid added to the solid support contained a photolabile protecting group instead of a t-Boc protecting group at its α-amino group. Illumination of selected regions of the solid support led to the release of the protecting group, which exposed the amino groups in these sites to make them reactive. The pattern of masks used in these illuminations and the sequence of reactants define the ultimate products and their locations.

25. Mass spectrometry is highly sensitive and capable of detecting the mass difference between a protein and its deuterated counterpart. Fragmentation techniques can be used to identify the amino acids that retained the isotope label. Alternatively, NMR spectroscopy can be used to detect the isotopically labeled atoms because the deuteron and the proton have very different nuclear-spin properties.

26. First amino acid: A
Last amino acid: R (not cleaved by carboxypeptidase).
Sequence of N-terminal tryptic peptide: AVR (tryptic peptide ends in K)
Sequence of N-terminal chymotryptic peptide: AVRY (chymotryptic peptide ends in Y)
Sequence: AVRYSR

27. First amino acid: S
Last amino acid: L
Cyanogen bromide cleavage: M is 10th position,
C-terminal residues are: (2S,L,W)
Amino-terminal residues: (G,K,S,Y), tryptic peptide, ends in K
Amino-terminal sequence: SYGK
Chymotryptic peptide order: (S,Y), (G,K,L), (F,I,S), (M,T), (S,W), (S,L)
Sequence: SYGKLSIFTMSWSL

28. If the protein did not contain any disulfide bonds, then the electrophoretic mobility of the trypsin fragments would be the same before and after performic acid treatment: all the fragments would lie along the diagonal of the paper. If one disulfide bond were present, the disulfide-linked trypsin fragments would run as a single peak in the first direction, then would run as two separate peaks after performic acid treatment. The result would be two peaks appearing off the diagonal:

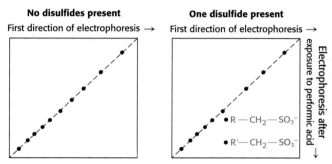

These fragments could then be isolated from the chromatography paper and analyzed by mass spectrometry to determine their amino acid composition and thus identify the cysteines participating in the disulfide bond.

Chapter 4

1. A nucleoside is a base attached to a ribose sugar. A nucleotide is a nucleoside with one or more phosphoryl groups attached to the ribose.
2. Hydrogen-bond pairing between the base A and the base T as well as hydrogen-bond pairing between the base G and the base C in DNA.
3. T is always equal to A, and so these two nucleotides constitute 40% of the bases. G is always equal to C, and so the remaining 60% must be 30% G and 30% C.
4. Nothing, because the base-pair rules do not apply to single-stranded nucleic acids.
5. (a) TTGATC; (b) GTTCGA; (c) ACGCGT; (d) ATGGTA.
6. (a) [T] + [C] = 0.46. (b) [T] = 0.30, [C] = 0.24, and [A] + [G] = 0.46.
7. Stable hydrogen bonding occurs only between GC and AT pairs. Moreover, two purines are too large to fit inside the double helix, and two pyrimidines are too small to form base pairs with each other.
8. The thermal energy causes the chains to wiggle about, which disrupts the hydrogen bonds between base pairs and the stacking forces between bases and thereby causes the strands to separate.
9. The probability that any sequence will appear is 4^n, where 4 is the number of nucleotides and n is the length of the sequence. The probability of any 15-base sequence appearing is $1/4^{15}$, or 1/1,073,741,824. Thus, a 15-nucleotide sequence would be likely to appear approximately three times (3 billion × probability of appearance). The probability of a 16-base sequence appearing is $1/4^{16}$, which is equal to 1/4,294,967,296. Such a sequence will be unlikely to appear more than once.

10. One end of a nucleic acid polymer ends with a free 5′-hydroxyl group (or a phosphoryl group esterified to the hydroxyl group), and the other end has a free 3′-hydroxyl group. Thus, the ends are different. Two chains of DNA can form a double helix only if the chains are running in different directions—that is, have opposite polarity.

11. Although the individual bonds are weak, the population of thousands to millions of such bonds provides much stability. There is strength in numbers.

12. There would be too much charge repulsion from the negative charges on the phosphoryl groups. These charges must be countered by the addition of cations.

13. The three forms are the A-DNA, the B-DNA and the Z-DNA, with B-DNA being the most common. There are many differences (see Table 4.2). Some key differences are: A-DNA and B-DNA are right-handed, whereas Z-DNA is left-handed. A-DNA forms in less-hydrated conditions than does B-DNA. The A form is shorter and wider than the B form.

14. 5.88×10^3 base pairs

15. In conservative replication, after 1.0 generation, half of the molecules would be ^{15}N-^{15}N, the other half ^{14}N-^{14}N. After 2.0 generations, one-quarter of the molecules would be ^{15}N-^{15}N, the other three-quarters ^{14}N-^{14}N. Hybrid ^{14}N-^{15}N molecules would not be observed in conservative replication.

16. (a) Tritiated thymine or tritiated thymidine.
(b) dATP, dGTP, dCTP, and TTP labeled with ^{32}P in the innermost (α) phosphorus atom.

17. Molecules in parts *a* and *b* would not lead to DNA synthesis, because they lack a 3′-OH group (a primer). The molecule in part *d* has a free 3′-OH group at one end of each strand but no template strand beyond. Only the molecule in part *c* would lead to DNA synthesis.

18. A retrovirus is a virus that has RNA as its genetic material. However, for the information to be expressed, it must first be converted into DNA, a reaction catalyzed by the enzyme reverse transcriptase. Thus, at least initially, information flow is opposite that of a normal cell: RNA $\longrightarrow$ DNA rather than DNA $\longrightarrow$ RNA.

19. A thymidylate oligonucleotide should be used as the primer. The poly(A) template specifies the incorporation of T; hence, radioactive thymidine triphosphate (labeled in the α phosphoryl group) should be used in the assay.

20. The ribonuclease serves to degrade the RNA strand, a necessary step in forming duplex DNA from the RNA–DNA hybrid.

21. Treat one aliquot of the sample with ribonuclease and another with deoxyribonuclease. Test these nuclease-treated samples for infectivity.

22. Deamination changes the original G · C base pair into a G · U pair. After one round of replication, one daughter duplex will contain a G · C pair and the other duplex will contain an A · U pair. After two rounds of replication, there will be two G · C pairs, one A · U pair, and one A · T pair.

23. (a) $4^8 = 65,536$. In computer terminology, there are 64K 8-mers of DNA.
(b) A bit specifies two bases (say, A and C) and a second bit specifies the other two (G and T). Hence, two bits are needed to specify a single nucleotide (base pair) in DNA. For example, 00, 01, 10, and 11 could encode A, C, G, and T. An 8-mer stores 16 bits ($2^{16} = 65,536$), the *E. coli* genome (4.6×10^6 bp) stores 9.2×10^6 bits, and the human genome (3.0×10^9 bases) stores 6.0×10^9 bits of genetic information.

(c) A standard CD can hold about 700 megabytes, which is equal to 5.6×10^9 bits. A large number of 8-mer sequences could be stored on such a CD. The DNA sequence of *E. coli,* could be written on a single CD with room to spare for a lot of music. One CD would not be quite enough to record the entire human genome.

24. (a) Deoxyribonucleoside triphosphates versus ribonucleoside triphosphates.
(b) 5′ $\longrightarrow$ 3′ for both.
(c) Semiconserved for DNA polymerase I; conserved for RNA polymerase.
(d) DNA polymerase I needs a primer, whereas RNA polymerase does not.

25. Messenger RNA encodes the information that, on translation, yields a protein. Ribosomal RNA is the catalytic component of ribosomes, the molecular complexes that synthesize proteins. Transfer RNA is an adaptor molecule, capable of binding a specific amino acid and recognizing a corresponding codon. Transfer RNAs with attached amino acids are substrates for the ribosome.

26. (a) 5′-UAACGGUACGAU-3′
(b) Leu-Pro-Ser-Asp-Trp-Met
(c) Poly(Leu-Leu-Thr-Tyr)

27. The 2′-OH group in RNA acts as an intramolecular nucleophile. In the alkaline hydrolysis of RNA, it forms a 2′-3′ cyclic intermediate.

28.

29. Gene expression is the process of expressing the information of a gene in its functional molecular form. For many genes, the functional information is a protein molecule. Thus, gene expression includes transcription and translation.

30. A nucleotide sequence whose bases represent the most-common, but not necessarily the only, members of the sequence. A consensus sequence can be thought of as the average of many similar sequences.

31. Cordycepin terminates RNA synthesis. An RNA chain containing cordycepin lacks a 3′-OH group.

32. Only single-stranded RNA can serve as a template for protein synthesis.

33. Degeneracy of the code refers to the fact that most amino acids are encoded by more than one codon.

34. If only 20 of the 64 possible codons encoded amino acids, then a mutation that changed a codon would likely result in a nonsense codon, leading to termination of protein synthesis. With degeneracy, a nucleotide change might yield a synonym or a codon for an amino acid with similar chemical properties.

35. (a) 2, 4, 8; (b) 1, 6, 10; (c) 3, 5, 7, 9.

36. (a) 3; (b) 6; (c) 2; (d) 5; (e) 7; (f) 1; (g) 4.

37. Incubation with RNA polymerase and only UTP, ATP, and CTP led to the synthesis of only poly(UAC). Only poly(GUA) was formed when GTP was used in place of CTP.

38. A peptide terminating with Lys (UGA is a stop codon), another containing -Asn-Glu-, and a third containing -Met-Arg-.

39. Highly abundant amino acid residues have the most codons (e.g., Leu and Ser each have six), whereas the least-abundant amino acids have the fewest (Met and Trp each have only one). Degeneracy (1) allows variation in base composition and (2) decreases the likelihood that a substitution for a base will change the encoded amino acid. If the degeneracy were equally distributed, each of the 20 amino acids would have three codons. Both benefits (1 and 2) are maximized by the assignment of more codons to prevalent amino acids than to less frequently used ones.

40. Phe-Cys-His-Val-Ala-Ala

41. Exon shuffling is a molecular process that can lead to the generation of new proteins by the rearrangement of exons within genes. Because many exons encode functional protein domains, exon shuffling is a rapid and efficient means of generating new genes.

42. It shows that the genetic code and the biochemical means of interpreting the code are common to even very distantly related life forms. It also testifies to the unity of life; that all life arose from a common ancestor.

43. (a) A codon for lysine cannot be changed to one for aspartate by the mutation of a single nucleotide. (b) Arg, Asn, Gln, Glu, Ile, Met, or Thr.

44. The genetic code is degenerate. Of the 20 amino acids, 18 are specified by more than one codon. Hence, many nucleotide changes (especially in the third base of a codon) do not alter the nature of the encoded amino acid. Mutations leading to an altered amino acid are usually more deleterious than those that do not and hence are subject to more stringent selection.

45. GC base pairs have three hydrogen bonds compared with two for AT base pairs. Thus, the higher content of GC means more hydrogen bonds and greater helix stability.

46. C_0t value essentially corresponds to the complexity of the DNA sequence—in other words, how long it will take for a sequence of DNA to find its complementary strand to form a double helix. The more complex the DNA, the slower it reassociates to make the double-stranded form.

Chapter 5

1. (a) 5'-GGCATAC-3'
(b) The Sanger dideoxy method of sequencing would give the gel pattern shown here.

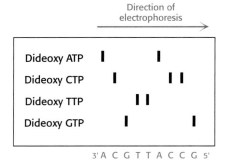

2. Ovalbumin cDNA should be used. *E. coli* lacks the machinery to splice the primary transcript arising from genomic DNA.

3. Consistent with its planar, aromatic structure, ethidium bromide is a DNA intercalator: it aligns itself between the paired bases in a DNA duplex.

4. The presence of the *Alu*I sequence would, on average, be $(1/4)^4$, or 1/256, because the likelihood of any base being at any position is one-fourth and there are four positions. By the same reasoning, the presence of the *Not*I sequence would be $(1/4)^8$, or 1/65,536. Thus, the average product of digestion by *Alu*I would be 250 base pairs (0.25 kb) in length, whereas that by *Not*I would be 66,000 base pairs (66 kb) in length.

5. No, because most human genes are much longer than 4 kb. A fragment would contain only a small part of a complete gene.

6. Southern blotting of an *Mst*II digest would distinguish between the normal and the mutant genes. The loss of a restriction site would lead to the replacement of two fragments on the Southern blot by a single longer fragment. Such a finding would not prove that GTG replaced GAG; other sequence changes at the restriction site could yield the same result.

7. Although the two enzymes cleave the same recognition site, they each break different bonds within the 6-bp sequence. Cleavage by *Kpn*I yields an overhang on the 3′ strand, whereas cleavage by *Acc*65I produces an overhang on the 5′ strand. These sticky ends do not overlap.

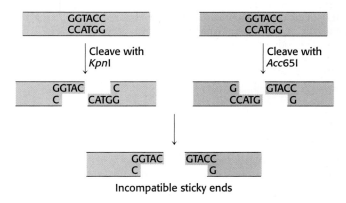

Incompatible sticky ends

8. A simple strategy for generating many mutants is to synthesize a degenerate set of cassettes by using a mixture of activated nucleosides in particular rounds of oligonucleotide synthesis. Suppose that the 30-bp coding region begins with GTT, which encodes valine. If a mixture of all four nucleotides is used in the first and second rounds of synthesis, the resulting oligonucleotides will begin with the sequence XYT (where X and Y denote A, C, G, or T). These 16 different versions of the cassette will encode proteins containing either Phe, Leu, Ile, Val, Ser, Pro, Thr, Ala, Tyr, His, Asn, Asp, Cys, Arg, or Gly at the first position. Likewise, degenerate cassettes can be made in which two or more codons are simultaneously varied.

9. Because PCR can amplify as little as one molecule of DNA, statements claiming the isolation of ancient DNA need to be greeted with some skepticism. The DNA would need to be sequenced. Is it similar to human, bacterial, or fungal DNA? If so, contamination is the likely source of the amplified DNA. Is it similar to that of birds or crocodiles? This sequence similarity would strengthen the case that it is dinosaur DNA because these species are evolutionarily close to dinosaurs.

10. PCR amplification is greatly hindered by the presence of G–C-rich regions within the template. Owing to their high melting temperatures, these templates do not denature easily, preventing the initiation of an amplification cycle. In addition, rigid secondary

structures prevent the progress of DNA polymerase along the template strand during elongation.

11. At high temperatures of hybridization, only very close matches between primer and target would be stable because all (or most) of the bases would need to find partners to stabilize the primer–target helix. As the temperature is lowered, more mismatches would be tolerated; so the amplification is likely to yield genes with less sequence similarity. In regard to the yeast gene, synthesize primers corresponding to the ends of the gene, and then use these primers and human DNA as the target. If nothing is amplified at 54°C, the human gene differs from the yeast gene, but a counterpart may still be present. Repeat the experiment at a lower temperature of hybridization.

12. Digest genomic DNA with a restriction enzyme, and select the fragment that contains the known sequence. Circularize this fragment. Then carry out PCR with the use of a pair of primers that serve as templates for the synthesis of DNA away from the known sequence.

13. The encoded protein contains four repeats of a specific sequence.

14. Use chemical synthesis or the polymerase chain reaction to prepare hybridization probes that are complementary to both ends of the known (previously isolated) DNA fragment. Challenge clones representing the library of DNA fragments with both of the hybridization probes. Select clones that hybridize to one of the probes but not the other; such clones are likely to represent DNA fragments that contain one end of the known fragment along with the adjacent region of the particular chromosome.

15. The codon(s) for each amino acid can be used to determine the number of possible nucleotide sequences that encode each peptide sequence (see Table 4.5):

Ala–Met–Ser–Leu–Pro–Trp:
$4 \times 1 \times 6 \times 6 \times 4 \times 1 \quad = 576$ total sequences

Gly–Trp–Asp–Met–His–Lys:
$4 \times 1 \times 2 \times 1 \times 2 \times 2 \quad = 32$ total sequences

Cys–Val–Trp–Asn–Lys–Ile:
$2 \times 4 \times 1 \times 2 \times 2 \times 3 \quad = 96$ total sequences

Arg–Ser–Met–Leu–Gln–Asn:
$6 \times 6 \times 1 \times 6 \times 2 \times 2 \quad = 864$ total sequences

The set of DNA sequences encoding the peptide Gly-Trp-Asp-Met-His-Lys would be most ideal for probe design because it encompasses only 32 total oligonucleotides.

16. Within a single species, individual dogs show enormous variation in body size and substantial diversity in other physical characteristics. Therefore, genomic analysis of individual dogs would provide valuable clues concerning the genes responsible for the diversity within the species.

17. On the basis of the comparative genome map shown in Figure 5.27, the region of greatest overlap with human chromosome 20 can be found on mouse chromosome 2.

18. T_m is the melting temperature of a double-stranded nucleic acid. If the melting temperatures of the primers are too different, the extent of hybridization with the target DNA will differ during the annealing phase, which would result in differential replications of the strands.

19. Careful comparison of the sequences reveals that there is a 7-bp region of complementarity at the 3′ ends of these two primers:

5′-GGATCGATGCTCGCGA-3′
```
       | | | | | | |
```
3′-GAGCGCTGGGCTAGGA-5′

In a PCR experiment, these primers would likely anneal to one another, preventing their interaction with the template DNA. During DNA synthesis by the polymerase, each primer would act as a template for the other primer, leading to the amplification of a 25-bp sequence corresponding to the overlapped primers.

20. A mutation in person B has altered one of the alleles for gene X, leaving the other intact. The fact that the mutated allele is smaller suggests that a deletion has occurred in one copy of the gene. The one functioning copy is transcribed and translated and apparently produces enough protein to render the person asymptomatic.

Person C has only the smaller version of the gene. This gene is neither transcribed (negative northern blot) nor translated (negative western blot).

Person D has a normal-size copy of the gene but no corresponding RNA or protein. There may be a mutation in the promoter region of the gene that prevents transcription.

Person E has a normal-size copy of the gene that is transcribed, but no protein is made, which suggests that a mutation prevents translation. There are a number of possible explanations, including a mutation that introduced a premature stop codon in the mRNA.

Person F has a normal amount of protein but still displays the metabolic problem. This finding suggests that the mutation affects the activity of the protein—for instance, a mutation that compromises the active site of enzyme Y.

21. Chongqing: residue 2, L ⟶ R, CTG ⟶ CGG
Karachi: residue 5, A ⟶ P, GCC ⟶ CCC
Swan River: residue 6, D ⟶ G, GAC ⟶ GGC

22. This particular person is heterozygous for this particular mutation: one allele is wild type, whereas the other carries a point mutation at this position. Both alleles are PCR amplified in this experiment, yielding the "dual peak" appearance on the sequencing chromatogram.

Chapter 6

1. There are 26 identities and two gaps for a score of 210. The two sequences are approximately 26% identical. This level of homology is likely to be statistically significant.

2. They are likely related by divergent evolution, because three-dimensional structure is more conserved than is sequence identity.

3. (a) Identity score = −25; Blosum score = 14; (b) identity score = 15; Blosum score = 3.

4. U

U   G

5. There are 4^{40}, or 1.2×10^{24}, different molecules. Each molecule has a mass of 2.2×10^{-20}, because 1 mol of polymer has a mass of 330 g mol$^{-1} \times 40$, and there are 6.02×10^{23} molecules per mole. Therefore, 26.4 kg of RNA would be required.

6. Because three-dimensional structure is much more closely associated with function than is sequence, tertiary structure is more evolutionarily conserved than is primary structure. In other words, protein function is the most important characteristic, and protein function is determined by structure. Thus, the structure must be conserved but not necessarily a specific amino acid sequence.

7. Alignment score of sequences (1) and (2) is $6 \times 10 = 60$. Many answers are possible, depending on the randomly reordered sequence. A possible result is

Shuffled sequence: (2) TKADKAGEYL

Alignment: (1) ASNFLDKAGK
               (2) TKADKAGEYL

Alignment score is $4 \times 10 = 40$.

8. (a) Almost certainly diverged from a common ancestor. (b) Almost certainly diverged from a common ancestor. (c) May have diverged from a common ancestor, but the sequence alignment may not provide supporting evidence. (d) May have diverged from a common ancestor, but the sequence alignment is unlikely to provide supporting evidence.

9. Replacement of cysteine, glycine, and proline never yields a positive score. Each of these residues exhibits features unlike those of its other 19 counterparts: cysteine is the only amino acid capable of forming disulfide bonds, glycine is the only amino acid without a side-chain and is highly flexible, and proline is the only amino acid that is highly constrained through the bonding of its side chain to its amine nitrogen.

10. Protein A is clearly homologous to protein B, given 65% sequence identity, and so A and B are expected to have quite similar three-dimensional structures. Likewise, proteins B and C are clearly homologous, given 55% sequence identity, and so B and C are expected to have quite similar three-dimensional structures. Thus, proteins A and C are likely to have similar three-dimensional structures, even though they are only 15% identical in sequence.

11. The likely secondary structure is

```
          N—N
      G⁄       ＼A
      C       G
      N       N
      N       N
      N       N
      N       N
      N       N
  N—N—N⁄       ＼N—N
```

12. To detect pairs of residues with correlated mutations, there must be variability in these sequences. If the alignment is over-represented by closely related organisms, there may not be enough changes in their sequences to allow the identification of potential base-pairing patterns.

13. After RNA molecules have been selected and reverse transcribed, PCR is performed to introduce additional mutations into these strands. The use of this error-prone, thermostable polymerase in the amplification step would enhance the efficiency of this random mutagenesis.

14. The initial pool of RNA molecules used in a molecular-evolution experiment is typically much smaller than the total number of possible sequences. Hence, the best possible RNA sequences will likely not be represented in the initial set of oligonucleotides. Mutagenesis of the initial selected RNA molecules allows for the iterative improvement of these sequences for the desired property.

15. 107 or 108 identities (depending on which annotated human sequence is chosen).

Chapter 7

1. The whale swims long distances between breaths. A high concentration of myoglobin in the whale muscle maintains a ready supply of oxygen for the muscle between breathing episodes.

2. (a) 2.96×10^{-11} g
(b) 2.74×10^{8} molecules
(c) No. There would be 3.17×10^{8} hemoglobin molecules in a red cell if they were packed in a cubic crystalline array. Hence, the actual packing density is about 84% of the maximum possible.

3. 2.65 g (or 4.75×10^{-2} mol) of Fe

4. (a) In human beings, 1.44×10^{-2} g (4.49×10^{-4} mol) of O_2 per kilogram of muscle. In sperm whale, 0.144 g (4.49×10^{-3} mol) of O_2 per kilogram.
(b) 128

5. The pK_a is (a) lowered; (b) raised; and (c) raised.

6. Deoxy Hb A contains a complementary site, and so it can add on to a fiber of deoxy Hb S. The fiber cannot then grow further, because the terminal deoxy Hb A molecule lacks a sticky patch.

7. 62.7% oxygen-carrying capacity

8. A higher concentration of BPG would shift the oxygen-binding curve to the right, causing an increase in P_{50}. The larger value of P_{50} would promote dissociation of oxygen in the tissues and would thereby increase the percentage of oxygen delivered to the tissues.

9. Oxygen binding appears to cause the copper ions and their associated histidine ligands to move closer to one another, thereby also moving the helices to which the histidines are attached (in similar fashion to the conformational change in hemoglobin).

10. The modified hemoglobin should not show cooperativity. Although the imidazole in solution will bind to the heme iron (in place of histidine) and will facilitate oxygen binding, the imidazole lacks the crucial connection to the particular α helix that must move so as to transmit the change in conformation.

11. Inositol pentaphosphate (part c) is highly anionic, much like 2,3-bisphosphoglycerate.

12.

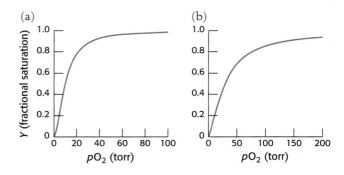

13. Release of acid will lower the pH. A lower pH promotes oxygen dissociation in the tissues. However, the enhanced release of oxygen in the tissues will increase the concentration of deoxy-Hb, thereby increasing the likelihood that the cells will sickle.

14. (a) $Y = 0.5$ when $pO_2 = 10$ torr. The plot of Y versus pO_2 appears to indicate little or no cooperativity.
(b) The Hill plot shows slight cooperativity with $n \cdot 1.3$ in the central region.
(c) Deoxy dimers of lamprey hemoglobin could have lower affinity for oxygen than do the monomers. If the binding of the first oxygen atom to a dimer causes dissociation of the dimer to give two monomers, then the process would be cooperative. In this mechanism, oxygen binding to each monomer would be easier than binding the first oxygen atom to a deoxy dimer.

15. (a) 2; (b) 4; (c) 2; (d) 1.

16. The electrostatic interactions between BPG and hemoglobin would be weakened by competition with water molecules. The T state would not be stabilized.

Chapter 8

1. Rate enhancement and substrate specificity
2. A cofactor
3. Coenzymes and metals
4. Vitamins are converted into coenzymes.
5. Enzymes facilitate the formation of the transition state.
6. The intricate three-dimensional structure of proteins allows the construction of active sites that will recognize only specific substrates.
7. The energy required to reach the transition state (the activation energy) is returned when the transition state proceeds to product.
8. Protein hydrolysis has a large activation energy. Protein synthesis must require energy to proceed.
9. The enzymes help protect the fluid that surrounds eyes from bacterial infection.
10. Transition states are very unstable. Consequently, molecules that resemble transition states are themselves likely to be unstable and, hence, difficult to synthesize.
11. (a) 0; (b) 28.53; (c) -22.84; (d) -11.42; (e) 5.69.
12. (a) $\Delta G^{\circ\prime} = -RT \ln K_{eq}'$

$$+1.8 = -(1.98 \times 10^{-3}\,\text{kcal}^{-1}\,\text{K}^{-1}\,\text{mol}^{-1})\,(298\,\text{K})$$
$$(\ln[\text{G1P}]/[\text{G6P}])$$

$$-3.05 = \ln[\text{G1P}]/[\text{G6P}]$$

$$+3.05 = \ln[\text{G6P}]/[\text{G1P}]$$

$$K_{eq}'^{-1} = 21 \quad \text{or} \quad K_{eq}' = 4.8 \times 10^{-2}$$

Because $[\text{G6P}]/[\text{G1P}] = 21$, there is 1 molecule of G1P for every 21 molecules of G6P. Because we started with 0.1 M, the [G1P] is $1/22(0.1\,\text{M}) = 0.0045\,\text{M}$ and [G6P] must be $21/22(0.1\,\text{M})$ or 0.096 M. Consequently, the reaction does not proceed as written to a significant extent.
(b) Supply G6P at a high rate and remove G1P at a high rate by other reactions. In other words, make sure that the [G6P]/[G1P] is kept large.
13. $K_{eq} = 19$, $\Delta G^{\circ\prime} = -7.41\,\text{kJ mol}^{-1}\,(-1.77\,\text{kcal mol}^{-1})$
14. The three-dimensional structure of an enzyme is stabilized by interactions with the substrate, reaction intermediates, and products. This stabilization minimizes thermal denaturation.
15. At substrate concentrations near the K_M, the enzyme displays significant catalysis yet is sensitive to changes in substrate concentration.
16. $A + S = 10\,K_M$, $V_0 = 0.91\,V_{max}$. $I + S = 20\,K_M$, $V_0 = 0.91\,V_{max}$.
So any Michaelis–Menten curves showing that the enzyme actually attains V_{max} are pernicious lies.
17. (a) 31.1 μmol; (b) 0.05 μmol; (c) 622 s^{-1}, a midrange value for enzymes (see Table 8.5).
18. (a) Yes, $K_M = 5.2 \times 10^{-6}$ M; (b) $V_{max} = 6.8 \times 10^{-10}$ mol minute^{-1}; (c) 337 s^{-1}.
19. Penicillinase, like glycopeptide transpeptidase, forms an acyl-enzyme intermediate with its substrate but transfers the intermediate to water rather than to the terminal glycine residue of the pentaglycine bridge.
20. (a) V_{max} is 9.5 μmol minute^{-1}. K_M is 1.1×10^{-5} M, the same as without inhibitor.
(b) Noncompetitive
(c) 2.5×10^{-5} M
(d) $f_{ES} = 0.73$, in the presence or absence of this noncompetitive inhibitor.

21. (a) $V = V_{max} - (V/[S])\,K_M$.
(b) Slope $= -K_M$, y-intercept $= V_{max}$, x-intercept $= V_{max}/K_M$.
(c) An Eadie–Hofstee plot

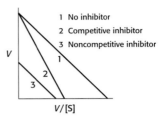

1 No inhibitor
2 Competitive inhibitor
3 Noncompetitive inhibitor

22. The rates of utilization of substrates A and B are given by

$$V_A = \left(\frac{k_{cat}}{K_M}\right)_A [E][A]$$

and

$$V_A = \left(\frac{k_{cat}}{K_M}\right)_B [E][B]$$

Hence, the ratio of these rates is

$$V_A/V_B = \left(\frac{k_{cat}}{K_M}\right)_B [A] / \left(\frac{k_{cat}}{K_M}\right)_A [B]$$

Thus, an enzyme discriminates between competing substrates on the basis of their values of k_{cat}/K_M rather than of K_M alone.
23. The mutation slows the reaction by a factor of 100 because the activation free energy is increased by 53.22 kJ mol^{-1} (12.72 kcal mol^{-1}). Strong binding of the substrate relative to the transition state slows catalysis.
24. 1.1 μmol minute^{-1}
25. (a) This piece of information is necessary for determining the correct dosage of succinylcholine to administer.
(b) The duration of the paralysis depends on the ability of the serum cholinesterase to clear the drug. If there were one-eighth the amount of enzyme activity, paralysis could last eight times as long, which is undesirable for two reasons. First, the respirator might break from extended use, which would not be good for the patient on the respirator; second, the doctors might miss their golf game.
(c) K_M is the concentration needed by the enzyme to reach $^1/_2 V_{max}$. Consequently, for a given concentration of substrate, the reaction catalyzed by the enzyme with the lower K_M will have the higher rate. The mutant patient with the higher K_M will clear the drug at a much lower rate.
26. If the total amount of enzyme (E_T) is increased, V_{max} will increase, because $V_{max} = k_2[E_T]$. But $K_M = (k_{-1} + k_2)/k_1$; that is, it is independent of substrate concentration. The middle graph describes this situation.
27. (a)

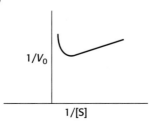

$1/V_0$

$1/[S]$

(b) This behavior is substrate inhibition: at high concentrations, the substrate forms unproductive complexes at the active site. The adjoining drawing shows what might happen. Substrate normally binds in a defined orientation, shown in the drawing as red to red and blue to blue. At high concentrations, the substrate may bind at the active site such that the proper orientation is met for each end of the molecule, but two different substrate molecules are binding.

Enzyme active site   Enzyme active site

Normal substrate binding at the active site. Substrate will be cleaved to red and blue balls.   Substrate inhibition

28. The first step will be the rate-limiting step. Enzymes E_B and E_C are operating at $\frac{1}{2} V_{max}$, whereas the K_M for enzyme E_A is greater than the substrate concentration. E_A would be operating at approximately $10^{-2} V_{max}$.

29. The fluorescence spectroscopy reveals the existence of an enzyme–serine complex and of an enzyme–serine–indole complex.

30. (a) When $[S^+]$ is much greater than the value of K_M, pH will have a negligible effect on the enzyme because S^+ will interact with E^- as soon as the enzyme becomes available.

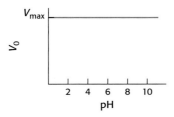

(b) When $[S^+]$ is much less than the value of K_M, the plot of V_0 versus pH becomes essentially a titration curve for the ionizable groups, with enzyme activity being the titration marker. At low pH, the high concentration of H^+ will keep the enzyme in the EH form and inactive. As the pH rises, more and more of the enzyme will be in the E^- form and active. At high pH (low H^+), all of the enzyme is E^-.

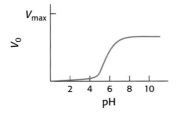

(c) The midpoint on this curve will be the pK_a of the ionizable group, which is stated to be pH 6.

31. (a) Incubating the enzyme at 37°C leads to a denaturation of enzyme structure and a loss of activity. For this reason, most enzymes must be kept cool if they are not actively catalyzing their reactions.

(b) The coenzyme apparently helps to stabilize enzyme structure, because enzyme from PLP-deficient cells denatures faster. Cofactors often help stabilize enzyme structure.

Chapter 9

1. For the amide substrate, the formation of the acyl-enzyme intermediate is slower than the hydrolysis of the acyl-enzyme intermediate, and so no burst is observed. A burst is observed for ester substrates; the formation of the acyl-enzyme intermediate is faster, leading to the observed burst.

2. The histidine residue in the substrate can substitute to some extent for the missing histidine residue of the catalytic triad of the mutant enzyme.

3. No. The catalytic triad works as a unit. After this unit has been made ineffective by the mutation of histidine to alanine, the further mutation of serine to alanine should have only a small effect.

4. The substitution corresponds to one of the key differences between trypsin and chymotrypsin, and so trypsinlike specificity (cleavage after lysine and arginine) might be predicted. In fact, additional changes are required to effect this specificity change.

5. Imidazole is apparently small enough to reach the active site of carbonic anhydrase. Buffers with large molecular components cannot do so, and the effects of the mutation are more evident.

6. No. The odds of such a sequence being present are approximately 1 in $4^{10} = 1,048,576$. Because a typical viral genome has only 50,000 bp, the target sequence would be unlikely to be present.

7. No, because the enzyme would destroy the host DNA before protective methylation could take place.

8. No. The bacteria receiving the enzyme would have their own DNA destroyed because they would likely lack the appropriate protective methylase.

9. EDTA will bind to Zn^{2+} and remove the ion, which is required for enzyme activity, from the enzyme.

10. (a) The aldehyde reacts with the active-site serine. (b) A hemiacetal is formed.

11. Trypsin

12. The reaction is expected to be slower by a factor of 10 because the rate depends on the pK_a of the zinc-bound water. $k_{cat} = 60,000 \text{ s}^{-1}$.

13. EDTA binds the magnesium necessary for the reaction.

14. ATP hydrolysis is reversible within the active site. ATP hydrolysis takes place within the active site with the incorporation of ^{18}O, ATP is re-formed, and the ATP is released back into solution.

15. If the aspartate is mutated, the protease is inactive and the virus will not be viable.

16. Water substitutes for the hydroxyl group of serine 236 in mediating proton transfer from the attacking water and the γ-phosphoryl group.

17. (a) Cysteine protease: The same as Figure 9.8, except that cysteine replaces serine in the active site and no aspartate is present. (b) Aspartyl protease:

(c) Metalloprotease:

Chapter 10

1. The enzyme catalyzes the first step in the synthesis of pyrimidines. It facilitates the condensation of carbamoyl phosphate and aspartate to form N-carbamoylaspartate and inorganic phosphate.

2. The protonated form of histidine probably stabilizes the negatively charged carbonyl oxygen atom of the scissile bond in the transition state. Deprotonation would lead to a loss of activity. Hence, the rate is expected to be half maximal at a pH of about 6.5 (the pK of an unperturbed histidine side chain in a protein) and to decrease as the pH is raised.

3. The inhibition of an allosteric enzyme by the end product of the pathway controlled by the enzyme. It prevents the production of too much end product and the consumption of substrates when product is not required.

4. High concentrations of ATP might signal two overlapping situations. The high levels of ATP might suggest that some *nucleotides* are available for nucleic acid synthesis, and consequently, CTP should be synthesized. The high levels of ATP indicate that *energy* is available for nucleic acid synthesis, and so CTP should be produced.

5. All of the enzyme would be in the R form all of the time. There would be no cooperativity. The kinetics would look like that of a Michaelis–Menten enzyme.

6. The enzyme would show simple Michaelis–Menten kinetics because it is essentially always in the R state.

7. CTP is formed by the addition of an amino group to UTP. Evidence indicates the UTP is also capable of inhibiting ATCase.

8. Homotropic effectors are the substrates of allosteric enzymes. Heterotropic effectors are the regulators of allosteric enzymes. Homotropic effectors account for the sigmoidal nature of the velocity versus substrate concentration curve, whereas heterotropic effectors alter the midpoint of K_M of the curve. Ultimately, both types of effectors work by altering the T/R ratio.

9. The reconstitution shows that the complex quaternary structure and the resulting catalytic and regulatory properties are ultimately encoded in the primary structure of individual components.

10. If substrates had been used, the enzyme would catalyze the reaction. Intermediates would not accumulate on the enzyme. Consequently, any enzyme that crystallized would have been free of substrates or products.

11. (a) 100. The change in the [R]/[T] ratio on binding one substrate molecule must be the same as the ratio of the substrate affinities of the two forms.
(b) 10. The binding of four substrate molecules changes the [R]/[T] by a factor of $100^4 = 10^8$. The ratio in the absence of substrate is 10^{-7}. Hence, the ratio in the fully liganded molecule is $10^8 \times 10^{-7} = 10$.

12. The fraction of molecules in the R form is 10^{-5}, 0.004, 0.615, 0.998, and 1 when 0, 1, 2, 3, and 4 ligands, respectively, are bound.

13. The sequential model can account for negative cooperativity, whereas the concerted model cannot.

14. The binding of PALA switches ATCase from the T to the R state because PALA acts as a substrate analog. An enzyme molecule containing bound PALA has fewer free catalytic sites than does an unoccupied enzyme molecule. However, the PALA-containing enzyme will be in the R state and, hence, have a higher affinity for the substrates. The dependence of the degree of activation on the concentration of PALA is a complex function of the allosteric constant L_0 and of the binding affinities of the R and T states for the analog and substrates.

15. The net outcome of the two reactions is the hydrolysis of ATP to ADP and P$_i$, which has a ΔG of -50 kJ mol^{-1} (-12 kcal mol^{-1}) under cellular conditions.

16. Isozymes are homologous enzymes that catalyze the same reaction but have different kinetic or regulatory properties.

17. Although the same reaction may be required in a variety of different tissues, the biochemical properties of tissues will differ according to their biological function. Isozymes allow the fine-tuning of catalytic and regulatory properties to meet the specific needs of the tissue.

18. (a) 7; (b) 8; (c) 11; (d) 6; (e) 1; (f) 12; (g) 3; (h) 4; (i) 5; (j) 2; (k) 10; (l) 9.

19. When phosphorylation takes place at the expense of ATP, sufficient energy is expended to dramatically alter the structure and hence activity of a protein. Moreover, because ATP is the cellular energy currency, protein modification is linked to the energy status of the cell.

20. Covalent modification is reversible, whereas proteolytic cleavage is irreversible.

21. Activation is independent of zymogen concentration because the reaction is intramolecular.

22. Although quite rare, cases of enteropeptidase deficiency have been reported. The affected person has diarrhea and fails to thrive because digestion is inadequate. In particular, protein digestion is impaired.

23. Add blood from the second patient to a sample from the first. If the mixture clots, the second patient has a defect different from that of the first. This type of assay is called a complementation test.

24. Activated factor X remains bound to blood-platelet membranes, which accelerates its activation of prothrombin.

25. Antithrombin III is a very slowly hydrolyzed substrate of thrombin. Hence, its interaction with thrombin requires a fully formed active site on the enzyme.

26. Residues a and d are located in the interior of an α-helical coiled coil, near the axis of the superhelix. Hydrophobic interactions between these side chains contribute to the stability of the coiled coil.

27. Leucine would be a good choice. It is resistant to oxidation and has nearly the same volume and degree of hydrophobicity as methionine has.

28. Inappropriate clot formation could block arteries in the brain, causing a stroke, or the heart, causing a heart attack.

29. Tissue-type plasminogen activator, or TPA, is a serine protease that leads to the dissolution of blood clots. TPA activates plasminogen that is bound to a fibrin clot, converting it into active plasmin, which then hydrolyzes the fibrin of the clot.

30. A mature clot is stabilized by amide linkages between the side chains of lysine and glutamine that are absent in a soft clot. The linkages are formed by transglutaminase.

31. The simple sequential model predicts that the fraction of catalytic chains in the R state, f_R, is equal to the fraction containing bound substrate, Y. The concerted model, in contrast, predicts that f_R increases more rapidly than Y as the substrate concentration is increased. The change in f_R leads to the change in Y on addition of substrate, as predicted by the concerted model.

32. The binding of succinate to the functional catalytic sites of the native c$_3$ moiety changed the visible absorption spectrum of nitrotyrosine residues in the *other* c$_3$ moiety of the hybrid enzyme. Thus, the binding of substrate analog to the active sites of one trimer altered the structure of the other trimer.

33. According to the concerted model, an allosteric activator shifts the conformational equilibrium of all subunits toward the R state, whereas an allosteric inhibitor shifts it toward the T state. Thus, ATP (an allosteric activator) shifted the equilibrium to the R form, resulting in an absorption change similar to that obtained when substrate is bound. CTP had a different effect. Hence, this allosteric inhibitor shifted the equilibrium to the T form. Thus, the concerted model accounts for the ATP-induced and CTP-induced (heterotropic), as well as for the substrate-induced (homotropic), allosteric interactions of ATCase.

34. In the R state, ATCase expands and becomes less dense. This decrease in density results in a decrease in the sedimentation value (see the formula on p. 76).

35. The interaction between trypsin and the inhibitor is so stable that the transition state is rarely formed. Recall that maximal binding energy is released when an enzyme binds to the transition state. If the substrate-enzyme interaction is too stable, the transition state rarely forms.

36.

37.

Chapter 11

1. Carbohydrates were originally regarded as *hydrates* of *carbon* because the empirical formula of many of them is $(CH_2O)_n$.

2. Three amino acids can be linked by peptide bonds in only six different ways. However, three different monosaccharides can be linked in a plethora of ways. The monosaccharides can be linked in a linear or branched manner, with α or β linkages, with bonds between C-1 and C-3, between C-1 and C-4, between C-1 and C-6, and so forth. In fact, the three monosaccharides can form 12,288 different trisaccharides.

3. (a) aldose-ketose; (b) epimers; (c) aldose-ketose (d) anomers; (e) aldose-ketose; (f) epimers.

4. Erythrose: tetrose aldose; Ribose: pentose aldose; Glyceraldehyde: triose aldose; Dihydroxyacetone: triose ketose; Erythrulose: tetrose ketose; Ribulose: pentose ketose; Fructose: hexose ketose.

5.

6. The proportion of the α anomer is 0.36, and that of the β anomer is 0.64.

7. Glucose is reactive because of the presence of an aldehyde group in its open-chain form. The aldehyde group slowly condenses with amino groups to form aldimine products of a type called Schiff-base adducts.

8. A pyranoside reacts with two molecules of periodate; formate is one of the products. A furanoside reacts with only one molecule of periodate; formate is not formed.

9. From methanol

10 (a) β-D-Mannose; (b) β-D-galactose; (c) β-D-fructose; (d) β-D-glucosamine.

11. The trisaccharide itself should be a competitive inhibitor of cell adhesion if the trisaccharide unit of the glycoprotein is critical for the interaction.

12. Reducing ends would form 1,2,3,6-tetramethylglucose. The branch points would yield 2,3-dimethylglucose. The remainder of the molecule would yield 2,3,6-trimethylglucose.

13. (a) not a reducing sugar; no open-chain forms are possible. (b) D-Galactose, D-glucose, D-fructose. (c) D-Galactose and sucrose (glucose + fructose).

14.

β-D-Mannose

The hemiketal linkage of the α anomer is broken to form the open form. Rotation about the C-1 and C-2 bonds allows the formation of the β anomer, and a mixture of isomers results.

15. Heating converts the very sweet pyranose form into the more-stable but less-sweet furanose form. Consequently, the sweetness of the preparation is difficult to accurately control, which also accounts for why honey loses sweetness with time. See Figure 11.5 for structures.

16. (a) Each glycogen molecule has one reducing end, whereas the number of nonreducing ends is determined by the number of branches, or α-1,6 linkages. (b) Because the number of nonreducing ends greatly exceeds the number of reducing ends in a collection of glycogen molecules, all of the degradation and synthesis of glycogen takes place at the nonreducing ends, thus maximizing the rate of degradation and synthesis.

17. No, sucrose is not a reducing sugar. The anomeric carbon atom acts as the reducing agent in both glucose and fructose but, in sucrose, the anomeric carbon atoms of fructose and glucose are joined by a covalent bond and are thus not available to react.

18. Glycogen is polymer of glucose linked by α-1,4-glycosidic bonds with branches formed approximately every 10 glucose units by α-1,6-glycosidic bonds. Starch consists of two polymers of glucose. Amylose is a straight-chain polymer formed by α-1,4-glycosidic bonds. Amylopectin is similar to glycogen but amylopectin has fewer branches, one branch per 30 or so glucose units.

19. Cellulose is a linear polymer of glucose joined by β-1,4 linkages. Glycogen is a branched polymer with the main chain being formed by α-1,4-glycosidic bonds. The β-1,4 linkages allow the formation of a linear polymer ideal for structural roles. The α-1,4 linkages of glycogen form a helical structure, which allows the storage of many glucose moieties in a small space.

20. Simple glycoproteins are often secreted proteins and thus play a variety of roles. For example, the hormone EPO is a glycoprotein. Usually, the protein component constitutes the bulk of the glycoprotein by mass. In contrast, proteoglycans and mucoproteins are predominantly carbohydrates. Proteoglycans have glycosaminoglycans attached, and play structural roles as in cartilage and the extracellular matrix. Mucoproteins often serve as lubricants and have multiple carbohydrates attached through an N-acetylgalactosamine moiety.

21. The attachment of the carbohydrate allows the EPO to stay in circulation longer and thus to function for longer periods of time than would a carbohydrate-free EPO.

22. The glycosaminoglycan, because it is heavily charged, binds many water molecules. When cartilage is stressed, such as when your heel hits the ground, the water is released, thus cushioning the impact. When you lift your heel, the water rebinds.

23. The lectin that binds the mannose 6-phosphate might be defective and not recognize a correctly addressed protein.

24. Different molecular forms of a glycoprotein that differ in the amount of carbohydrate attached or the location of attachment or both.

25. The total collection of carbohydrates synthesized by a cell at particular times and under particular environmental conditions.

26. The genome comprises all of the genes present in an organism. The proteome includes all of the possible protein products and modified proteins that a cell expresses under any particular set of circumstances. The glycome consists of all of the carbohydrates synthesized by the cell under any particular set of circumstances. Because the genome is static, but any given protein can be variously expressed and modified, the proteome is more complex than the genome. The glycome, which includes not only glycoforms of proteins, but also many possible carbohydrate structures, must be even more complex.

27. It suggests that carbohydrates are on the cell surfaces of all organisms for the purpose of recognition by other organisms or the environment.

28. A glycoprotein is a protein that is decorated with carbohydrates. A lectin is a protein that specifically recognizes carbohydrates. A lectin can also be a glycoprotein.

29. Each site either is or is not glycosylated, and so there are $2^6 = 64$ possible proteins.

30. As discussed in Chapter 9, many enzymes display stereochemical specificity. Clearly, the enzymes of sucrose synthesis are able to distinguish between the isomers of the substrates and link only the correct pair.

31. If the carbohydrate specificity of the lectin is known, an affinity column with the appropriate carbohydrate attached could be prepared. The protein preparation containing the lectin of interest could be passed over the column. The use of this method was indeed how the glucose-binding lectin concanavalin A was purified.

32. (a) Aggrecan is heavily decorated with glycosaminoglycans. If glycosaminoglycans are released into the media, aggrecan must be undergoing degradation.

(b) Another enzyme might be present that cleaves glycosaminoglycans from aggrecan without degrading aggrecan. Other experiments not shown established that glycosaminoglycan release is an accurate measure of aggrecan destruction.

(c) The control provides a baseline of "background" degradation inherent in the assay.

(d) Aggrecan degradation is greatly enhanced.

(e) Aggrecan degradation is reduced to the background system.

(f) It is an in vitro system in which not all the factors contributing to cartilage stabilization in vivo are present.

Chapter 12

1. 2.86×10^6 molecules, because each leaflet of the bilayer contains 1.43×10^6 molecules.

2. Essentially an "inside-out" membrane. The hydrophilic groups would come together on the interior of the structure, away from the solvent, whereas the hydrocarbon chains would interact with the solvent.

3. 2×10^{-7} cm, 6×10^{-6} cm, and 2×10^{-4} cm.

4. The radius of this molecule is 3.1×10^{-7} cm, and its diffusion coefficient is 7.4×10^{-9} cm^2 s^{-1}. The average distances traversed are 1.7×10^{-7} cm in 1 μs, 5.4×10^{-6} cm in 1 ms, and 1.7×10^{-4} cm in 1 s.

5. The membrane underwent a phase transition from a highly fluid to a nearly frozen state when the temperature was lowered. A carrier can shuttle ions across a membrane only when the bilayer is highly fluid. A channel, in contrast, allows ions to traverse its pore even when the bilayer is quite rigid.

6. The presence of a cis double bond introduces a kink in the fatty acid chain that prevents tight packing and reduces the number of atoms in van der Waals contact. The kink lowers the melting point compared with that of a saturated fatty acid. Trans fatty acids do not have the kink, and so their melting temperatures are higher, more similar to those of saturated fatty acids.

Because trans fatty acids have no structural effect, they are rarely observed.

7. Palmitic acid is shorter than stearic acid. Thus, when the chains pack together, there is less opportunity for van der Waals interaction and the melting point is thus lower than that of the longer stearic acid.

8. Hibernators selectively feed on plants that have a high proportion of polyunsaturated fatty acids with lower melting temperature.

9. The initial decrease in fluorescence with the first addition of sodium dithionite results from the quenching of NBD-PS molecules in the outer leaflet of the bilayer. Sodium dithionite does not traverse the membrane under these experimental conditions; hence, it does not quench the labeled phospholipids in the inner leaflet. A second addition of sodium dithionite has no effect, as the NBD-PS molecules in the outer leaflet remain quenched. However, after a 6.5 hour incubation, about half the NBD-PS has flipped over to the outer leaflet of the bilayer, resulting in the 50% decrease in fluorescence when sodium dithionite is added.

10. The addition of the carbohydrate introduces a significant energy barrier to the flip-flop because a hydrophilic carbohydrate moiety would need to be moved through a hydrophobic environment. This energetic barrier enhances membrane asymmetry.

11. The C_{16} alkyl chain is attached by an ether linkage. The C-2 carbon atom of glycerol has only an acetyl group attached by an ester linkage instead of a fatty acid, as is the case with most phospholipids.

12. In a hydrophobic environment, the formation of intrachain hydrogen bonds stabilizes the amide hydrogen atoms and carbonyl oxygen atoms of the polypeptide chain, and so an α helix forms. In an aqueous environment, these groups are stabilized by interaction with water, and so there is no energetic reason to form an α helix. Thus, the α helix would be more likely to form in a hydrophobic environment.

13. The protein may contain an α helix that passes through the hydrophobic core of the protein. This helix is likely to feature a stretch of hydrophobic amino acids similar to those observed in transmembrane helices.

14. The shift to the lower temperature would decrease fluidity by enhancing the packing of the hydrophobic chains by van der Waals interactions. To prevent this packing, new phospholipids having shorter chains and a greater number of cis double bonds would be synthesized. The shorter chains would reduce the number of van der Waals interactions, and the cis double bonds, which cause the kink in structure, would prevent the packing of the fatty acid tails of the phospholipids.

15. Each of the 21 v-SNARE proteins could interact with each of 7 t-SNARE partners. Multiplication gives the total number of different interacting pairs: $7 \times 21 = 147$ different v-SNARE–t-SNARE pairs.

16. (a) The graph shows that, as temperature increases, the phospholipid bilayer becomes more fluid. T_m is the temperature of the transition from the predominantly less fluid state to the predominantly more fluid state. Cholesterol broadens the transition from the less-fluid to the more-fluid state. In essence, cholesterol makes membrane fluidity less sensitive to temperature changes.

(b) This effect is important because the presence of cholesterol tends to stabilize membrane fluidity by preventing sharp transitions. Because protein function depends on the proper fluidity of the membrane, cholesterol maintains the proper environment for membrane-protein function.

17. The protein plotted in part c is a transmembrane protein from *C. elegans*. It spans the membrane with four α helices that are prominently displayed as hydrophobic peaks in the hydropathy plot. Interestingly, the protein plotted in part a also is a membrane protein, a porin. This protein is made primarily of β strands, which lack the prominent hydrophobic window of membrane helices. This example shows that, although hydropathy plots are useful, they are not infallible.

18. To purify any protein, the protein must first be solubilized. For a membrane protein, solubilization usually requires a detergent—hydrophobic molecules that bind to the protein and thus replace the lipid environment of the membrane. If the detergent is removed, the protein aggregates and precipitates from solution. Often, the steps in purification, such as ion-exchange chromatography, are difficult to perform in the presence of sufficient detergent to solubilize the protein. Crystals of appropriate protein–detergent complexes must be generated.

Chapter 13

1. In simple diffusion, the substance in question can diffuse down its concentration gradient through the membrane. In facilitated diffusion, the substance is not lipophilic and cannot directly diffuse through the membrane. A channel or carrier is required to facilitate movement down the gradient.

2. The two forms are (1) ATP hydrolysis and (2) the movement of one molecule down its concentration gradient coupled with the movement of another molecule up its concentration gradient.

3. The three types of carriers are symporters, antiporters, and uniporters. Symporters and antiporters can mediate secondary active transport.

4. The free-energy cost is 32 kJ mol^{-1} (7.6 kcal mol^{-1}). The chemical work performed is 20.4 kJ mol^{-1} (4.9 kcal mol^{-1}), and the electrical work performed is 11.5 kJ mol^{-1} (2.8 kcal mol^{-1}).

5. For chloride, $z = -1$; for calcium $z = +2$. At the concentrations given, the equilibrium potential for chloride is -97 mV and the equilibrium potential for calcium is $+122$ mV.

6. The concentration of glucose inside the cell is 66 times as great as that outside the cell [$(c_2/c_1) = 66$] when the free-energy input is 10.8 kJ mol^{-1} (2.6 kcal mol^{-1}).

7. By analogy with the Ca^{2+} ATPase, with three Na^+ ions binding from inside the cell to the E_1 conformation and with two K^+ ions binding from outside the cell to the E_2 conformation, a plausible mechanism is as follows:

(i) A catalytic cycle could begin with the enzyme in its unphosphorylated state (E_1) with three sodium ions bound.
(ii) The E_1 conformation binds ATP. A conformational change traps sodium ions inside the enzyme.
(iii) The phosphoryl group is transferred from ATP to an aspartyl residue.
(iv) On ADP release, the enzyme changes its overall conformation, including the membrane domain. This new conformation (E_2) releases the sodium ions to the side of the membrane opposite that at which they entered and binds two potassium ions from the side where sodium ions are released.
(v) The phosphorylaspartate residue is hydrolyzed to release inorganic phosphate. With the release of phosphate, the interactions stabilizing E_2 are lost, and the enzyme everts to the E_1 conformation. Potassium ions are released to the cytoplasmic side of the membrane. The binding of three sodium ions from the cytoplasmic side of the membrane completes the cycle.

8. Establish a lactose gradient across vesicle membranes that contain properly oriented lactose permease. Initially, the pH should be the same on both sides of the membrane and the lactose concentration should be higher on the "exit" side of lactose

permease. As the lactose flows "in reverse" through the permease, down its concentration gradient, it can be tested whether or not a pH gradient becomes established as the lactose gradient is dissipated.

9. Ligand-gated channels open in response to the binding of a molecule by the channel, whereas voltage-gated channels open in response to changes in the membrane potential.

10. An ion channel must transport ions in either direction at the same rate. The net flow of ions is determined only by the composition of the solutions on either side of the membrane.

11. Uniporters act as enzymes do; their transport cycles include large conformational changes, and only a few molecules interact with the protein per transport cycle. In contrast, channels, after having opened, provide a pore in the membrane through which many ions may pass. As such, channels mediate transport at a much higher rate than do uniporters.

12. FCCP effectively creates a pore in the bacterial membrane through which protons can pass rapidly. Protons that are pumped out of the bacteria will pass through this pore preferentially (the "path of least resistance"), rather than participate in H^+/lactose symport.

13. Cardiac muscle must contract in a highly coordinated manner in order to pump blood effectively. Gap junctions mediate the orderly cell-to-cell propagation of the action potential through the heart during each beat.

14. The positively charged guanidinium group resembles Na^+ and binds to negatively charged carboxylate groups in the mouth of the channel.

15. SERCA, a P-type ATPase, uses a mechanism by which a covalent phosphorylated intermediate (at an aspartate residue) is formed. At steady state, a subset of the SERCA molecules are trapped in the E_2-P state and, as a result, radiolabeled. The MDR protein is an ABC transporter and does not operate through a phosphorylated intermediate. Hence, a radiolabeled band would not be observed for MDR.

16. The blockage of ion channels inhibits action potentials, leading to loss of nervous function. Like tetrodotoxin, these toxin molecules are useful for isolating and specifically inhibiting particular ion channels.

17. After repolarization, the ball domains of the ion channels engage the channel pore, rendering them inactive for a short period of time. During this time, the channels cannot be reopened until the ball domains disengage and the channel returns to the "closed" state.

18. Because sodium ions are charged and because sodium channels carry only sodium ions (but not anions), the accumulation of excess positive charge on one side of the membrane dominates the chemical gradients.

19. A mutation that impairs the ability of the sodium channel to inactivate would prolong the duration of the depolarizing sodium current, thus lengthening the cardiac action potential.

20. No. Channels will likely open or close in response to an external stimulus, but the unit conductance of the open channel will be influenced very little.

21. The ratio of closed to open forms of the channel is 10^5, 5000, 250, 12.5, and 0.625 when zero, one, two, three, and four ligands, respectively, are bound. Hence, the fraction of open channels is 1.0 $\times$ 10^{-5}, 2.0×10^{-4}, 4.0×10^{-3}, 7.4×10^{-2}, and 0.62.

22. These organic phosphates inhibit acetylcholinesterase by reacting with the active-site serine residue to form a stable phosphorylated derivative. They cause respiratory paralysis by blocking synaptic transmission at cholinergic synapses.

23. (a) The binding of the first acetylcholine molecule increases the open-to-closed ratio by a factor of 240, and the binding of

the second increases it by a factor of 11,700. (b) The free-energy contributions are 14 kJ mol^{-1} (3.3 kcal mol^{-1}) and 23 kJ mol^{-1} (5.6 kcal mol^{-1}), respectively. (c) No; the MWC model predicts that the binding of each ligand will have the same effect on the open-to-closed ratio.

24. Batrachotoxin blocks the transition from the open to the closed state.

25. (a) Chloride ions flow into the cell. (b) Chloride flux is inhibitory because it hyperpolarizes the membrane. (c) The channel consists of five subunits.

26. After the addition of ATP and calcium, SERCA will pump Ca^{2+} ions into the vesicle. However, the accumulation of Ca^{2+} ions inside the vesicle will rapidly lead to the formation of an electrical gradient that cannot be overcome by ATP hydrolysis. The addition of calcimycin will allow the pumped Ca^{2+} ions to flow back out of the vesicle, dissipating the charge buildup, and enabling the pump to operate continuously.

27. The catalytic prowess of acetylcholinesterase ensures that the duration of the nerve stimulus will be short.

28. See reaction below.

29. (a) Only ASIC1a is inhibited by the toxin. (b) Yes; when the toxin was removed, the activity of the acid-sensing channel began to be restored. (c) 0.9 nM.

30. This mutation is one of a class of mutations that result in slow-channel syndrome (SCS). The results suggest a defect in channel closing; so the channel remains open for prolonged periods. Alternatively, the channel may have a higher affinity for acetylcholine than does the control channel.

31. The mutation reduces the affinity of acetylcholine for the receptor. The recordings would show the channel opening only infrequently.

32. Glucose displays a transport curve that suggests the participation of a carrier because the initial rate is high but then levels off

at higher concentrations, consistent with saturation of the carrier, which is reminiscent of Michaelis–Menten enzymes (Section 8.4). Indole shows no such saturation phenomenon, which implies that the molecule is lipophilic and simply diffuses across the membrane. Ouabain is a specific inhibitor the Na^+-K^+ pump. If ouabain were to inhibit glucose transport, then a Na^+-glucose cotransporter would be assisting in transport.

Chapter 14

1. The negatively charged glutamate residues mimic the negatively charged phosphoserine or phosphothreonine residues and stabilize the active conformation of the enzyme.
2. No. Phosphoserine and phosphothreonine are considerably shorter than phosphotyrosine.
3. The GTPase activity terminates the signal. Without such activity, after a pathway has been activated, it remains activated and is unresponsive to changes in the initial signal. If the GTPase activity were more efficient, the lifetime of the GTP-bound G_α subunit would be too short to achieve downstream signaling.
4. Two identical receptor molecules must recognize different aspects of the same signal molecule.
5. Growth-factor receptors can be activated by dimerization. If an antibody causes a receptor to dimerize, the signal-transduction pathway in a cell will be activated.
6. The mutated α subunit will always be in the GTP form and, hence, in the active form, which would stimulate its signaling pathway.
7. A G protein is a component of the signal-transduction pathway. GTPγS is not hydrolyzed by the G_α subunit, leading to prolonged activation.
8. Calcium ions diffuse slowly because they bind to many protein surfaces within a cell, impeding their free motion. Cyclic AMP does not bind as frequently, and so it diffuses more rapidly.
9. Fura-2 is a highly negatively charged molecule, with five carboxylate groups. Its charge prevents it from effectively crossing the hydrophobic region of the plasma membrane.
10. $G_{\alpha s}$ stimulates adenylate cyclase, leading to the generation of cAMP. This signal then leads to glucose mobilization (see Chapter 21). If cAMP phosphodiesterase were inhibited, then cAMP levels would remain high even after the termination of the epinephrine signal, and glucose mobilization would continue.
11. If the two kinase domains are forced to be within close proximity of each other, the activation loop of one kinase, in its inactivating conformation, can be displaced by the activation loop of the neighboring kinase, which acts as a substrate for phosphorylation.
12. The full network of pathways initiated by insulin includes a large number of proteins and is substantially more elaborate than indicated in Figure 14.25. Furthermore, many additional proteins take part in the termination of insulin signaling. A defect in any of the proteins in the insulin signaling pathways or in the subsequent termination of the insulin response could potentially cause problems. Therefore, it is not surprising that many different gene defects can cause type 2 diabetes.
13. The binding of growth hormone causes its monomeric receptor to dimerize. The dimeric receptor can then activate a separate tyrosine kinase to which the receptor binds. The signaling pathway can then continue in similar fashion to the pathways that are activated by the insulin receptor or other mammalian EGF receptors.
14. The truncated receptor will dimerize with the full-length monomers on EGF-binding, but cross-phosphorylation cannot take place, because the truncated receptor possesses neither the substrate for the neighboring kinase domain nor its own kinase domain to phosphorylate the C-terminal tail of the other monomer. Hence, these mutant receptors will block normal EGF signaling.

15. Insulin would elicit the response that is normally caused by EGF. Insulin binding will likely stimulate dimerization and phosphorylation of the chimeric receptor and thereby signal the downstream events that are normally triggered by EGF binding. Exposure of these cells to EGF would have no effect.
16. 10^5
17. The formation of diacylglycerol implies the participation of phospholipase C. A simple pathway would entail receptor activation by cross-phosphorylation, followed by the binding of phospholipase Cγ (through its SH2 domains). The participation of phospholipase C indicates that IP_3 would be formed and, hence, calcium concentrations would increase.
18. Other potential drug targets within the EGF signaling cascade include, but are not limited to, the kinase active sites of the EGF receptor, Raf, MEK, or ERK.
19. In the reaction catalyzed by adenylate cyclase, the 3′-OH group nucleophilically attacks the α-phosphorus atom attached to the 5′-OH group, leading to displacement of pyrophosphate. The reaction catalyzed by DNA polymerase is similar except that the 3′-OH group is on a different nucleotide.
20. ATP-competitive inhibitors are likely to act on multiple kinases because every kinase domain contains an ATP-binding site. Hence, these drugs may not be selective for the desired kinase target.
21. (a) $X \approx 10^{-7}$ M; $Y \approx 5 \times 10^{-6}$ M; $Z \approx 10^{-3}$ M. (b) Because much less X is required to fill half of the sites, X displays the highest affinity. (c) The binding affinity almost perfectly matches the ability to stimulate adenylate cyclase, suggesting that the hormone–receptor complex leads to the stimulation of adenylate cyclase. (d) Try performing the experiment in the presence of antibodies to $G_{\alpha s}$.
22. (a) The total binding does not distinguish binding to a specific receptor from binding to different receptors or from nonspecific binding to the membrane.
(b) The rationale is that the receptor will have a high affinity for the ligand. Thus, in the presence of excess nonradioactive ligand, the receptor will bind to nonradioactive ligand. Therefore, any binding of the radioactive ligand must be nonspecific.
(c) The plateau suggests that the number of receptor-binding sites in the cell membrane is limited.
23. Number of receptors per cell =

$$\frac{10^4 \text{ cpm}}{\text{mg of membrane protein}} \times \frac{\text{mg of membrane protein}}{10^{10} \text{ cells}} \times$$

$$\frac{\text{mmol}}{10^{12} \text{ cpm}} \times \frac{6.023 \times 10^{20} \text{ molecules}}{\text{mmol}} = 600$$

Chapter 15

1. The highly integrated biochemical reactions that take place inside the cell.
2. Anabolism is the set of biochemical reactions that use energy to build new molecules and ultimately new cells. Catabolism is the set of biochemical reactions that extract energy from fuel sources or breakdown biomolecules.
3. Cellular movements and the performance of mechanical work; active transport; biosynthetic reactions.
4. 1. f; 2. h; 3. i; 4. a; 5. g; 6. b; 7. c; 8. e; 9. j; 10. d.
5. Charge repulsion, resonance stabilization, and stabilization by hydration.
6. Trick question. The answer is not known. Adenine appears to form more readily under prebiotic conditions; so ATP may have predominated initially.

7. Having only one nucleotide represent the available energy allows the cell to better monitor its energy status.

8. Increasing the concentration of ATP or decreasing the concentration cellular ADP or P_i (by rapid removal by other reactions, for instance) would make the reaction more exergonic. Likewise, altering the Mg^{2+} concentration could raise or lower the ΔG of the reaction.

9. The free-energy changes of the individual steps in a pathway are summed to determine the overall free-energy change of the entire pathway. Consequently, a reaction with a positive free-energy value can be powered to take place if coupled to a sufficiently exergonic reaction.

10. Reactions in parts *a* and *c*, to the left; reactions in parts *b* and *d*, to the right.

11. None whatsoever

12. (a) $\Delta G^{\circ\prime} = 31.4$ kJ mol^{-1} (7.5 kcal mol^{-1}) and $K'_{eq} = 3.06 \times 10^{-6}$; (b) 3.28×10^4.

13. $\Delta G^{\circ\prime} = 7.1$ kJ mol^{-1} (1.7 kcal mol^{-1}). The equilibrium ratio is 17.8.

14. (a) Acetate + CoA + H^+ goes to acetyl CoA + H_2O, $\Delta G^{\circ\prime} = -31.4$ kJ mol^{-1} (-7.5 kcal mol^{-1}). ATP hydrolysis to AMP and PP_i, $\Delta G^{\circ\prime} = -45.6$ kJ mol^{-1} (-10.9 kcal mol^{-1}). Overall reaction, $\Delta G^{\circ\prime} = -14.2$ kJ mol^{-1} (-3.4 kcal mol^{-1}).
(b) With pyrophosphate hydrolysis, $\Delta G^{\circ\prime} = -33.4$ kJ mol^{-1} (-7.98 kcal mol^{-1}). Pyrophosphate hydrolysis makes the overall reaction even more exergonic.

15. (a) For an acid AH,

$$\text{AH} \rightleftharpoons \text{A}^{-1} + \text{H}^+ \quad K = \frac{[\text{A}^-]\,[\text{H}^+]}{[\text{AH}]}$$

The pK is defined as p$K = -\log_{10} K$. $\Delta G^{\circ\prime}$ is the standard free-energy change at pH 7. Thus, $\Delta G^{\circ\prime} = -RT \ln K = -2.303\,RT$ $\log_{10} K = +2.303\,RT$ pK.
(b) $\Delta G^{\circ\prime} = 27.32$ kJ mol^{-1} (6.53 kcal mol^{-1}).

16. Arginine phosphate in invertebrate muscle, like creatine phosphate in vertebrate muscle, serves as a reservoir of high-potential phosphoryl groups. Arginine phosphate maintains a high level of ATP in muscular exertion.

17. An ADP unit

18. (a) The rationale behind creatine supplementation is that it would be converted into creatine phosphate and thus serve as a rapid means of replenishing ATP after muscle contraction. (b) If creatine supplementation is beneficial, it would affect activities that depend on short bursts of activity; any sustained activity would require ATP generation by fuel metabolism, which, as Figure 15.7 shows, requires more time.

19. Under standard conditions, $\Delta G^{\circ\prime} = -RT \ln$ [products]/ [reactants]. Substituting 23.8 kJ mol^{-1} (5.7 kcal mol^{-1}) for $\Delta G^{\circ\prime}$ and solving for [products]/[reactants] yields 7×10^{-5}. In other words, the forward reaction does not take place to a significant extent. Under intracellular conditions, ΔG is -1.3 kJ mol^{-1} (-0.3 kcal mol^{-1}). Using the equation $\Delta G = \Delta G^{\circ\prime} + RT \ln$ [products]/[reactants] and solving for [products]/[reactants] gives a ratio of 3.7×10^{-5}. Thus, a reaction that is endergonic under standard conditions can be converted into an exergonic reaction by maintaining the [products]/[reactants] ratio below the equilibrium value. This conversion is usually attained by using the products in another coupled reaction as soon as they are formed.

20. Under standard conditions,

$$K'_{eq} = \frac{[\text{B}]_{eq}}{[\text{A}]_{eq}} \times \frac{[\text{ADP}]_{eq}\,[\text{P}_i]_{eq}}{[\text{ATP}]_{eq}} = 10^{3.3/1.36} = 2.67 \times 10^2$$

At equilibrium, the ratio of [B] to [A] is given by

$$\frac{[\text{B}]_{eq}}{[\text{A}]_{eq}} = K'_{eq} \frac{[\text{ATP}]_{eq}}{[\text{ADP}]_{eq}\,[\text{P}_i]_{eq}}$$

The ATP-generating system of cells maintains the [ATP]/[ADP] [P_i] ratio at a high level, typically about 500 M^{-1}. For this ratio,

$$\frac{[\text{B}]_{eq}}{[\text{A}]_{eq}} = 2.67 \times 10^2 \times 500 = 1.34 \times 10^5$$

This equilibrium ratio is strikingly different from the value of 1.15×10^{-3} for the reaction A $\longrightarrow$ B in the absence of ATP hydrolysis. In other words, coupling the hydrolysis of ATP with the conversion of A into B has changed the equilibrium ratio of B to A by a factor of about 10^8.

21. Liver: -45.2 kJ mol^{-1} (-10.8 kcal mol^{-1}); muscle: -48.1 kJ mol^{-1} (-11.5 kcal mol^{-1}); brain: -48.5 kJ mol^{-1} (-11.6 kcal mol^{-1}). The ΔG is most negative in brain cells.

22. (a) Ethanol; (b) lactate; (c) succinate; (d) isocitrate; (e) malate; (f) 2-phosphoglycerate.

23. Recall that $\Delta G = \Delta G^{\circ\prime} + RT \ln$ [products]/[reactants]. Altering the ratio of products to reactants will cause ΔG to vary. In glycolysis, the concentrations of the components of the pathway result in a value of ΔG greater than that of $\Delta G^{\circ\prime}$.

24. Unless the ingested food is converted into molecules capable of being absorbed by the intestine, no energy can ever be extracted by the body.

25. NADH and $FADH_2$ are electron carriers for catabolism; NADPH is the carrier for anabolism.

26. The electrons of the C–O bond cannot form resonance structures with the C–S bond that are as stable as those that they can form with the C–O bond. Thus, the thioester is not stabilized by resonance to the same degree as an oxygen ester is stabilized.

27. Oxidation–reduction reactions; ligation reactions; isomerization reactions; group-transfer reactions; hydrolytic reactions; the addition of functional groups to double bonds to form single bonds or the removal of functional groups to form double bonds.

28. Controlling the amount of enzymes; controlling enzyme activity; controlling the availability of substrates.

29. Although the reaction is thermodynamically favorable, the reactants are kinetically stable because of the large activation energy. Enzymes lower the activation energy so that reactions take place on time scales required by the cell.

30. The activated form of sulfate in most organisms is 3′-phosphoadenosine-5′-phosphosulfate.

31. (a) As the Mg^{2+} concentration falls, the ΔG of hydrolysis rises. Note that pMg is a logarithmic plot, and so each number on the *x*-axis represents a 10-fold change in [Mg^{2+}].
(b) Mg^{2+} would bind to the phosphates of ATP and help to mitigate charge repulsion. As the [Mg^{2+}] falls, charge stabilization of ATP would be less, leading to greater charge repulsion and an increase in ΔG on hydrolysis.

Chapter 16

1. Two molecules of ATP are produced per molecule of glyceraldehyde 3-phosphate and, because two molecules of GAP are produced per molecule of glucose, the total ATP yield is four. However, two molecules of ATP are required to convert glucose into fructose 1,6-bisphosphate. Thus, the net yield is only two molecules of ATP.

2. In both cases, the electron donor is glyceraldehyde 3-phosphate. In lactic acid fermentation, the electron acceptor is pyruvate, converting it into lactate. In alcoholic fermentation, acetaldehyde is the electron acceptor, forming ethanol.

3. (a) 3 ATP; (b) 2 ATP; (c) 2 ATP; (d) 2 ATP; (e) 4 ATP.

4. Glucokinase enables the liver to remove glucose from the blood when hexokinase is saturated, ensuring that glucose is captured for later use.

5. Glycolysis is a component of alcoholic fermentation, the pathway that produces alcohol for beer and wine. The belief was that understanding the biochemical basis of alcohol production might lead to a more-efficient means of producing beer.

6. The conversion of glyceraldehyde 3-phosphate into 1,3-bisphosphoglycerate would be impaired. Glycolysis would be less effective.

7. Glucose 6-phosphate must have other fates. Indeed, it can be converted into glycogen (Chapter 21) or be processed to yield reducing power for biosynthesis (Chapter 20).

8. The energy needs of a muscle cell vary widely, from rest to intense exercise. Consequently, the regulation of phosphofructokinase by energy charge is vital. In other tissues, such as the liver, ATP concentration is less likely to fluctuate and will not be a key regulator of phosphofructokinase.

9. The $\Delta G^{\circ\prime}$ for the reverse of glycolysis is $+96$ kJ mol^{-1} ($+23$ kcal mol^{-1}), far too endergonic to take place.

10. The conversion of glucose into glucose 6-phosphate by hexokinase; the conversion of fructose 6-phosphate into fructose 1,6-bisphosphate by phosphofructokinase; the formation of pyruvate from phosphoenolpyruvate by pyruvate kinase.

11. Lactic acid is a strong acid. If it remained in the cell, the pH of the cell would fall, which could lead to the denaturation of muscle protein and result in muscle damage.

12. GLUT2 transports glucose only when the blood concentration of glucose is high, which is precisely the condition in which the β cells of the pancreas secrete insulin.

13. Fructose + ATP $\longrightarrow$ fructose 1-phosphate + ADP: Fructokinase

Fructose 1-phosphate $\longrightarrow$ dihydroxyacetone phosphate + glyceraldehyde: Fructose 1-phosphate aldolase

Glyceraldehyde + ATP $\longrightarrow$ glyceraldehyde 3-phosphate + ADP: Triose kinase

The primary controlling step of glycolysis catalyzed by phosphofructokinase is bypassed by the preceding reactions. Glycolysis will proceed in an unregulated fashion.

14. Without triose isomerase, only one of the two three-carbon molecules generated by aldolase could be used to generate ATP. Only two molecules of ATP would result from the metabolism of each glucose. But two molecules of ATP would still be required to form fructose 1,6-bisphosphate, the substrate for aldolase. The net yield of ATP would be zero, a yield incompatible with life.

15. Glucose is reactive because its open-chain form contains an aldehyde group.

16. (a) The label is in the methyl carbon atom of pyruvate. (b) 5 mCi mM^{-1}. The specific activity is halved because the number of moles of product (pyruvate) is twice that of the labeled substrate (glucose).

17. (a) Glucose + 2 P$_i$ + 2 ADP $\longrightarrow$ 2 lactate + 2 ATP. (b) $\Delta G = -114$ kJ mol^{-1} (-27.2 kcal mol^{-1}).

18. 3.06×10^{-5}

19. The equilibrium concentrations of fructose 1,6-bisphosphate, dihydroxyacetone phosphate, and glyceraldehyde 3-phosphate are 7.8×10^{-4} M, 2.2×10^{-4} M, and 2.2×10^{-4} M, respectively.

20. All three carbon atoms of 2,3-BPG are ^{14}C labeled. The phosphorus atom attached to the C-2 hydroxyl group is ^{32}P labeled.

21. Hexokinase has a low ATPase activity in the absence of a sugar because it is in a catalytically inactive conformation. The addition of xylose closes the cleft between the two lobes of the enzyme. However, xylose lacks a hydroxymethyl group, and so it cannot be phosphorylated. Instead, a water molecule at the site normally occupied by the C-6 hydroxymethyl group acts as the acceptor of the phosphoryl group from ATP.

22. (a) The fructose 1-phosphate pathway forms glyceraldehyde 3-phosphate. (b) Phosphofructokinase, a key control enzyme, is bypassed. Furthermore, fructose 1-phosphate stimulates pyruvate kinase.

23. The reverse of glycolysis is highly endergonic under cellular conditions. The expenditure of six NTP molecules in gluconeogenesis renders gluconeogenesis exergonic.

24. Lactic acid is capable of being further oxidized and is thus useful energy. The conversion of this acid into glucose saves the carbon atoms for future combustion.

25. In glycolysis, the formation of pyruvate and ATP by pyruvate kinase is irreversible. This step is bypassed by two reactions in gluconeogenesis: (1) the formation of oxaloacetate from pyruvate and CO$_2$ by pyruvate carboxylase and (2) the formation of phosphoenolpyruvate from oxaloacetate and GTP by phosphoenolpyruvate carboxykinase. The formation of fructose 1,6-bisphosphate by phosphofructokinase is bypassed by fructose 1,6-bisphosphatase in gluconeogenesis, which catalyzes the conversion of fructose 1,6-bisphosphate into fructose 6-phosphate. Finally, the hexokinase-catalyzed formation of glucose 6-phosphate in glycolysis is bypassed by glucose 6-phosphatase, but only in the liver.

26. Reciprocal regulation at the key allosteric enzymes in the two pathways. For instance, PFK is stimulated by fructose 2,6-bisphosphate and AMP. The effect of these signals is opposite that of fructose 1,6-bisphosphatase. If both pathways were operating simultaneously, a futile cycle would result. ATP would be hydrolyzed, yielding only heat.

27. Muscle is likely to produce lactic acid during contraction. Lactic acid is a strong acid and cannot accumulate in muscle or blood. Liver removes the lactic acid from the blood and converts it into glucose. The glucose can be released into the blood or stored as glycogen for later use.

28. Glucose produced by the liver could not be released into the blood. Tissues that rely on glucose as an energy source would not function as well unless glucose was provided in the diet.

29. Glucose is an important energy source for both tissues and is essentially the only energy source for the brain. Consequently, these tissues should never release glucose. Glucose release is prevented by the absence of glucose 6-phosphatase.

30. 6 NTP (4 ATP and 2 GTP); 2 NADH.

31. (a) None; (b) none; (c) 4 (2 ATP and 2 GTP); (d) none.

32. If the amino groups are removed from alanine and aspartate, the ketoacids pyruvate and oxaloacetate are formed. Both of these molecules are components of the gluconeogenic pathway.

33. (a) Increased; (b) increased; (c) increased; (d) decreased.

34. Fructose 2,6-bisphosphate, present at high concentration when glucose is abundant, normally inhibits gluconeogenesis by blocking fructose 1,6-bisphosphatase. In this genetic disorder, the phosphatase is active irrespective of the glucose level. Hence, substrate cycling is increased. The level of fructose 1,6-bisphosphate is

consequently lower than normal. Less pyruvate is formed and thus less ATP is generated.

35. Reactions in parts *b* and *e* would be blocked.

36. There will be no labeled carbons. The CO_2 added to pyruvate (formed from the lactate) to form oxaloacetate is lost with the conversion of oxaloacetate into phosphoenolpyruvate.

37. The net reaction in the presence of arsenate is

Glyceraldehyde 3-phosphate + NAD^+ + H_2O $\longrightarrow$
3-phosphoglycerate + NADH + 2 H^+

Glycolysis proceeds in the presence of arsenate, but the ATP normally formed in the conversion of 1,3-bisphosphoglycerate into 3-phosphoglycerate is lost. Thus, arsenate uncouples oxidation and phosphorylation by forming a highly labile acyl arsenate.

38. This example illustrates the difference between the *stoichiometric* and the *catalytic* use of a molecule. If cells used NAD^+ stoichiometrically, a new molecule of NAD^+ would be required each time a molecule of lactate was produced. As we will see, the synthesis of NAD^+ requires ATP. On the other hand, if the NAD^+ that is converted into NADH could be recycled and reused, a small amount of the molecule could regenerate a vast amount of lactate, which is the case in the cell. NAD^+ is regenerated by the oxidation of NADH and reused. NAD^+ is thus used catalytically.

39. Consider the equilibrium equation of adenylate kinase:

$$K_{eq} = [ATP][AMP]/[ADP]^2 \ (1)$$

or

$$AMP = K_{eq}[ADP_2]/[ATP] \ (2)$$

Recall that [ATP] > [ADP] > [AMP] in the cell. As ATP is utilized, a small decrease in its concentration will result in a larger percentage increase in [ADP] because its concentration is greater than that of ADP. This larger percentage increase in [ADP] will result in an even greater percentage increase in [AMP] because the concentration of AMP is related to the square of [ADP]. In essence, equation 2 shows that monitoring the energy status with AMP magnifies small changes in [ATP], leading to tighter control.

40. The synthesis of glucose during intense exercise provides a good example of interorgan cooperation in higher organisms. When muscle is actively contracting, lactate is produced from glucose by glycolysis. The lactate is released into the blood and absorbed by the liver, where it is converted by gluconeogenesis into glucose. The newly synthesized glucose is then released and taken up by the muscle for energy generation.

41. The input of four additional high-phosphoryl-transfer-potential molecules in gluconeogenesis changes the equilibrium constant by a factor of 10^{32}, which makes the conversion of pyruvate into glucose thermodynamically feasible. Without this energetic input, gluconeogenesis would not take place.

42. The mechanism is analogous to that for triose phosphate isomerase (Figure 16.5). It proceeds through an enediol intermediate. The active site would be expected to have a general base (analogous to Glu 165 in TPI) and a general acid (analogous to His 95 in TPI).

43. Galactose is a component of glycoproteins. Possibly, the absence of galactose leads to the improper formation or function of glycoproteins required in the central nervous system. More generally, the fact that the symptoms arise in the absence of galactose suggests that galactose is required in some fashion.

44. Fructose 2,6-bisphosphate stabilizes the R state of the enzyme.

45. (a) Curiously, the enzyme uses ADP as the phosphoryl donor rather than ATP.
(b) Both AMP and ATP behave as competitive inhibitors of ADP, the phosphoryl donor. Apparently, the *P. furiosus* enzyme is not allosterically inhibited by ATP.

46. (a) If both enzymes operated simultaneously, the following reactions would take place:

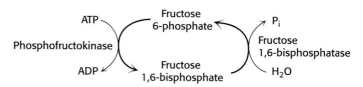

The net result would be simply:

$$ATP + H_2O \longrightarrow ADP + P_i$$

The energy of ATP hydrolysis would be released as heat.
(b) Not really. For the cycle to generate heat, both enzymes must be functional at the same time in the same cell.
(c) The species *B. terrestris* and *B. rufocinctus* might show some futile cycling because both enzymes are active to a substantial degree.
(d) No. These results simply suggest that simultaneous activity of phosphofructokinase and fructose 1,6-bisphosphatase is unlikely to be employed to generate heat in the species shown.

Chapter 17

1. Pyruvate dehydrogenase catalyzes the decarboxylation of pyruvate and the formation of acetyllipoamide. Dihydrolipoyl transacetylase catalyzes the formation of acetyl CoA. Dihydrolipoyl dehydrogenase catalyzes the reduction of the oxidized lipoic acid. The kinase associated with the complex phosphorylates and inactivates the complex, whereas the phosphatase dephosphorylates and activates the complex.

2. Thiamine pyrophosphate plays a role in the decarboxylation of pyruvate. Lipoic acid (as lipoamide) transfers the acetyl group. Coenzyme A accepts the acetyl group from lipoic acid to form acetyl CoA. FAD accepts the electrons and hydrogen ions when reduced lipoic acid is oxidized. NAD^+ accepts electrons from $FADH_2$.

3. Catalytic coenzymes (TPP, lipoic acid, and FAD) are modified but regenerated in each reaction cycle. Thus, they can play a role in the processing of many molecules of pyruvate. Stoichiometric coenzymes (coenzyme A and NAD^+) are used in only one reaction because they are the components of products of the reaction.

4. The advantages are as follows:
   The reaction is facilitated by having the active sites in proximity.
   The reactants do not leave the enzyme until the final product is formed.
   Constraining the reactants minimizes loss due to diffusion and minimizes side reactions.
   All of the enzymes are present in the correct amounts.
   Regulation is more efficient because the regulatory enzymes—the kinase and phosphatase—are part of the complex.

5. (a) After one round of the citric acid cycle, the label emerges in C-2 and C-3 of oxaloacetate. (b) The label emerges in CO_2 in the formation of acetyl CoA from pyruvate. (c) After one round of the citric acid cycle, the label emerges in C-1 and C-4 of oxaloacetate. (d) and (e) Same fate as that in part *a*.

6. (a) Isocitrate lyase and malate synthase are required in addition to the enzymes of the citric acid cycle.
(b) 2 Acetyl CoA + 2 NAD$^+$ + FAD + 3 H$_2$O → oxaloacetate + 2 CoA + 2 NADH + FADH$_2$ + 3 H$^+$.
(c) No. Hence, mammals cannot carry out the net synthesis of oxaloacetate from acetyl CoA.

7. -41.0 kJ mol^{-1} (-9.8 kcal mol^{-1})

8. Enzymes or enzyme complexes are biological catalysts. Recall that a catalyst facilitates a chemical reaction without the catalyst itself being permanently altered. Oxaloacetate can be thought of as a catalyst because it binds to an acetyl group, leads to the oxidative decarboxylation of the two carbon atoms, and is regenerated at the completion of a cycle. In essence, oxaloacetate (and any cycle intermediate) acts as a catalyst.

9. Thiamine thiazolone pyrophosphate is a transition-state analog. The sulfur-containing ring of this analog is uncharged, and so it closely resembles the transition state of the normal coenzyme in thiamine-catalyzed reactions (e.g., the uncharged resonance form of hydroxyethyl-TPP).

10. A decrease in the amount of O$_2$ will necessitate an increase in anaerobic glycolysis for energy production, leading to the generation of a large amount of lactic acid. Under conditions of shock, the kinase inhibitor is administered to ensure that pyruvate dehydrogenase is operating maximally.

11. Acetyllipoamide and acetyl CoA

12. In muscle, the acetyl CoA generated by the complex is used for energy generation. Consequently, signals that indicate an energy-rich state (high ratios of ATP/ADP and NADH/NAD$^+$) inhibit the complex, whereas the reverse conditions stimulate the enzyme. Calcium as the signal for muscle contraction (and, hence, energy need) also stimulates the enzyme. In liver, acetyl CoA derived from pyruvate is used for biosynthetic purposes, such as fatty acid synthesis. Insulin, the hormone denoting the fed state, stimulates the complex.

13. (a) Enhanced kinase activity will result in a decrease in the activity of the PDH complex because phosphorylation by the kinase inhibits the complex.
(b) Phosphatase activates the complex by removing a phosphate. If the phosphatase activity is diminished, the activity of the PDH complex also will decrease.

14. She might have been ingesting, in some fashion, the arsenite from the peeling paint or the wallpaper. Also, she might have been breathing arsine gas from the wallpaper, which would be oxidized to arsenite in her body. In any of these circumstances, the arsenite inhibited enzymes that require lipoic acid—notably, the PDH complex.

15. The TCA cycle depends on a steady supply of NAD$^+$, which is typically generated from NADH by reaction of the NADH with oxygen. If there is no oxygen to accept the electrons, the citric acid cycle will cease to operate.

16. (a) The steady-state concentrations of the products are low compared with those of the substrates. (b) The ratio of malate to oxaloacetate must be greater than 1.57×10^4 for oxaloacetate to be formed.

17.

$$\text{Pyruvate} + \text{CoA} + \text{NAD}^+ \xrightarrow{\substack{\text{Pyruvate} \\ \text{dehydrogenase} \\ \text{complex}}} \text{acetyl CoA} + \text{CO}_2 + \text{NADH}$$

$$\text{Pyruvate} + \text{CO}_2 + \text{ATP} + \text{H}_2\text{O} \xrightarrow{\substack{\text{Pyruvate} \\ \text{carboxylase}}} \text{oxaloacetate} + \text{ADP} + \text{P}_i + \text{H}^+$$

$$\text{Oxaloacetate} + \text{acetyl CoA} + \text{H}_2\text{O} \xrightarrow{\substack{\text{Citrate} \\ \text{synthase}}} \text{citrate} + \text{CoA} + \text{H}^+$$

$$\text{Citrate} \xrightarrow{\text{Aconitase}} \text{isocitrate}$$

$$\text{Isocitrate} + \text{NAD}^+ \xrightarrow{\substack{\text{Isocitrate} \\ \text{dehydrogenase}}} \alpha\text{-ketoglutarate} + \text{CO}_2 + \text{NADH}$$

Net: $2 \text{ Pyruvate} + 2 \text{ NAD}^+ + \text{ATP} + \text{H}_2\text{O} \longrightarrow \alpha\text{-ketoglutarate} + \text{CO}_2 + \text{ADP} + \text{P}_i + 2 \text{ NADH} + 3 \text{ H}^+$

18. Succinate will increase in concentration, followed by α-ketoglutarate and the other intermediates "upstream" of the site of inhibition. Succinate has two methylene groups that are required for the dehydrogenation, whereas malonate has but one.

19. Pyruvate carboxylase should be active only when the acetyl CoA concentration is high. Acetyl CoA might accumulate if the energy needs of the cell are not being met, because of a deficiency of oxaloacetate. Under these conditions the pyruvate carboxylase catalyzes an anapleurotic reaction. Alternatively, acetyl CoA might accumulate because the energy needs of the cell have been met. In this circumstance, pyruvate will be converted back into glucose, and the first step in this conversion is the formation of oxaloacetate.

20. The energy released when succinate is reduced to fumarate is not sufficient to power the synthesis of NADH but is sufficient to reduce FAD.

21. Citrate is a tertiary alcohol that cannot be oxidized, because oxidation requires a hydrogen atom to be removed from the alcohol and a hydrogen atom to be removed from the carbon atom bonded to the alcohol. No such hydrogen exists in citrate. The isomerization converts the tertiary alcohol into isocitrate, which is a secondary alcohol that can be oxidized.

22. Because the enzyme nucleoside diphosphokinase transfers a phosphoryl group from GTP (or any nucleoside triphosphate) to ADP according to the reversible reaction:

$$\text{GTP} + \text{ADP} \rightleftharpoons \text{GDP} + \text{ATP}$$

23. The reaction is powered by the hydrolysis of a thioester. Acetyl CoA provides the thioester that is converted into citryl CoA. When this thioester is hydrolyzed, citrate is formed in an irreversible reaction.

24. We cannot get the net conversion of fats into glucose, because the only means to get the carbon atoms from fats into oxaloacetate, the precursor of glucose, is through the citric acid cycle. However, although two carbon atoms enter the cycle as acetyl CoA, two carbon atoms are lost as CO$_2$ before oxaloacetate is formed. Thus, although some carbon atoms from fats may end up as carbon atoms in glucose, we cannot obtain a *net* synthesis of glucose from fats.

25. Acetyl CoA will inhibit the complex. Glucose metabolism to pyruvate will be slowed because acetyl CoA is being derived from an alternative source.

26. The enol intermediate of acetyl CoA attacks the carbonyl carbon atom of glyoxylate to form a C–C bond. This reaction is like the condensation of oxaloacetate with the enol intermediate of acetyl CoA in the reaction catalyzed by citrate synthase. Glyoxylate contains a hydrogen atom in place of the –CH$_2$COO$^-$ group of oxaloacetate; the reactions are otherwise nearly identical.

27. Citrate is a symmetric molecule. Consequently, the investigators assumed that the two –CH$_2$COO$^-$ groups in it would react identically. Thus, for every citrate molecule undergoing the reactions shown in path 1, they thought that another citrate

molecule would react as shown in path 2. If so, then only *half* the label should have emerged in the CO_2.

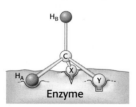

Path 1

Path 2 (does not occur)

28. Call one hydrogen atom A and the other B. Now suppose that an enzyme binds three groups of this substrate—X, Y, and H—at three complementary sites. The adjoining diagram shows X, Y, and H_A bound to three points on the enzyme. In contrast, X, Y, and H_B cannot be bound to this active site; two of these three groups can be bound, but not all three. Thus, H_A and H_B will have different fates.

Sterically nonequivalent groups such as H_A and H_B will almost always be distinguished in enzymatic reactions. The essence of the differentiation of these groups is that the enzyme holds the substrate in a specific orientation. Attachment at three points, as depicted in the diagram, is a readily visualized way of achieving a particular orientation of the substrate, but it is not the only means of doing so.
29. (a) The complete oxidation of citrate requires 4.5 μmol of O_2 for every micromole of citrate.

$$C_6H_8O_7 + 4.5\ O_2 \longrightarrow 6\ CO_2 + 4\ H_2O$$

Thus, 13.5 μmol of O_2 would be consumed by 3 μmol of citrate.
(b) Citrate led to the consumption of far more O_2 than can be accounted for simply by the oxidation of citrate itself. Citrate thus facilitated O_2 consumption.

30. (a) In the absence of arsenite, the amount of citrate remained constant. In its presence, the concentration of citrate fell, suggesting that it was being metabolized.
(b) The action of arsenite is not altered. Citrate still disappears.
(c) Arsenite is preventing the regeneration of citrate. Recall (pp. 517–518) that arsenite inhibits the pyruvate dehydrogenase complex.
31. (a) The initial infection is unaffected by the absence of isocitrate lyase, but the absence of this enzyme inhibits the latent phase of the infection.
(b) Yes
(c) A critic could say that, in the process of deleting the isocitrate lyase gene, some other gene was damaged, and it is the absence of this other gene that prevents latent infection. Reinserting the isocitrate lyase gene into the bacteria from which it had been removed renders the criticism less valid.
(d) Isocitrate lyase enables the bacteria to synthesize carbohydrates that are necessary for survival, including carbohydrate components of the cell membrane.

Chapter 18
1. In fermentations, organic compounds are both the donors and the acceptors of electrons. In respiration, the electron donor is usually an organic compound, whereas the electron acceptor is an inorganic molecule, such as oxygen.
2. Biochemists use E'_0, the value at pH 7, whereas chemists use E_0, the value in 1 M H^+. The prime denotes that pH 7 is the standard state.
3. The reduction potential of $FADH_2$ is less than that of NADH (see Table 18.1). Consequently, when those electrons are passed along to oxygen, less energy is released. The consequence of the difference is that electron flow from $FADH_2$ to O_2 pumps fewer protons than do the electrons from NADH.
4. The $\Delta G^{o'}$ for the reduction of oxygen by $FADH_2$ is -200 kJ mol^{-1} (-48 kcal mol^{-1}).
5. $\Delta G^{o'}$ is $+67$ kJ mol^{-1} ($+16.1$ kcal mol^{-1}) for oxidation by NAD^+ and -3.8 kJ mol^{-1} (-0.92 kcal mol^{-1}) for oxidation by FAD. The oxidation of succinate by NAD^+ is not thermodynamically feasible.
6. Pyruvate accepts electrons and is thus the oxidant. NADH gives up electrons and is the reductant.
7. $\Delta G^{o'} = -nF\Delta E'_0$
8. The $\Delta E'_0$ value of iron can be altered by changing the environment of the ion.
9. c, e, b, a, d.
10. (a) 4; (b) 3; (c) 1; (d) 5; (e) 2.
11. The 10 isoprene units render coenzyme Q soluble in the hydrophobic environment of the inner mitochondrial membrane. The two oxygen atoms can reversibly bind two electrons and two protons as the molecule transitions between the quinone form and quinol form.
12. Rotenone: NADH, NADH-Q oxidoreductase will be reduced. The remainder will be oxidized. Antimycin A: NADH, NADH-Q oxidoreductase and coenzyme Q will be reduced. The remainder will be oxidized. Cyanide: All will be reduced.
13. Complex I would be reduced, whereas Complexes II, III, and IV would be oxidized. The citric acid cycle would become reduced because it has no way to oxidize NADH.
14. The respirasome is another example of the use of supramolecular complexes in biochemistry. Having the three complexes that are proton pumps associated with one another will enhance the efficiency of electron flow from complex to complex, which in turn will cause more-efficient proton pumping.
15. Hydroxyl radical (OH ·), hydrogen peroxide (H_2O_2), superoxide ion ($O_2^{\cdot -}$), and peroxide (O_2^{2-}). These small molecules react

with a host of macromolecules—including proteins, nucleotides, and membranes—to disrupt cell structure and function.

16. The ATP is recycled by ATP-generating processes, most notably oxidative phosphorylation.

17. (a) 12.5; (b) 14; (c) 32; (d) 13.5; (e) 30; (f) 16.

18. (a) It blocks electron transport and proton pumping at Complex IV. (b) It blocks electron transport and ATP synthesis by inhibiting the exchange of ATP and ADP across the inner mitochondrial membrane. (c) It blocks electron transport and proton pumping at Complex I. (d) It blocks ATP synthesis without inhibiting electron transport by dissipating the proton gradient. (e) It blocks electron transport and proton pumping at Complex IV. (f) It blocks electron transport and proton pumping at Complex III.

19. If the proton gradient is not dissipated by the influx of protons into a mitochondrion with the generation of ATP, eventually the outside of the mitochondrion develops such a large positive charge that the electron-transport chain can no longer pump protons against the gradient.

20. The subunits are jostled by background thermal energy (Brownian motion). The proton gradient makes clockwise rotation more likely because that direction results in protons flowing down their concentration gradient.

21. In the presence of poorly functioning mitochondria, the only means of generating ATP is by anaerobic glycolysis, which will lead to an accumulation of lactic acid in blood.

22. If ADP cannot get into mitochondria, the electron-transport chain will cease to function because there will be no acceptor for the energy. NADH will build up in the matrix. Recall that NADH inhibits some citric acid cycle enzymes and that NAD^+ is required by several citric acid cycle enzymes. Glycolysis will stop functioning aerobically but will switch to anaerobic glycolysis so that the NADH can be reoxidized to NAD^+ by lactate dehydrogenase.

23. (a) No effect; mitochondria cannot metabolize glucose.
(b) No effect; no fuel is present to power the synthesis of ATP.
(c) The $[O_2]$ falls because citrate is a fuel and ATP can be formed from ADP and P_i.
(d) Oxygen consumption stops because oligomycin inhibits ATP synthesis, which is coupled to the activity of the electron-transport chain.
(e) No effect, for the reasons given in part d.
(f) $[O_2]$ falls rapidly because the system is uncoupled and does not require ATP synthesis to lower the proton-motive force.
(g) $[O_2]$ falls, though at a lower rate. Rotenone inhibits Complex I, but the presence of succinate will enable electrons to enter at Complex II.
(h) Oxygen consumption ceases because Complex IV is inhibited and the entire chain backs up.

24. (a) The P : O ratio is equal to the product of ($H^+/2\ e^-$) and (P/H^+). Note that the P : O ratio is identical with the P : 2 e^- ratio.
(b) 2.5 and 1.5, respectively.

25. Cyanide can be lethal because it binds to the ferric form of cytochrome oxidase and thereby inhibits oxidative phosphorylation. Nitrite converts ferrohemoglobin into ferrihemoglobin, which also binds cyanide. Thus, ferrihemoglobin competes with cytochrome oxidase for cyanide. This competition is therapeutically effective because the amount of ferrihemoglobin that can be formed without impairing oxygen transport is much greater than the amount of cytochrome oxidase.

26. Such a defect (called Luft syndrome) was found in a 38-year-old woman who was incapable of performing prolonged physical work. Her basal metabolic rate was more than twice normal, but her thyroid function was normal. A muscle biopsy showed that her mitochondria were highly variable and atypical in structure.

Biochemical studies then revealed that oxidation and phosphorylation were not tightly coupled in these mitochondria. In this patient, much of the energy of fuel molecules was converted into heat rather than ATP.

27. Triose phosphate isomerase converts dihydroxyacetone phosphate (a potential dead end) into glyceraldehyde 3-phosphate (a mainstream glycolytic intermediate).

28. This inhibitor (like antimycin A) blocks the reduction of cytochrome c_1 by QH_2, the crossover point.

29. If oxidative phosphorylation were uncoupled, no ATP could be produced. In a futile attempt to generate ATP, much fuel would be consumed. The danger lies in the dose. Too much uncoupling would lead to tissue damage in highly aerobic organs such as the brain and heart, which would have severe consequences for the organism as a whole. The energy that is normally transformed into ATP would be released as heat. To maintain body temperature, sweating might increase, although the very process of sweating itself depends on ATP.

30. If ATP and ADP cannot exchange between the matrix and the mitochondria, ATP synthase will cease to function because its substrate ADP is absent. The proton gradient will eventually become so large that the energy released by the electron-transport chain will not be great enough to pump protons against the larger-than-normal gradient.

31. Add the inhibitor with and without an uncoupler, and monitor the rate of O_2 consumption. If the O_2 consumption increases again in the presence of inhibitor and uncoupler, the inhibitor must be inhibiting ATP synthase. If the uncoupler has no effect on the inhibition, the inhibitor is inhibiting the electron-transport chain.

32. Presumably, because the muscle has greater energy needs, especially during exercise, it will require more ATP. This requirement means that more sites of oxidative phosphorylation are called for, and these sites can be provided by an increase in the amount of cristae.

33. The arginine residue, with its positive charge, will facilitate proton release from aspartic acid by stabilizing the negatively charged aspartate.

34. 4; 4.7

35. The ATP synthase would pump protons at the expense of ATP hydrolysis, thus maintaining the proton-motive force. The synthase would function as an ATPase. There is some evidence that damaged mitochondria use this tactic to maintain, at least temporarily, the proton-motive force.

36. It suggests that malfunctioning mitochondria may play a role in the development of Parkinson disease. Specifically, it implicates Complex I.

37. The extra negative charge on ATP relative to that on ADP accounts for ATP's more-rapid translocation out of the mitochondrial matrix. If the charge differences between ATP and ADP were lessened by the binding of Mg^{2+}, ADP might more readily compete with ATP for transport to the cytoplasm.

38. When all of the available ADP has been converted into ATP, ATP synthase can no longer function. The proton gradient becomes large enough that the energy of the electron-transport chain is not enough to pump against the gradient, and electron transport and, hence, oxygen consumption falls.

39. The effect on the proton gradient is the same in each case.

40. ATP export from the matrix. Phosphate import into the matrix.

41. Recall from the discussion of enzyme-catalyzed reactions that the direction of a reaction is determined by the ΔG difference between substrate and products. An enzyme speeds up the rate of both the forward and the backward reactions. The hydrolysis of ATP is exergonic, and so ATP synthase will enhance the hydrolytic reaction.

42. The cytoplasmic kinases thereby obtaining preferential access to the exported ATP.
43. The organic acids in the blood are indications that the mice are deriving a large part of their energy needs through anaerobic glycolysis. Lactate is the end product of anaerobic glycolysis. Alanine is an aminated transport form of lactate. Alanine formation plays a role in succinate formation, which is caused by the reduced state of the mitochondria.

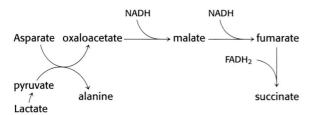

The electron-transport chain is slowed because the inner mitochondrial membrane is hyperpolarized. Without ADP to accept the energy of the proton-motive force, the membrane becomes polarized to such an extent that protons can no longer be pumped. The excess H_2O_2 is probably due to the fact that the superoxide radical is present in higher concentration because the oxygen can no longer be effectively reduced.

$$O_2 \cdot^- + O_2 \cdot^- + 2\,H^+ \longrightarrow O_2 + H_2O_2$$

Indeed, these mice display evidence of such oxidative damage.
44. (a) Vitamins C and E.
(b) Exercise induces superoxide dismutase, which converts ROS in hydrogen peroxide and oxygen.
(c) The answer to this question is not fully established. Two possibilities are (1) the suppression of ROS by vitamins prevents the expression of more superoxide dismutase and (2) some ROS may be signal molecules required to stimulate insulin-sensitivity pathways.
45. (a) Succinate is oxidized by Complex II, and the electrons are used to establish a proton-motive force that powers ATP synthesis.
(b) The ability to synthesize ATP is greatly reduced.
(c) Because the goal was to measure ATP hydrolysis. If succinate had been added in the presence of ATP, no reaction would have taken place, because of respiratory control.
(d) The mutation has little effect on the ability of the enzyme to catalyze the hydrolysis of ATP.
(e) They suggest two things: (1) the mutation did not affect the catalytic site on the enzyme, because ATP synthase is still capable of catalyzing the reverse reaction, and (2) the mutation did not affect the amount of enzyme present, given that the controls and patients had similar amounts of activity.
46. The absolute configuration of thiophosphate indicates that inversion at phosphorus has taken place in the reaction catalyzed by ATP synthase. This result is consistent with an in-line phosphoryl-transfer reaction taking place in a single step. The retention of configuration in the Ca^{2+}-ATPase reaction points to two phosphoryl-transfer reactions—inversion by the first and a return to the starting configuration by the second. The Ca^{2+}-ATPase reaction proceeds by a phosphorylated enzyme intermediate.

Chapter 19

1. Photosystem I generates ferredoxin, which reduces $NADP^+$ to NADPH, a biosynthetic reducing power. Photosystem II activates the manganese complex, an oxidant capable of oxidizing water, generating electrons for photosynthesis, and generating protons to form a proton gradient and to reduce $NADP^+$ and O_2.

2. The light reactions take place on thylakoid membranes. Increasing the membrane surface increases the number of ATP- and NADH-generating sites.
3. These complexes absorb more light than can a reaction center alone. The light-harvesting complexes funnel light to the reaction centers.
4. $NADP^+$ is the acceptor. H_2O is the donor. Light energy.
5. The charge gradient, a component of the proton-motive force in mitochondria, is neutralized by the influx of Mg^{2+} into the lumen of the thylakoid membranes.
6. Chlorophyll is readily inserted into the hydrophobic interior of the thylakoid membranes.
7. Protons released by the oxidation of water; protons pumped into the lumen by the cytochrome bf complex; protons removed from the stroma by the reduction of $NADP^+$ and plastoquinone.
8. 700-nm photons have an energy content of 172 kJ mol^{-1}. The absorption of light by photosystem I results in a $\Delta E_0'$ of -1.0 V. Recall that $\Delta G_0' = -nF\,\Delta E_0'$, where $F = 96.48$ kJ $mol^{-1}\,V^{-1}$. Under standard conditions, the energy change for the electrons is 96.5 kJ. Thus, the efficiency is $96.5/172 = 56\%$.
9. The electron flow from PS II to PS I is uphill, or exergonic. For this uphill flow, ATP would need to be consumed, defeating the purpose of photosynthesis.
10. $\Delta E_0' = 10.11$ V, and $\Delta G^{\circ\prime} = -21.3$ kJ mol^{-1} (-5.1 kcal mol^{-1}).
11. (a) All ecosystems require an energy source from outside the system, because the chemical-energy sources will ultimately be limited. The photosynthetic conversion of sunlight is one example of such a conversion.
(b) Not at all. Spock would point out that chemicals other than water can donate electrons and protons.
12. DCMU inhibits electron transfer in the link between photosystems II and I. O_2 can evolve in the presence of DCMU if an artificial electron acceptor such as ferricyanide can accept electrons from Q.
13. DCMU will have no effect, because it blocks photosystem II, and cyclic photophosphorylation uses photosystem I and the cytochrome bf complex.
14. (a) 120 kJ einstein^{-1} (28.7 kcal einstein^{-1})
(b) 1.24 V
(c) One 1000-nm photon has the free energy content of 2.4 molecules of ATP. A minimum of 0.42 photon is needed to drive the synthesis of a molecule of ATP.
15. At this distance, the expected rate is one electron per second.
16. The distance doubles, and so the rate should decrease by a factor of 64 to 640 ps.
17. The cristae.
18. In eukaryotes, both processes take place in specialized organelles. Both depend on high-energy electrons to generate ATP. In oxidative phosphorylation, the high-energy electrons originate in fuels and are extracted as reducing power in the form of NADH. In photosynthesis, the high-energy electrons are generated by light and are captured as reducing power in the form of NADPH. Both processes use redox reactions to generate a proton gradient, and the enzymes that convert the proton gradient into ATP are very similar in both processes. In both systems, electron transport takes place in membranes inside organelles.
19. We need to factor in the NADPH because it is an energy-rich molecule. Recall from Chapter 18, that NADH is worth 2.5 ATP if oxidized by the electron-transport chain. 12 NADPH = 30 ATP. Eighteen molecules of ATP are used directly, and so the equivalent of 48 molecules of ATP is required for the synthesis of glucose.
20. Both photosynthesis and cellular respiration are powered by high-energy electrons flowing toward a more-stable state. In cellular respiration, the high-energy electrons are derived from the

oxidation of carbon fuels as NADH and FADH$_2$. They release their energy as they reduce oxygen. In photosynthesis, high-energy electrons are generated by absorbing light energy, and they find stability in photosystem I and ferridoxin.

21. The electrons flow through photosystem II directly to ferricyanide. No other steps are required.

22. (a) Thioredoxin

(b) The control enzyme is unaffected, but the mitochondrial enzyme with part of the chloroplast γ subunit increases activity as the concentration of DTT increases.

(c) The increase was even larger when thioredoxin was present. Thioredoxin is the natural reductant for the chloroplast enzyme, and so it presumably operates more efficiently than would DTT, which probably functions to keep the thioredoxin reduced.

(d) They seem to have done so.

(e) The enzyme is susceptible to control by the redox state. In plant cells, reduced thioredoxin is generated by photosystem I. Thus, the enzyme is active when photosynthesis is taking place.

(f) Cysteine

(g) Group-specific modification or site-specific mutagenesis.

Chapter 20

1. The Calvin cycle is the primary means of converting gaseous CO$_2$ into organic matter—that is, biomolecules. Essentially, every carbon atom in your body passed through rubisco and the Calvin cycle at some time in the past.

2.

Calvin cycle	Krebs cycle
Stroma	Matrix
Carbon chemistry for photosynthesis	Carbon chemistry for oxidative phosphorylation
Fixes CO$_2$	Releases CO$_2$
Requires high-energy electrons (NADPH)	Generates high-energy electrons (NADPH)
Regenerates starting compound (ribulose 1.5-bisphosphate	Regenerates starting compound (oxaloacetate)
Requires ATP	Generates ATP or GTP
Complex stoichiometry	Simple stoichiometry

3. (a) 3-Phosphoglycerate. (b) The other members of the Calvin cycle.

4. Stage 1 is the fixation of CO$_2$ with ribulose 1,5-bisphosphate and the subsequent formation of 3-phosphoglycerate. Stage 2 is the conversion of some of the 3-phosphoglycerate into hexose. Stage 3 is the regeneration of ribulose 1,5-bisphosphate.

5. It catalyzes a crucial reaction, but it is highly inefficient. Consequently, it is required in large amounts to overcome its slow catalysis.

6. Because carbamate forms only in the presence of CO$_2$, this property prevents rubisco from catalyzing the oxygenase reaction exclusively when CO$_2$ is absent.

7. Because NADPH is generated in the chloroplasts by the light reactions.

8. The concentration of 3-phosphoglycerate would increase, whereas that of ribulose 1,5-bisphosphate would decrease.

9. The concentration of 3-phosphoglycerate would decrease, whereas that of ribulose 1,5-bisphosphate would increase.

10. Aspartate + glyoxylate $\longrightarrow$ oxaloacetate + glycine

11. The oxygenase activity of rubisco increases with temperature. Crabgrass is a C$_4$ plant, whereas most grasses lack this capability. Consequently, the crabgrass will thrive at the hottest part of the summer because the C$_4$ pathway provides an ample supply of CO$_2$.

12. The C$_4$ pathway allows the CO$_2$ concentration to increase at the site of carbon fixation. High concentrations of CO$_2$ inhibit the oxygenase reaction of rubisco. This inhibition is important for tropical plants because the oxygenase activity increases more rapidly with temperature than does the carboxylase activity.

13. ATP is required to form phosphoenolpyruvate (PEP) from pyruvate. The PEP combines with CO$_2$ to form oxaloacetate and, subsequently, malate. Two ATP molecules are required because a second ATP molecule is required to phosphorylate AMP to ADP.

14. Photorespiration is the consumption of oxygen by plants with the production of CO$_2$, but it does not generate energy. Photorespiration is due to the oxygenase activity of rubisco. It is wasteful because, instead of fixing CO$_2$ for conversion into hexoses, rubisco is generating CO$_2$.

15. As global warming progresses, C$_4$ plants will invade the higher latitudes, and C$_3$ plants will retreat to cooler regions.

16. The light reactions lead to an increase in the stromal concentrations of NADPH, reduced ferredoxin, and Mg^{2+}, as well as an increase in pH.

17. The enzymes catalyze the transformation of the five-carbon sugar formed by the oxidative phase of the pentose phosphate pathway into fructose 6-phosphate and glyceraldehyde 3-phosphate, intermediates in glycolysis (and gluconeogenesis).

18. The label emerges at C-5 of ribulose 5-phosphate.

19. Oxidative decarboxylation of isocitrate to α-ketoglutarate. A β-ketoacid intermediate is formed in both reactions.

20. (a) 5 Glucose 6-phosphate + ATP $\longrightarrow$ 6 ribose 5-phosphate + ADP + H$^+$.

(b) Glucose 6-phosphate + 12 NADP$^+$ + 7 H$_2$O $\longrightarrow$ 6 CO$_2$ + 12 NADPH + 12 H$^+$ + P$_i$.

21. The nonoxidative phase of the pentose phosphate pathway can be used to convert three molecules of ribose 5-phosphate into two molecules of fructose 6-phosphate and one molecule of glyceraldehyde 3-phosphate. These molecules are components of the glycolytic pathway.

22. The conversion of fructose 6-phosphate into fructose 1,6-bisphosphate by phosphofructokinase requires ATP.

23. When much NADPH is required. The oxidative phase of the pentose phosphate pathway is followed by the nonoxidative phase. The resulting fructose 6-phosphate and glyceraldehyde 3-phosphate are used to generate glucose 6-phosphate through gluconeogenesis, and the cycle is repeated until the equivalent of one glucose molecule is oxidized to CO$_2$.

24. Fava beans contain pamaquine, a purine glycoside that can lead to the generation of peroxides—reactive oxygen species that can damage membranes as well as other biomolecules. Glutathione is used to detoxify the ROS. The regeneration of glutathione depends on an adequate supply of NADPH, which is synthesized by the oxidative phase of the pentose phosphate pathway. People with low levels of the dehydrogenase are especially susceptible to pamaquine toxicity.

25. Because red blood cells do not have mitochondria and the only means to obtain NADPH is through the pentose phosphate pathway. There are biochemical means to convert mitochondrial NADH into cytoplasmic NADPH.

26. Reactive peroxides are a type of reactive oxygen species. The enzyme glutathione peroxidase uses reduced glutathione to neutralize peroxides by converting them into alcohols while generating oxidized glutathione. Reduced glutathione is regenerated by glutathione reductase with the use of NADPH, the product of the oxidative phase of the pentose phosphate pathway.

27. $\Delta E_0'$ for the reduction of glutathione by NADPH is $+0.09$ V. Hence, $\Delta G^{\circ\prime}$ is -17.4 kJ mol^{-1} (-4.2 kcal mol^{-1}), which corresponds to an equilibrium constant of 1126. The required [NADPH]/[NADP$^+$] ratio is 8.9×10^{-5}.

28.

Dihydroxyacetone phosphate

Fructose 1,6-bisphosphate

29.

Ribose 5-phosphate   **Enediol intermediate**

Ribulose 5-phosphate

30. Incubate an aliquot of a tissue homogenate with glucose labeled with ^{14}C at C-1, and incubate another with glucose labeled with ^{14}C at C-6. Compare the radioactivity of the CO$_2$ produced by the two samples. The rationale of this experiment is that only C-1 is decarboxylated by the pentose phosphate pathway, whereas C-1 and C-6 are decarboxylated equally when glucose is metabolized by the glycolytic pathway, the pyruvate dehydrogenase complex, and the citric acid cycle. The reason for the equivalence of C-1 and C-6 in the latter set of reactions is that glyceraldehyde 3-phosphate and dihydroxyacetone phosphate are rapidly interconverted by triose phosphate isomerase.

31. The reduction of each mole of CO$_2$ to the level of a hexose requires two moles of NADPH. The reduction of NADP$^+$ is a two-electron process. Hence, the formation of two moles of NADPH requires the pumping of four moles of electrons by photosystem I. The electrons given up by photosystem I are replenished by photosystem II, which needs to absorb an equal number of photons. Hence, eight photons are needed to generate the

required NADPH. The energy input of eight moles of photons is 1594 kJ (381 kcal). Thus, the overall efficiency of photosynthesis under standard conditions is at least 477/1594, or 30%.

32. It is neither a violation nor a miracle. The equation on page 580 requires not only 18 ATP, but also 12 NADPH. These electrons, if transferred to NAD$^+$ and used in the electron-transport chain, would yield 30 ATP. Thus, the synthesis of glucose requires the equivalent of 48 ATP.

33. (a) The curve on the right in graph A was generated by the C$_4$ plant. Recall that the oxygenase activity of rubisco increases with temperature more rapidly than does the carboxylase activity. Consequently, at higher temperatures, the C$_3$ plants would fix less carbon. Because C$_4$ plants can maintain a higher CO$_2$ concentration, the rise in temperature is less deleterious.
(b) The oxygenase activity will predominate. Additionally, when the temperature rise is very high, the evaporation of water might become a problem. The higher temperatures can begin to damage protein structures as well.
(c) The C$_4$ pathway is a very effective active-transport system for concentrating CO$_2$, even when environmental concentrations are very low.
(d) With the assumption that the plants have approximately the same capability to fix CO$_2$, the C$_4$ pathway is apparently the rate-limiting step in C$_4$ plants.

Chapter 21

1. Glycogen is an important fuel reserve for several reasons. The controlled breakdown of glycogen and release of glucose increase the amount of glucose that is available between meals. Hence, glycogen serves as a buffer to maintain blood-glucose levels. Glycogen's role in maintaining blood-glucose levels is especially important because glucose is virtually the only fuel used by the brain, except during prolonged starvation. Moreover, the glucose from glycogen is readily mobilized and is therefore a good source of energy for sudden, strenuous activity. Unlike fatty acids, the released glucose can provide energy in the absence of oxygen and can thus supply energy for anaerobic activity.

2. As an unbranched polymer, α-amylose has only one nonreducing end. Therefore, only one glycogen phosphorylase molecule could degrade each α-amylose molecule. Because glycogen is highly branched, there are many nonreducing ends per molecule. Consequently, many phosphorylase molecules can release many glucose molecules per glycogen molecule.

3. The patient has a deficiency of the branching enzyme.

4. In muscle, the b form of phosphorylase is activated by AMP. In the liver, the a form is inhibited by glucose. The difference corresponds to the difference in the metabolic role of glycogen in each tissue. Muscle uses glycogen as a fuel for contraction, whereas the liver uses glycogen to maintain blood-glucose levels.

5. Cells maintain the [P$_i$]/[glucose 1-phosphate] ratio at greater than 100, substantially favoring phosphorolysis. We see here an example of how the cell can alter the free-energy change to favor a reaction taking place by altering the ratio of substrate and product.

6. The high level of glucose 6-phosphate in von Gierke disease, resulting from the absence of glucose 6-phosphatase or the transporter, shifts the allosteric equilibrium of phosphorylated glycogen synthase toward the active form.

7. The phosphoryl donor is glucose 1,6-bisphosphate, which is formed from glucose 1-phosphate and ATP in a reaction catalyzed by phosphoglucokinase.

8. The different manifestations correspond to the different roles of the liver and muscle. Liver glycogen phosphorylase plays a crucial role in the maintenance of blood-glucose levels. Recall that glucose

is the primary fuel for the brain. Muscle glycogen phosphorylase provides glucose only for the muscle and, even then, only when the energy needs of the muscle are high, as during exercise. The fact that there are two different diseases suggests that there are two different isozymic forms of the glycogen phosphorylase—a liver-specific isozyme and a muscle-specific isozyme.

9. Water is excluded from the active site to prevent hydrolysis. The entry of water could lead to the formation of glucose rather than glucose 1-phosphate. A site-specific mutagenesis experiment is revealing in this regard. In phosphorylase, Tyr 573 is hydrogen bonded to the 2′-OH group of a glucose residue. The ratio of glucose 1-phosphate to glucose product is 9000 : 1 for the wild-type enzyme, and 500 : 1 for the Phe 573 mutant. Model building suggests that a water molecule occupies the site normally filled by the phenolic OH group of tyrosine and occasionally attacks the oxocarbonium ion intermediate to form glucose.

10. The amylase activity was necessary to remove all of the glycogen from the glycogenin. Recall that glycogenin synthesizes oligosaccharides of about eight glucose units, and then activity stops. Consequently, if the glucose residues are not removed by extensive amylase treatment, glycogenin will not function.

11. The substrate can be handed directly from the transferase site to the debranching site.

12. During exercise, [ATP] falls and [AMP] rises. Recall that AMP is an allosteric activator of glycogen phosphorylase b. Thus, even in the absence of covalent modification by phosphorylase kinase, glycogen is degraded.

13. Although glucose 1-phosphate is the actual product of the phosphorylase reaction, glucose 6-phosphate is a more versatile molecule with respect to metabolism. Among other fates, glucose-6-phosphate can be processed to yield energy or building blocks. In the liver, glucose 6-phosphate can be converted into glucose and released into the blood.

14. Epinephrine binds to its G-protein-coupled receptor. The resulting structural changes activate a G_α protein, which in turn activates adenyl cyclase. Adenyl cyclase synthesizes cAMP, which activates protein kinase A. Protein kinase A partly activates phosphoryl kinase, which phosphorylates and activates glycogen phosphorylase. The calcium released during muscle contraction further activates the phosphorylase kinase, leading to further stimulation of glycogen phosphorylase.

15. First, the signal-transduction pathway is shut down when the initiating hormone is no longer present. Second, the inherent GTPase activity of the G protein converts the bound GTP into inactive GDP. Third, phosphodiesterases convert cyclic AMP into AMP. Fourth, PP1 removes the phosphoryl group from glycogen phosphorylase, converting the enzyme into the usually inactive b form.

16. It prevents both from operating simultaneously, which would lead to a useless expenditure of energy. See the answer to Problem 24.

17. All these symptoms suggest central nervous system problems. If exercise is exhaustive enough or the athlete has not prepared well enough or both, liver glycogen also can be depleted. The brain depends on glucose derived from liver glycogen. The symptoms suggest that the brain is not getting enough fuel.

18. Liver phosphorylase a is inhibited by glucose, which facilitates the R $\longrightarrow$ T transition. This transition releases PP1, which inactivates glycogen breakdown and stimulates glycogen synthesis. Muscle phosphorylase is insensitive to glucose.

19. The presence of high concentrations of glucose 6-phosphate indicates that glucose is abundant and that it is not being used by glycolysis. Therefore, this valuable resource is saved by incorporation into glycogen.

20. Free glucose must be phosphorylated at the expense of a molecule of ATP. Glucose 6-phosphate derived from glycogen is formed by phosphorolytic cleavage, thus sparing one molecule of ATP. Thus, the net yield of ATP when glycogen-derived glucose is processed to pyruvate is three molecules of ATP compared with two molecules of ATP from free glucose.

21. Breakdown: Phosphoglucomutase converts glucose 1-phosphate, liberated from glycogen breakdown, into glucose 6-phosphate, which can be released as free glucose (liver) or processed in glycolysis (muscle and liver). Synthesis: Converts glucose 6-phophosphate into glucose 1-phosphate, which reacts with UTP to form UDP-glucose, the substrate for glycogen synthase.

22. $Glycogen_n + P_i \longrightarrow glycoge_{n-1} + glucose\ 6\text{-phosphate}$

Glucose 6-phosphate $\longrightarrow$ glucose 1-phosphate

UTP + glucose 1-phosphate $\longrightarrow$ UDP-glucose + 2 P_i

$Glycogen_{n-1}$ + UDP-glucose $\longrightarrow glycogen_n$ + UDP

Sum: $Glycogen_n$ + UTP $\longrightarrow glycogen_n$ + UDP + P_i

23. In principle, having glycogen be the only primer for the further synthesis of glycogen should be a successful strategy. However, if the glycogen granules were not evenly divided between daughter cells, glycogen stores for future generations of cells might be compromised. Glycogenin synthesizes the primer for glycogen synthase.

24. Insulin binds to its receptor and activates the tyrosine kinase activity of the receptor, which in turn triggers a pathway that activates protein kinases. The kinases phosphorylate and inactivate glycogen synthase kinase. Protein phosphatase 1 then removes the phosphate from glycogen synthase and thereby activates the synthase.

25.

Transferase reaction

α-1,6-Glucosidase reaction

26. Galactose + ATP + UTP + H_2O + glycogen$_n$ $\longrightarrow$
glycogen$_{n+1}$ + ADP + UDP + 2 P_i + H^+.

27. Phosphorylase, transferase, glucosidase, phosphoglucomutase, and glucose 6-phosphatase.

28. Glucose is an allosteric inhibitor of phosphorylase a. Hence, crystals grown in its presence are in the T state. The addition of glucose 1-phosphate, a substrate, shifts the R-to-T equilibrium toward the R state. The conformational differences between these states are sufficiently large that the crystal shatters unless it is stabilized by chemical cross-links.

29. Galactose is converted into UDP-galactose to eventually form glucose 6-phosphate.

30. This disease can also be produced by a mutation in the gene that encodes the glucose 6-phosphate transporter. Recall that glucose 6-phosphate must be transported into the lumen of the endoplasmic reticulum to be hydrolyzed by phosphatase. Mutations in the other three essential proteins of this system can likewise lead to von Gierke disease.

31. (a) Glycogen was too large to enter the gel and, because analysis was by western blot with the use of an antibody specific to glycogenin, we would not expect to see background proteins.
(b) α-Amylase degrades glycogen, releasing the protein glycogenin, which can be visualized by a western blot.
(c) Glycogen phosphorylase, glycogen synthase, and protein phosphatase 1. These proteins might be visible if the gel were stained for protein, but a western analysis reveals the presence of glycogenin only.

32. (a) The smear was due to molecules of glycogenin with increasingly large amounts of glycogen attached to them.
(b) In the absence of glucose in the medium, glycogen is metabolized, resulting in a loss of the high-molecular-weight material.
(c) Glycogen could have been resynthesized and added to the glycogenin when the cells were fed glucose again.
(d) No difference between lanes 3 and 4 suggests that, by 1 hour, the glycogen molecules had attained maximum size in this cell line. Prolonged incubation does not apparently increase the amount of glycogen.
(e) α-Amylase removes essentially all of the glycogen, and so only the glycogenin remains.

Chapter 22

1. Glycerol + 2 NAD^+ + P_i + ADP $\longrightarrow$
    pyruvate + ATP + H_2O + 2 NADH + H^+

Glycerol kinase and glycerol phosphate dehydrogenase

2. The ready reversibility is due to the high-energy nature of the thioester in the acyl CoA.

3. To return the AMP to a form that can be phosphorylated by oxidative phosphorylation or substrate-level phosphorylation, another molecule of ATP must be expended in the reaction:

$$ATP + AMP \rightleftharpoons 2\ ADP$$

4. b, c, a, g, h, d, e, f.

5. The citric acid cycle. The reactions that take succinate to oxaloacetate, or the reverse, are similar to those of fatty acid metabolism (Section 17.2).

6. The next-to-last degradation product, acetoacetyl CoA, yields two molecules of acetyl CoA with the thiolysis by only one molecule of CoA.

7. Palmitic acid yields 106 molecules of ATP. Palmitoleic acid has a double bond between carbons C-9 and C-10. When palmitoleic acid is processed in β oxidation, one of the oxidation steps

(to introduce a double bond before the addition of water) will not take place, because a double bond already exists. Thus, $FADH_2$ will not be generated, and palmitoleic acid will yield 1.5 fewer molecules of ATP than palmitic acid, for a total of 104.5 molecules of ATP.

8.

Activation fee to form the acyl CoA	−2 ATP
Seven rounds of yield:	
7 acetyl CoA at 10 ATP/acetyl CoA	+ 70 ATP
7 NADH at 2.5 ATP/NADH	+ 17.5 ATP
7 $FADH_2$ at 1.5 ATP/$FADH_2$	+ 10.5 ATP
Propionyl CoA, which requires an ATP to be converted into succinyl CoA	− 1 ATP
Succinyl CoA $\rightarrow$ succinate	+ 1 ATP (GTP)
Succinate $\rightarrow$ fumarate + $FADH_2$ $FADH_2$ at 1.5 ATP/$FADH_2$	+ 1.5 ATP
Fumarate $\rightarrow$ malate	
Malate $\rightarrow$ oxaloacetate + NADH NADH at 2.5 ATP/NADH	+ 2.5 ATP
Total	120 ATP

9. You might hate yourself in the morning, but at least you won't have to worry about energy. To form stearoyl CoA requires the equivalent of 2 molecules of ATP.

Stearoyl CoA + 8 FAD + 8 NAD^+ + 8 CoA + 8 H_2O $\longrightarrow$
    9 acetyl CoA + 8 $FADH_2$ + 8 NADH + 8 H^+

9 acetyl CoA at 10 ATP/acetyl CoA	+ 90 ATP
8 NADH at 2.5 ATP/NADH	+ 20 ATP
8 $FADH_2$ at 1.5 ATP/$FADH_2$	+ 12 ATP
Activation fee	−2.0
Total	122 ATP

10. Keep in mind that, in the citric acid cycle, 1 molecule of $FADH_2$ yields 1.5 ATP, 1 molecule of NADH yields 2.5 ATP, and 1 molecule of acetyl CoA yields 10 ATP. Two molecules of ATP are produced when glucose is degraded to 2 molecules of pyruvate. Two molecules of NADH also are produced, but the electrons are transferred to $FADH_2$ to enter the mitochondria. Each molecule of $FADH_2$ can generate 1.5 ATP. Each molecule of pyruvate will produce 1 molecule of NADH. Each molecule of acetyl CoA generates 3 molecules of NADH, 1 molecule of $FADH_2$, and 1 molecule of ATP. So, we have a total of 10 ATP per acetyl CoA, or 20 for the 2 molecules of acetyl CoA. The total for glucose is 30 ATP. Now, what about hexanoic acid? Caprioic acid is activated to caprioic CoA at the expense of 2 ATP, and so we are 2 ATP in the hole. The first cycle of β oxidation generates 1 $FADH_2$, 1 NADH, and 1 acetyl CoA. After the acetyl CoA has been run through the citric acid cycle, this step will have generated a total of 14 ATP. The second cycle of β oxidation generates 1 $FADH_2$ and 1 NADH but 2 acetyl CoA. After the acetyl CoA has been run through the citric acid cycle, this step will have generated a total of 24 ATP. The total is 36 ATP. Thus, the foul-smelling caprioic acid has a net yield of 36 ATP. So on a per carbon basis, this fat yields 20% more ATP than does glucose, a manifestation of the fact that fats are more reduced than carbohydrates.

11. Stearate + ATP + 13.5 H_2O + 8 FAD + 8 NAD^+ $\rightarrow$
4.5 acetoacetate + 14.5 H^+ + 8 $FADH_2$ + 8 NADH + AMP + 2 P_i.

12. Palmitate is activated and then processed by β oxidation according to the following reactions.

Palmitate + CoA + ATP $\longrightarrow$ palmitoyl CoA + AMP + 2 P$_i$

Palmitoyl CoA + 7 FAD + 7 NAD + 7 CoASH + H$_2$O $\longrightarrow$
8 acetyl CoA + 7 FADH$_2$ + 7 NADH + 7 H$^+$

The eight molecules of acetyl CoA combine to form four molecules of acetoacetate for release into the blood, and so they do not contribute to the energy yield in the liver. However, the FADH$_2$ and NADH generated in the preparation of acetyl CoA can be processed by oxidative phosphorylation to yield ATP.

$$1.5\ \text{ATP/FADH}_2 \times 7 = 10.5\ \text{ATP}$$

$$2.5\ \text{ATP/NADH} \times 7 = 17.5\ \text{ATP}$$

The equivalent of 2 ATP were used to form palmitoyl CoA. Thus, 26 ATP were generated for use by the liver.

13. NADH produced with the oxidation to acetoacetate = 2.5 ATP. Acetoacetate is converted into acetoacetyl CoA.

Two molecules of acetyl CoA result from the hydrolysis of acetoacetyl CoA, each worth 10 ATP when processed by the citric acid cycle. Total ATP yield is 22.5.

14. Because a molecule of succinyl CoA is used to form acetoacetyl CoA. Succinyl CoA could be used to generate one molecule of ATP (GTP), and so someone could argue that the yield is 21.5.

15. For fats to be combusted, not only must they be converted into acetyl CoA, but the acetyl CoA must be processed by the citric acid cycle. In order for acetyl CoA to enter the citric acid cycle, there must be a supply of oxaloacetate. Oxaloacetate can be formed by the metabolism of glucose to pyruvate and the subsequent carboxylation of pyruvate to form oxaloacetate.

16. (a)

Phytanic acid

The problem with phytanic acid is that, as it undergoes β oxidation, we encounter the dreaded pentavalent carbon atom. Because the pentavalent carbon atom doesn't exist, β oxidation cannot take place and phytanic acid accumulates.

The dreaded pentavalent carbon atom

(b) Removing methyl groups, though theoretically possible, would be time consuming and, lacking in elegance. What would we do with the methyl groups? Our livers solve the problem by inventing α oxidation.

One round of α oxidation rather than β oxidation converts phytanic acid into a β-oxidation substrate.

17. The first oxidation removes two tritium atoms. The hydration adds nonradioactive H and OH. The second oxidation removes another tritium atom from the β-carbon atom. Thiolysis removes an acetyl CoA with only one tritium atom; so the tritium-to-carbon ratio is 1/2. This ratio will be the same for two of the acetates. The last one, however, does not undergo oxidation, and so all tritium remains. The ratio for this acetate is 3/2. The ratio for the entire molecule is then 5/6.

18. In the absence of insulin, lipid mobilization will take place to an extent that it overwhelms the ability of the liver to convert the lipids into ketone bodies.

19. (a) Oxidation in mitochondria; synthesis in the cytoplasm. (b) Coenzyme A in oxidation; acyl carrier protein for synthesis. (c) FAD and NAD$^+$ in oxidation; NADPH for synthesis. (d) the L isomer of 3-hydroxyacyl CoA in oxidation; the D isomer in synthesis. (e) From carboxyl to methyl in oxidation; from methyl to carboxyl in synthesis. (f) The enzymes of fatty acid synthesis, but not those of oxidation, are organized in a multienzyme complex.

20. 7 acetyl CoA + 6 ATP + 12 NADPH +12 H$^+$ $\rightarrow$ myristate + 7 CoA + 6 ADP + 6 Pi + 12 NADP$^+$ + 5H$_2$O.

21. We will need six acetyl CoA units. One acetyl CoA unit will be used directly to become the two carbon atoms farthest from the acid end. The other five units must be converted into malonyl CoA. The synthesis of each malonyl CoA molecule costs a molecule of ATP; so 5 molecules of ATP will be required. Each round of elongation requires 2 molecules of NADPH, 1 molecule to reduce the keto group to an alcohol and 1 molecule to reduce the double bond. As a result, 10 molecules of NADPH will be required. Therefore, 5 molecules of ATP and 10 molecules of NADPH are required to synthesize lauric acid.

22. e, b, d, a, c.

23. Such a mutation would inhibit fatty acid synthesis because the enzyme cleaves cytoplasmic citrate to yield acetyl CoA for fatty acid synthesis.

24. (a) False. Biotin is required for acetyl CoA carboxylase activity. (b) True. (c) False. ATP is required to synthesize malonyl CoA. (d) True. (e) True. (f) False. Fatty acid synthase is a dimer. (g) True. (h) False. Acetyl CoA carboxylase is stimulated by citrate, which is cleaved to yield its substrate acetyl CoA.

25. Fatty acids with odd numbers of carbon atoms are synthesized starting with propionyl ACP (instead of acetyl ACP), which is formed from propionyl CoA by acetyl transacetylase.

26. All of the labeled carbon atoms will be retained. Because we need 8 acetyl CoA molecules and only 1 carbon atom is labeled in the acetyl group, we will have 8 labeled carbon atoms. The only acetyl CoA used

directly will retain 3 tritium atoms. The 7 acetyl CoA molecules used to make malonyl CoA will lose 1 tritium atom on addition of the CO_2 and another one at the dehydration step. Each of the 7 malonyl CoA molecules will retain 1 tritium atom. Therefore, the total retained tritium is 10 atoms. The ratio of tritium to carbon is 1.25.

27. With a diet rich in raw eggs, avidin will inhibit fatty acid synthesis by reducing the amount of biotin required by acetyl CoA carboxylase. Cooking the eggs will denature avidin, and so it will no longer bind biotin.

28. The only acetyl CoA used directly, not in the form of malonyl CoA, provides the two carbon atoms at the ω end of the fatty acid chain. Because palmitic acid is a C_{16} fatty acid, acetyl CoA will have provided carbons 15 and 16.

29. HCO_3^- is attached to acetyl CoA to form malonyl CoA. When malonyl CoA condenses with acetyl CoA to form the four-carbon keto acyl CoA, the HCO_3^- is lost as CO_2.

30. Phosphofructokinase controls the flux down the glycolytic pathway. Glycolysis functions to generate ATP or building blocks for biosynthesis, depending on the tissue. The presence of citrate in the cytoplasm indicates that those needs are met, and there is no need to metabolize glucose.

31. C-1 is more radioactive.

32. The mutant enzyme will be persistently active because it cannot be inhibited by phosphorylation. Fatty acid synthesis will be abnormally active. Such a mutation might lead to obesity.

33. (a) Palmitoleate; (b) linoleate; (c) linoleate; (d) oleate; (e) oleate; (f) linolenate.

34. Decarboxylation drives the condensation of malonyl ACP and acetyl ACP. In contrast, the condensation of two molecules of acetyl ACP is energetically unfavorable. In gluconeogenesis, decarboxylation drives the formation of phosphoenolpyruvate from oxaloacetate.

35. Fat mobilization in adipocytes is activated by phosphorylation. Hence, overproduction of the cAMP-activated kinase will lead to an accelerated breakdown of triacylglycerols and a depletion of fat stores.

36. Carnitine translocase deficiency and glucose 6-phosphate transporter deficiency.

37. In the fifth round of β oxidation, *cis*-Δ^2-enoyl CoA is formed. Dehydration by the classic hydratase yields D-3-hydroxyacyl CoA, the wrong isomer for the next enzyme in β oxidation. This dead end is circumvented by a second hydratase that removes water to give *trans*-Δ^2-enoyl CoA. The addition of water by the classic hydratase then yields L-3-hydroxyacyl CoA, the appropriate isomer. Thus, hydratases of opposite stereospecificities serve to *epimerize* (invert the configuration of) the 3-hydroxyl group of the acyl CoA intermediate.

38. The probability of synthesizing an error-free polypeptide chain decreases as the length of the chain increases. A single mistake can make the entire polypeptide ineffective. In contrast, a defective subunit can be spurned in the formation of a noncovalent multienzyme complex; the good subunits are not wasted.

39. The absence of ketone bodies is due to the fact that the liver, the source of ketone bodies in the blood, cannot oxidize fatty acids to produce acetyl CoA. Moreover, because of the impaired fatty acid oxidation, the liver becomes more dependent on glucose as an energy source. This dependency results in a decrease in gluconeogenesis and a drop in blood-glucose levels, which is exacerbated by the lack of fatty acid oxidation in muscle and a subsequent increase in glucose uptake from the blood.

40. Peroxisomes enhance the degradation of fatty acids. Consequently, increasing the activity of peroxisomes could help to lower levels of blood triglycerides. In fact, clofibrate is rarely used because of serious side effects.

41. Citrate works by facilitating the formation of active filaments from inactive monomers. In essence, it increases the number of active sites available, or the concentration of enzyme. Consequently, its effect is visible as an increase in the value of V_{max}. Allosteric enzymes that alter their V_{max} values in response to regulators are sometimes called V-class enzymes. The more common type of allosteric enzyme, in which K_m is altered, comprises K-class enzymes. Palmitoyl CoA causes depolymerization and thus inactivation.

42. The thiolate anion of CoA attacks the 3-keto group to form a tetrahedral intermediate. This intermediate collapses to form acyl CoA and the enolate anion of acetyl CoA. Protonation of the enolate yields acetyl CoA.

43.

Malonyl-ACP

Acetyl-ACP

Acetoacetyl-ACP

44. (a) Fats burn in the flame of carbohydrates. Without carbohydrates, there would be no anapleurotic reactions to replenish the components of the citric acid cycle. With a diet of fats only, the acetyl CoA from fatty acid degradation would build up.
(b) Acetone from ketone bodies
(c) Yes. Odd-chain fatty acids would lead to the production of propionyl CoA, which can be converted into succinyl CoA, a citric acid cycle component. It would serve to replenish the citric acid cycle and mitigate the halitosis.

45. A labeled fat can enter the citric acid cycle as acetyl CoA and yield labeled oxaloacetate, but only after two carbon atoms have been lost as CO_2. Consequently, even though oxaloacetate may be labeled, there can be no net synthesis of oxaloacetate and hence no net synthesis of glucose or glycogen.

46. (a) The V_{max} is decreased and the K_m is increased. V_{max} (wild type) = 13 nmol minute^{-1} mg^{-1}; K_m (wild type) = 45 μM; V_{max} (mutant) = 8.3 nmol minute^{-1} mg^{-1}; K_m (mutant) = 74 μM.
(b) Both the V_{max} and the K_m are decreased. V_{max} (wild type) = 41 nmol minute^{-1} mg^{-1}; K_m (wild type) = 104 μM; V_{max} (mutant) = 23 nmol minute^{-1} mg^{-1}; K_m (mutant) = 69 μM.
(c) The wild type is significantly more sensitive to malonyl CoA.
(d) With respect to carnitine, the mutant displays approximately 65% of the activity of the wild type; with respect to palmitoyl CoA, approximately 50% activity. On the other hand, 10 μM of malonyl CoA inhibits approximately 80% of the wild type but has essentially no effect on the mutant enzyme.

(e) The glutamate appears to play a more prominent role in regulation by malonyl CoA than in catalysis.

Chapter 23

1. When the proteins are denatured, all of the peptide bonds are accessible to proteolytic enzymes. If the three-dimensional structure of a protein is maintained, access to many peptide bonds is denied to the proteolytic enzymes.

2. First, the ubiquitin-activating enzyme (E1) links ubiquitin to a sulfhydryl group on E1 itself. Next, the ubiquitin is transferred to a cysteine residue on the ubiquitin-conjugating enzyme (E2) by E2. The ubiquitin–protein ligase (E3), using the ubiquitinated E2 as a substrate, transfers the ubiquitin to the target protein.

3. (a) 7; (b) 4; (c) 2; (d) 10; (e) 5; (f) 3; (g) 9; (h) 1; (i) 6; (j) 8.

4. (a) The ATPase activity of the 26S proteasome resides in the 19S subunit. The energy of ATP hydrolysis could be used to unfold the substrate, which is too large to enter the catalytic barrel. ATP may also be required for translocation of the substrate into the barrel.
(b) Substantiates the answer in part *a*. Because they are small, the peptides do not need to be unfolded. Moreover, small peptides could probably enter all at once and not require translocation.

5. (a) Pyruvate; (b) oxaloacetate; (c) α-ketoglutarate; (d) α-ketoisocaproate; (e) phenylpyruvate; (f) hydroxyphenylpyruvate.

6. (a) Aspartate + α-ketoglutarate + GTP + ATP + 2 H_2O + NADH + H^+ ⟶ ½ glucose + glutamate + CO_2 + ADP + GDP + NAD^+ + 2 P_i.
The required coenzymes are pyridoxal phosphate in the transamination reaction and NAD^+/NADH in the redox reactions.
(b) Aspartate + CO_2 + NH_4^+ + 3 ATP + NAD^+ + 4 H_2O ⟶ oxaloacetate + urea + 2 ADP + 4 P_i + AMP + NADH + H^+.

7. In the eukaryotic proteasome, the distinct β subunits have different substrate specificities, allowing proteins to be more thoroughly degraded.

8. The six subunits probably exist as a heterohexamer. Cross-linking experiments could test the model and help determine which subunits are adjacent to one another.

9. Thiamine pyrophosphate

10. Aminotransferases transfer the α-amino group to α-ketoglutarate to form glutamate. Glutamate is oxidatively deaminated to form an ammonium ion.

11. Aspartate (oxaloacetate), glutamate (α-ketoglutarate), alanine (pyruvate)

12. Serine and threonine

13. They are either fuels for the citric acid cycle, components of the citric acid cycle, or molecules that can be converted into a fuel for the citric acid cycle in one step.

14. It acts as an electron sink.

15. Carbamoyl phosphate and aspartate

16. (a) 4; (b) 5; (c) 1; (d) 6; (e) 7; (f) 3; (g) 2.

17. A, arginine; B, citrulline; C, ornithine; D, arginosuccinate. The order of appearance: C, B, D, E.

18. CO_2 + NH_4^+ + 3 ATP + NAD^+ + aspartate + 3 H_2O ⟶ urea + 2 ADP + 2 P_i + AMP + PP_i + NADH + H^+ + oxaloacetate.
Four high-transfer-potential phosphoryl groups are spent. Note, however, that an NADH is generated if fumarate is converted into oxaloacetate. NADH can generate 2.5 ATP in the electron-transport chain. Taking these ATP into account, only 1.5 high-transfer-potential phosphoryl groups are spent.

19. The synthesis of fumarate by the urea cycle is important because it links the urea cycle and the citric acid cycle. Fumarate is hydrated to malate, which, in turn, is oxidized to oxaloacetate. Oxaloacetate has several possible fates: (1) transamination to aspartate, (2) conversion into glucose by the gluconeogenic pathway, (3) condensation with acetyl CoA to form citrate, or (4) conversion into pyruvate. You can collect.

20. Ornithine transcarbamoylase (analogous to PALA; see Chapter 10).

21. Ammonia could lead to the amination of α-ketoglutarate, producing a high concentration of glutamate in an unregulated fashion. α-Ketoglutarate for glutamate synthesis could be removed from the citric acid cycle, thereby diminishing the cell's respiration capacity.

22. The mass spectrometric analysis strongly suggests that three enzymes—pyruvate dehydrogenase, α-ketoglutarate dehydrogenase, and the branched-chain α-ketoacid dehydrogenase—are deficient. Most likely, the common E3 component of these enzymes is missing or defective. This proposal could be tested by purifying these three enzymes and assaying their ability to catalyze the regeneration of lipoamide.

23. Benzoate, phenylacetate, and arginine would be given to supply a protein-restricted diet. Nitrogen would emerge in hippurate, phenylacetylglutamine, and citrulline.

24. The liver is the primary tissue for capturing nitrogen as urea. If the liver is damaged (for instance, by hepatitis or the excessive consumption of alcohol), free ammonia is released into the blood.

25. This defect can be partly bypassed by providing a surplus of arginine in the diet and restricting the total protein intake. In the liver, arginine is split into urea and ornithine, which then reacts with carbamoyl phosphate to form citrulline. This urea-cycle intermediate condenses with aspartate to yield argininosuccinate, which is then excreted. Note that two nitrogen atoms—one from carbamoyl phosphate and the other from aspartate—are eliminated from the body per molecule of arginine provided in the diet. In essence, argininosuccinate substitutes for urea in carrying nitrogen out of the body. The formation of argininosuccinate removes the nitrogen, and the restriction on protein intake relieves the aciduria.

26. Aspartame, a dipeptide ester (L-aspartyl-L-phenylalanine methyl ester), is hydrolyzed to L-aspartate and L-phenylalanine. High levels of phenylalanine are harmful in phenylketonurics.

27. N-Acetylglutamate is synthesized from acetyl CoA and glutamate. Once again, acetyl CoA serves as an activated acetyl donor. This reaction is catalyzed by N-acetylglutamate synthase.

28. Not all proteins are created equal: some are more important than others. Some proteins would be degraded to provide the missing amino acid. The nitrogen from the other amino acids would be excreted as urea. Consequently, more nitrogen would be excreted than ingested.

29. The carbon skeletons of ketogenic amino acids can be converted into ketone bodies or fatty acids. Only leucine and lysine are purely ketogenic. Glucogenic amino acids are those whose carbon skeletons can be converted into glucose.

30. The branched-chain amino acids leucine, isoleucine, and valine. The required enzyme is the branched-chain α-ketoacid dehydrogenase complex.

31. Pyruvate (glycolysis and gluconeogenesis), acetyl CoA (citric acid cycle and fatty acid synthesis), acetoacetyl CoA (ketone-body formation), α-ketoglutarate (citric acid cycle), succinyl CoA (citric acid cycle), fumarate (citric acid cycle), and oxaloacetate (citric acid cycle and gluconeogenesis).

32.

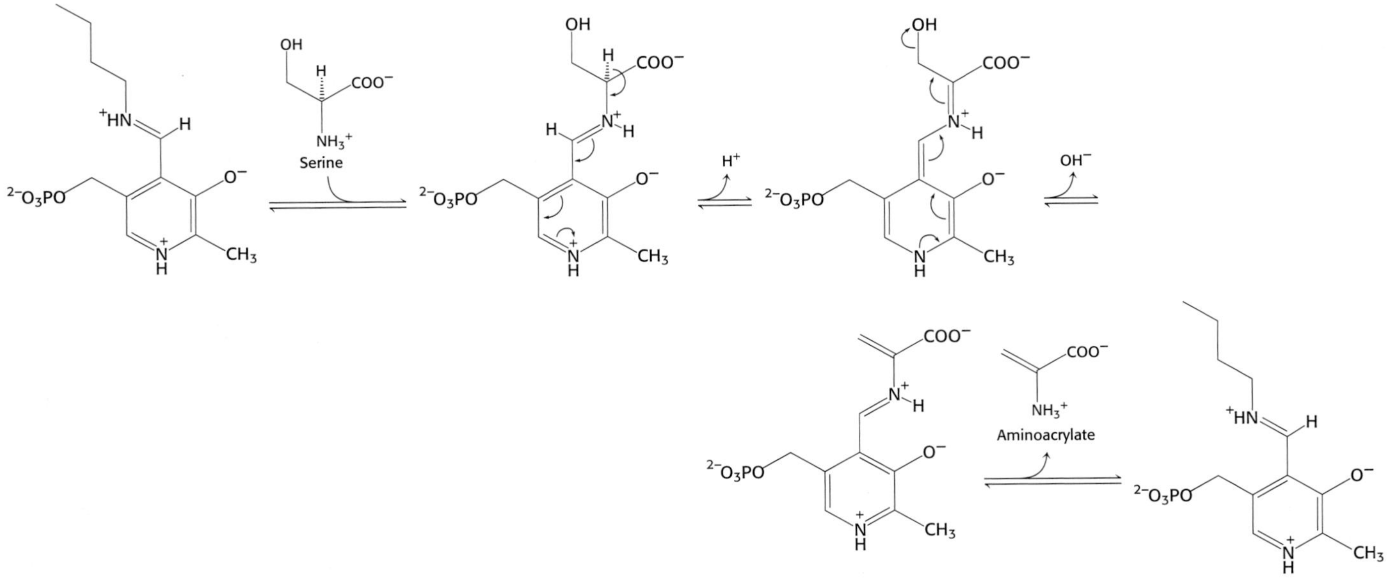

Serine

L-Serine

Aminoacrylate

33.

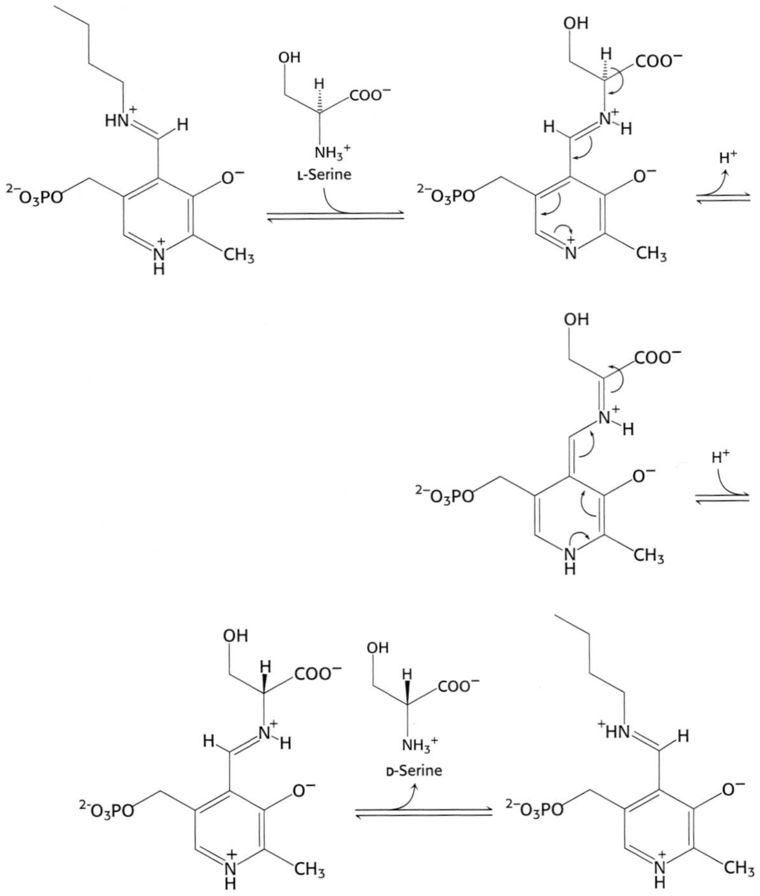

L-Serine

D-Serine

The equilibrium constant for the interconversion of L-serine and D-serine is exactly 1.

34. Exposure of such a domain suggests that a component of a multiprotein complex has failed to form properly or that one component has been synthesized in excess. This exposure leads to rapid degradation and the restoration of appropriate stoichiometries.

35. (a) Depletion of glycogen stores. When they are gone, proteins must be degraded to meet the glucose needs of the brain. The resulting amino acids are deaminated, and the nitrogen atoms are excreted as urea.
(b) The brain has adapted to the use of ketone bodies, which are derived from fatty acid catabolism. In other words, the brain is being powered by fatty acid breakdown.
(c) When the glycogen and lipid stores are gone, the only available energy source is protein.

36. Deamination to α-keto-β-methylvalerate; oxidative decarboxylation to α-methylbutyryl CoA; oxidation to tiglyl CoA; hydration, oxidation, and thiolysis yield acetyl CoA and propionyl CoA; propionyl CoA to succinyl CoA.

37. Glycogen phosphorylase. The coenzyme serves as an acid–base catalyst.

38. In the Cori cycle, the carbon atoms are transferred from muscle to liver as lactate. For lactate to be of any use, it must be reduced to pyruvate. This reduction requires high-energy electrons in the form of NADH. When the carbon atoms are transferred as alanine, transamination yields pyruvate directly.

39. (a) Virtually no digestion in the absence of nucleotides. (b) Protein digestion is greatly stimulated by the presence of ATP. (c) AMP-PNP, a nonhydrolyzable analog of ATP, is no more effective than ADP. (d) The proteasome requires neither ATP nor PAN to digest small substrates. (e) PAN and ATP hydrolysis may be required to unfold the peptide and translocate it into the proteasome. (f) Although *Thermoplasma* PAN is not as effective with the other proteasomes, it nonetheless results in threefold to fourfold stimulation of digestion. (g) In light of the fact that the archaea and eukarya diverged several billion years ago, the fact that

Thermoplasma PAN can stimulate rabbit muscle suggests homology not only between the proteasomes, but also between PAN and the 19S subunit (most likely the ATPases) of the mammalian 26S proteasome.

Chapter 24

1. Nitrogen fixation is the conversion of atmospheric N_2 into NH_3^+. Diazotrophic (nitrogen-fixing) microorganisms are able to fix nitrogen.

2. Oxaloacetate, pyruvate, ribose-5-phosphate, phosphoenolpyruvate, erythrose-4-phosphate, α-ketoglutarate, and 3-phosphoglycerate.

3. Human beings do not have the biochemical pathways to synthesize certain amino acids from simpler precursors. Consequently, these amino acids are "essential" and must be obtained from the diet.

4. Glucose + 2 ADP + 2 P_i + 2 NAD^+ + 2 glutamate $\longrightarrow$ 2 alanine + 2 α-ketoglutrate + 2 ATP + 2 NADH + 2 H_2O + 2 H^+.

5. $N_2 \longrightarrow NH_4^+ \longrightarrow$ glutamate $\longrightarrow$ serine $\longrightarrow$ glycine $\longrightarrow$ δ-aminolevulinate $\longrightarrow$ porphobilinogen $\longrightarrow$ heme.

6. False. Nitrogen fixation is thermodynamically favorable. Nitrogenase is required because the process is kinetically disfavored.

7. Pyridoxal phosphate (PLP)

8. S-Adenosylmethionine, tetrahydrofolate, and methylcobalamin.

9. (a) N^5,N^{10}-Methylenetetrahydrofolate; (b) N^5-methyltetrahydrofolate.

10. γ-Glutamyl phosphate is a likely reaction intermediate.

11. The synthesis of asparagine from aspartate passes through an acyl-adenylate intermediate. One of the products of the reaction will be ^{18}O-labeled AMP.

12. The administration of glycine leads to the formation of isovalerylglycine. This water-soluble conjugate, in contrast with isovaleric acid, is excreted very rapidly by the kidneys.

13. The nitrogen atom shaded red is derived from glutamine. The carbon atom shaded blue is derived from serine.

14. They carry out nitrogen fixation. The absence of photosystem II provides an environment in which O_2 is not produced. Recall that the nitrogenase is very rapidly inactivated by O_2.

15. The cytoplasm is a reducing environment, whereas the extracellular milieu is an oxidizing environment.

16. (a) None; (b) D-glutamate and oxaloacetate.

17. Succinyl CoA is formed in the mitochondrial matrix.

18. Alanine from pyruvate; aspartate from oxaloacetate; glutamate from α-ketoglutarate.

19. Lysine cyclodeaminase converts L-lysine into the six-membered ring analog of proline, also referred to as L-homoproline or L-pipecolate:

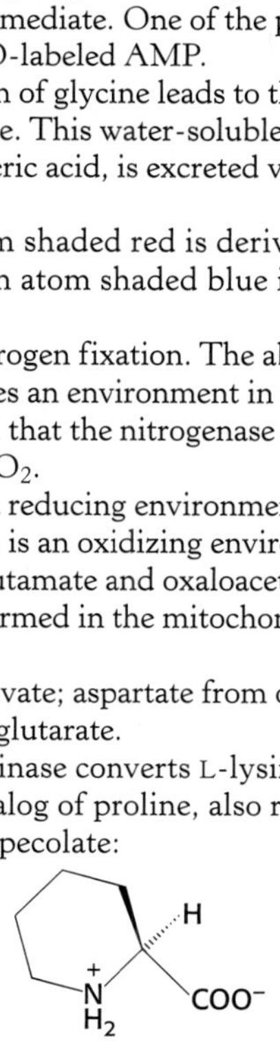

Pipecolate

20. Y could inhibit the C $\longrightarrow$ D step, Z could inhibit the C $\longrightarrow$ F step, and C could inhibit A $\longrightarrow$ B. This scheme is an example of sequential feedback inhibition. Alternatively, Y could inhibit the C $\longrightarrow$ D step, Z could inhibit the C $\longrightarrow$ F step, and the A $\longrightarrow$ B

step would be inhibited only in the presence of both Y and Z. This scheme is called concerted feedback inhibition.

21. The rate of the A $\longrightarrow$ B step in the presence of high levels of Y and Z would be 24 s^{-1} ($0.6 \times 0.4 \times 100\ s^{-1}$).

22. Lysine 258 is absolutely essential for the activity of aspartate aminotransferase, as it is responsible both for the formation of the internal aldimine with the pyridoxal phosphate cofactor and for transferring the proton between the ketimine and quinonoid intermediates. Mutation of this residue to cysteine would be expected to dramatically impair catalysis, as cysteine cannot occupy the same space as lysine and also exhibits differing pK_a properties. Upon treatment with 2-bromoethylamine, however, the resulting thioether now has a shape and pK_a similar to the original lysine side chain. Hence, some catalytic activity is restored.

23. An external aldimine forms with SAM, which is deprotonated to form the quinonoid intermediate. The deprotonated carbon atom attacks the carbon atom adjacent to the sulfur atom to form the cyclopropane ring and release methylthioadenosine, the other product.

24. An external aldimine forms with L-serine, which is deprotonated to form the quinonoid intermediate. This intermediate is reprotonated on its opposite face to form an aldimine with D-serine. This compound is cleaved to release D-serine. The equilibrium constant for a racemization reaction is 1 because the reactant and product are exact mirror images of each other.

25. (a) In the first step, histidine attacks the methylene group from the methionine subgroup of SAM (rather than the usual methyl substituent), resulting in the transfer of an aminocarboxypropyl group. Three subsequent conventional SAM-mediated methylations of the primary amine yield diphthine.

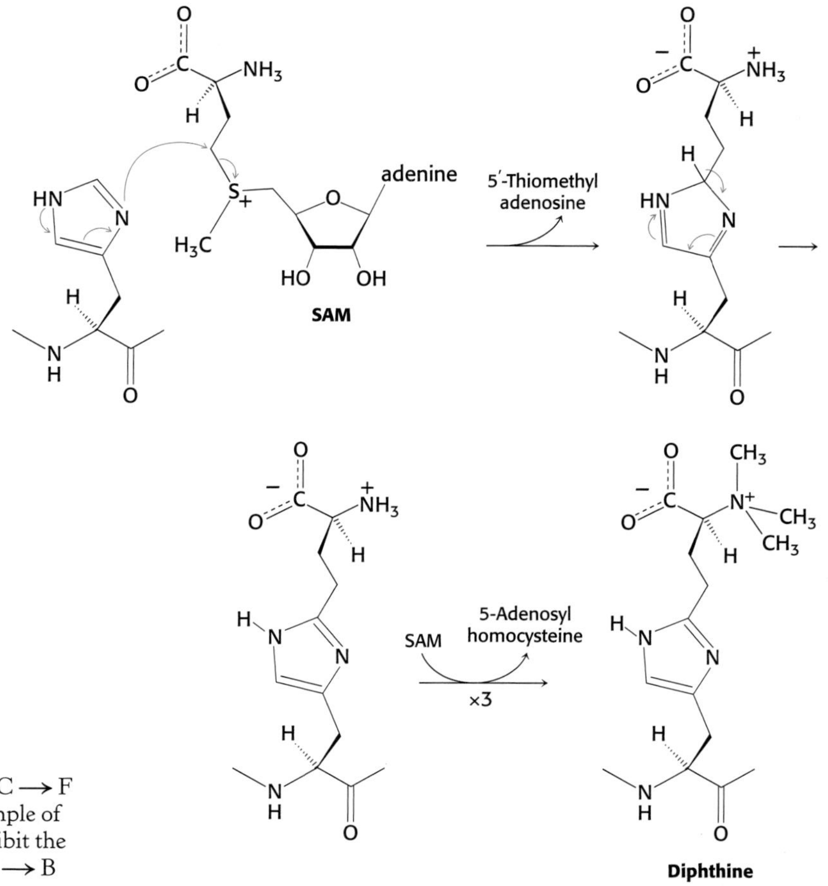

Diphthine

(b) In this chapter, we have observed two examples of an ATP-dependent conversion of a carboxylate into an amide: glutamine synthetase, which uses an acyl-phosphate intermediate, and asparagine synthetase, which uses an acyl-adenylate intermediate. Either mechanism is possible in formation of diphthamide from diphthine.

26. Synthesis from oxaloacetate and α-ketoglutarate would deplete the citric acid cycle, which would decrease ATP production. Anapleurotic reactions would be required to replenish the citric acid cycle.

27. SAM is the donor for DNA methylation reactions that protect a host from digestion by its own restriction enzymes. A lack of SAM would render the bacterial DNA susceptible to digestion by the cell's own restriction enzymes.

28. Acetate $\longrightarrow$ acetyl-CoA $\longrightarrow$ citrate $\longrightarrow$ isocitrate $\longrightarrow$ α-ketoglutarate $\longrightarrow$ succinyl-CoA.

29. (a) Asparagine is much more abundant in the dark. More glutamine is present in the light. These amino acids show the most dramatic effects. Glycine also is more abundant in the light.
(b) Glutamine is a more metabolically reactive amino acid, used in the synthesis of many other compounds. Consequently, when energy is available as light, glutamine will be preferentially synthesized. Asparagine, which carries more nitrogen per carbon atom and is thus a more-efficient means of storing nitrogen when energy is short, is synthesized in the dark. Glycine is more prevalent in the light because of photorespiration.
(c) White asparagus has an especially high concentration of asparagine, which accounts for its intense taste. All asparagus has a large amount of asparagine. In fact, as suggested by its name, asparagine was first isolated from asparagus.

Chapter 25

1. In de novo synthesis, the nucleotides are synthesized from simpler precursor compounds, in essence from scratch. In salvage pathways, preformed bases are recovered and attached to riboses.

2. Carbon 2 and nitrogen 3 come from carbamoyl phosphate. Nitrogen 1 and carbons 4, 5, and 6 are derived from aspartate.

3. Nitrogen 1: aspartate; carbon 2: N^{10}-formyltetrahydrofolate; nitrogen 3: glutamine; carbons 4 and 5 and nitrogen 7: glycine; carbon 6: CO_2; carbon 8: N^{10}-formyltetrahydrofolate; nitrogen 9: glutamine.

4. Energy currency: ATP; signal transduction: ATP and GTP; RNA synthesis: ATP, GTP, CTP, and UTP; DNA synthesis: dATP, dCTP, dGTP, and TTP; components of coenzymes: ATP in CoA, FAD, and NAD(P)$^+$; carbohydrate synthesis: UDP-glucose. They are just some of the uses.

5. A nucleoside is a base attached to ribose. A nucleotide is a nucleoside with the ribose bearing one or more phosphates.

6. (a) 9; (b) 7; (c) 6; (d) 10; (e) 2; (f) 4; (g) 1; (h) 11; (i) 8; (j) 3; (k) 5.

7. Substrate channeling is the process whereby the product of one active site moves to become a substrate at another active site without ever leaving the enzyme. A channel connects the active sites. Substrate channeling greatly enhances enzyme efficiency and minimizes the diffusion of a substrate to an active site.

8. Glucose + 2 ATP + 2 NADP$^+$ + H_2O $\longrightarrow$ PRPP + CO_2 + ADP + AMP + 2 NADPH + 3 H$^+$.

9. Glutamine + aspartate + CO_2 + 2 ATP + NAD$^+$ $\longrightarrow$ orotate + 2 ADP + 2 P$_i$ + glutamate + NADH + H$^+$.

10. (a, c, and d) PRPP; (b) carbamoyl phosphate.

11. PRPP and formylglycinamide ribonucleotide

12. dUMP + serine + NADPH + H$^+$ $\longrightarrow$ dTMP + NADP$^+$ + glycine.

13. There is a deficiency of N^{10}-formyltetrahydrofolate. Sulfanilamide inhibits the synthesis of folate by acting as an analog of p-aminobenzoate, one of the precursors of folate.

14. (a) Cell A cannot grow in a HAT medium, because it cannot synthesize TMP either from thymidine or from dUMP. Cell B cannot grow in this medium, because it cannot synthesize purines by either the de novo pathway or the salvage pathway. Cell C can grow in a HAT medium because it contains active thymidine kinase from cell B (enabling it to phosphorylate thymidine to TMP) and hypoxanthine guanine phosphoribosyltransferase from cell A (enabling it to synthesize purines from hypoxanthine by the salvage pathway).
(b) Transform cell A with a plasmid containing foreign genes of interest and a functional thymidine kinase gene. The only cells that will grow in a HAT medium are those that have acquired a thymidylate kinase gene; nearly all of these transformed cells will also contain the other genes on the plasmid.

15. The reciprocal substrate relation refers to the fact that AMP synthesis requires GTP, whereas GMP synthesis requires ATP. These requirements tend to balance the synthesis of ATP and GTP.

16. Ring carbon 6 in cytosine will be labeled. In guanine, only carbon 5 will be labeled with ^{13}C.

17. The enzyme that uses ammonia synthesizes carbamoyl phosphate for a reaction with ornithine, the first step of the urea cycle. The enzyme that uses glutamine synthesizes carbamoyl phosphate for use in the first step of pyrimidine biosynthesis.

18. These patients have a high level of urate because of the breakdown of nucleic acids. Allopurinol prevents the formation of kidney stones and blocks other deleterious consequences of hyperuricemia by preventing the formation of urate.

19. The free energies of binding are -57.7 (wild type), -49.8 (Asn 27), and -38.1 (Ser 27) kJ mol^{-1} (-13.8, -11.9, and -9.1 kcal mol^{-1}, respectively). The loss in binding energy is 7.9 kJ mol^{-1} (1.9 kcal mol^{-1}) and 19.7 kJ mol^{-1} (4.7 kcal mol^{-1}).

20. Inosine or hypoxanthine could be administered.

21. N-1 in both cases, and the amine group linked to C-6 in ATP.

22. Nitrogen atoms 3 and 9 in the purine ring

23. Allopurinol, an analog of hypoxanthine, is a suicide inhibitor of xanthine oxidase.

24. An oxygen atom is added to allopurinol to form alloxanthine.

25.

The synthesis of carbamoyl phosphate requires 2 ATP	2 ATP
The formation of PRPP from ribose 5-phosphate yields an AMP*	2 ATP
The conversion of UMP to UTP requires 2 ATP	2 ATP
The conversion of UTP to CTP requires 1 ATP	1 ATP
Total	7 ATP

*Remember that AMP is the equivalent of 2 ATP because an ATP must be expended to generate ADP, the substrate for ATP synthesis.

26. (a) Carboxyaminoimidazole ribonucleotide; (b) glycinamide ribonucleotide; (c) phosphoribosyl amine; (d) formylglycinamide ribonucleotide.

27. The first reaction proceeds by phosphorylation of glycine to form an acyl phosphate followed by nucleophilic attack by the amine of phosphoribosylamine to displace orthophosphate. The second reaction consists of adenylation of the carbonyl group of xanthylate followed by nucleophilic attack by ammonia to displace AMP.

28. The $-NH_2$ group attacks the carbonyl carbon atom to form a tetrahedral intermediate. Removal of a proton leads to the elimination of water to form inosinate.

29. PRPP is the activated intermediate in the synthesis of phosphoribosylamine in the de novo pathway of purine formation; of purine nucleotides from free bases by the salvage pathway; of orotidylate in the formation of pyrimidines; of nicotinate ribonucleotide; of phosphoribosyl ATP in the pathway leading to histidine; and of phosphoribosylanthranilate in the pathway leading to tryptophan.

30. (a) cAMP; (b) ATP; (c) UDP-glucose; (d) acetyl CoA; (e) NAD^+, FAD; (f) dideoxynucleotides; (g) fluorouracil; (h) CTP inhibits ATCase.

31. In vitamin B_{12} deficiency, methyltetrahydrofolate cannot donate its methyl group to homocysteine to regenerate methionine. Because the synthesis of methyltetrahydrofolate is irreversible, the cell's tetrahydrofolate will ultimately be converted into this form. No formyl or methylene tetrahydrofolate will be left for nucleotide synthesis. Vitamin B_{12} is also required to metabolize propionyl CoA generated in the oxidation of odd-chain fatty acids and in the degradation of methionine.

32. Because folate is required for nucleotide synthesis, cells that are dividing rapidly would be most readily affected. They would include cells of the intestine, which are constantly replaced, and precursors to blood cells. A lack of intestinal cells and blood cells would account for the symptoms often observed.

33. The cytoplasmic level of ATP in the liver falls and that of AMP rises above normal in all three conditions. The excess AMP is degraded to urate.

34. Succinate $\longrightarrow$ malate $\longrightarrow$ oxaloacetate by the citric acid cycle. Oxaloacetate $\longrightarrow$ aspartate by transamination, followed by pyrimidine synthesis. Carbons 4, 5, and 6 are labeled.

35. Glucose will most likely be converted into two molecules of pyruvate, one of which will be labeled in the 2 position:

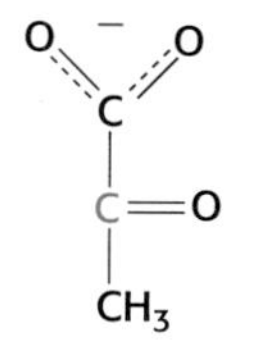

Now consider two common fates of pyruvate—conversion into acetyl CoA and subsequent processing by the citric acid cycle or carboxylation by pyruvate carboxylase to form oxaloacetate. Formation of citrate by condensing the labeled pyruvate with oxaloacetate will yield labeled citrate:

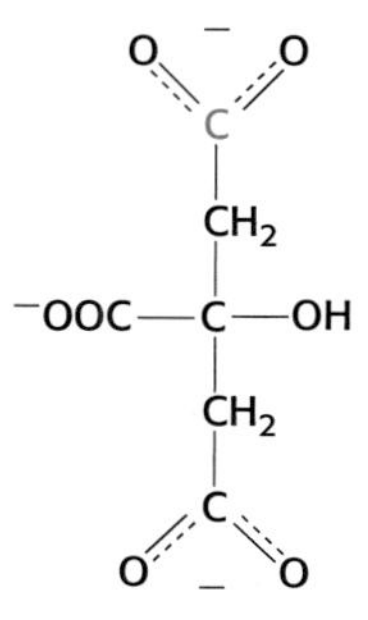

The labeled carbon will be retained through one round of the citric acid cycle but, on the formation of the symmetric succinate, the label will appear in two different positions. Thus, when succinate

is metabolized to oxaloacetate, which may be aminated to form aspartate, two carbons will be labeled:

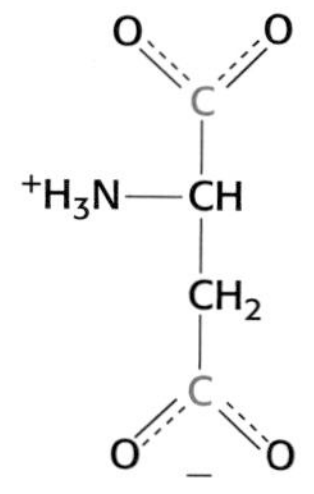

When this aspartate is used to form uracil, the labeled COO^- attached to the α-carbon is lost and the other COO^- becomes incorporated into uracil as carbon 4.

Suppose, instead, that labeled 2-[^{14}C]pyruvate is carboxylated to form oxaloacetate and processed to form aspartate. In this case, the α-carbon of aspartate bears the label.

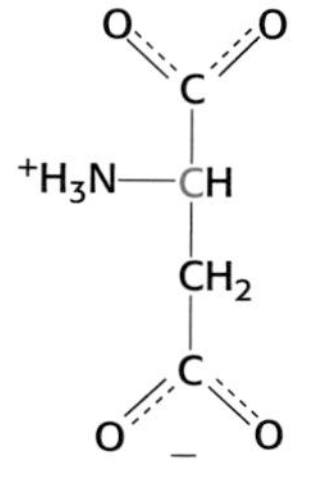

When this aspartate is used to synthesize uracil, carbon 6 bears the label.

36. (a) Some ATP can be salvaged from the ADP that is being generated. (b) There are equal numbers of high-phosphoryl-transfer-potential groups on each side of the equation. (c) Because the adenylate kinase reaction is at equilibrium, the removal of AMP would lead to the formation of more ATP. (d) Essentially, the cycle serves as an anaplerotic reaction for the generation of the citric acid cycle intermediate fumarate.

37. (i) The formation of 5-aminoididazole-4-carboxamide ribonucleotide from 5-aminoimidazole-4-(N-succinylcarboxamide) ribonucleotide in the synthesis of IMP. (ii) The formation of AMP from adenylosuccinate. (iii) The formation of arginine from argininosuccinate in the urea cycle.

38. Allopurinol is an inhibitor of xanthine oxidase, which is on the pathway for urate synthesis. In your pet duck, this pathway is the means by which excess nitrogen is excreted. If xanthine oxidase were inhibited in your duck, nitrogen could not be excreted, with severe consequences such as the formation of a dead duck.

Chapter 26

1. Glycerol 3-phosphate is the foundation for both triacylglycerol and phospholipid synthesis. Glycerol 3-phosphate is acylated twice to form phosphatidate. In triacylglycerol synthesis, the phosphoryl group is removed from glycerol 3-phosphate to form diacylglycerol, which is then acylated to form triacylglycerol. In phospholipid synthesis, phosphatidate commonly reacts with CTP to form CDP-diacylglycerol, which then reacts with an alcohol to form a phospholipid. Alternatively, diacylglycerol may react with a CDP-alcohol to form a phospholipid.

2. Glycerol 3-phosphate is formed primarily by the reduction of dihydroxyacetone phosphate, a gluconeogenic intermediate, and to a lesser extent by the phosphorylation of glycerol.

3. Glycerol + 4 ATP + 3 fatty acids + 4 H_2O → triacylglycerol + ADP + 3 AMP + 7 P_i + 4 H^+.

4. Glycerol + 3 ATP + 2 fatty acids + 2 H_2O + CTP + ethanolamine → phosphatidylethanolamine + CMP + ADP + 2 AMP + 6 P_i + 3 H^+.

5. Three. One molecule of ATP to form phosphorylethanolamine and two molecules of ATP to regenerate CTP from CMP.

6. All are synthesized from ceramide. In sphingomyelin, the terminal hydroxyl group of ceramide is modified with phosphorylcholine. In a cerebroside, the hydroxyl group has a glucose or galactose attached. In a ganglioside, oligosaccharide chains are attached to the hydroxyl group.

7. (i) Activate the diacylglycerol as CDP-DAG. (ii) Activate the alcohol as CDP-alcohol. (iii) Use the base-exchange reaction.

8. (a) CDP-diacylglycerol; (b) CDP-ethanolamine; (c) acyl CoA; (d) phosphatidylcholine; (e) UDP-glucose or UDP-galactose; (f) UDP-galactose; (g) geranyl pyrophosphate.

9. Such mutations are seen in mice. The amount of adipose tissue would decrease severely because diacylglycerol could not be formed. Normally, diacylglycerol is acylated to form triacylglycerols. If there were deficient phosphatidic acid phosphatase activity, no triacylglycerols would form.

10. (i) The synthesis of activated isoprene units (isopentyl pyrophosphate), (ii) the condensation of six of the activated isoprene units to form squalene, and (iii) cyclization of the squalene to form cholesterol.

11. The amount of reductase and its activity control the regulation of cholesterol biosynthesis. Transcriptional control is mediated by SREBP. Translation of the reductase mRNA also is controlled. The reductase itself may undergo regulated proteolysis. Finally, the activity of the reductase is inhibited by phosphorylation by AMP kinase when ATP levels are low.

12. (a and b) None, because the label is lost as CO_2.

13. The hallmark of this genetic disease is elevated cholesterol levels in the blood of even young children. The excess cholesterol is taken up by marcrophages, which eventually results in the formation of plaques and heart disease. There are many mutations that cause the disease, but all result in malfunctioning of the LDL receptor.

14. The categories of mutations are: (i) no receptor is synthesized; (ii) receptors are synthesized but do not reach the plasma membrane, because they lack signals for intracellular transport or do not fold properly; (iii) receptors reach the cell surface, but they fail to bind LDL normally because of a defect in the LDL-binding domain; (iv) receptors reach the cell surface and bind LDL, but they fail to cluster in coated pits because of a defect in their carboxyl-terminal regions.

15. "None of your business" and "I don't talk biochemistry until after breakfast" are appropriate but rude and uninformative answers. A better answer might be: "Although it is true that cholesterol is a precursor to steroid hormones, the rest of the statement is oversimplified. Cholesterol is a component of membranes, and membranes literally define cells, and cells make up tissues. But to say that cholesterol 'makes' cells and tissues is wrong."

16. Statins are competitive inhibitors of HMG-CoA reductase. They are used as drugs to inhibit cholesterol synthesis in patients with high levels of cholesterol.

17. No. Cholesterol is essential for membrane function and as a precursor for bile salts and steroid hormones. The complete lack of cholesterol would be lethal.

18. Deamination of cytidine to uridine changes CAA (Gln) into UAA (stop).

19. The LDL contains apolipoprotein B-100, which binds to an LDL receptor on the cell surface in a region known as a coated pit. On binding, the complex is internalized by endocytosis to form an internal vesicle. The vesicle is separated into two components. One, with the receptor, is transported back to the cell surface and fuses with the membrane, allowing continued use of the receptor. The other vesicle fuses with lysosomes inside the cell. The cholesteryl esters are hydrolyzed, and free cholesterol is made available for cellular use. The LDL protein is hydrolyzed to free amino acids.

20. Benign prostatic hypertrophy can be treated by inhibiting 5α-reductase. Finasteride, the 4-azasteroid analog of dihydrotestosterone, competitively inhibits the reductase but does not act on androgen receptors. Patients taking finasteride have a markedly lower plasma level of dihydrotestosterone and a nearly normal level of testosterone. The prostate gland becomes smaller, whereas testosterone-dependent processes such as fertility, libido, and muscle strength appear to be unaffected.

Finasteride

21. Patients who are most sensitive to debrisoquine have a deficiency of a liver P450 enzyme encoded by a member of the *CYP2* subfamily. This characteristic is inherited as an autosomal recessive trait. The capacity to degrade other drugs may be impaired in people who hydroxylate debrisoquine at a slow rate, because a single P450 enzyme usually handles a broad range of substrates.

22. Many hydrophobic odorants are deactivated by hydroxylation. Molecular oxygen is activated by a cytochrome P450 monooxygenase. NADPH serves as the reductant. One oxygen atom of O_2 goes into the odorant substrate, whereas the other is reduced to water.

23. Recall that dihydrotestosterone is crucial for the development of male characteristics in the embryo. If a pregnant woman were to be exposed to Propecia, the 5α-reductase of the male embryo would be inhibited, which could result in severe developmental abnormalities.

24. The oxygenation reactions catalyzed by the cytochrome P450 family permit greater flexibility in biosynthesis. Because plants are not mobile, they must rely on physical defenses, such as thorns, and chemical defenses, such as toxic alkaloids. The larger P450 array might permit greater biosynthetic versatility.

25. This knowledge would enable clinicians to characterize the likelihood of a patient's having an adverse drug reaction or being susceptible to chemical-induced illnesses. It would also permit a personalized and especially effective drug-treatment regime for diseases such as cancer.

26. The honey bees may be especially sensitive to environmental toxins, including pesticides, because these chemicals are not readily detoxified, owing to the minimal P450 system.

27. The core structure of a steroid is four fused rings: three cyclohexane rings and one cyclopentane ring. In vitamin D, the B ring is split by ultraviolet light.

28. The negatively charged phosphoserine residue interacts with the positively charged protonated histidine residue and decreases its ability to transfer a proton to the thiolate.

His

29. The methyl group is first hydroxylated. The hydroxymethyl-amine eliminated formaldehyde to form methylamine.

30. Note that a cytidine nucleotide plays the same role in the synthesis of these phosphoglycerides as a uridine nucleotide does in the formation of glycogen (Section 21.4). In all of these biosyntheses, an activated intermediate (UDP-glucose, CDP-diacylglycerol, or CDP-alcohol) is formed from a phosphorylated substrate (glucose 1-phosphate, phosphatidate, or a phosphorylalcohol) and a nucleoside triphosphate (UTP or CTP). The activated intermediate then reacts with a hydroxyl group (the terminus of glycogen, the side chain of serine, or a diacylglycerol).

31. The attachment of isoprenoid side chains confers hydrophobic character. Proteins having such a modification are targeted to membranes.

32. 3-Hydroxy-3-methylglutaryl CoA is also a precursor for ketone-body synthesis. If fuel is needed elsewhere in the body, as might be the case during a fast, 3-hydroxy-3-methylglutaryl CoA is converted into the ketone acetoacetate. If energy needs are met, the liver will synthesize cholesterol.

33. One way in which phosphatidylcholine can be synthesized is by the addition of three methyl groups to phosphatidylethanolamine. The methyl donor is a modified form of methionine, S-adenosylmethionine or SAM (Section 24.2).

34. Citrate is transported out of the mitochondria in times of plenty. ATP-citrate lyase yields acetyl CoA and oxaloacetate. The acetyl CoA can then be used to synthesize cholesterol.

35. (a) There is no effect. (b) Because actin is not controlled by cholesterol, the amount isolated should be the same in both experimental groups; a difference would suggest a problem in the RNA isolation. (c) The presence of cholesterol in the diet dramatically reduces the amount of HMG-CoA reductase protein. (d) A common means of regulating the amount of a protein present is to regulate transcription, which is clearly not the case here. (e) The translation of mRNA could be inhibited, and the protein could be rapidly degraded.

Chapter 27

1. Adipose tissue is now known to be an active endocrine organ, secreting signal molecules called adipokines.

2. Caloric homeostasis is the condition in which the energy expenditure of an organism is equal to the energy intake.

3. Leptin and insulin

4. CCK produces a feeling of satiety and stimulates the secretion of digestive enzymes by the pancreas and the secretion of bile salts by the gall bladder. GLP-1 also produces a feeling of satiety; in addition, it potentiates the glucose-induced secretion of insulin by the β cells of the pancreas.

5. Obviously, something is amiss. Although the answer is not known, the leptin-signaling pathway appears to be inhibited by suppressors of cytokine signaling, the regulatory proteins.

6. 1: a, b; 2: f; 3: c, d, f; 4: c, d; 5: c; 6: f; 7: e; 8: e; 9: e.

7. Phosphorylation of dietary glucose after it enters the liver; gluconeogenesis; glycogen breakdown.

8. Type 1 diabetes is due to autoimmune destruction of the insulin-producing cells of the pancreas. Type 1 diabetes is also called insulin-dependent diabetes because affected people require insulin to survive. Type 2 diabetes is characterized by insulin resistance. Insulin is produced, but the tissues that should respond to insulin, such as muscle, do not.

9. Leptin stimulates processes impaired in diabetes. For instance, leptin stimulates fatty acid oxidation, inhibits triacylglycerol synthesis, and increases the sensitivity of muscle and the liver to insulin.

10. (a) A watt is equal to 1 joule (J) per second (0.239 calorie per second). Hence, 70 W is equivalent to 0.07 kJ s^{-1} ($0.017 \text{ kcal s}^{-1}$). (b) A watt is a current of 1 ampere (A) across a potential of 1 volt (V). For simplicity, let us assume that all the electron flow is from NADH to O_2 (a potential drop of 1.14 V). Hence, the current is 61.4 A, which corresponds to 3.86×10^{20} electrons per second ($1 \text{ A} = 1 \text{ coulomb s}^{-1} = 6.28 \times 10^{18} \text{ charge s}^{-1}$). (c) About 2.5 molecules of ATP are formed per molecule of NADH oxidized (two electrons). Hence, 1 molecule of ATP is formed per 0.8 electron transferred. A flow of 3.86×10^{20} electrons per second therefore leads to the generation of 4.83×10^{20} molecules of ATP per second, or 0.80 mmol s^{-1}. (d) The molecular weight of ATP is 507. The total body content of ATP of 50 g is equal to 0.099 mol. Hence, ATP turns over about once in 125 seconds when the body is at rest.

11. (a) The stoichiometry of the complete oxidation of glucose is

$$C_6H_{12}O_6 + 6 O_2 \longrightarrow 6 CO_2 + 6 H_2O$$

and that of tripalmitoylglycerol is

$$C_{51}H_{98}O_2 + 72.5 O_2 \longrightarrow 51 CO_2 + 49 H_2O$$

Hence, the RQ values are 1.0 and 0.703, respectively. (b) An RQ value reveals the relative use of carbohydrates and fats as fuels. The RQ of a marathon runner typically decreases from 0.97 to 0.77 in the course of a race. The lowering of the RQ indicates the shift in fuel from carbohydrates to fat.

12. One gram of glucose (molecular weight 180.2) is equal to 5.55 mmol, and one gram of tripalmitoylglycerol (molecular weight 807.3) is equal to 1.24 mmol. The reaction stoichiometries (see Problem 11) indicate that 6 mol of H_2O is produced per mole of glucose oxidized, and 49 mol of H_2O is produced per mole of tripalmitoylglycerol oxidized. Hence, the H_2O yields per gram of fuel are 33.3 mmol (0.6 g) for glucose and 60.8 mmol (1.09 g) for tripalmitoylglycerol. Thus, complete oxidation of this fat gives 1.82 times as much water as does glucose. Another advantage of triacylglycerols is that they can be stored in essentially anhydrous form, whereas glucose is stored as glycogen, a highly hydrated polymer. A hump consisting mainly of glycogen would be an intolerable burden—far more than the straw that broke the camel's back.

13. The starved–fed cycle is the nightly hormonal cycle that humans experience during sleep and on eating. The cycle maintains adequate amounts of blood glucose. The starved part—sleep—is characterized by increased glucagon secretion and decreased insulin secretion. After a meal, glucagon concentration falls and insulin concentration rises.

14. Ethanol is oxidized to yield acetaldehyde by alcohol dehydrogenase, which is subsequently oxidized to acetate acetaldehyde. Ethanol is also metabolized to acetaldehyde by the MEOS, with the subsequent depletion of NADPH.

15. First, fatty liver develops owing to the increased amounts of NADH that inhibit fatty acid oxidation and stimulate fatty acid

synthesis. Second, alcoholic hepatitis begins owing to oxidative damage and damage due to excess acetaldehyde that results in cell death. Finally, fibrous tissues form, creating scars that impair blood flow and biochemical function. Ammonia cannot be converted into urea, and its toxicity leads to coma and death.

16. A typical macadamia nut has a mass of about 2 g. Because it consists mainly of fats ($\sim$37 kJ g^{-1}, $\sim$9 kcal g^{-1}), a nut has a value of about 75 kJ (18 kcal). The ingestion of 10 nuts results in an intake of about 753 kJ (180 kcal). As stated in the answer to Problem 10, a power consumption of 1 W corresponds to 1 J s^{-1} (0.239 cal s^{-1}), and so 400-W running requires 0.4 kJ s^{-1} (0.0956 kcal s^{-1}). Hence, a person would have to run 1882 s, or about 31 minutes, to spend the calories provided by 10 nuts.

17. A high blood-glucose level triggers the secretion of insulin, which stimulates the synthesis of glycogen and triacylglycerols. A high insulin level would impede the mobilization of fuel reserves during the marathon.

18. A lack of adipose tissue leads to an accumulation of fats in the muscle, with the generation of insulin resistance. The experiment shows that adipokines secreted by the adipose tissue, here leptin, facilitate in some fashion the action of insulin in muscle.

19. Such a mutation would increase the phosphorylation of the insulin receptor and IRS in muscle and would improve insulin sensitivity. Indeed, PTP1B is an attractive therapeutic target for type 2 diabetes.

20. Lipid mobilization can be so rapid that it exceeds the ability of the liver to oxidize the lipids or convert them into ketone bodies. The excess is reesterified and released into the blood as VLDLs.

21. A role of the liver is to provide glucose for other tissues. In the liver, glycolysis is used not for energy production but for biosynthetic purposes. Consequently, in the presence of glucagon, liver glycolysis stops so that the glucose can be released into the blood.

22. The urea cycle and gluconeogenesis

23. (a) Insulin inhibits lipid utilization.
(b) Insulin stimulates protein synthesis, but there are no amino acids in the children's diet. Moreover, insulin inhibits protein breakdown. Consequently, muscle proteins cannot be broken down and used for the synthesis of essential proteins.
(c) Because proteins cannot be synthesized, blood osmolarity is too low. Consequently, fluid leaves the blood. An especially important protein for maintaining blood osmolarity is albumin.

24. During strenuous exercise, muscle converts glucose into pyruvate through glycolysis. Some of the pyruvate is processed by cellular respiration. However, some of it is converted into lactate and released into the blood. The liver takes up the lactate and converts it into glucose through gluconeogenesis. Muscle may process the carbon skeletons of branched-chain amino acids aerobically. The nitrogens of these amino acids are transferred to pyruvate to form alanine, which is released into the blood and taken up by the liver. After the transamination of the amino group to α-ketoglutarate, the resulting pyruvate is converted into glucose. Finally, muscle glycogen may be mobilized, and the released glucose can be used by muscle.

25. This conversion allows muscle to function anaerobically. NAD$^+$ is regenerated when pyruvate is reduced to lactate, and so energy can continue to be extracted from glucose during strenuous exercise. The liver converts the lactate into glucose.

26. Fatty acids and glucose, respectively.

27. This practice is called carbo-loading. Depleting the glycogen stores will initially cause the muscles to synthesis a large amount of glycogen when dietary carbohydrates are provided and will lead to the supercompensation of glycogen stores.

28. The oxygen consumption at the end of exercise is used to replenish ATP and creatine phosphate and to oxidize any lactate produced.

29. Oxygen is used in oxidative phosphorylation to resynthesize ATP and creatine phosphate. The liver converts lactate released by the muscle into glucose. Blood must be circulated to return the body temperature to normal, and so the heart cannot return to its resting rate immediately. Hemoglobin must be reoxygenated to replace the oxygen used in exercise. The muscles that power breathing must continue working at the same time as the exercised muscles are returning to resting states. In essence, all the biochemical systems activated in intense exercise need increased oxygen to return to the resting state.

30. Ethanol may replace water that is hydrogen bonded to proteins and membrane surfaces. This alteration of the hydration state of the protein would alter its conformation and hence function. Ethanol may also alter phospholipid packing in membranes. The two effects suggest that integral membrane proteins would be most sensitive to ethanol, as indeed seems to be the case.

31. Cells from the type I fiber would be rich in mitochondria, whereas those of the type II fiber would have few mitochondria.

32. (a) The ATP expended during this race amounts to about 8380 kg, or 18,400 pounds. (b) The cyclist would need about $1,260,000,000 to complete the race.

33. 55 pounds = 25 kg = 25,000 g = total weight gain

40 years × 365 days year^{-1} = 14,600 days

25,000 g/14,600 days = 1.7 g day^{-1}

which is equivalent to an extra pat of butter per day. Her BMI is 26.5, and she would be considered overweight but not obese.

34. Exercise greatly enhances the ATP needs of muscle cells. To more efficiently meet these needs, more mitochondria are synthesized.

35. The inability of muscle mitochondria to process all of the fatty acids produced by overnutrition leads to excessive levels of diacylglycerol and ceramide in the muscle cytoplasm. These second-messenger molecules activate enzymes that impair insulin signaling.

36. Both are due to a lack of thiamine (vitamin B$_1$). Thiamine, which is sometimes called aneurin, is required most notably for the proper functioning of pyruvate dehydrogenase.

37. (a) Red blood cells always produce lactate, and fast-twitch muscle fibers (see Problem 31) also produce a large amount of lactate.
(b) At that point, the athlete is beginning to move into anaerobic exercise, in which most energy is produced by anaerobic glycolysis.
(c) The lactate threshold is essentially the point at which the athlete switches from aerobic exercise, which can be done for extended periods, to anaerobic exercise, essentially sprinting, which can be done for only short periods. The idea is to race at the extreme of his or her aerobic capacity until the finish line is in sight and then to switch to anaerobic.
(d) Training increases the amount of blood vessels and the number of muscle mitochondria. Together, they increase the ability to process glucose aerobically. Consequently, a greater effort can be expended before the switch to anaerobic energy production.

Chapter 28

1. DNA polymerase I uses deoxyribonucleoside triphosphates; pyrophosphate is the leaving group. DNA ligase uses DNA–adenylate (AMP joined to the 5′-phosphoryl group) as a reaction partner; AMP is the leaving group. Topoisomerase I uses a DNA–tyrosyl intermediate (5′-phosphoryl group linked to the phenolic OH group); the tyrosine residue of the enzyme is the leaving group.

2. Positive supercoiling resists the unwinding of DNA. The melting temperature of DNA increases in proceeding from negatively supercoiled to relaxed to positively supercoiled DNA. Positive supercoiling is probably an adaptation to high temperature.

3. The nucleotides used for DNA synthesis have the triphosphate attached to the 5′-hydroxyl group with free 3′-hydroxyl groups. Such nucleotides can be utilized only for 5′-to-3′ DNA synthesis.
4. DNA replication requires RNA primers. Without appropriate ribonucleotides, such primers cannot be synthesized.
5. This close contact prevents the incorporation of ribonucleotides rather than 2′-deoxyribonucleotides.
6. (a) 96.2 revolutions per second (1000 nucleotides per second divided by 10.4 nucleotides per turn for B-DNA gives 96.2 rps). (b) 0.34 μm s^{-1} (1000 nucleotides per second corresponds to 3400 Å s^{-1} because the axial distance between nucleotides in B-DNA is 3.4 Å).
7. Eventually, the DNA would become so tightly wound that movement of the replication complex would be energetically impossible.
8. Linking number $Lk = Tw + Wr = 48 + 3 = 51$. If $Tw = 50$, the $Wr = 1$.
9. A hallmark of most cancer cells is prolific cell division, which requires DNA replication. If the telomerase were not activated, the chromosomes would shorten until they became nonfunctional, leading to cell death.
10. No.
11. Treat the DNA briefly with endonuclease to occasionally nick each strand. Add the polymerase with the radioactive dNTPs. At the broken bond, or nick, the polymerase will degrade the existing strand with its 5′ ⟶ 3′ exonuclease activity and replace it with a radioactive complementary copy by using its polymerase activity. This reaction scheme is referred to as nick translation because the nick is moved, or translated, along the DNA molecule without ever becoming sealed.
12. If replication were unidirectional, tracks with a low grain density at one end and a high grain density at the other end would be seen. On the other hand, if replication were bidirectional, the middle of a track would have a low density, as shown in the diagram below. For *E. coli*, the grain tracks are denser on both ends than in the middle, indicating that replication is bidirectional.

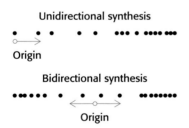

13. (a) Pro (CCC), Ser (UCC), Leu (CUC), and Phe (UUC). Alternatively, the last base of each of these codons could be U.
(b) Nitrous acid.
14. Potentially deleterious side reactions are prevented. The enzyme itself might be damaged by light if it could be activated by light in the absence of bound DNA harboring a pyrimidine dimer.
15. The free DNA ends that appear in the absence of telomeres are repaired by DNA fusion.
16. The free energy of ATP hydrolysis under standard conditions is -30.5 kJ mol^{-1} (-7.3 kcal mol^{-1}). In principle, it could be used to break three base pairs.
17. The oxidation of guanine could lead to DNA repair: DNA strand cleavage could allow looping out of the triplet repeat regions and triplet expansion.

18. The release of DNA topoisomerase II after the enzyme has acted on its DNA substrate requires ATP hydrolysis. Negative supercoiling requires only the binding of ATP, not its hydrolysis.
19. (a) Size; the top is relaxed and the bottom is supercoiled DNA. (b) Topoisomers. (c) The DNA is becoming progressively more unwound, or relaxed, and thus slower moving.
20. (a) It was used to determine the number of spontaneous revertants—that is, the background mutation rate.
(b) To firmly establish that the system was working. A known mutagen's failure to produce revertants would indicate that something was wrong with the experimental system.
(c) The chemical itself has little mutagenic ability but is apparently activated into a mutagen by the liver homogenate.
(d) Cytochrome P450 system.

Chapter 29
1. The sequence of the coding (+, sense) strand is

5′-ATGGGGAACAGCAAGAGTGGGGCCCTGTCCAAGGAG-3′

and the sequence of template (−, antisense) strand is

3′-TACCCCTTGTCGTTCTCACCCCGGGACAGGTTCCTC-5′

2. An error will affect only one molecule of mRNA of many synthesized from a gene. In addition, the errors do not become a permanent part of the genomic information.
3. At any given instant, only a fraction of the genome (total DNA) is being transcribed. Consequently, speed is not essential.
4. The active sites are related by convergent evolution.
5. Heparin, a glycosaminoglycan, is highly anionic. Its negative charges, like the phosphodiester bridges of DNA templates, allow it to bind to lysine and arginine residues of RNA polymerase.
6. This mutant σ will competitively inhibit the binding of holoenzyme and prevent the specific initiation of RNA chains at promoter sites.
7. The core enzyme without σ binds more tightly to the DNA template than does the holoenzyme. The retention of σ after chain initiation would make the mutant RNA polymerase less processive. Hence, RNA synthesis would be much slower than normal.
8. A 100-kd protein contains about 910 residues, which are encoded by 2730 nucleotides. At a maximal transcription rate of 50 nucleotides per second, the mRNA would be synthesized in 54.6 s.
9. The RNA polymerase slides along the DNA rapidly rather than simply diffusing through three-dimensional space.
10. The start site is in red type:

5′-GCCGTTGACACCGTTCGGCGATCGATCCGCTATAATGTGTGGATCCGCTT-3′

11. Initiation at strong promoters takes place every 2 s. In this interval, 100 nucleotides are transcribed. Hence, centers of transcription bubbles are 34 nm (340 Å) apart.
12. (a) The lowest band on the gel will be that of strand 3 alone (*i*), whereas the highest will be that of stands 1, 2, and 3 and core polymerase (*v*). Band *ii* will be at the same position as band *i* because the RNA is not complementary to the nontemplate strand, whereas band *iii* will be higher because a complex is formed between RNA and the template strand. Band *iv* will be higher than the others because strand 1 is complexed to 2, and strand 2 is complexed to 3. Band *v* is the highest because core polymerase associates with the three strands.
(b) None, because rifampicin acts before the formation of the open complex.

(c) RNA polymerase is processive. When the template is bound, heparin cannot enter the DNA-binding site.
(d) When GTP is absent, synthesis stops when the first cytosine residue downstream of the bubble is encountered in the template strand. In contrast, with all four nucleoside triphosphates present, synthesis will continue to the end of the template.
13. RNA polymerase must backtrack before cleavage, leading to dinucleotide products.
14. The base-pairing energy of the di- and trinucleotide DNA–RNA hybrids formed at the very beginning of transcription is not sufficient to prevent strand separation and loss of product.
15. (a) Because cordycepin lacks a 3'-OH group, it cannot participate in $3' \longrightarrow 5'$ bond formation. (b) Because the poly(A) tail is a long stretch of adenosine nucleotides, the likelihood that a molecule of cordycepin would become incorporated is higher than with most RNA. (c) Yes, it must be converted into cordycepin 5'-triphosphate.
16. There are $2^8 = 256$ possible products.
17. The relation between the -10 and -35 sequences could be affected by torsional strain. The fact that topoisomerase II introduces negative supercoils in DNA prevents this enzyme from overstimulating the expression of its own gene.
18. Ser-Ile-Phe-His-Pro-Stop
19. A mutation that disrupted the normal AAUAAA recognition sequence for the endonuclease could account for this finding. In fact, a change from U to C in this sequence caused this defect in a thalassemic patient. Cleavage was at the AAUAAA 900 nucleotides downstream of this mutant AACAAA site.
20. One possibility is that the 3' end of the poly(U) donor strand cleaves the phosphodiester bond on the 5' side of the insertion site. The newly formed 3' terminus of the acceptor strand then cleaves the poly(U) strand on the 5' side of the nucleotide that initiated the attack. In other words, a uridine residue could be added by two transesterification reactions. This postulated mechanism is similar to the one in RNA splicing.
21. Alternative splicing and RNA editing. Covalent modification of the proteins subsequent to synthesis further enhances the complexity.
22. Attach an oligo(dT) or oligo(U) sequence to an inert support to create an affinity column. When RNA is passed through the column, only poly(A)-containing RNA will be retained.
23. (a) Different amounts of RNA are present for the various genes.
(b) Although all of the tissues have the same genes, the genes are expressed to different extents in different tissues.
(c) These genes are called housekeeping genes—genes that most tissues express. They might include genes for glycolysis or citric acid cycle enzymes.
(d) The point of the experiment is to determine which genes are initiated in vivo. The initiation inhibitor is added to prevent initiation at start sites that may have been activated during the isolation of the nuclei.
24. DNA is the single strand that forms the trunk of the tree. Strands of increasing length are RNA molecules; the beginning of transcription is where growing chains are the smallest; the end of transcription is where chain growth stops. Direction is left to right. Many enzymes are actively transcribing each gene.

Chapter 30

1. The Oxford English Dictionary defines translation as the action or process of turning from one language into another. Protein synthesis converts nucleic acid sequence information into amino acid sequence information.
2. An error frequency of 1 incorrect amino acid every 10^4 incorporations allows for the rapid and accurate synthesis of proteins as large as 1000 amino acids. Higher error rates would result in too many defective proteins. Lower error rates would likely slow the rate of protein synthesis without a significant gain in accuracy.
3. (i) Each is a single chain. (ii) They contain unusual bases. (iii) Approximately half of the bases are base-paired to form double helices. (iv) The 5' end is phosphorylated and is usually pG. (v) The amino acid is attached to the hydroxyl group of the A residue of the CCA sequence at the 3' end of the tRNA. (vi) The anticodon is located in a loop near the center of the tRNA sequence. (vii) The molecules are L-shaped.
4. First is the formation of the aminoacyl adenylate, which then reacts with the tRNA to form the aminoacyl-tRNA. Both steps are catalyzed by aminoacyl-tRNA synthetase.
5. Unique features are required so that the aminoacyl-tRNA synthetases can distinguish among the tRNAs and attach the correct amino acid to the proper tRNA. Common features are required because all tRNAs must interact with the same protein-synthesizing machinery.
6. An activated amino acid is one linked to the appropriate tRNA.
7. (a) No; (b) no; (c) yes.
8. The ATP is cleaved to AMP and PP_i. Consequently, a second ATP is required to convert AMP into ADP, the substrate for oxidative phosphorylation.
9. Amino acids larger than the correct amino acid cannot fit into the active site of the tRNA. Smaller but incorrect amino acids that become attached to the tRNA fit into the editing site and are cleaved from the tRNA.
10. Recognition sites on both faces of the tRNAs may be required to uniquely identify the 20 different tRNAs.
11. The first two bases in a codon form Watson–Crick base pairs that are checked for fidelity by bases of the 16S rRNA. The third base is not inspected for accuracy, and so some variation is tolerated.
12. Four bands: light, heavy, a hybrid of light 30S and heavy 50S, and a hybrid of heavy 30S and light 50S.
13. Two hundred molecules of ATP are converted into 200 AMP + 400 P_i to activate the 200 amino acids, which is equivalent to 400 molecules of ATP. One molecule of GTP is required for initiation, and 398 molecules of GTP are needed to form 199 peptide bonds.
14. (a, d, and e) Type 2; (b, c, and f) type 1.
15. The reading frame is a set of contiguous, nonoverlapping three-nucleotide codons that begins with a start codon and ends with a stop codon.
16. A mutation caused by the insertion of an extra base can be suppressed by a tRNA that contains a fourth base in its anticodon. For example, UUUC rather than UUU is read as the codon for phenylalanine by a tRNA that contains 3'-AAAG-5' as its anticodon.
17. One approach is to synthesize a tRNA that is acylated with a reactive amino acid analog. For example, bromoacetyl-phenylalanyl-tRNA is an affinity-labeling reagent for the P site of E. coli ribosomes.
18. The sequence GAGGU is complementary to a sequence of five bases at the 3' end of 16S rRNA and is located several bases upstream of an AUG start codon. Hence, this region is a start signal for protein synthesis. The replacement of G by A would be expected to weaken the interaction of this mRNA with the 16S rRNA and thereby diminish its effectiveness as an initiation signal. In fact, this mutation results in a 10-fold decrease in the rate of synthesis of the protein specified by this mRNA.
19. The peptide would be Phe-Cys-His-Val-Ala-Ala. The codons UGC and UGU encode cysteine but, because the

cysteine was modified to alanine, alanine is incorporated in place of cysteine.

20. Proteins are synthesized from the amino to the carboxyl end on ribosomes, whereas they are synthesized in the reverse direction in the solid-phase method. The activated intermediate in ribosomal synthesis is an aminoacyl-tRNA; in the solid-phase method, it is the adduct of the amino acid and dicyclohexylcarbodiimide.

21. The error rates of DNA, RNA, and protein synthesis are of the order of 10^{-10}, 10^{-5}, and 10^{-4}, respectively, per nucleotide (or amino acid) incorporated. The fidelity of all three processes depends on the precision of base-pairing to the DNA or mRNA template. Few errors are corrected in RNA synthesis. In contrast, the fidelity of DNA synthesis is markedly increased by the $3' \longrightarrow 5'$ proofreading nuclease activity and by postreplicative repair. In protein synthesis, the mischarging of some tRNAs is corrected by the hydrolytic action of aminoacyl-tRNA synthetase. Proofreading also takes place when aminoacyl-tRNA occupies the A site on the ribosome; the GTPase activity of EF-Tu sets the pace of this final stage of editing.

22. GTP is not hydrolyzed until aminoacyl-tRNA is delivered to the A site of the ribosome. An earlier hydrolysis of GTP would be wasteful because EF-Tu–GDP has little affinity for aminoacyl-tRNA.

23. The translation of an mRNA molecule can be blocked by antisense RNA, an RNA molecule with the complementary sequence. The antisense–sense RNA duplex cannot serve as a template for translation; single-stranded mRNA is required. Furthermore, the antisense–sense duplex is degraded by nucleases. Antisense RNA added to the external medium is spontaneously taken up by many cells. A precise quantity can be delivered by microinjection. Alternatively, a plasmid encoding the antisense RNA can be introduced into target cells.

24. (a) A_5. (b) $A_5 > A_4 > A_3 > A_2$. (c) Synthesis is from the amino terminus to the carboxyl terminus.

25. These enzymes convert nucleic acid information into protein information by interpreting the tRNA and linking it to the proper amino acid.

26. The rate would fall because the elongation step requires that the GTP be hydrolyzed before any further elongation can take place.

27. Protein factors modulate the initiation of protein synthesis. The role of IF1 and IF3 is to prevent premature binding of the 30S and 50S ribosomal subunits, whereas IF2 delivers Met-tRNA$_f$ to the ribosome. Protein factors are also required for elongation (EF-G and EF-Tu), for termination (release factors, RFs), and for ribosome dissociation (ribosome release factors, RRFs).

28. The signal sequence, signal-recognition particle (SRP), the SRP receptor, and the translocon.

29. The formation of peptide bonds, which in turn are powered by the hydrolysis of the aminoacyl-tRNAs.

30. The Shine–Dalgarno sequence of the mRNA base-pairs with a part of the 16S rRNA of the 30S subunit, which positions the subunit so that the initiator AUG is recognized.

31.

	Prokaryote	Eukaryote
Ribosome size	60S	80S
mRNA	polycistronic	Not polycistronic
Initiation	Shine–Dalgarno is required	First AUG is used
Protein factors	Required	Many more required
Relation to transcription	Translation can start before transcription is completed	Transcription and translation are spatially separated
First amino acid	fMet	Met

32. The SRP binds to the signal sequence and inhibits further translation. The SRP ushers the inhibited ribosome to the ER, where it interacts with the SRP receptor (SR). The SRP–SR complex binds the translocon and simultaneously hydrolyzes GTP. On GTP hydrolysis, SRP and SR dissociate from each other and from the ribosome. Protein synthesis resumes and the nascent protein is channeled through the translocon.

33. The alternative would be to have a single ribosome translating a single mRNA molecule. The use of polysomes allows more protein synthesis per mRNA molecule in a given period of time and thus the production of more protein.

34. (a) 1, 2, 3, 5, 6, 10; (b) 1, 2, 7, 8,; (c) 1, 4, 8, 9.

35. Transfer RNAs have roles in several recognition processes. A tRNA must be recognized by the appropriate aminoacyl-tRNA synthetase, and the tRNA must interact with the ribosome and, in particular, with the peptidyl transferase.

36. The nucleophile is the amino group of the aminoacyl-tRNA. This amino group attacks the carbonyl group of the ester of peptidyl-tRNA to form a tetrahedral intermediate, which eliminates the tRNA alcohol to form a new peptide bond.

37. The aminoacyl-tRNA can be initially synthesized. However, the side-chain amino group attacks the ester linkage to form a six-membered amide, releasing the tRNA.

38. EF-Ts catalyzes the exchange of GTP for GDP bound to EF-Tu. In G-protein cascades, an activated 7TM receptor catalyzes GTP–GDP exchange in a G protein.

39. The α subunits of G proteins are inhibited by a similar mechanism in cholera and whooping cough (Section 14.5).

40. Glu-tRNA^{Gln} is formed by misacylation. The activated glutamate is subsequently amidated to form Gln-tRNA^{Gln}. Ways in which glutamine is formed from glutamate were discussed in Section 24.2. In regard to *H. pylori*, a specific enzyme, Glu-tRNA^{Gln} amidotransferase, catalyzes the following reaction:

$$\text{Gln} + \text{Glu-tRNA}^{Gln} + \text{ATP} \longrightarrow \\ \text{Gln-tRNA}^{Gln} + \text{glu} + \text{ADP} + P_i$$

Glu-tRNA^{Glu} is not a substrate for the enzyme; so the transferase must also recognize aspects of the structure of tRNA^{Gln}.

41. The primary structure determines the three-dimensional structure of the protein. Thus, the final phase of information transfer from DNA to RNA to protein synthesis is the folding of the protein into its functional state.

42. (a) eIF-4H has two effects: (1) the extent of unwinding is increased and (2) the rate of unwinding is increased, as indicated by the increased rise in activity at early reaction times. (b) To firmly establish that the effect of eIF-H4 was not due to any inherent helicase activity. (c) Half-maximal activity was achieved at 0.11 μM of eIF-4H. Therefore, maximal stimulation would be achieved at a ratio of 1:1. (d) eIF-4H enhances the rate of unwinding of all helices, but the effect is greater as the helices increase in stability. (e) The results in graph C suggest that eIF-4H increases the processivity.

43. (a) The three peaks represent, from left to right, the 40S ribosomal subunit, the 60S ribosomal subunit, and the 80S ribosome. (b) Not only are ribosomal subunits and the 80S ribosome present, but polysomes of various lengths also are apparent. The individual peaks in the polysome region represent polysomes of discrete length. (c) The treatment significantly inhibited the number of polysomes while increasing the number of free ribosomal subunits. This outcome could be due to inhibited protein-synthesis initiation or inhibited transcription.

Chapter 31

1. (a) Cells will express β-galactosidase, *lac* permease, and thiogalactoside transacetylase even in the absence of lactose. (b) Cells will express β-galactosidase, *lac* permease, and thiogalactoside transacetylase even in the absence of lactose. (c) The levels of catabolic enzymes such as β-galactosidase and arabinose isomerase will remain low even at low levels of glucose.

2. The concentration is $1/(6 \times 10^{23})$ moles per 10^{-15} liter $= 1.7 \times 10^{-9}$ M. Because $K_d = 10^{-13}$ M, the single molecule should be bound to its specific binding site.

3. The number of possible 8-bp sites is $4^8 = 65{,}536$. In a genome of 4.6×10^6 base pairs, the average site should appear $(4.6 \times 10^6)/65{,}536 = 70$ times. Each 10-bp site should appear 4 times. Each 12-bp site should appear 0.27 times (many 12-bp sites will not appear at all).

4. The *lac* repressor does not bind DNA when the repressor is bound to a small molecule (the inducer), whereas the *pur* repressor binds DNA only when the repressor is bound to a small molecule (the corepressor). The *E. coli* genome contains only a single *lac* repressor-binding region, whereas it has many sites for the *pur* repressor

5. Anti-inducers bind to the conformation of repressors, such as the *lac* repressor, that are capable of binding DNA. They occupy a site that overlaps that for the inducer and, therefore, compete for binding to the repressor.

6. The inverted repeat may be a binding site for a dimeric DNA-binding protein or it may correspond to a stem-loop structure in the encoded RNA.

7. Bacteriophage λ would be more likely to enter the lytic phase because the cooperative binding of the λ repressor to O_R2 and O_R1, which supports the lysogenic pathway, would be disrupted.

8. λ repressor gene −10 region GATTTA −35 region TAGATA
   Cro gene −10 region TAATGG −35 region TTGACT
There are four differences in the −10 region and three differences in the −35 region.

9. Increased Cro concentration reduces the expression of the λ repressor gene. Increased λ repressor concentration reduces the expression of the Cro gene. At low λ repressor concentration, increased λ repressor concentration increases the expression of the λ repressor gene. At higher λ repressor concentrations, increased λ repressor concentration decreases the expression of the λ repressor gene.

10. Normally, bacterial mRNAs have a leader sequence in which a Shine–Delgarno sequence precedes the AUG start codon. The absence of a leader would be expected to lead to inefficient translation.

11. Add each compound to a culture of *V. fischeri* at low density and look for the development of luminescence.

12. ACC, 7; ACA, 1, ACU, 0; ACG, 0.

13. The reaction takes place with overall retention of configuration. Each step likely takes place with inversion of configuration, which suggests that the reaction consists of two (or some other even number of) steps. A possible mechanism is nucleophilic attack by the carboxylate group of Glu 537 on the C-1 carbon atom of the galactose moiety within glucose, releasing glucose and forming an intermediate with the galactose linked to the enzyme through an ester linkage. Water then attacks this carbon atom, displacing the glutamate carboxylate and releasing galactose.

14. The binding appears to be half complete at a concentration of λ repressor near 3.7 nM. Thus, K_d is approximately 3.7 nM and $\Delta G° = -48$ kJ/mol (-11 kcal/mol) at 298 K.

Chapter 32

1. The distribution of charged amino acids is H2A (13 K, 13 R, 2 D, 7 E, charge $= +17$), H2B (20 K, 8 R, 3 D, 7 E, charge $= +18$), H3 (13 K, 18 R, 4 D, 7 E, charge $= +20$), H4 (11 K, 14 R, 3 D, 4 E, charge $= +18$). The total charge of the histone octamer is estimated to be $2 \times (17 + 18 + 20 + 18) = +146$. The total charge on 150 base pairs of DNA is -300. Thus, the histone octamer neutralizes approximately one-half of the charge.

2. The presence of a particular DNA fragment could be detected by hybridization, by PCR, or by direct sequencing.

3. The total length of the DNA is estimated to be 145 bp $\times$ 3.4 Å/bp $= 493$ Å, which represents 1.75 turns or $1.75 \times 2\pi r = 11.0r$. Thus, the radius is estimated to be $r = 493$ Å$/11.0 = 44.8$ Å.

4. 5-Azacytidine cannot be methylated. Some genes, normally repressed by methylation, will be active.

5. Proteins containing these domains will be targeted to methylated DNA in repressed promoter regions. They would likely bind in the major groove because that is where the methyl group is located.

6. Gene expression is not expected to respond to the presence of estrogen. However, genes for which expression normally responds to estrogen will respond to the presence of progesterone.

7. The acetylation of lysine will reduce the charge from $+1$ to 0. The methylation of lysine will not reduce the charge.

8. On the basis of the pattern of cysteine and histidine residues, this region appears to contain three zinc-finger domains.

9. $10/4000 = 0.25\%$. 0.25% of 12 Mb $=$ 30 kilobase pairs.

10. The addition of an IRE to the 5′ end of the mRNA is expected to block translation in the absence of iron. The addition of an IRE to the 3′ end of the mRNA is not expected to block translation, but it might affect mRNA stability.

11. The sequences of all of the mRNAs would be searched for sequences that are fully or nearly complementary to the sequence of the miRNA. These sequences would be candidates for regulation by this mRNA.

12. The amino group of the lysine residue, formed from the protonated form by a base, attacks the carbonyl group of acetyl CoA to generate a tetrahedral intermediate. This intermediate collapses to form the amide bond and release CoA.

13. In mouse DNA, most of the *Hpa*II sites are methylated and therefore not cut by the enzyme, resulting in large fragments. Some small fragments are produced from CpG islands that are unmethylated. For *Drosophila* and *E. coli* DNA, there is no methylation and all sites are cut.

Chapter 33

1. The transgenic nematode would avoid the compound. The identity of the ligand is determined by the receptor, whereas the behavioral response is dictated by the neuron in which the receptor is expressed.

2. Only a mixture of compounds C_5-COOH and HOOC-C_7-COOH is predicted to yield this pattern.

3. Bitter and sweet sensations are mediated by G proteins coupled to 7TM receptors, leading to millisecond time resolution. Salty and sour sensations are mediated directly by ion channels, which may lead to faster time resolution.

4. Sound travels 0.15 m in 428 μs. The human hearing system is capable of sensing time differences of close to a microsecond, and so the difference in arrival times at the two ears is substantial. A system based on G proteins is unlikely to be able to reliably distinguish between signals arriving at the two ears, because G proteins typically respond in milliseconds.

5. If a plant tastes bitter, animals will avoid eating it even if it is nontoxic, which may provide a selective advantage to the plant.

6. Using mice in which either the gene for T1R1 or the gene for T1R3 has been disrupted, test the taste responses of these mice to glutamate, aspartate, and a wide variety of other amino acids.

7. These women have four functional color receptors: blue, red, green, and a red–green hybrid. The additional color receptor allows some colors that appear identical to most people to be distinguished.

8. 380 (one for each receptor); there are $(380 \times 379)/2! = 72{,}010$ combinations of two receptors; $(380 \times 379 \times 378)/3! = 9{,}073{,}260$ combinations of three receptors.

9. The absorption of light converts 11-*cis*-retinal into all-*trans*-retinal.

10. These compounds are enantiomers and must bind to protein receptors to elicit a smell. Even these subtle structural differences can affect relative receptor binding affinities and, hence, the elicited odor.

11. Vision: cGMP-gated channel; taste: amiloride-sensitive sodium channel; hearing; tip-link channel.

12. For all senses, ATP hydrolysis is required to generate and maintain ion gradients and membrane potential. Olfaction: ATP is required for the synthesis of cAMP. Gustation: ATP is required for the synthesis of cyclic nucleotides, and GTP is required for the action of gustducin in the detection of bitter and sweet tastes. Vision: GTP is required for the synthesis of cGMP and for the action of transducin. Hearing and touch: ATP hydrolysis is required to generate and maintain ion gradients and membrane potential and may be required for other roles as well.

13.

Chapter 34

1. The innate immune system responds rapidly to common features present in many pathogens. The genes for the innate immune system's key molecules are expressed without substantial modification. In contrast, the adaptive immune system responds to specific features present only in a given pathogen. Its genes undergo significant rearrangement and mutation to enable specific recognition of a vast number of potential binding surfaces.

2. VJ and V(D)J recombination; variability in segment joining by the action of terminal deoxyribonucleotidyl transferase; somatic mutation.

3. *Affinity* refers to the strength of a single interaction; avidity refers to the cumulative strength of multiple independent binding interactions. *Avidity* may play a significant role in the interaction between IgM and antigen because this immunoglobulin class features 10 binding sites.

4. The intracellular signaling domain common to each of the TLRs is responsible for docking other proteins and reporting that a targeted pathogen-associated molecular pattern (PAMP), such as LPS, has been detected. If a mutation within this domain interfered with the intracellular docking and signal transduction, then TLR-4 would not respond to LPS.

5. Viruses that contain dsRNA genomes would be expected to stimulate a TLR-3-mediated immune response.

6. (a) $\Delta G^{\circ\prime} = -37$ kJ mol^{-1} (-8.9 kcal mol^{-1})
(b) $K_a = 3.3 \times 10^6$ M^{-1}
(c) $k_{on} = 4 \times 10^8$ M^{-1} s^{-1}. This value is close to the diffusion-controlled limit for the combination of a small molecule with a

protein (see p. 245). Hence, the extent of structural change is likely to be small; extensive conformational transitions take time.

7. The fluorescence enhancement and the shift to blue indicate that water is largely excluded from the combining site when the hapten is bound. Hydrophobic interactions contribute significantly to the formation of most antigen–antibody complexes.

8. (a) An antibody combining site is formed by CDRs from both the H and the L chains. The V_H and V_L domains are essential. A small proportion of F_{ab} fragments can be further digested to produce F_v, a fragment that contains just these two domains. C_H1 and C_L contribute to the stability of F_{ab} but not to antigen binding.
(b) A synthetic F_v analog 248 residues long was prepared by expressing a synthetic gene consisting of a V_H gene joined to a V_L gene through a linker. See J. S. Huston et al., *Proc. Natl. Acad. Sci. U. S. A.* 85:5879–5883, 1988.

9. (a) Multivalent antigens lead to the dimerization or oligomerization of transmembrane immunoglobulins, an essential step in their activation. This mode of activation is reminiscent of that of receptor tyrosine kinases (Section 14.2).
(b) An antibody specific for a transmembrane immunoglobulin will activate a B cell by cross-linking these receptors. This experiment can be carried out by using, for example, a goat antibody to cross-link receptors on a mouse B cell.

10. B cells do not express T-cell receptors. The hybridization of T-cell cDNAs with B-cell mRNAs removes cDNAs that are expressed in both cells. Hence, the mixture of cDNAs subsequent to this hybridization are enriched in those encoding T-cell receptors. This procedure, called subtractive hybridization, is generally useful in isolating low-abundance cDNAs. Hybridization should be carried out by using mRNAs from a closely related cell that does not express the gene of interest. See S. M. Hedrick, M. M. Davis, D. I. Cohen, E. A. Nielsen, and M. M. Davis, *Nature* 308:149–153, 1984, for an interesting account of how this method was used to obtain genes for T-cell receptors.

11. TLR-4 is the receptor for LPS, a toxin found specifically in the walls of Gram-negative bacteria. Mutations that inhibit the function of TLR4 impair an affected person's defenses against this class of bacteria.

12. If the HLA alleles are not matched, then the recipient's T cell receptors will identify the MHC proteins of the transplanted tissue as nonself and transplant rejection is likely.

13. Purify an antibody with a specificity to one antigen. Unfold the antibody and allow it to re-fold either in the presence of the antigen or in the absence of the antigen. Test the re-folded antibodies for antigen-binding ability.

14. In some cases, V–D–J rearrangement will result in combining V, D, and J segments out of frame. mRNA molecules produced from such rearranged genes will produce truncated molecules if translated. This possibility is excluded by degrading the mRNA.

15. The mutant bacteria may still stimulate an immune response without causing disease. Hence, they may be valuable starting points for the design of a live attenuated vaccine for the original pathogenic strain.

16. The peptide is LLQATYSAV (L in second position, V in last).

17. Catalysis is likely to require a base for removing a proton from a water molecule. A histidine, glutamate, or aspartate residue is most likely. In addition, a potential hydrogen-bond donor may be present and will interact with the negatively charged oxygen atom that forms in the transition state.

18. A phosphotyrosine residue in the carboxyl terminus of Src and related protein tyrosine kinases binds to its own SH2 domain to generate the inhibited from of Src (Section 14.5). Removal of the phosphoryl group from this residue will activate the kinase.

19. (a) $K_d = 10^{-7}$ M; (b) $K_d = 10^{-9}$ M. The gene was probably generated by a point mutation in the gene for antibody A rather than by de novo rearrangement.

Chapter 35

1. (a) Skeletal muscle and eukaryotic cilia derive their free energy from ATP hydrolysis; the bacterial flagellar motor uses a proton-motive force.
(b) Skeletal muscle requires myosin and actin. Eukaryotic cilia require microtubules and dynein. The bacterial flagellar motor requires MotA, MotB, and FliG, as well as many ancillary components.
2. 6400 Å/80 Å = 80 body lengths per second. For a 10-foot automobile, this body-length speed corresponds to a speed of 80 × 10 feet = 800 feet per second, or 545 miles per hour.
3. 4 pN = 8.8×10^{-13} pounds. The weight of a single motor domain is 100,000 g mol^{-1}/(6.023 × 10^{23} molecules mol^{-1}) = 1.7×10^{-19} g = 3.7×10^{-22} pounds. Thus, a motor domain can lift $(8.8 \times 10^{-13}/3.7 \times 10^{-22}) = 2.4 \times 10^9$ times its weight.
4. Both actin filaments and microtubules are built from subunits and these subunits bind and hydrolyze nucleoside triphosphates. Actin filaments are built of a single type of subunit and these subunits bind ATP. Microtubules are built of two different types of subunits and these subunits bind GTP.
5. The light chains in myosin stiffen the lever arm. The light chains in kinesin bind cargo to be transported.
6. After death, the ratio of ADP to ATP increases rapidly. In the ADP form, myosin motor domains bind tightly to actin. Myosin–actin interactions are possible because the drop in ATP concentration also allows the calcium concentration to rise, clearing the blockage of actin by tropomyosin through the action of the troponin complex.
7. Above its critical concentration, ATP-actin will polymerize. The ATP will hydrolyze through time to form ADP-actin, which has a higher critical concentration. Thus, if the initial subunit concentration is between the critical concentrations of ATP-actin and ADP-actin, filaments will form initially and then disappear on ATP hydrolysis.
8. A one-base step is approximately 3.4 Å = 3.4×10^{-4} μm. If a stoichiometry of one molecule of ATP per step is assumed, this distance corresponds to a velocity of 0.017 μm s^{-1}. Kinesin moves at a velocity of 6400 Å per second, or 0.64 μm s^{-1}.
9. A proton-motive force across the plasma membrane is necessary to drive the flagellar motor. Under conditions of starvation, this proton-motive force is depleted. In acidic solution, the pH difference across the membrane is sufficient to power the motor.
10. The mean distance between tumbles would be longer when the bacterium is moving up a gradient of a chemoattractant.
11. (a) 1.13×10^{-9} dyne
(b) 6.8×10^{14} erg
(c) 6.6×10^{-11} erg per 80 molecules of ATP. A single kinesin motor provides more than enough free energy to power the transport of micrometer-size cargoes at micrometer-per-second velocities.
12. The spacing between identical subunits on microtubules is 8 nm. Thus, a kinesin molecule with a step size that is not a multiple of 8 nm would have to be able to bind at more than one type of site on the microtubule surface.
13. KIF1A must be tethered to an additional microtubule-binding element that retains an attachment to the microtubule when the motor domain releases.
14. Filaments built from subunits can be arbitrarily long, can be dynamically assembled and disassembled, and require only a small amount of genetic information to encode.

15. Protons still flow from outside to inside the cell. Each proton might pass into the outer half-channel of one MotA–MotB complex, bind to the MS ring, rotate clockwise, and pass into the inner half-channel of the neighboring MotA–MotB complex.
16. At a high concentration of calcium ion, Ca^{2+} binds to calmodulin. In turn, calmodulin binds to a protein kinase that phosphorylates myosin light chains and activates it. At low calcium ion concentration, the light chains are dephosphorylated by a Ca^{2+}-independent phosphatase.
17. (a) The value of k_{cat} is approximately 13 molecules per second, whereas the K_M value for ATP is approximately 12 μM.
(b) The step size is approximately (380 – 120)/7 = 37 nm.
(c) The step size is very large, which is consistent with the presence of six light-chain-binding sites and, hence, very long lever arms. The rate of ADP release is essentially identical with the overall k_{cat}; so ADP release is rate limiting, which suggests that both motor domains can bind to sites 37 nm apart simultaneously. ADP release from the hindmost domain allows ATP to bind, leading to actin release and lever-arm motion.

Chapter 36

1. (a) Before; (b) after; (c) after; (d) after; (e) before; (f) after.
2. (a) Yes; (b) yes; (c) no (MW > 600).
3. If computer programs could estimate log(P) values on the basis of chemical structure, then the required laboratory time for drug development could be shortened. The determination of the relative solubilities of pharmaceutical candidates by allowing each compound to equilibrate between water and an organic phase would no longer be necessary.
4. Perhaps N-acetylcysteine would conjugate to some of the N-acetyl-p-benzoquinone imine that is produced by the metabolism of acetaminophen, thereby preventing the depletion of the liver's supply of glutathione.
5. In phase 1 clinical trials, approximately 10 to 100 healthy volunteers are typically enrolled in a study designed to assess safety. In contrast, a larger number of subjects are enrolled in a typical phase 2 trial. Moreover, these persons may benefit from the drug administered. In a phase 2 trial, efficacy, dosage, and safety can be assessed.
6. The binding of other drugs to albumin could cause extra coumadin to be released. (Albumin is a general carrier for hydrophobic molecules.)
7. A drug that inhibits a P450 enzyme may dramatically affect the disposition of another drug that is metabolized by that same enzyme. If this inhibited metabolism is not accounted for when dosing, the second drug may reach very high, and sometimes toxic, levels in the blood.
8. Unlike competitive inhibition, noncompetitive inhibition cannot be overcome with additional substrate. Hence, a drug that acts by a noncompetitive mechanism will be unaffected by changing levels of the physiological substrate.
9. An inhibitor of MDR could prevent the efflux of a chemotherapeutic drug from tumor cells. Hence, this type of an inhibitor could be useful in averting resistance to cancer chemotherapy.
10. Agents that inhibit one or more enzymes of the glycolytic pathway could act to deprive trypanosomes of energy and thus be useful for treating sleeping sickness. A difficulty is that glycolysis in the host cells also would be inhibited.
11. Imatinib is an inhibitor of the Bcr-Abl kinase, a mutant kinase present only in tumor cells that have undergone a translocation between chromosomes 9 and 22 (see Figure 14.33). Before initiating treatment with imatinib, we could sequence the DNA of the tumor cells and determine (a) whether this translocation has taken place and (b) whether the sequence of *bcr-abl* carries any mutations

that would render the kinase resistant to imatinib. If the translocation has not taken place or if the gene carries resistance mutations, then imatinib would likely not be an effective treatment for the patient carrying this particular tumor.

12. Sildenafil increases cGMP levels by inhibiting the phosphodiesterase-mediated breakdown of cGMP to GMP. Intracellular cGMP levels can also be increased by activating its synthesis. This activation can be achieved with the use of NO donors (such as sodium nitroprusside and nitroglycerin) or compounds that activate guanylate cyclase activity. Drugs that act by the latter mechanism are currently in clinical trials.

13. A reasonable mechanism would be an oxidative deamination following an overall mechanism similar to that in Figure 36.9, with release of ammonia.

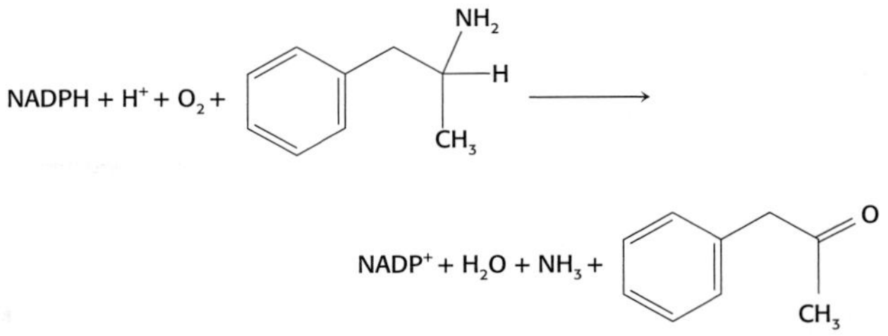

$NADPH + H^+ + O_2 + $

$NADP^+ + H_2O + NH_3 + $

14. $K_I \approx 0.3$ nM. $IC_{50} \approx 2.0$ nM. Yes, compound A should be effective when taken orally because 400 nM is much greater than the estimated values of K_I and IC_{50}.

SELECTED READINGS

Chapter 2

Where to Start

Service, R. F. 2008. Problem solved*(*sort of) (a brief review of protein folding). *Science* 321:784–786.

Doolittle, R. F. 1985. Proteins. *Sci. Am.* 253(4):88–99.

Richards, F. M. 1991. The protein folding problem. *Sci. Am.* 264(1): 54–57.

Weber, A. L., and Miller, S. L. 1981. Reasons for the occurrence of the twenty coded protein amino acids. *J. Mol. Evol.* 17:273–284.

Books

Petsko, G. A., and Ringe, D. 2004. *Protein Structure and Function.* New Science Press.

Tanford, C., and Reynolds, J. 2004. *Nature's Robots: A History of Proteins.* Oxford.

Branden, C., and Tooze, J. 1999. *Introduction to Protein Structure* (2d ed.). Garland.

Creighton, T. E. 1992. *Proteins: Structures and Molecular Principles* (2d ed.). W. H. Freeman and Company.

Conformation of Proteins

Smock, R. G., and Gierasch, L. M. 2009. Sending signals dynamically. *Science* 324:198–203.

Tokuriki, N., and Tawfik, D. S. 2009. Protein dynamism and evolvability. *Science* 324:203–207.

Pace, C. N., Grimsley, G. R., and Scholtz, J. M. 2009. Protein ionizable groups: pK values and their contribution to protein stability and solubility. *J. Biol. Chem.* 284:13285–13289.

Ronald Breslow, R., and Cheng, Z.-L. 2009. On the origin of terrestrial homochirality for nucleosides and amino acids. *Proc. Natl. Acad. Sci. U.S.A.* 106:9144–9146.

Secondary Structure

Shoulders, M. D., and Raines, R. T. 2009. Collagen structure and stability. *Annu. Rev. Biochem.* 78:929–58.

O'Neil, K. T., and DeGrado, W. F. 1990. A thermodynamic scale for the helix-forming tendencies of the commonly occurring amino acids. *Science* 250:646–651.

Zhang, C., and Kim, S. H. 2000. The anatomy of protein beta-sheet topology. *J. Mol. Biol.* 299:1075–1089.

Regan, L. 1994. Protein structure: Born to be beta. *Curr. Biol.* 4:656–658.

Srinivasan, R., and Rose, G. D. 1999. A physical basis for protein secondary structure. *Proc. Natl. Acad. Sci. U.S.A.* 96:14258–14263.

Intrinsically Unstructured Proteins

Galea, C. A., Wang, Y., Sivakolundu, S. G., and Kriwacki, R. W. 2008. Regulation of cell division by intrinsically unstructured proteins: Intrinsic flexibility, modularity, and signaling conduits. *Biochemistry* 47:7598–7609.

Raychaudhuri, S., Dey, S., Bhattacharyya, N. P., and Mukhopadhyay, D. 2009. The role of intrinsically unstructured proteins in neurodegenerative diseases. *PLoS One* 4:e5566.

Tompa, P., and Fuxreiter, M. 2008. Fuzzy complexes: Polymorphism and structural disorder in protein–protein interactions. *Trends Biochem. Sci.* 33:2–8.

Tuinstra, R. L., Peterson, F. C., Kutlesa, E. S., Elgin, S., Kron, M. A., and Volkman, B. F. 2008. Interconversion between two unrelated protein folds in the lymphotactin native state. *Proc. Natl. Acad. Sci. U.S.A.* 105:5057–5062.

Domains

Jin, J., Xie, X., Chen, C., Park, J. G., Stark, C., James, D. A., Olhovsky, M., Linding, R., Mao, Y., and Pawson, T. 2009. Eukaryotic protein domains as functional units of cellular evolution. *Sci. Signal.* 2:ra76.

Bennett, M. J., Choe, S., and Eisenberg, D. 1994. Domain swapping: Entangling alliances between proteins. *Proc. Natl. Acad. Sci. U.S.A.* 91:3127–3131.

Bergdoll, M., Eltis, L. D., Cameron, A. D., Dumas, P., and Bolin, J. T. 1998. All in the family: Structural and evolutionary relationships among three modular proteins with diverse functions and variable assembly. *Protein Sci.* 7:1661–1670.

Hopfner, K. P., Kopetzki, E., Kresse, G. B., Bode, W., Huber, R., and Engh, R. A. 1998. New enzyme lineages by subdomain shuffling. *Proc. Natl. Acad. Sci. U.S.A.* 95:9813–9818.

Ponting, C. P., Schultz, J., Copley, R. R., Andrade, M. A., and Bork, P. 2000. Evolution of domain families. *Adv. Protein Chem.* 54:185–244.

Protein Folding

Caughey, B., Baron, G. S., Chesebro, B., and Jeffrey, M. 2009. Getting a grip on prions: Oligomers, amyloids, and pathological membrane interactions. *Annu. Rev. Biochem.* 78:177–204.

Cobb, N. J., and Surewicz, W. K. 2009. Prion diseases and their biochemical mechanisms. *Biochemistry* 48:2574–2585.

Daggett, V., and Fersht, A. R. 2003. Is there a unifying mechanism for protein folding? *Trends Biochem. Sci.* 28:18–25.

Selkoe, D. J. 2003. Folding proteins in fatal ways. *Nature* 426:900–904.

Anfinsen, C. B. 1973. Principles that govern the folding of protein chains. *Science* 181:223–230.

Baldwin, R. L., and Rose, G. D. 1999. Is protein folding hierarchic? I. Local structure and peptide folding. *Trends Biochem. Sci.* 24:26–33.

Baldwin, R. L., and Rose, G. D. 1999. Is protein folding hierarchic? II. Folding intermediates and transition states. *Trends Biochem. Sci.* 24:77–83.

Kuhlman, B., Dantas, G., Ireton, G. C., Varani, G., Stoddard, B. L., and Baker, D. 2003. Design of a novel globular protein with atomic-level accuracy. *Science* 302:1364–1368.

Staley, J. P., and Kim, P. S. 1990. Role of a subdomain in the folding of bovine pancreatic trypsin inhibitor. *Nature* 344:685–688.

Covalent Modification of Proteins

Tarrant, M. K., and Cole, P. A. 2009. The chemical biology of protein phosphorylation. *Annu. Rev. Biochem.* 78:797–825.

Krishna, R. G., and Wold, F. 1993. Post-translational modification of proteins. *Adv. Enzymol. Relat. Areas. Mol. Biol.* 67:265–298.

Aletta, J. M., Cimato, T. R., and Ettinger, M. J. 1998. Protein methylation: A signal event in post-translational modification. *Trends Biochem. Sci.* 23:89–91.

Tsien, R. Y. 1998. The green fluorescent protein. *Annu. Rev. Biochem.* 67:509–544.

Chapter 3

Where to Start

Sanger, F. 1988. Sequences, sequences, sequences. *Annu. Rev. Biochem.* 57:1–28.

Merrifield, B. 1986. Solid phase synthesis. *Science* 232:341–347.

Hunkapiller, M. W., and Hood, L. E. 1983. Protein sequence analysis: Automated microsequencing. *Science* 219:650–659.

Milstein, C. 1980. Monoclonal antibodies. *Sci. Am.* 243(4):66–74.

Moore, S., and Stein, W. H. 1973. Chemical structures of pancreatic ribonuclease and deoxyribonuclease. *Science* 180:458–464.

Books

Methods in Enzymology. Academic Press.

Wilson, K., and Walker, J. (Eds.). 2000. *Principles and Techniques of Practical Biochemistry* (5th ed.). Cambridge University Press.

Van Holde, K. E., Johnson, W. C., and Ho, P.-S. 1998. *Principles of Physical Biochemistry.* Prentice Hall.

SELECTED READINGS

Wilkins, M. R., Williams, K. L., Appel, R. D., and Hochstrasser, D. F. 1997. *Proteome Research: New Frontiers in Functional Genomics (Principles and Practice)*. Springer Verlag.

Johnstone, R. A. W. 1996. *Mass Spectroscopy for Chemists and Biochemists* (2d ed.). Cambridge University Press.

Kyte, J. 1994. *Structure in Protein Chemistry*. Garland.

Creighton, T. E. 1993. *Proteins: Structure and Molecular Properties* (2d ed.). W. H. Freeman and Company.

Cantor, C. R., and Schimmel, P. R. 1980. *Biophysical Chemistry*. W. H. Freeman and Company.

Protein Purification and Analysis

Blackstock, W. P., and Weir, M. P. 1999. Proteomics: Quantitative and physical mapping of cellular proteins. *Trends Biotechnol.* 17:121–127.

Deutscher, M. (Ed.). 1997. *Guide to Protein Purification*. Academic Press.

Dunn, M. J. 1997. Quantitative two-dimensional gel electrophoresis: From proteins to proteomes. *Biochem. Soc. Trans.* 25:248–254.

Scopes, R. K., and Cantor, C. 1994. *Protein Purification: Principles and Practice* (3d ed.). Springer Verlag.

Aebersold, R., Pipes, G. D., Wettenhall, R. E., Nika, H., and Hood, L. E. 1990. Covalent attachment of peptides for high sensitivity solid-phase sequence analysis. *Anal. Biochem.* 187:56–65.

Ultracentrifugation and Mass Spectrometry

Steen, H., and Mann, M. 2004. The ABC's (and XYZ's) of peptide sequencing. *Nat. Rev. Mol. Cell Biol.* 5:699–711.

Glish, G. L., and Vachet, R. W. 2003. The basics of mass spectrometry in the twenty-first century. *Nat. Rev. Drug Discovery* 2:140–150.

Li, L., Garden, R. W., and Sweedler, J. V. 2000. Single-cell MALDI: A new tool for direct peptide profiling. *Trends Biotechnol.* 18: 151–160.

Yates, J. R., 3d. 1998. Mass spectrometry and the age of the proteome. *J. Mass Spectrom.* 33:1–19.

Pappin, D. J. 1997. Peptide mass fingerprinting using MALDI-TOF mass spectrometry. *Methods Mol. Biol.* 64:165–173.

Schuster, T. M., and Laue, T. M. 1994. *Modern Analytical Ultracentrifugation*. Springer Verlag.

Arnott, D., Shabanowitz, J., and Hunt, D. F. 1993. Mass spectrometry of proteins and peptides: Sensitive and accurate mass measurement and sequence analysis. *Clin. Chem.* 39:2005–2010.

Chait, B. T., and Kent, S. B. H. 1992. Weighing naked proteins: Practical, high-accuracy mass measurement of peptides and proteins. *Science* 257:1885–1894.

Edmonds, C. G., Loo, J. A., Loo, R. R., Udseth, H. R., Barinaga, C. J., and Smith, R. D. 1991. Application of electrospray ionization mass spectrometry and tandem mass spectrometry in combination with capillary electrophoresis for biochemical investigations. *Biochem. Soc. Trans.* 19:943–947.

Jardine, I. 1990. Molecular weight analysis of proteins. *Methods Enzymol.* 193:441–455.

Proteomics

Yates, J. R., 3d. 2004. Mass spectral analysis in proteomics. *Annu. Rev. Biophys. Biomol. Struct.* 33:297–316.

Weston, A. D., and Hood, L. 2004. Systems biology, proteomics, and the future of health care: Toward predictive, preventative, and personalized medicine. *J. Proteome Res.* 3:179–196.

Pandey, A., and Mann, M. 2000. Proteomics to study genes and ge-nomes. *Nature* 405:837–846.

Dutt, M. J., and Lee, K. H. 2000. Proteomic analysis. *Curr. Opin. Biotechnol.* 11:176–179.

Rout, M. P., Aitchison, J. D., Suprapto, A., Hjertaas, K., Zhao, Y., and Chait, B. T. 2000. The yeast nuclear pore complex: Composition, architecture, and transport mechanism. *J. Cell Biol.* 148:635–651.

X-ray Crystallography and NMR Spectroscopy

Rhodes, G. 2006. *Crystallography Made Crystal Clear*. Elsevier/Academic Press.

Moffat, K. 2003. The frontiers of time-resolved macromolecular crystallography: Movies and chirped X-ray pulses. *Faraday Discuss.* 122:65–88.

Bax, A. 2003. Weak alignment offers new NMR opportunities to study protein structure and dynamics. *Protein Sci.* 12:1–16.

Wery, J. P., and Schevitz, R. W. 1997. New trends in macromolecular x-ray crystallography. *Curr. Opin. Chem. Biol.* 1:365–369.

Glusker, J. P. 1994. X-ray crystallography of proteins. *Methods Biochem. Anal.* 37:1–72.

Clore, G. M., and Gronenborn, A. M. 1991. Structures of larger proteins in solution: Three- and four-dimensional heteronuclear NMR spectroscopy. *Science* 252:1390–1399.

Wüthrich, K. 1989. Protein structure determination in solution by nuclear magnetic resonance spectroscopy. *Science* 243:45–50.

Wüthrich, K. 1986. *NMR of Proteins and Nucleic Acids*. Wiley-Interscience.

Monoclonal Antibodies and Fluorescent Molecules

Immunology Today. 2000. Volume 21, issue 8.

Tsien, R. Y. 1998. The green fluorescent protein. *Annu. Rev. Biochem.* 67:509–544.

Kendall, J. M., and Badminton, M. N. 1998. *Aequorea victoria* bioluminescence moves into an exciting era. *Trends Biotechnol.* 16:216–234.

Goding, J. W. 1996. *Monoclonal Antibodies: Principles and Practice*. Academic Press.

Köhler, G., and Milstein, C. 1975. Continuous cultures of fused cells secreting antibody of predefined specificity. *Nature* 256:495–497.

Chemical Synthesis of Proteins

Bang, D., Chopra, N., and Kent, S. B. 2004. Total chemical synthesis of crambin. *J. Am. Chem. Soc.* 126:1377–1383.

Dawson, P. E., and Kent, S. B. 2000. Synthesis of native proteins by chemical ligation. *Annu. Rev. Biochem.* 69:923–960.

Mayo, K. H. 2000. Recent advances in the design and construction of synthetic peptides: For the love of basics or just for the technology of it. *Trends Biotechnol.* 18:212–217.

Chapter 4

Where to Start

Felsenfeld, G. 1985. DNA. *Sci. Am.* 253(4):58–67.

Darnell, J. E., Jr. 1985. RNA. *Sci. Am.* 253(4):68–78.

Dickerson, R. E. 1983. The DNA helix and how it is read. *Sci. Am.* 249(6):94–111.

Crick, F. H. C. 1954. The structure of the hereditary material. *Sci. Am.* 191(4): 54–61.

Chambon, P. 1981. Split genes. *Sci. Am.* 244(5):60–71.

Watson, J. D., and Crick, F. H. C. 1953. Molecular structure of nucleic acids: A structure for deoxyribose nucleic acid. *Nature* 171:737–738.

Watson, J. D., and Crick, F. H. C. 1953. Genetic implications of the structure of deoxyribonucleic acid. *Nature* 171:964–967.

Meselson, M., and Stahl, F. W. 1958. The replication of DNA in *Escherichia coli*. *Proc. Natl. Acad. Sci. U.S.A.* 44:671–682.

Books

Bloomfield, V. A., Crothers, D. M., Tinoco, I., and Hearst, J. 2000. *Nucleic Acids: Structures, Properties, and Functions*. University Science Books.

Singer, M., and Berg, P. 1991. *Genes and Genomes: A Changing Perspective*. University Science Books.

Lodish, H., Berk, A., Kaiser, C. A., Krieger, M., Scott, M. P., Bretscher, A., Ploegh, H., and Matsudaira, P. 2007. *Molecular Cell Biology* (6th ed.). W. H. Freeman and Company.

Lewin, B. 2007. *Genes IX*. Jones and Bartlett.

Watson, J. D., Baker, T. A., Bell, S. P., Gann, A., Levine, M., and Losick, R. 2007. *Molecular Biology of the Gene* (6th ed.). Benjamin Cummings.

DNA Structure

Neidle, S. 2007. *Principles of Nucleic Acid Structure*. Academic Press.

Dickerson, R. E., Drew, H. R., Conner, B. N., Wing, R. M., Fratini, A. V., and Kopka, M. L. 1982. The anatomy of A-, B-, and Z-DNA. *Science* 216:475–485.

Sinden, R. R. 1994. *DNA Structure and Function*. Academic Press.

DNA Replication

Lehman, I. R. 2003. Discovery of DNA polymerase. *J. Biol. Chem.* 278:34733–34738.

Hübscher, U., Maga, G., and Spardari, S. 2002. Eukaryotic DNA polymerases. *Annu. Rev. Biochem.* 71:133–163.

Hübscher, U., Nasheuer, H.-P., and Syväoja, J. E. 2000. Eukaryotic DNA polymerases: A growing family. *Trends Biochem. Sci.* 25:143–147.

Brautigam, C. A., and Steitz, T. A. 1998. Structural and functional insights provided by crystal structures of DNA polymerases and their substrate complexes. *Curr. Opin. Struct. Biol.* 8:54–63.

Kornberg, A., and Baker, T. A. 1992. *DNA Replication* (2d ed.). W. H. Freeman and Company.

Discovery of Messenger RNA

Jacob, F., and Monod, J. 1961. Genetic regulatory mechanisms in the synthesis of proteins. *J. Mol. Biol.* 3:318–356.

Brenner, S., Jacob, F., and Meselson, M. 1961. An unstable intermediate carrying information from genes to ribosomes for protein synthesis. *Nature* 190:576–581.

Hall, B. D., and Spiegelman, S. 1961. Sequence complementarity of T2-DNA and T2-specific RNA. *Proc. Natl. Acad. Sci. U.S.A.* 47:137–146.

Genetic Code

Koonin, E. V., and Novozhilov, A. S. 2009. Origin and evolution of the genetic code: The universal enigma. *IUBMB Life* 61:99–111.

Yarus, M., Caporaso, J. G., and Knight, R. 2005. Origins of the genetic code: The escaped triplet theory. *Annu. Rev. Biochem.* 74:179–198.

Freeland, S. J., and Hurst, L. D. 2004. Evolution encoded. *Sci. Am.* 290(4):84–91.

Crick, F. H. C., Barnett, L., Brenner, S., and Watts-Tobin, R. J. 1961. General nature of the genetic code for proteins. *Nature* 192:1227–1232.

Woese, C. R. 1967. *The Genetic Code*. Harper & Row.

Knight, R. D., Freeland, S. J., and Landweber L. F. 1999. Selection, history and chemistry: The three faces of the genetic code. *Trends Biochem. Sci.* 24(6):241–247.

Introns, Exons, and Split Genes

Liu, M., and Grigoriev, A. 2004. Protein domains correlate strongly with exons in multiple eukaryotic genomes—evidence of exon shuffling? *Trends Genet.* 20:399–403.

Dorit, R. L., Schoenbach, L., and Gilbert, W. 1990. How big is the universe of exons? *Science* 250:1377–1382.

Cochet, M., Gannon, F., Hen, R., Maroteaux, L., Perrin, F., and Chambon, P. 1979. Organization and sequence studies of the 17-piece chicken conalbumin gene. *Nature* 282:567–574.

Tilghman, S. M., Tiemeier, D. C., Seidman, J. G., Peterlin, B. M., Sullivan, M., Maizel, J. V., and Leder, P. 1978. Intervening sequence of DNA identified in the structural portion of a mouse β-globin gene. *Proc. Natl. Acad. Sci. U.S.A.* 75:725–729.

Reminiscences and Historical Accounts

Nirenberg, M. 2004. Deciphering the genetic code—a personal account. *Trends Biochem. Sci.* 29:46–54.

Clayton, J., and Dennis, C. (Eds.). 2003. *50 Years of DNA*. Palgrave Macmillan.

Watson, J. D. 1968. *The Double Helix*. Atheneum.

McCarty, M. 1985. *The Transforming Principle: Discovering That Genes Are Made of DNA*. Norton.

Cairns, J., Stent, G. S., and Watson, J. D. 2000. *Phage and the Origins of Molecular Biology*. Cold Spring Harbor Laboratory.

Olby, R. 1974. *The Path to the Double Helix*. University of Washington Press.

Portugal, F. H., and Cohen, J. S. 1977. *A Century of DNA: A History of the Discovery of the Structure and Function of the Genetic Substance*. MIT Press.

Judson, H. F. 1996. *The Eighth Day of Creation*. Cold Spring Harbor Laboratory.

Sayre, A. 2000. *Rosalind Franklin and DNA*. Norton.

Chapter 5

Where to Start

Berg, P. 1981. Dissections and reconstructions of genes and chromosomes. *Science* 213:296–303.

Gilbert, W. 1981. DNA sequencing and gene structure. *Science* 214:1305–1312.

Sanger, F. 1981. Determination of nucleotide sequences in DNA. *Science* 214:1205–1210.

Mullis, K. B. 1990. The unusual origin of the polymerase chain reaction. *Sci. Am.* 262(4):56–65.

Books on Recombinant DNA Technology

Watson, J. D., Myers, R. M., Caudy, A. A., and Witkowski, J. 2007. *Recombinant DNA: Genes and Genomes* (3d ed.). W. H. Freeman and Company.

Grierson, D. (Ed.). 1991. *Plant Genetic Engineering*. Chapman and Hall.

Mullis, K. B., Ferré, F., and Gibbs, R. A. (Eds.). 1994. *The Polymerase Chain Reaction*. Birkhäuser.

Russel, D., Sambrook, J., and Russel, D. 2000. *Molecular Cloning: A Laboratory Manual* (3d ed.). Cold Spring Harbor Laboratory Press.

Ausubel, F. M., Brent, R., Kingston, R. E., and Moore, D. D. (Eds.). 1999. *Short Protocols in Molecular Biology: A Compendium of Methods from Current Protocols in Molecular Biology*. Wiley.

Birren, B., Green, E. D., Klapholz, S., Myers, R. M., Roskams, J., Riethamn, H., and Hieter, P. (Eds.). 1999. *Genome Analysis* (vols. 1–4). Cold Spring Harbor Laboratory Press.

Methods in Enzymology. Academic Press. [Many volumes in this series deal with recombinant DNA technology.]

DNA Sequencing and Synthesis

Hunkapiller, T., Kaiser, R. J., Koop, B. F., and Hood, L. 1991. Large-scale and automated DNA sequence determination. *Science* 254:59–67.

Sanger, F., Nicklen, S., and Coulson, A. R. 1977. DNA sequencing with chain-terminating inhibitors. *Proc. Natl. Acad. Sci. U.S.A.* 74:5463–5467.

Maxam, A. M., and Gilbert, W. 1977. A new method for sequencing DNA. *Proc. Natl. Acad. Sci. U.S.A.* 74:560–564.

Smith, L. M., Sanders, J. Z., Kaiser, R. J., Hughes, P., Dodd, C., Connell, C. R., Heiner, C., Kent, S. B. H., and Hood, L. E. 1986. Fluorescence detection in automated DNA sequence analysis. *Nature* 321:674–679.

Pease, A. C., Solas, D., Sullivan, E. J., Cronin, M. T., Holmes, C. P., and Fodor, S. P. A. 1994. Light-generated oligonucleotide arrays for rapid DNA sequence analysis. *Proc. Natl. Acad. Sci. U.S.A.* 91:5022–5026.

Venter, J. C., Adams, M. D., Sutton, G. G., Kerlavage, A. R., Smith, H. O., and Hunkapiller, M. 1998. Shotgun sequencing of the human genome. *Science* 280:1540–1542.

SELECTED READINGS

Mardis, E. R. 2008. Next-generation DNA sequencing methods. *Annu. Rev. Genomics Hum. Genet.* 9:387–402.

Polymerase Chain Reaction
Arnheim, N., and Erlich, H. 1992. Polymerase chain reaction strategy. *Annu. Rev. Biochem.* 61:131–156.

Kirby, L. T. (Ed.). 1997. *DNA Fingerprinting: An Introduction.* Stockton Press.

Eisenstein, B. I. 1990. The polymerase chain reaction: A new method for using molecular genetics for medical diagnosis. *N. Engl. J. Med.* 322:178–183.

Foley, K. P., Leonard, M. W., and Engel, J. D. 1993. Quantitation of RNA using the polymerase chain reaction. *Trends Genet.* 9:380–386.

Pääbo, S. 1993. Ancient DNA. *Sci. Am.* 269(5):86–92.

Hagelberg, E., Gray, I. C., and Jeffreys, A. J. 1991. Identification of the skeletal remains of a murder victim by DNA analysis. *Nature* 352:427–429.

Lawlor, D. A., Dickel, C. D., Hauswirth, W. W., and Parham, P. 1991. Ancient HLA genes from 7500-year-old archaeological remains. *Nature* 349:785–788.

Krings, M., Geisert, H., Schmitz, R. W., Krainitzki, H., and Pääbo, S. 1999. DNA sequence of the mitochondrial hypervariable region II for the Neanderthal type specimen. *Proc. Natl. Acad. Sci. U.S.A.* 96:5581–5585.

Ovchinnikov, I. V., Götherström, A., Romanova, G. P., Kharitonov, V. M., Lidén, K., and Goodwin, W. 2000. Molecular analysis of Neanderthal DNA from the northern Caucasus. *Nature* 404:490–493.

Genome Sequencing
International Human Genome Sequencing Consortium. 2004. Finishing the euchromatic sequence of the human genome. *Nature* 431:931–945.

Lander, E. S., Linton, L. M., Birren, B., Nusbaum, C., Zody, M. C., Baldwin, J., Devon, K., Dewar, K., Doyle, M., FitzHugh, W., et al. 2001. Initial sequencing and analysis of the human genome. *Nature* 409:860–921.

Venter, J. C., Adams, M. D., Myers, E. W., Li, P. W., Mural, R. J., Sutton, G. G., Smith, H. O., Yandell, M., Evans, C. A., Holt, R. A., et al. 2001. The sequence of the human genome. *Science* 291:1304–1351.

Waterston, R. H., Lindblad-Toh, K., Birney, E., Rogers, J., Abril, J. F., Agarwal, P., Agarwala, R., Ainscough, R., Alexandersson, M., An, P., et al. 2002. Initial sequencing and comparative analysis of the mouse genome. *Nature* 420:520–562.

Koonin, E. V. 2003. Comparative genomics, minimal gene-sets and the last universal common ancestor. *Nat. Rev. Microbiol.* 1:127–236.

Gilligan, P., Brenner, S., and Venkatesh, B. 2002. Fugu and human sequence comparison identifies novel human genes and conserved non-coding sequences. *Gene* 294:35–44.

Enard, W., and Pääbo, S. 2004. Comparative primate genomics. *Annu. Rev. Genomics Hum. Genet.* 5:351–378.

Quantitative PCR and DNA Arrays
Duggan, D. J., Bittner, J. M., Chen, Y., Meltzer, P., and Trent, J. M. 1999. Expression profiling using cDNA microarrays. *Nat. Genet.* 21:10–14.

Golub, T. R., Slonim, D. K., Tamayo, P., Huard, C., Gaasenbeek, M., Mesirov, J. P., Coller, H., Loh, M. L., Downing, J. R., Caligiuri, M. A., Bloomfield, C. D., and Lander, E. S. 1999. Molecular classification of cancer: Class discovery and class prediction by gene expression monitoring. *Science* 286:531–537.

Perou, C. M., Sørlie, T., Eisen, M. B., van de Rijn, M., Jeffery, S. S., Rees, C. A., Pollack, J. R., Ross, D. T., Johnsen, H., Akslen, L. A., Fluge, Ø., Pergamenschikov, A., Williams, C., Zhu, S. X., Lønning, P. E., Børresen-Dale, A.-L., Brown, P. O., and Botstein, D. 2000. Molecular portraits of human breast tumours. *Nature* 406:747–752.

Walker, N. J. 2002. A technique whose time has come. *Science* 296:557–559.

Introduction of Genes into Animal Cells
Anderson, W. F. 1992. Human gene therapy. *Science* 256:808–813.

Friedmann, T. 1997. Overcoming the obstacles to gene therapy. *Sci. Am.* 277(6):96–101.

Blaese, R. M. 1997. Gene therapy for cancer. *Sci. Am.* 277 (6): 111–115.

Brinster, R. L., and Palmiter, R. D. 1986. Introduction of genes into the germ lines of animals. *Harvey Lect.* 80:1–38.

Capecchi, M. R. 1989. Altering the genome by homologous recombination. *Science* 244:1288–1292.

Hasty, P., Bradley, A., Morris, J. H., Edmondson, D. G., Venuti, J. M., Olson, E. N., and Klein, W. H. 1993. Muscle deficiency and neonatal death in mice with a targeted mutation in the myogenin gene. *Nature* 364:501–506.

Parkmann, R., Weinberg, K., Crooks, G., Nolta, J., Kapoor, N., and Kohn, D. 2000. Gene therapy for adenosine deaminase deficiency. *Annu. Rev. Med.* 51:33–47.

RNA Interference
Rana, T. M. 2007. Illuminating the silence: Understanding the structure and function of small RNAs. *Nat. Rev. Mol. Cell Biol.* 8:23–36.

Novina, C. D., and Sharp, P. A. 2004. The RNAi revolution. *Nature* 430:161–164.

Hannon, G. J., and Rossi, J. J. 2004. Unlocking the potential of the human genome with RNA interference. *Nature* 431:371–378.

Meister, G., and Tuschl, T. 2004. Mechanisms of gene silencing by double-stranded RNA. *Nature* 431:343–349.

Elbashir, S. M., Harborth, J., Lendeckel, W., Yalcin, A., Weber, K., and Tuschl, T. 2001. Duplexes of 21-nucleotide RNAs mediate RNA interference in cultured mammalian cells. *Nature* 411:494–498.

Fire, A., Xu, S., Montgomery, M. K., Kostas, S. A., Driver, S. E., and Mello, C. C. 1998. Potent and specific genetic interference by double-stranded RNA in *Caenorhabditis elegans*. *Nature* 391:806–811.

Genetic Engineering of Plants
Gasser, C. S., and Fraley, R. T. 1992. Transgenic crops. *Sci. Am.* 266(6):62–69.

Gasser, C. S., and Fraley, R. T. 1989. Genetically engineering plants for crop improvement. *Science* 244:1293–1299.

Shimamoto, K., Terada, R., Izawa, T., and Fujimoto, H. 1989. Fertile transgenic rice plants regenerated from transformed protoplasts. *Nature* 338:274–276.

Chilton, M.-D. 1983. A vector for introducing new genes into plants. *Sci. Am.* 248(6):50–59.

Hansen, G., and Wright, M. S. 1999. Recent advances in the transformation of plants. *Trends Plant Sci.* 4:226–231.

Hammond, J. 1999. Overview: The many uses of transgenic plants. *Curr. Top. Microbiol. Immunol.* 240:1–20.

Finer, J. J., Finer, K. R., and Ponappa, T. 1999. Particle bombardment mediated transformation. *Curr. Top. Microbiol. Immunol.* 240:60–80.

Amyotrophic Lateral Sclerosis
Siddique, T., Figlewicz, D. A., Pericak-Vance, M. A., Haines, J. L., Rouleau, G., Jeffers, A. J., Sapp, P., Hung, W.-Y., Bebout, J., McKenna-Yasek, D., et al. 1991. Linkage of a gene causing familial amyotrophic lateral sclerosis to chromosome 21 and evidence of genetic-locus heterogeneity. *New Engl. J. Med.* 324:1381–1384.

Rosen, D. R., Siddique, T., Patterson, D., Figlewicz, D. A., Sapp, P., Hentati, A., Donaldson, D., Goto, J., O'Regan, J. P., Deng, H.-X., et al. 1993. Mutations in Cu/Zn superoxide dismutase gene are associated with familial amyotrophic lateral sclerosis. *Nature* 362:59–62.

Gurney, M. E., Pu, H., Chiu, A. Y., Dal Canto, M. C., Polchow, C. Y., Alexander, D. D., Caliendo, J., Hentati, A., Kwon, Y. W., Deng, H.-X., Chen, W., Zhai, P., Sufit, R. L., and Siddique, T. 1994. Motor neuron degeneration in mice that express a human Cu,Zn superoxide dismutase mutation. *Science* 264:1772–1774.

Borchelt, D. R., Lee, M. K., Slunt, H. S., Guarnieri, M., Xu, Z.-S., Wong, P. C. Brown, R. H., Jr., Price, D. L., Sisodia, S. S., and Cleveland, D. W. 1994. Superoxide dismutase 1 with mutations linked to familial amyotrophic lateral sclerosis possesses significant activity. *Proc. Natl. Acad. Sci. U.S.A.* 91:8292–8296.

Chapter 6

Books

Claverie, J.-M., and Notredame, C. 2003. *Bioinformatics for Dummies.* Wiley.

Pevsner, J. 2003. *Bioinformatics and Functional Genomics.* Wiley-Liss.

Doolittle, R. F. 1987. *Of URFS and ORFS.* University Science Books.

Sequence Alignment

Schaffer, A. A., Aravind, L., Madden, T. L., Shavirin, S., Spouge, J. L., Wolf, Y. I., Koonin, E. V., and Altschul, S. F. 2001. Improving the accuracy of PSI-BLAST protein database searches with composition-based statistics and other refinements. *Nucleic Acids Res.* 29:2994–3005.

Henikoff, S., and Henikoff, J. G. 1992. Amino acid substitution matrices from protein blocks. *Proc. Natl. Acad. Sci. U.S.A.* 89:10915–10919.

Johnson, M. S., and Overington, J. P. 1993. A structural basis for sequence comparisons: An evaluation of scoring methodologies. *J. Mol. Biol.* 233:716–738.

Eddy, S. R. 2004. Where did the BLOSUM62 alignment score matrix come from? *Nat. Biotechnol.* 22:1035–1036.

Aravind, L., and Koonin, E. V. 1999. Gleaning non-trivial structural, functional and evolutionary information about proteins by iterative database searches. *J. Mol. Biol.* 287:1023–1040.

Altschul, S. F., Madden, T. L., Schaffer, A. A., Zhang, J., Zhang, Z., Miller, W., and Lipman, D. J. 1997. Gapped BLAST and PSI-BLAST: A new generation of protein database search programs. *Nucleic Acids Res.* 25:3389–3402.

Structure Comparison

Orengo, C. A., Bray, J. E., Buchan, D. W., Harrison, A., Lee, D., Pearl, F. M., Sillitoe, I., Todd, A. E., and Thornton, J. M. 2002. The CATH protein family database: A resource for structural and functional annotation of genomes. *Proteomics* 2:11–21.

Bashford, D., Chothia, C., and Lesk, A. M. 1987. Determinants of a protein fold: Unique features of the globin amino acid sequences. *J. Mol. Biol.* 196:199–216.

Harutyunyan, E. H., Safonova, T. N., Kuranova, I. P., Popov, A. N., Teplyakov, A. V., Obmolova, G. V., Rusakov, A. A., Vainshtein, B. K., Dodson, G. G., Wilson, J. C., et al. 1995. The structure of deoxy- and oxy-leghaemoglobin from lupin. *J. Mol. Biol.* 251:104–115.

Flaherty, K. M., McKay, D. B., Kabsch, W., and Holmes, K. C. 1991. Similarity of the three-dimensional structures of actin and the ATPase fragment of a 70-kDa heat shock cognate protein. *Proc. Natl. Acad. Sci. U.S.A.* 88:5041–5045.

Murzin, A. G., Brenner, S. E., Hubbard, T., and Chothia, C. 1995. SCOP: A structural classification of proteins database for the investigation of sequences and structures. *J. Mol. Biol.* 247: 536–540.

Hadley, C., and Jones, D. T. 1999. A systematic comparison of protein structure classification: SCOP, CATH and FSSP. *Struct. Fold. Des.* 7:1099–1112.

Domain Detection

Marchler-Bauer, A., Anderson, J. B., DeWeese-Scott, C., Fedorova, N. D., Geer, L. Y., He, S., Hurwitz, D. I., Jackson, J. D., Jacobs, A. R., Lanczycki, C. J., Liebert, C. A., Liu, C., Madej, T., Marchler, G. H., Mazumder, R., Nikolskaya, A. N., Panchenko, A. R., Rao, B. S., Shoemaker, B. A., Simonyan, V., Song, J. S., Thiessen, P. A., Vasudevan, S., Wang, Y., Yamashita, R. A., Yin, J. J., and Bryant, S. H. 2003. CDD: A curated Entrez database of conserved domain alignments. *Nucleic Acids Res.* 31:383–387.

Ploegman, J. H., Drent, G., Kalk, K. H., and Hol, W. G. 1978. Structure of bovine liver rhodanese I: Structure determination at 2.5 Å resolution and a comparison of the conformation and sequence of its two domains. *J. Mol. Biol.* 123:557–594.

Nikolov, D. B., Hu, S. H., Lin, J., Gasch, A., Hoffmann, A., Horikoshi, M., Chua, N. H., Roeder, R. G., and Burley, S. K. 1992. Crystal structure of TFIID TATA-box binding protein. *Nature* 360: 40–46.

Doolittle, R. F. 1995. The multiplicity of domains in proteins. *Annu. Rev. Biochem.* 64:287–314.

Heger, A., and Holm, L. 2000. Rapid automatic detection and alignment of repeats in protein sequences. *Proteins* 41:224–237.

Evolutionary Trees

Wolf, Y. I., Rogozin, I. B., Grishin, N. V., and Koonin, E. V. 2002. Genome trees and the tree of life. *Trends Genet.* 18:472–479.

Doolittle, R. F. 1992. Stein and Moore Award address. Reconstructing history with amino acid sequences. *Protein Sci.* 1:191–200.

Zuckerkandl, E., and Pauling, L. 1965. Molecules as documents of evolutionary history. *J. Theor. Biol.* 8:357–366.

Ancient DNA

Green, R. E., Malaspinas, A.-S., Krause, J., Briggs, A. W., Johnson, P. L. F., Uhler, C., Meyer, M., Good, J. M., Maricic, T., Stenzel, U., Prüfer, K., Siebauer, M., Burbano, H. A., Ronan, M., Rothberg, J. M., Egholm, M., Rudan, P., Brajković, D., Kućan, Ž., Gušić, I., Wikström, M., Laakkonen, L., Kelso, J., Slatkin, M., and Pääbo, S. 2008. A complete Neandertal mitochondrial genome sequence determined by high-throughput sequencing. *Cell* 134:416–426.

Pääbo, S., Poinar, H., Serre, D., Jaenicke-Despres, V., Hebler, J., Rohland, N., Kuch, M., Krause, J., Vigilant, L., and Hofreiter, M. 2004. Genetic analyses from ancient DNA. *Annu. Rev. Genet.* 38:645–679.

Krings, M., Stone, A., Schmitz, R. W., Krainitzki, H., Stoneking, M., and Pääbo, S. 1997. Neandertal DNA sequences and the origin of modern humans. *Cell* 90:19–30.

Krings, M., Geisert, H., Schmitz, R. W., Krainitzki, H., and Pääbo, S. 1999. DNA sequence of the mitochondrial hypervariable region II from the Neanderthal type specimen. *Proc. Natl. Acad. Sci. U.S.A.* 96:5581–5585.

Evolution in the Laboratory

Sassanfar, M., and Szostak, J. W. 1993. An RNA motif that binds ATP. *Nature* 364:550–553.

Gold, L., Polisky, B., Uhlenbeck, O., and Yarus, M. 1995. Diversity of oligonucleotide functions. *Annu. Rev. Biochem.* 64:763–797.

Wilson, D. S., and Szostak, J. W. 1999. In vitro selection of functional nucleic acids. *Annu. Rev. Biochem.* 68:611–647.

Hermann, T., and Patel, D. J. 2000. Adaptive recognition by nucleic acid aptamers. *Science* 287:820–825.

Web Sites

The Protein Data Bank (PDB) site is the repository for three-dimensional macromolecular structures. It currently contains more than 30,000 structures. (http://www.rcsb.org/pdb/).

National Center for Biotechnology Information (NCBI) contains molecular biological databases and software for analysis. (http://www.ncbi.nlm.nih.gov/).

Chapter 7

Where to Start

Perutz, M. F. 1978. Hemoglobin structure and respiratory transport. *Sci. Am.* 239(6):92–125.

Perutz, M. F. 1980. Stereochemical mechanism of oxygen transport by haemoglobin. *Proc. R. Soc. Lond. Biol. Sci.* 208:135–162.

Kilmartin, J. V. 1976. Interaction of haemoglobin with protons, CO_2, and 2,3-diphosphoglycerate. *Brit. Med. Bull.* 32:209–222.

Structure

Kendrew, J. C., Bodo, G., Dintzis, H. M., Parrish, R. G., Wyckoff, H., and Phillips, D. C. 1958. A three-dimensional model of the myoglobin molecule obtained by x-ray analysis. *Nature* 181:662–666.

Shaanan, B. 1983. Structure of human oxyhaemoglobin at 2.1 Å resolution. *J. Mol. Biol.* 171:31–59.

Frier, J. A., and Perutz, M. F. 1977. Structure of human foetal deoxyhaemoglobin. *J. Mol. Biol.* 112:97–112.

Perutz, M. F. 1969. Structure and function of hemoglobin. *Harvey Lect.* 63:213–261.

Perutz, M. F. 1962. Relation between structure and sequence of haemoglobin. *Nature* 194:914–917.

Interaction of Hemoglobin with Allosteric Effectors

Benesch, R., and Beesch, R. E. 1969. Intracellular organic phosphates as regulators of oxygen release by haemoglobin. *Nature* 221:618–622.

Fang, T. Y., Zou, M., Simplaceanu, V., Ho, N. T., and Ho, C. 1999. Assessment of roles of surface histidyl residues in the molecular basis of the Bohr effect and of β 143 histidine in the binding of 2,3-bisphosphoglycerate in human normal adult hemoglobin. *Biochemistry* 38:13423–13432.

Arnone, A. 1992. X-ray diffraction study of binding of 2,3-diphosphoglycerate to human deoxyhaemoglobin. *Nature* 237:146–149.

Models for Cooperativity

Monod, J., Wyman, J., and Changeux, J.-P. 1965. On the nature of allosteric interactions: A plausible model. *J. Mol. Biol.* 12:88–118.

Koshland, D. L., Jr., Nemethy, G., and Filmer, D. 1966. Comparison of experimental binding data and theoretical models in proteins containing subunits. *Biochemistry* 5:365–385.

Ackers, G. K., Doyle, M. L., Myers, D., and Daugherty, M. A. 1992. Molecular code for cooperativity in hemoglobin. *Science* 255: 54–63.

Sickle-Cell Anemia and Thalasssemia

Herrick, J. B. 1910. Peculiar elongated and sickle-shaped red blood corpuscles in a case of severe anemia. *Arch. Intern. Med.* 6: 517–521.

Pauling, L., Itano, H. A., Singer, S. J., and Wells, L. C. 1949. Sickle cell anemia: A molecular disease. *Science* 110:543–548.

Ingram, V. M. 1957. Gene mutation in human hemoglobin: The chemical difference between normal and sickle cell haemoglobin. *Nature* 180:326–328.

Eaton, W. A., and Hofrichter, J. 1990. Sickle cell hemoglobin polymerization. *Adv. Prot. Chem.* 40:63–279.

Weatherall, D. J. 2001. Phenotype genotype relationships in monogenic disease: Lessons from the thalassemias. *Nat. Rev. Genet.* 2:245–255.

Globin-Binding Proteins and Other Globins

Kihm, A. J., Kong, Y., Hong, W., Russell, J. E., Rouda, S., Adachi, K., Simon, M. C., Blobel, G. A., and Weiss, M. J. 2002. An abundant erythroid protein that stabilizes free α-haemoglobin. *Nature* 417:758–763.

Feng, L., Zhou, S., Gu, L., Gell, D. A., Mackay, J. P., Weiss, M. J., Gow, A. J., and Shi, Y. 2005. Structure of oxidized α-haemoglobin bound to AHSP reveals a protective mechanism for haem. *Nature* 435:697–701.

Yu, X., Kong, Y., Dore, L. C., Abdulmalik, O., Katein, A. M., Zhou, S., Choi, J. K., Gell, D., Mackay, J. P., Gow, A. J., and Weiss, M. J. 2007. An erythroid chaperone that facilitates folding of α-globin subunits for hemoglobin synthesis. *J. Clin. Invest.* 117:1856–1865.

Burmester, T., Haberkamp, M., Mitz, S., Roesner, A., Schmidt, M., Ebner, B., Gerlach, F., Fuchs, C., and Hankeln, T. 2004. Neuroglobin and cytoglobin: Genes, proteins and evolution. *IUBMB Life* 56:703–707.

Hankeln, T., Ebner, B., Fuchs, C., Gerlach, F., Haberkamp, M., Laufs, T. L., Roesner, A., Schmidt, M., Weich, B., Wystub, S., Saaler-Reinhardt, S., Reuss, S., Bolognesi, M., De Sanctis, D., Marden, M. C., Kiger, L., Moens, L., Dewilde, S., Nevo, E., Avivi, A., Weber, R. E., Fago, A., and Burmester, T. 2005. Neuroglobin and cytoglobin in search of their role in the vertebrate globin family. *J. Inorg. Biochem.* 99:110–119.

Burmester, T., Ebner, B., Weich, B., and Hankeln, T. 2002. Cytoglobin: A novel globin type ubiquitously expressed in vertebrate tissues. *Mol. Biol. Evol.* 19:416–421.

Zhang, C., Wang, C., Deng, M., Li, L., Wang, H., Fan, M., Xu, W., Meng, F., Qian, L., and He, F. 2002. Full-length cDNA cloning of human neuroglobin and tissue expression of rat neuroglobin. *Biochem. Biophys. Res. Commun.* 290:1411–1419

Chapter 8

Where to Start

Zalatan, J. G., and Herschlag, D. 2009. The far reaches of enzymology. *Nat. Chem. Biol.* 5:516–520.

Hammes, G. G. 2008. How do enzymes really work? *J. Biol. Chem.* 283:22337–22346.

Koshland, D. E., Jr. 1987. Evolution of catalytic function. *Cold Spring Harbor Symp. Quant. Biol.* 52:1–7.

Jencks, W. P. 1987. Economics of enzyme catalysis. *Cold Spring Harbor Symp. Quant. Biol.* 52:65–73.

Lerner, R. A., and Tramontano, A. 1988. Catalytic antibodies. *Sci. Am.* 258(3):58–70.

Books

Cook, P. F., and Cleland, W. W. 2007. *Enzyme Kinetics and Mechanism.* Garland Press.

Fersht, A. 1999. *Structure and Mechanism in Protein Science: A Guide to Enzyme Catalysis and Protein Folding.* W. H. Freeman and Company.

Walsh, C. 1979. *Enzymatic Reaction Mechanisms.* W. H. Freeman and Company.

Page, M. I., and Williams, A. (Eds.). 1987. *Enzyme Mechanisms.* Royal Society of Chemistry.

Bender, M. L., Bergeron, R. J., and Komiyama, M. 1984. *The Bioorganic Chemistry of Enzymatic Catalysis.* Wiley-Interscience.

Abelson, J. N., and Simon, M. I. (Eds.). 1992. *Methods in Enzymology.* Academic Press.

Boyer, P. D. (Ed.). 1970. *The Enzymes* (3d ed.). Academic Press.

Friedmann, H. C. (Ed.). 1981. *Benchmark Papers in Biochemistry.* Vol. 1, *Enzymes.* Hutchinson Ross.

Transition-State Stabilization, Analogs, and Other Enzyme Inhibitors

Schramm, V. L. 2007. Enzymatic transition state theory and transition state analog design. *J. Biol. Chem.* 282:28297–28300.

Pauling, L. 1948. Nature of forces between large molecules of biological interest. *Nature* 161:707–709.

Leinhard, G. E. 1973. Enzymatic catalysis and transition-state theory. *Science* 180:149–154.

Kraut, J. 1988. How do enzymes work? Science 242:533–540.

Waxman, D. J., and Strominger, J. L. 1983. Penicillin-binding proteins and the mechanism of action of β-lactam antibiotics. *Annu. Rev. Biochem.* 52:825–869.

Abraham, E. P. 1981. The β-lactam antibiotics. *Sci. Am.* 244:76–86.

Walsh, C. T. 1984. Suicide substrates, mechanism-based enzyme inactivators: Recent developments. *Annu. Rev. Biochem.* 53:493–535.

Catalytic Antibodies

Hilvert, D. 2000. Critical analysis of antibody catalysis. *Annu. Rev. Biochem.* 69:751–794.

Wade, H., and Scanlan, T. S. 1997. The structural and functional basis of antibody catalysis. *Annu. Rev. Biophys. Biomol. Struct.* 26:461–493.

Lerner, R. A., Benkovic, S. J., and Schultz, P. G. 1991. At the crossroads of chemistry and immunology: Catalytic antibodies. *Science* 252:659–667.

Cochran, A. G., and Schultz, P. G. 1990. Antibody-catalyzed porphyrin metallation. *Science* 249:781–783.

Enzyme Kinetics and Mechanisms

Hammes-Schiller, S. and Benkovic, S. J. 2006. Relating protein motion to catalysis. *Annu. Rev. Biochem.* 75:519–541.

Benkovic, S. J., and Hammes-Schiller, S. 2003. A perspective on enzyme catalysis. *Science* 301:1196–1202.

Hur, S., and Bruice, T. C. 2003. The near attack conformation approach to the study of the chorismate to prephenate reaction. *Proc. Natl. Acad. Sci. U.S.A.* 100:12015–12020.

Xie, X. S., and Lu, H. P. 1999. Single-molecule enzymology. *J. Biol. Chem.* 274:15967–15970.

Miles, E. W., Rhee, S., and Davies, D. R. 1999. The molecular basis of substrate channeling. *J. Biol. Chem.* 274:12193–12196.

Warshel, A. 1998. Electrostatic origin of the catalytic power of enzymes and the role of preorganized active sites. *J. Biol. Chem.* 273:27035–27038.

Cannon, W. R., and Benkovic, S. J. 1999. Solvation, reorganization energy, and biological catalysis. *J. Biol. Chem.* 273:26257–26260.

Cleland, W. W., Frey, P. A., and Gerlt, J. A. 1998. The low barrier hydrogen bond in enzymatic catalysis. *J. Biol. Chem.* 273:25529–25532.

Romesberg, F. E., Santarsiero, B. D., Spiller, B., Yin, J., Barnes, D., Schultz, P. G., and Stevens, R. C. 1998. Structural and kinetic evidence for strain in biological catalysis. *Biochemistry* 37:14404–14409.

Lu, H. P., Xun, L., and Xie, X. S. 1998. Single-molecule enzymatic dynamics. *Science* 282:1877–1882.

Fersht, A. R., Leatherbarrow, R. J., and Wells, T. N. C. 1986. Binding energy and catalysis: A lesson from protein engineering of the tyrosyl-tRNA synthetase. *Trends Biochem. Sci.* 11:321–325.

Jencks, W. P. 1975. Binding energy, specificity, and enzymic catalysis: The Circe effect. *Adv. Enzymol.* 43:219–410.

Knowles, J. R., and Albery, W. J. 1976. Evolution of enzyme function and the development of catalytic efficiency. *Biochemistry* 15:5631–5640.

Chapter 9

Where to Start

Stroud, R. M. 1974. A family of protein-cutting proteins. *Sci. Am.* 231(1):74–88.

Kraut, J. 1977. Serine proteases: Structure and mechanism of catalysis. *Annu. Rev. Biochem.* 46:331–358.

Lindskog, S. 1997. Structure and mechanism of carbonic anhydrase. *Pharmacol. Ther.* 74:1–20.

Jeltsch, A., Alves, J., Maass, G., and Pingoud, A. 1992. On the catalytic mechanism of *Eco*RI and *Eco*RV: A detailed proposal based on biochemical results, structural data and molecular modelling. *FEBS Lett.* 304:4–8.

Bauer, C. B., Holden, H. M., Thoden, J. B., Smith, R., and Rayment, I. 2000. X-ray structures of the apo and MgATP-bound states of *Dictyostelium discoideum* myosin motor domain. *J. Biol. Chem.* 275:38494–38499.

Lolis, E., and Petsko, G. A. 1990. Transition-state analogues in protein crystallography: Probes of the structural source of enzyme catalysis. *Annu. Rev. Biochem.* 59:597–630.

Books

Fersht, A. 1999. *Structure and Mechanism in Protein Science: A Guide to Enzyme Catalysis and Protein Folding.* W. H. Freeman and Company.

Silverman, R. B. 2000. *The Organic Chemistry of Enzyme-Catalyzed Reactions.* Academic Press.

Page, M., and Williams, A. 1997. *Organic and Bio-organic Mechanisms.* Addison Wesley Longman.

Chymotrypsin and Other Serine Proteases

Fastrez, J., and Fersht, A. R. 1973. Demonstration of the acyl-enzyme mechanism for the hydrolysis of peptides and anilides by chymotrypsin. *Biochemistry* 12:2025–2034.

Sigler, P. B., Blow, D. M., Matthews, B. W., and Henderson, R. 1968. Structure of crystalline-chymotrypsin II: A preliminary report including a hypothesis for the activation mechanism. *J. Mol. Biol.* 35:143–164.

Kossiakoff, A. A., and Spencer, S. A. 1981. Direct determination of the protonation states of aspartic acid-102 and histidine-57 in the tetrahedral intermediate of the serine proteases: Neutron structure of trypsin. *Biochemistry* 20:6462–6474.

Carter, P., and Wells, J. A. 1988. Dissecting the catalytic triad of a serine protease. *Nature* 332:564–568.

Carter, P., and Wells, J. A. 1990. Functional interaction among catalytic residues in subtilisin BPN′. *Proteins* 7:335–342.

Koepke, J., Ermler, U., Warkentin, E., Wenzl, G., and Flecker, P. 2000. Crystal structure of cancer chemopreventive Bowman-Birk inhibitor in ternary complex with bovine trypsin at 2.3 Å resolution: Structural basis of Janus-faced serine protease inhibitor specificity. *J. Mol. Biol.* 298:477–491.

Gaboriaud, C., Rossi, V., Bally, I., Arlaud, G. J., and Fontecilla-Camps, J. C. 2000. Crystal structure of the catalytic domain of human complement C1s: A serine protease with a handle. *EMBO J.* 19:1755–1765.

Other Proteases

Vega, S., Kang, L. W., Velazquez-Campoy, A., Kiso, Y., Amzel, L. M., and Freire, E. 2004. A structural and thermodynamic escape mechanism from a drug resistant mutation of the HIV-1 protease. *Proteins* 55:594–602.

Kamphuis, I. G., Kalk, K. H., Swarte, M. B., and Drenth, J. 1984. Structure of papain refined at 1.65 Å resolution. *J. Mol. Biol.* 179:233–256.

Kamphuis, I. G., Drenth, J., and Baker, E. N. 1985. Thiol proteases: Comparative studies based on the high-resolution structures of papain and actinidin, and on amino acid sequence information for cathepsins B and H, and stem bromelain. *J. Mol. Biol.* 182:317–329.

Sivaraman, J., Nagler, D. K., Zhang, R., Menard, R., and Cygler, M. 2000. Crystal structure of human procathepsin X: A cysteine protease with the proregion covalently linked to the active site cysteine. *J. Mol. Biol.* 295:939–951.

Davies, D. R. 1990. The structure and function of the aspartic proteinases. *Annu. Rev. Biophys. Biophys. Chem.* 19:189–215.

Dorsey, B. D., Levin, R. B., McDaniel, S. L., Vacca, J. P., Guare, J. P., Darke, P. L., Zugay, J. A., Emini, E. A., Schleif, W. A., Quintero, J. C., et al. 1994. L-735,524: The design of a potent and orally bioavailable HIV protease inhibitor. *J. Med. Chem.* 37:3443–3451.

Chen, Z., Li, Y., Chen, E., Hall, D. L., Darke, P. L., Culberson, C., Shafer, J. A., and Kuo, L. C. 1994. Crystal structure at 1.9-Å resolution of human immunodeficiency virus (HIV) II protease complexed with L-735,524, an orally bioavailable inhibitor of the HIV proteases. *J. Biol. Chem.* 269:26344–26348.

Ollis, D. L., Cheah, E., Cygler, M., Dijkstra, B., Frolow, F., Franken, S. M., Harel, M., Remington, S. J., Silman, I., Schrag, J., et al. 1992. The α/β hydrolase fold. *Protein Eng.* 5:197–211.

Carbonic Anhydrase

Strop, P., Smith, K. S., Iverson, T. M., Ferry, J. G., and Rees, D. C. 2001. Crystal structure of the "cab"-type beta class carbonic anhydrase from the archaeon *Methanobacterium thermoautotrophicum.* *J. Biol. Chem.* 276:10299–10305.

Lindskog, S., and Coleman, J. E. 1973. The catalytic mechanism of carbonic anhydrase. *Proc. Natl. Acad. Sci. U.S.A.* 70:2505–2508.

Kannan, K. K., Notstrand, B., Fridborg, K., Lovgren, S., Ohlsson, A., and Petef, M. 1975. Crystal structure of human erythrocyte carbonic anhydrase B: Three-dimensional structure at a nominal 2.2-Å resolution. *Proc. Natl. Acad. Sci. U.S.A.* 72:51–55.

Boriack-Sjodin, P. A., Zeitlin, S., Chen, H. H., Crenshaw, L., Gross, S., Dantanarayana, A., Delgado, P., May, J. A., Dean, T., and Christianson, D. W. 1998. Structural analysis of inhibitor binding to human carbonic anhydrase II. *Protein Sci.* 7:2483–2489.

Wooley, P. 1975. Models for metal ion function in carbonic anhydrase. *Nature* 258:677–682.

Jonsson, B. H., Steiner, H., and Lindskog, S. 1976. Participation of buffer in the catalytic mechanism of carbonic anhydrase. *FEBS Lett.* 64:310–314.

Sly, W. S., and Hu, P. Y. 1995. Human carbonic anhydrases and carbonic anhydrase deficiencies. *Annu. Rev. Biochem.* 64:375–401.

Maren, T. H. 1988. The kinetics of HCO_3^- synthesis related to fluid secretion, pH control, and CO_2 elimination. *Annu. Rev. Physiol.* 50:695–717.

Kisker, C., Schindelin, H., Alber, B. E., Ferry, J. G., and Rees, D. C. 1996. A left-hand beta-helix revealed by the crystal structure of a carbonic anhydrase from the archaeon *Methanosarcina thermophila*. *EMBO J.* 15:2323–2330.

Restriction Enzymes

Selvaraj, S., Kono, H., and Sarai, A. 2002. Specificity of protein-DNA recognition revealed by structure-based potentials: Symmetric/asymmetric and cognate/non-cognate binding. *J. Mol. Biol.* 322:907–915.

Winkler, F. K., Banner, D. W., Oefner, C., Tsernoglou, D., Brown, R. S., Heathman, S. P., Bryan, R. K., Martin, P. D., Petratos, K., and Wilson, K. S. 1993. The crystal structure of *Eco*RV endonuclease and of its complexes with cognate and non-cognate DNA fragments. *EMBO J.* 12:1781–1795.

Kostrewa, D., and Winkler, F. K. 1995. Mg^{2+} binding to the active site of *Eco*RV endonuclease: A crystallographic study of complexes with substrate and product DNA at 2 Å resolution. *Biochemistry* 34:683–696.

Athanasiadis, A., Vlassi, M., Kotsifaki, D., Tucker, P. A., Wilson, K. S., and Kokkinidis, M. 1994. Crystal structure of *Pvu*II endonuclease reveals extensive structural homologies to *Eco*RV. *Nat. Struct. Biol.* 1:469–475.

Sam, M. D., and Perona, J. J. 1999. Catalytic roles of divalent metal ions in phosphoryl transfer by *Eco*RV endonuclease. *Biochemistry* 38:6576–6586.

Jeltsch, A., and Pingoud, A. 1996. Horizontal gene transfer contributes to the wide distribution and evolution of type II restriction-modification systems. *J. Mol. Evol.* 42:91–96.

Myosins

Grigorenko, B. L., Rogov, A. V., Topol, I. A., Burt, S. K., Martinez, H. M., and Nemukhin, A. V. 2007. Mechanism of the myosin catalyzed hydrolysis of ATP as rationalized by molecular modeling. *Proc. Natl. Acad. Sci. U.S.A.* 104:7057–7061.

Gulick, A. M., Bauer, C. B., Thoden, J. B., and Rayment, I. 1997. X-ray structures of the MgADP, MgATPγS, and MgAMPPNP complexes of the *Dictyostelium discoideum* myosin motor domain. *Biochemistry* 36:11619–11628.

Kovacs, M., Malnasi-Csizmadia, A., Woolley, R. J., and Bagshaw, C. R. 2002. Analysis of nucleotide binding to *Dictyostelium* myosin II motor domains containing a single tryptophan near the active site. *J. Biol. Chem.* 277:28459–28467.

Kuhlman, P. A., and Bagshaw, C. R. 1998. ATPase kinetics of the *Dictyostelium discoideum* myosin II motor domain. *J. Muscle Res. Cell Motil.* 19:491–504.

Smith, C. A., and Rayment, I. 1996. X-ray structure of the magnesium(II) ADP vanadate complex of the *Dictyostelium discoideum* myosin motor domain to 1.9 Å resolution. *Biochemistry* 35: 5404–5417.

Chapter 10

Where to Start

Kantrowitz, E. R., and Lipscomb, W. N. 1990. *Escherichia coli* aspartate transcarbamoylase: The molecular basis for a concerted allosteric transition. *Trends Biochem. Sci.* 15:53–59.

Schachman, H. K. 1988. Can a simple model account for the allosteric transition of aspartate transcarbamoylase? *J. Biol. Chem.* 263: 18583–18586.

Neurath, H. 1989. Proteolytic processing and physiological regulation. *Trends Biochem. Sci.* 14:268–271.

Bode, W., and Huber, R. 1992. Natural protein proteinase inhibitors and their interaction with proteinases. *Eur. J. Biochem.* 204:433–451.

Aspartate Transcarbamoylase and Allosteric Interactions

Rabinowitz, J. D., Hsiao, J. J., Gryncel, K. R., Kantrowitz, E. R., Feng, X.-J., Li, G., and Rabitz H. 2008. Dissecting enzyme regulation by multiple allosteric effectors: Nucleotide regulation of aspartate transcarbamoylase. *Biochemistry* 47:5881–5888.

West, J. M., Tsuruta, H., and Kantrowitz, E. R. 2004. A fluorescent probe-labeled *Escherichia coli* aspartate transcarbamoylase that monitors the allosteric conformation state. *J. Biol. Chem.* 279:945–951.

Endrizzi, J. A., Beernink, P. T., Alber, T., and Schachman, H. K. 2000. Binding of bisubstrate analog promotes large structural changes in the unregulated catalytic trimer of aspartate transcarbamoylase: Implications for allosteric regulation. *Proc. Natl. Acad. Sci. U. S. A.* 97:5077–5082.

Beernink, P. T., Endrizzi, J. A., Alber, T., and Schachman, H. K. 1999. Assessment of the allosteric mechanism of aspartate transcarbamoylase based on the crystalline structure of the unregulated catalytic subunit. *Proc. Natl. Acad. Sci. U.S.A.* 96:5388–5393.

Wales, M. E., Madison, L. L., Glaser, S. S., and Wild, J. R. 1999. Divergent allosteric patterns verify the regulatory paradigm for aspartate transcarbamoylase. *J. Mol. Biol.* 294:1387–1400.

Eisenstein, E., Markby, D. W., and Schachman, H. K. 1990. Heterotropic effectors promote a global conformational change in aspartate transcarbamoylase. *Biochemistry* 29:3724–3731.

Newell, J. O., Markby, D. W., and Schachman, H. K. 1989. Cooperative binding of the bisubstrate analog N-(phosphonacetyl)-L-aspartate to aspartate transcarbamoylase and the heterotropic effects of ATP and CTP. *J. Biol. Chem.* 264:2476–2481.

Stevens, R. C., Reinisch, K. M., and Lipscomb, W. N. 1991. Molecular structure of *Bacillus subtilis* aspartate transcarbamoylase at 3.0 Å resolution. *Proc. Natl. Acad. Sci. U.S.A.* 88:6087–6091.

Stevens, R. C., Gouaux, J. E., and Lipscomb, W. N. 1990. Structural consequences of effector binding to the T state of aspartate carbamoyltransferase: Crystal structures of the unligated and ATP- and CTP-complexed enzymes at 2.6-Å resolution. *Biochemistry* 29:7691–7701.

Gouaux, J. E., and Lipscomb, W. N. 1990. Crystal structures of phosphonoacetamide ligated T and phosphonoacetamide and malonate ligated R states of aspartate carbamoyltransferase at 2.8-Å resolution and neutral pH. *Biochemistry* 29:389–402.

Labedan, B., Boyen, A., Baetens, M., Charlier, D., Chen, P., Cunin, R., Durbeco, V., Glansdorff, N., Herve, G., Legrain, C., Liang, Z., Purcarea, C., Roovers, M., Sanchez, R., Toong, T. L., Van de Casteele, M., van Vliet, F., Xu, Y., and Zhang, Y. F. 1999. The evolutionary history of carbamoyltransferases: A complex set of paralogous genes was already present in the last universal common ancestor. *J. Mol. Evol.* 49:461–473.

Covalent Modification

Tarrant, M. K., and Cole, P.A. 2009. The chemical biology of protein phosphorylation *Annu. Rev. Biochem.* 78:797–825.

Johnson, L. N., and Barford, D. 1993. The effects of phosphorylation on the structure and function of proteins. *Annu. Rev. Biophys. Biomol. Struct.* 22:199–232.

Ziegler, M. 2000. New functions of a long-known molecule: Emerging roles of NAD in cellular signaling. *Eur. J. Biochem.* 267:1550–1564.

Ng, H. H., and Bird, A. 2000. Histone deacetylases: Silencers for hire. *Trends Biochem. Sci.* 25:121–126.

Jacobson, M. K., and Jacobson, E. L. 1999. Discovering new ADP-ribose polymer cycles: Protecting the genome and more. *Trends Biochem. Sci.* 24:415–417.

Barford, D., Das, A. K., and Egloff, M. P. 1998. The structure and mechanism of protein phosphatases: Insights into catalysis and regulation. *Annu. Rev. Biophys. Biomol. Struct.* 27:133–164.

Protein Kinase A

Taylor, S. S., Knighton, D. R., Zheng, J., Sowadski, J. M., Gibbs, C. S., and Zoller, M. J. 1993. A template for the protein kinase family. *Trends Biochem. Sci.* 18:84–89.

Gibbs, C. S., Knighton, D. R., Sowadski, J. M., Taylor, S. S., and Zoller, M. J. 1992. Systematic mutational analysis of cAMP-dependent protein kinase identifies unregulated catalytic subunits and defines regions important for the recognition of the regulatory subunit. *J. Biol. Chem.* 267:4806–4814.

Knighton, D. R., Zheng, J. H., TenEyck, L., Ashford, V. A., Xuong, N. H., Taylor, S. S., and Sowadski, J. M. 1991. Crystal structure of the catalytic subunit of cyclic adenosine monophosphate-dependent protein kinase. *Science* 253:407–414.

Knighton, D. R., Zheng, J. H., TenEyck, L., Xuong, N. H., Taylor, S. S., and Sowadski, J. M. 1991. Structure of a peptide inhibitor bound to the catalytic subunit of cyclic adenosine monophosphate-dependent protein kinase. *Science* 253:414–420.

Adams, S. R., Harootunian, A. T., Buechler, Y. J., Taylor, S. S., and Tsien, R. Y. 1991. Fluorescence ratio imaging of cyclic AMP in single cells. *Nature* 349:694–697.

Zymogen Activation

Neurath, H. 1986. The versatility of proteolytic enzymes. *J. Cell. Biochem.* 32:35–49.

Bode, W., and Huber, R. 1986. Crystal structure of pancreatic serine endopeptidases. In *Molecular and Cellular Basis of Digestion* (pp. 213–234), edited by P. Desnuelle, H. Sjostrom, and O. Noren. Elsevier.

James, M. N. 1991. Refined structure of porcine pepsinogen at 1.8 Å resolution. *J. Mol. Biol.* 219:671–692.

Protease Inhibitors

Carrell, R., and Travis, J. 1985. α_1-Antitrypsin and the serpins: Variation and countervariation. *Trends Biochem. Sci.* 10:20–24.

Carp, H., Miller, F., Hoidal, J. R., and Janoff, A. 1982. Potential mechanism of emphysema: α_1-Proteinase inhibitor recovered from lungs of cigarette smokers contains oxidized methionine and has decreased elastase inhibitory capacity. *Proc. Natl. Acad. Sci. U.S.A.* 79:2041–2045.

Owen, M. C., Brennan, S. O., Lewis, J. H., and Carrell, R. W. 1983. Mutation of antitrypsin to antithrombin. *New Engl. J. Med.* 309:694–698.

Travis, J., and Salvesen, G. S. 1983. Human plasma proteinase inhibitors. *Annu. Rev. Biochem.* 52:655–709.

Clotting Cascade

Furie, B., and Furie, B. C. 2008. Mechanisms of thrombus formation. *New Engl. J. Med.* 359:938–949.

Orfeo, T., Brufatto, N., Nesheim, M. E., Xu, H., Butenas, S., and Mann, K. G. 2004. The factor V activation paradox. *J. Biol. Chem.* 279:19580–19591.

Mann, K. G. 2003. Thrombin formation. *Chest* 124:4S–10S.

Rose, T., and Di Cera, E. 2002. Three-dimensional modeling of thrombin–fibrinogen interaction. *J. Biol. Chem.* 277:18875–18880.

Krem, M. M., and Di Cera, E. 2002. Evolution of cascades from embryonic development to blood coagulation. *Trends Biochem. Sci.* 27: 67–74.

Fuentes-Prior, P., Iwanaga, Y., Huber, R., Pagila, R., Rumennik, G., Seto, M., Morser, J., Light, D. R., and Bode, W. 2000. Structural basis for the anticoagulant activity of the thrombin–thrombomodulin complex. *Nature* 404:518–525.

Lawn, R. M., and Vehar, G. A. 1986. The molecular genetics of hemophilia. *Sci. Am.* 254(3):48–65.

Brown, J. H., Volkmann, N., Jun, G., Henschen-Edman, A. H., and Cohen, C. 2000. The crystal structure of modified bovine fibrinogen. *Proc. Natl. Acad. Sci. U.S.A.* 97:85–90.

Stubbs, M. T., Oschkinat, H., Mayr, I., Huber, R., Angliker, H., Stone, S. R., and Bode, W. 1992. The interaction of thrombin with fibrinogen: A structural basis for its specificity. *Eur. J. Biochem.* 206:187–195.

Chapter 11

Where to Start

Glycochemistry and glycobiology. A series of review articles. 2007. *Nature* 446:999–1051.

Maeder, T. 2002. Sweet medicines. *Sci. Am.* 287(1):40–47.

Sharon, N., and Lis, H. 1993. Carbohydrates in cell recognition. *Sci. Am.* 268(1):82–89.

Lasky, L. A. 1992. Selectins: Interpreters of cell-specific carbohydrate information during inflammation. *Science* 258:964–969.

Woods, R. J. 1995. Three-dimensional structures of oligosaccharides. *Curr. Opin. Struct. Biol.* 5:591–598.

Books

Varki, A., Cummings, R., Esko, J., Freeze, H., Stanley, P., Bertozzi, C., Hart, G., and Etzler, M. E. 2009. *Essentials of Glycobiology*, 2d ed. Cold Spring Harbor Laboratory Press.

Stick, R. V., and Williams, S. 2008. *Carbohydrates: The Essential Molecules of Life*, 2d ed. Elsevier Science.

Sansome, C., and Markman, O. 2007. *Glycobiology*. Scion.

Lindhorst, T. K. 2007. *Essentials of Carbohydrate Chemistry and Biochemistry*, 3d ed. Wiley-VCH.

Taylor, M. E. 2006. *Introduction to Glycobiology*, 2d ed. Oxford University Press.

Carbohydrate-Binding Proteins and Glycoproteins

Lairson, L. L., Henrissat, B., Davies, G. J., and Withers, S. G. 2008. Glycosyltransferases: Structures, functions and mechanisms. *Annu. Rev. Biochem.* 77:521–555.

Foley, R. N. 2008. Erythropoietin: Physiology and molecular mechanisms. *Heart Failure Rev.* 13:404–414.

Yan, A., and Lennarz, W. J. 2005. Unraveling the mechanism of protein N-glycosylation. *J. Biol. Chem.* 280:3121–3124.

Qasba, P. K., Ramakrishnan, B., and Boeggeman, E. 2005. Substrate-induced conformational changes in glycosyltransferases. *Trends Biochem. Sci.* 30:53–62.

Pratta, M. A., Yao, W., Decicco, C., Tortorella, M., Liu, R.-Q., Copeland, R. A., Magolda, R., Newton, R. C., Trzaskos, J. M., and Arner, E. C. 2003. Aggrecan protects cartilage collagen from proteolytic cleavage. *J. Biol. Chem.* 278:45539–45545.

Fisher, J. W. 2003. Erythropoietin: Physiology and pharmacology update. *Exp. Biol. Med.* 228:1–14.

Cheetham, J. C., Smith, D. M., Aoki, K. H., Stevenson, J. L., Hoeffel, T. J., Syed, R. S., Egrie, J., and Harvey, T. S. 1998. NMR structure of human erythropoietin and a comparison with its receptor bound conformation. *Nat. Struct. Biol.* 5:861–866.

Bouckaert, J., Hamelryck, T., Wyns, L., and Loris, R. 1999. Novel structures of plant lectins and their complexes with carbohydrates. *Curr. Opin. Struct. Biol.* 9:572–577.

Weis, W. I., and Drickamer, K. 1996. Structural basis of lectin–carbohydrate recognition. *Annu. Rev. Biochem.* 65:441–473.

Vyas, N. K. 1991. Atomic features of protein–carbohydrate interactions. *Curr. Opin. Struct. Biol.* 1:732–740.

Weis, W. I., Drickamer, K., and Hendrickson, W. A. 1992. Structure of a C-type mannose-binding protein complexed with an oligosaccharide. *Nature* 360:127–134.

Shaanan, B., Lis, H., and Sharon, N. 1991. Structure of a legume lectin with an ordered N-linked carbohydrate in complex with lactose. *Science* 254:862–866.

Glycoproteins

Hattrup, C. L., and Gendler, S. J. 2008. Structure and function of the cell surface (tethered) mucins. *Annu. Rev. Physiol.* 70:431–457.

Thorton, D. J., Rousseau, K., and McGuckin, M. A. 2008. Structure and function of mucins in airways mucus. *Annu. Rev. Physiol.* 70:459–486.

Rose, M. C., and Voynow, J. A. 2007. Respiratory tract mucin genes and mucin glycoproteins in health and disease. *Physiol. Rev.* 86:245–278.

Lamoureux, F., Baud'huin, M., Duplomb, L., Heymann, D., and Rédini, F. 2007. Proteoglycans: Key partners in bone cell biology. *Bioessays* 29:758–771.

Carraway, K. L., Funes, M., Workman, H. C., and Sweeney, C. 2007. Contribution of membrane mucins to tumor progression through modulation of cellular growth signaling pathways. *Curr. Top. Dev. Biol.* 78:1–22.

Bernfield, M., Götte, M., Park, P. W., Reizes, O., Fitzgerald, M. L., Lincecum, J., and Zako, M. 1999. Functions of cell surface heparan sulfate proteoglycans. *Annu. Rev. Biochem.* 68:729–777.

Iozzo, R. V. 1998. Matrix proteoglycans: From molecular design to cellular function. *Annu. Rev. Biochem.* 67:609–652.

Yanagishita, M., and Hascall, V. C. 1992. Cell surface heparan sulfate proteoglycans. *J. Biol. Chem.* 267:9451–9454.

Iozzo, R. V. 1999. The biology of small leucine-rich proteoglycans: Functional network of interactive proteins. *J. Biol. Chem.* 274:18843–18846.

Carbohydrates in Recognition Processes

Wasserman, P. M. 2008. Zona pellucida glycoproteins. *J. Biol. Chem.* 283:24285–24289.

Sharon, N. 2008. Lectins: Past, present and future. *Biochem. Soc. Trans.* 36:1457–1460.

Balzarini, J, 2007. Targeting the glycans of glycoproteins: A novel paradigm for antiviral therapy. *Nat. Rev. Microbiol.* 5:583–597.

Sharon, N. 2007. Lectins: Carbohydrate-specific reagents and biological recognition molecules. *J. Biol. Chem.* 282:2753–2764.

Stevens, J., Blixt, O., Tumpey, T. M., Taubenberger, J. K., Paulson, J. C., and Wilson, I. A. 2006. Structure and receptor specificity of hemagglutinin from an H5N1 influenza virus. *Science* 312: 404–409.

Cambi, A., Koopman, M., and Figdor, C. G. 2005. How C-type lectins detect pathogens. *Cell. Microbiol.* 7:481–488.

Turner, M. L. 1992. Cell adhesion molecules: A unifying approach to topographic biology. *Biol. Rev. Camb. Philos. Soc.* 67:359–377.

Feizi, T. 1992. Blood group–related oligosaccharides are ligands in cell-adhesion events. *Biochem. Soc. Trans.* 20:274–278.

Jessell, T. M., Hynes, M. A., and Dodd, J. 1990. Carbohydrates and carbohydrate-binding proteins in the nervous system. *Annu. Rev. Neurosci.* 13:227–255.

Clothia, C., and Jones, E. V. 1997. The molecular structure of cell adhesion molecules. *Annu. Rev. Biochem.* 66:823–862.

Carbohydrate Sequencing

Venkataraman, G., Shriver, Z., Raman, R., and Sasisekharan, R. 1999. Sequencing complex polysaccharides. *Science* 286:537–542.

Zhao, Y., Kent, S. B. H., and Chait, B. T. 1997. Rapid, sensitive structure analysis of oligosaccharides. *Proc. Natl. Acad. Sci. U.S.A.* 94:1629–1633.

Rudd, P. M., Guile, G. R., Küster, B., Harvey, D. J., Opdenakker, G., and Dwek, R. A. 1997. Oligosaccharide sequencing technology. *Nature* 388:205–207.

Chapter 12

Where to Start

De Weer, P. 2000. A century of thinking about cell membranes. *Annu. Rev. Physiol.* 62:919–926.

Bretscher, M. S. 1985. The molecules of the cell membrane. *Sci. Am.* 253(4):100–108.

Unwin, N., and Henderson, R. 1984. The structure of proteins in biological membranes. *Sci. Am.* 250(2):78–94.

Deisenhofer, J., and Michel, H. 1989. The photosynthetic reaction centre from the purple bacterium *Rhodopseudomonas viridis*. *EMBO J.* 8:2149–2170.

Singer, S. J., and Nicolson, G. L. 1972. The fluid mosaic model of the structure of cell membranes. *Science* 175:720–731.

Jacobson, K., Sheets, E. D., and Simson, R., 1995. Revisiting the fluid mosaic model of membranes. *Science* 268:1441–1442.

Books

Gennis, R. B. 1989. *Biomembranes: Molecular Structure and Function.* Springer Verlag.

Vance, D. E., and Vance, J. E. (Eds.). 1996. *Biochemistry of Lipids, Lipoproteins, and Membranes.* Elsevier.

Lipowsky, R., and Sackmann, E. 1995. *The Structure and Dynamics of Membranes.* Elsevier.

Racker, E. 1985. *Reconstitutions of Transporters, Receptors, and Pathological States.* Academic Press.

Tanford, C. 1980. *The Hydrophobic Effect: Formation of Micelles and Biological Membranes* (2d ed.). Wiley-Interscience.

Membrane Lipids and Dynamics

Lingwood, D., and Simons, K. 2010. Lipid rafts as a membrane-organizing principle. *Science.* 327:46–50.

Pike, L. J. 2009. The challenge of lipid rafts. *J. Lipid Res.* 50:S323–S328.

Simons, K., and Vaz, W. L. 2004. Model systems, lipid rafts, and cell membranes. *Annu. Rev. Biophys. Biomol. Struct.* 33:269–295.

Anderson, T. G., and McConnell, H. M. 2002. A thermodynamic model for extended complexes of cholesterol and phospholipid. *Biophys. J.* 83:2039–2052.

Saxton, M. J., and Jacobson, K. 1997. Single-particle tracking: Applications to membrane dynamics. *Annu. Rev. Biophys. Biomol. Struct.* 26:373–399.

Bloom, M., Evans, E., and Mouritsen, O. G. 1991. Physical properties of the fluid lipid-bilayer component of cell membranes: A perspective. *Q. Rev. Biophys.* 24:293–397.

Elson, E. L. 1986. Membrane dynamics studied by fluorescence correlation spectroscopy and photobleaching recovery. *Soc. Gen. Physiol. Ser.* 40:367–383.

Zachowski, A., and Devaux, P. F. 1990. Transmembrane movements of lipids. *Experientia* 46:644–656.

Devaux, P. F. 1992. Protein involvement in transmembrane lipid asymmetry. *Annu. Rev. Biophys. Biomol. Struct.* 21:417–439.

Silvius, J. R. 1992. Solubilization and functional reconstitution of biomembrane components. *Annu. Rev. Biophys. Biomol. Struct.* 21:323–348.

Yeagle, P. L., Albert, A. D., Boesze-Battaglia, K., Young, J., and Frye, J. 1990. Cholesterol dynamics in membranes. *Biophys. J.* 57:413–424.

Nagle, J. F., and Tristram-Nagle, S. 2000. Lipid bilayer structure. *Curr. Opin. Struct. Biol.* 10:474–480.

Dowhan, W. 1997. Molecular basis for membrane phospholipid diversity: Why are there so many lipids? *Annu. Rev. Biochem.* 66:199–232.

Huijbregts, R. P. H., de Kroon, A. I. P. M., and de Kruijff, B. 1998. Rapid transmembrane movement of newly synthesized phosphatidylethanolamine across the inner membrane of *Escherichia coli.* *J. Biol.Chem.* 273:18936–18942.

Structure of Membrane Proteins

Walian, P., Cross, T. A., and Jap, B. K. 2004. Structural genomics of membrane proteins. *Genome Biol.* 5:215.

Werten, P. J., Remigy, H. W., de Groot, B. L., Fotiadis, D., Philippsen, A., Stahlberg, H., Grubmuller, H., and Engel, A. 2002. Progress in the analysis of membrane protein structure and function. *FEBS Lett.* 529:65–72.

Popot, J.-L., and Engleman, D. M. 2000. Helical membrane protein folding, stability and evolution. *Annu. Rev. Biochem.* 69:881–922.

White, S. H., and Wimley, W. C. 1999. Membrane protein folding and stability: Physical principles. *Annu. Rev. Biophys. Biomol. Struct.* 28:319–365.

Marassi, F. M., and Opella, S. J. 1998. NMR structural studies of membrane proteins. *Curr. Opin. Struct. Biol.* 8:640–648.

Lipowsky, R. 1991. The conformation of membranes. *Nature* 349:475–481.

Altenbach, C., Marti, T., Khorana, H. G., and Hubbell, W. L. 1990. Transmembrane protein structure: Spin labeling of bacteriorhodopsin mutants. *Science* 248:1088–1092.

Fasman, G. D., and Gilbert, W. A. 1990. The prediction of transmembrane protein sequences and their conformation: An evaluation. *Trends Biochem. Sci.* 15:89–92.

Jennings, M. L. 1989. Topography of membrane proteins. *Annu. Rev. Biochem.* 58:999–1027.

Engelman, D. M., Steitz, T. A., and Goldman, A. 1986. Identifying non-polar transbilayer helices in amino acid sequences of membrane proteins. *Annu. Rev. Biophys. Biophys. Chem.* 15:321–353.

Udenfriend, S., and Kodukola, K. 1995. How glycosyl-phosphatidyl-inositol-anchored membrane proteins are made. *Annu. Rev. Biochem.* 64:563–591.

Intracellular Membranes

Skehel, J. J., and Wiley, D. C. 2000. Receptor binding and membrane fusion in virus entry: The influenza hemagglutinin. *Annu. Rev. Biochem.* 69:531–569.

Roth, M. G. 1999. Lipid regulators of membrane traffic through the Golgi complex. *Trends Cell Biol.* 9:174–179.

Jahn, R., and Sudhof, T. C. 1999. Membrane fusion and exocytosis. *Annu. Rev. Biochem.* 68:863–911.

Stroud, R. M., and Walter, P. 1999. Signal sequence recognition and protein targeting. *Curr. Opin. Struct. Biol.* 9:754–759.

Teter, S. A., and Klionsky, D. J. 1999. How to get a folded protein across a membrane. *Trends Cell Biol.* 9:428–431.

Hettema, E. H., Distel, B., and Tabak, H. F. 1999. Import of proteins into peroxisomes. *Biochim. Biophys. Acta* 1451:17–34.

Membrane Fusion

Sollner, T. H., and Rothman, J. E. 1996. Molecular machinery mediating vesicle budding, docking and fusion. *Experientia* 52:1021–1025.

Ungar, D., and Hughson, F. M. 2003. SNARE protein structure and function. *Annu. Rev. Cell Dev. Biol.* 19:493–517.

Chapter 13

Where to Start

Lancaster, C. R. 2004. Structural biology: Ion pump in the movies. *Nature* 432:286–287.

Unwin, N. 2003. Structure and action of the nicotinic acetylcholine receptor explored by electron microscopy. *FEBS Lett.* 555:91–95.

Abramson, J., Smirnova, I., Kasho, V., Verner, G., Iwata, S., and Kaback, H. R. 2003. The lactose permease of *Escherichia coli*: Overall structure, the sugar-binding site and the alternating access model for transport. *FEBS Lett.* 555:96–101.

Lienhard, G. E., Slot, J. W., James, D. E., and Mueckler, M. M. 1992. How cells absorb glucose. *Sci. Am.* 266(1):86–91.

King, L. S., Kozono, D., and Agre, P. 2004. From structure to disease: The evolving tale of aquaporin biology. *Nat. Rev. Mol. Cell Biol.* 5:687–698.

Neher, E., and Sakmann, B. 1992. The patch clamp technique. *Sci. Am.* 266(3):28–35.

Sakmann, B. 1992. Elementary steps in synaptic transmission revealed by currents through single ion channels. *Science* 256:503–512.

Books

Ashcroft, F. M. 2000. *Ion Channels and Disease*. Academic Press.

Conn, P. M. (Ed.). 1998. *Ion Channels*, vol. 293, *Methods in Enzymology*. Academic Press.

Aidley, D. J., and Stanfield, P. R. 1996. *Ion Channels: Molecules in Action*. Cambridge University Press.

Hille, B. 2001. *Ionic Channels of Excitable Membranes* (3d ed.). Sinauer.

Läuger, P. 1991. *Electrogenic Ion Pumps*. Sinauer.

Stein, W. D. 1990. *Channels, Carriers, and Pumps: An Introduction to Membrane Transport*. Academic Press.

Hodgkin, A. 1992. *Chance and Design: Reminiscences of Science in Peace and War*. Cambridge University Press.

P-Type ATPases

Sorensen, T. L., Moller, J. V., and Nissen, P. 2004. Phosphoryl transfer and calcium ion occlusion in the calcium pump. *Science* 304:1672–1675.

Sweadner, K. J., and Donnet, C. 2001. Structural similarities of Na,K-ATPase and SERCA, the Ca^{2+}-ATPase of the sarcoplasmic reticulum. *Biochem. J.* 356:685–704.

Toyoshima, C., and Mizutani, T. 2004. Crystal structure of the calcium pump with a bound ATP analogue. *Nature* 430:529–535.

Toyoshima, C., Nakasako, M., Nomura, H., and Ogawa, H. 2000. Crystal structure of the calcium pump of sarcoplasmic reticulum at 2.6 Å resolution. *Nature* 405:647–655.

Auer, M., Scarborough, G. A., and Kuhlbrandt, W. 1998. Three-dimensional map of the plasma membrane H^+-ATPase in the open conformation. Nature 392:840–843.

Axelsen, K. B., and Palmgren, M. G. 1998. Evolution of substrate specificities in the P-type ATPase superfamily. *J. Mol. Evol.* 46:84–101.

Pedersen, P. A., Jorgensen, J. R., and Jorgensen, P. L. 2000. Importance of conserved a-subunit segment [709]GDGVND for Mg^{2+} binding, phosphorylation, energy transduction in Na,K-ATPase. *J. Biol. Chem.* 275:37588–37595.

Blanco, G., and Mercer, R. W. 1998. Isozymes of the Na-K-ATPase: heterogeneity in structure, diversity in function. *Am. J. Physiol.* 275:F633–F650.

Estes, J. W., and White, P. D. 1965. William Withering and the purple foxglove. Sci. Am. 212(6):110–117.

ATP-Binding Cassette Proteins

Ward, A., Reyes, C. L., Yu, J., Roth, C. B., and Chang, G. 2007. Flexibility in the ABC transporter MsbA: Alternating access with a twist. *Proc. Natl. Acad. Sci. U.S.A.* 104:19005–19010.

Locher, K. P. 2004. Structure and mechanism of ABC transporters. *Curr. Opin. Struct. Biol.* 14:426–431.

Locher, K. P., Lee, A. T., and Rees, D. C. 2002. The *E. coli* BtuCD structure: A framework for ABC transporter architecture and mechanism. *Science* 296:1091–1098.

Borths, E. L., Locher, K. P., Lee, A. T., and Rees, D. C. 2002. The structure of *Escherichia coli* BtuF and binding to its cognate ATP binding cassette transporter. *Proc. Natl. Acad. Sci. U.S.A.* 99:16642–16647.

Dong, J., Yang, G., and McHaourab, H. S. 2005. Structural basis of energy transduction in the transport cycle of MsbA. *Science* 308:1023–1028.

Akabas, M. H. 2000. Cystic fibrosis transmembrane conductance regulator: Structure and function of an epithelial chloride channel. *J. Biol. Chem.* 275:3729–3732.

Chen, J., Sharma, S., Quiocho, F. A., and Davidson, A. L. 2001. Trapping the transition state of an ATP-binding cassette transporter: Evidence for a concerted mechanism of maltose transport. *Proc. Natl. Acad. Sci. U.S.A.* 98:1525–1530.

Sheppard, D. N., and Welsh, M. J. 1999. Structure and function of the CFTR chloride channel. *Physiol. Rev.* 79:S23–S45.

Jones, P. M., and George, A. M. 2000. Symmetry and structure in P-glycoprotein and ABC transporters: What goes around comes around. *Eur. J. Biochem.* 287:5298–5305.

Chen, Y., and Simon, S. M. 2000. In situ biochemical demonstration that P-glycoprotein is a drug efflux pump with broad specificity. *J. Cell Biol.* 148:863–870.

Saier, M. H., Jr., Paulsen, I. T., Sliwinski, M. K., Pao, S. S., Skurray, R. A., and Nikaido, H. 1998. Evolutionary origins of multidrug and drug-specific efflux pumps in bacteria. *FASEB J.* 12:265–274.

Symporters and Antiporters

Abramson, J., Smirnova, I., Kasho, V., Verner, G., Kaback, H. R., and Iwata, S. 2003. Structure and mechanism of the lactose permease of *Escherichia coli. Science* 301:610–615.

Philipson, K. D., and Nicoll, D. A. 2000. Sodium-calcium exchange: A molecular perspective. *Annu. Rev. Physiol.* 62:111–133.

Pao, S. S., Paulsen, I. T., and Saier, M. H., Jr. 1998. Major facilitator superfamily. *Microbiol. Mol. Biol. Rev.* 62:1–34.

Wright, E. M., Hirsch, J. R., Loo, D. D., and Zampighi, G. A. 1997. Regulation of Na$^+$/glucose cotransporters. *J. Exp. Biol.* 200:287–293.

Kaback, H. R., Bibi, E., and Roepe, P. D. 1990. β-Galactoside transport in *E. coli:* A functional dissection of lac permease. *Trends Biochem. Sci.* 8:309–314.

Hilgemann, D. W., Nicoll, D. A., and Philipson, K. D. 1991. Charge movement during Na$^+$ translocation by native and cloned cardiac Na$^+$/Ca^{2+} exchanger. *Nature* 352:715–718.

Hediger, M. A., Turk, E., and Wright, E. M. 1989. Homology of the human intestinal Na$^+$/glucose and *Escherichia coli* Na$^+$/proline cotransporters. *Proc. Natl. Acad. Sci. U.S.A.* 86:5748–5752.

Ion Channels

Zhou, Y., and MacKinnon, R. 2003. The occupancy of ions in the K$^+$ selectivity filter: Charge balance and coupling of ion binding to a protein conformational change underlie high conduction rates. *J. Mol. Biol.* 333:965–975.

Zhou, Y., Morais-Cabral, J. H., Kaufman, A., and MacKinnon, R. 2001. Chemistry of ion coordination and hydration revealed by a K$^+$ channel-Fab complex at 2.0 Å resolution. *Nature* 414:43–48.

Jiang, Y., Lee, A., Chen, J., Cadene, M., Chait, B. T., and MacKinnon, R. 2002. The open pore conformation of potassium channels. *Nature* 417:523–526.

Jiang, Y., Lee, A., Chen, J., Ruta, V., Cadene, M., Chait, B. T., and MacKinnon, R. 2003. X-ray structure of a voltage-dependent K$^+$ channel. *Nature* 423:33–41.

Jiang, Y., Ruta, V., Chen, J., Lee, A., and MacKinnon, R. 2003. The principle of gating charge movement in a voltage-dependent K$^+$ channel. *Nature* 423:42–48.

Mackinnon, R. 2004. Structural biology: Voltage sensor meets lipid membrane. *Science* 306:1304–1305.

Bezanilla, F. 2000. The voltage sensor in voltage-dependent ion channels. *Physiol. Rev.* 80:555–592.

Shieh, C.-C., Coghlan, M., Sullivan, J. P., and Gopalakrishnan, M. 2000. Potassium channels: Molecular defects, diseases, and therapeutic opportunities. *Pharmacol. Rev.* 52:557–594.

Horn, R. 2000. Conversation between voltage sensors and gates of ion channels. *Biochemistry* 39:15653–15658.

Perozo, E., Cortes, D. M., and Cuello, L. G. 1999. Structural rearrangements underlying K$^+$-channel activation gating. *Science* 285:73–78.

Doyle, D. A., Morais Cabral, J., Pfuetzner, R. A., Kuo, A., Gulbis, J. M., Cohen, S. L., Chait, B. T., and MacKinnon R. 1998. The structure of the potassium channel: Molecular basis of K$^+$ conduction and selectivity. *Science* 280:69–77.

Marban, E., Yamagishi, T., and Tomaselli, G. F. 1998. Structure and function of the voltage-gated Na$^+$ channel. *J. Physiol.* 508:647–657.

Miller, R. J. 1992. Voltage-sensitive Ca^{2+} channels. *J. Biol. Chem.* 267:1403–1406.

Catterall, W. A. 1991. Excitation-contraction coupling in vertebrate skeletal muscle: A tale of two calcium channels. *Cell* 64:871–874.

Ligand-Gated Ion Channels

Unwin, N. 2005. Refined structure of the nicotinic acetylcholine receptor at 4 Å resolution. *J. Mol. Biol.* 346:967–989.

Miyazawa, A., Fujiyoshi, Y., Stowell, M., and Unwin, N. 1999. Nicotinic acetylcholine receptor at 4.6 Å resolution: Transverse tunnels in the channel wall. *J. Mol. Biol.* 288:765–786.

Jiang, Y., Lee, A., Chen, J., Cadene, M., Chait, B. T., and MacKinnon, R. 2002. Crystal structure and mechanism of a calcium-gated potassium channel. *Nature* 417:515–522.

Barrantes, F. J., Antollini, S. S., Blanton, M. P., and Prieto, M. 2000. Topography of the nicotinic acetylcholine receptor membrane-embedded domains. *J. Biol. Chem.* 275:37333–37339.

Cordero-Erausquin, M., Marubio, L. M., Klink, R., and Changeux, J. P. 2000. Nicotinic receptor function: New perspectives from knockout mice. *Trends Pharmacol. Sci.* 21:211–217.

Le Novère, N., and Changeux, J. P. 1995. Molecular evolution of the nicotinic acetylcholine receptor: An example of multigene family in excitable cells. *J. Mol. Evol.* 40:155–172.

Kunishima, N., Shimada, Y., Tsuji, Y., Sato, T., Yamamoto, M., Kumasaka, T., Nakanishi, S., Jingami, H., and Morikawa, K. 2000. Structural basis of glutamate recognition by dimeric metabotropic glutamate receptor. *Nature* 407:971–978.

Betz, H., Kuhse, J., Schmieden, V., Laube, B., Kirsch, J., and Harvey, R. J. 1999. Structure and functions of inhibitory and excitatory glycine receptors. *Ann. N. Y. Acad. Sci.* 868:667–676.

Unwin, N. 1995. Acetylcholine receptor channel imaged in the open state. *Nature* 373:37–43.

Colquhoun, D., and Sakmann, B. 1981. Fluctuations in the microsecond time range of the current through single acetylcholine receptor ion channels. *Nature* 294:464–466.

Long QT Syndrome and hERG

Saenen, J. B., and Vrints, C. J. 2008. Molecular aspects of the congenital and acquired Long QT Syndrome: clinical implications. *J. Mol. Cell. Cardiol.* 44:633–646.

Zaręba, W. 2007. Drug induced QT prolongation. *Cardiol. J.* 14:523–533.

Fernandez, D., Ghanta, A., Kauffman, G. W., and Sanguinetti, M. C. 2004. Physicochemical features of the hERG channel drug binding site. *J. Biol. Chem.* 279:10120–10127.

Mitcheson, J. S., Chen, J., Lin, M., Culberson, C., and Sanguinetti, M. C. 2000. A structural basis for drug-induced long QT syndrome. *Proc. Natl. Acad. Sci. U.S.A.* 97:12329–12333.

Gap Junctions

Saez, J. C., Berthoud, V. M., Branes, M. C., Martinez, A. D., and Beyer, E. C. 2003. Plasma membrane channels formed by connexins: Their regulation and functions. *Physiol. Rev.* 83:1359–1400.

Revilla, A., Bennett, M. V. L., and Barrio, L. C. 2000. Molecular determinants of membrane potential dependence in vertebrate gap junction channels. *Proc. Natl. Acad. Sci. U.S.A.* 97:14760–14765.

Unger, V. M., Kumar, N. M., Gilula, N. B., and Yeager, M. 1999. Three-dimensional structure of a recombinant gap junction membrane channel. *Science* 283:1176–1180.

Simon, A. M. 1999. Gap junctions: More roles and new structural data. *Trends Cell Biol.* 9:169–170.

Beltramello, M., Piazza, V., Bukauskas, F. F., Pozzan, T., and Mammano, F. 2005. Impaired permeability to Ins(1,4,5)P$_3$ in a mutant connexin underlies recessive hereditary deafness. *Nat. Cell Biol.* 7:63–69.

White, T. W., and Paul, D. L. 1999. Genetic diseases and gene knockouts reveal diverse connexin functions. *Annu. Rev. Physiol.* 61:283–310.

Water Channels

Agre, P., King, L. S., Yasui, M., Guggino, W. B., Ottersen, O. P., Fujiyoshi, Y., Engel, A., and Nielsen, S. 2002. Aquaporin water channels: From atomic structure to clinical medicine. *J. Physiol.* 542:3–16.

Agre, P., and Kozono, D. 2003. Aquaporin water channels: Molecular mechanisms for human diseases. *FEBS Lett.* 555:72–78.

de Groot, B. L., Engel, A., and Grubmuller, H. 2003. The structure of the aquaporin-1 water channel: A comparison between cryo-electron microscopy and X-ray crystallography. *J. Mol. Biol.* 325:485–493.

Chapter 14

Where to Start

Scott, J. D., and Pawson, T. 2000. Cell communication: The inside story. *Sci. Am.* 282(6):7279.

Pawson, T. 1995. Protein modules and signalling networks. *Nature* 373:573–580.

Okada, T., Ernst, O. P., Palczewski, K., and Hofmann, K. P. 2001. Activation of rhodopsin: New insights from structural and biochemical studies. *Trends Biochem. Sci.* 26:318–324.

Tsien, R. Y. 1992. Intracellular signal transduction in four dimensions: From molecular design to physiology. *Am. J. Physiol.* 263:C723–C728.

Loewenstein, W. R. 1999. *Touchstone of Life: Molecular Information, Cell Communication, and the Foundations of Life.* Oxford University Press.

G Proteins and 7TM Receptors

Palczewski, K., Kumasaka, T., Hori, T., Behnke, C. A., Motoshima, H., Fox, B. A., Le Trong, I., Teller, D. C., Okada, T., Stenkamp, R. E., Yamamoto, M., and Miyano, M. 2000. Crystal structure of rhodopsin: A G protein-coupled receptor. *Science* 289:739–745.

Rasmussen, S. G. F., Choi, H.-J., Rosenbaum, D. M., Kobilka, T. S., Thian, F. S., Edwards, P. C., Burghammer, M., Ratnala, V. R. P., Sanishvili, R., Fischetti, R. F., Schertler, G. F. X., Weis, W. I., and Kobilka, B. K. 2007. Crystal structure of the human β$_2$ adrenergic G-protein-coupled receptor. *Nature* 450:383–387.

Rosenbaum, D. M., Cherezov, V., Hanson, M. A., Rasmussen, S. G. F., Thian, F. S., Kobilka, T. S., Choi, H.-J., Yao, X.-J., Weis, W. I., Stevens, R. C., and Kobilka, B. K. 2007. GPCR engineering yields high-resolution structural insights into β$_2$-adrenergic receptor function. *Science* 318:1266–1273.

Lefkowitz, R. J. 2000. The superfamily of heptahelical receptors. *Nat. Cell Biol.* 2:E133–E136.

Bourne, H. R., Sanders, D. A., and McCormick, F. 1991. The GTPase superfamily: Conserved structure and molecular mechanism. *Nature* 349:117–127.

Lambright, D. G., Noel, J. P., Hamm, H. E., and Sigler, P. B. 1994. Structural determinants for activation of the α-subunit of a heterotrimeric G protein. *Nature* 369:621–628.

Noel, J. P., Hamm, H. E., and Sigler, P. B. 1993. The 2.2 Å crystal structure of transducin-α complexed with GTPγS. *Nature* 366:654–663.

Sondek, J., Lambright, D. G., Noel, J. P., Hamm, H. E., and Sigler, P. B. 1994. GTPase mechanism of G proteins from the 1.7-Å crystal structure of transducin α-GDP-AIF$^-_4$. *Nature* 372:276–279.

Sondek, J., Bohm, A., Lambright, D. G., Hamm, H. E., and Sigler, P. B. 1996. Crystal structure of a G-protein βγ dimer at 2.1 Å resolution. *Nature* 379:369–374.

Wedegaertner, P. B., Wilson, P. T., and Bourne, H. R. 1995. Lipid modifications of trimeric G proteins. *J. Biol. Chem.* 270:503–506.

Farfel, Z., Bourne, H. R., and Iiri, T. 1999. The expanding spectrum of G protein diseases. *N. Engl. J. Med.* 340:1012–1020.

Bockaert, J., and Pin, J. P. 1999. Molecular tinkering of G protein-coupled receptors: An evolutionary success. *EMBO J.* 18:1723–1729.

Cyclic AMP Cascade

Hurley, J. H. 1999. Structure, mechanism, and regulation of mammalian adenylyl cyclase. *J. Biol. Chem.* 274:7599–7602.

Kim, C., Xuong, N. H., and Taylor, S. S. 2005. Crystal structure of a complex between the catalytic and regulatory (RI) subunits of PKA. *Science* 307:690–696.

Tesmer, J. J., Sunahara, R. K., Gilman, A. G., and Sprang, S. R. 1997. Crystal structure of the catalytic domains of adenylyl cyclase in a complex with G$_{s\alpha}$-GTPγS. *Science* 278:1907–1916.

Smith, C. M., Radzio-Andzelm, E., Madhusudan, Akamine, P., and Taylor, S. S. 1999. The catalytic subunit of cAMP-dependent protein kinase: Prototype for an extended network of communication. *Prog. Biophys. Mol. Biol.* 71:313–341.

Taylor, S. S., Buechler, J. A., and Yonemoto, W. 1990. cAMP-dependent protein kinase: Framework for a diverse family of regulatory enzymes. *Annu. Rev. Biochem.* 59:971–1005.

Phosphoinositide Cascade

Berridge, M. J., and Irvine, R. F. 1989. Inositol phosphates and cell signalling. *Nature* 341:197–205.

Berridge, M. J. 1993. Inositol trisphosphate and calcium signalling. *Nature* 361:315–325.

Essen, L. O., Perisic, O., Cheung, R., Katan, M., and Williams, R. L. 1996. Crystal structure of a mammalian phosphoinositide-specific phospholipase C δ. *Nature* 380:595–602.

Ferguson, K. M., Lemmon, M. A., Schlessinger, J., and Sigler, P. B. 1995. Structure of the high affinity complex of inositol trisphosphate with a phospholipase C pleckstrin homology domain. *Cell* 83:1037–1046.

Baraldi, E., Carugo, K. D., Hyvonen, M., Surdo, P. L., Riley, A. M., Potter, B. V., O'Brien, R., Ladbury, J. E., and Saraste, M. 1999. Structure of the PH domain from Bruton's tyrosine kinase in complex with inositol 1,3,4,5-tetrakisphosphate. *Struct. Fold. Design* 7:449–460.

Calcium

Ikura, M., Clore, G. M., Gronenborn, A. M., Zhu, G., Klee, C. B., and Bax, A. 1992. Solution structure of a calmodulin-target peptide complex by multidimensional NMR. *Science* 256:632–638.

Kuboniwa, H., Tjandra, N., Grzesiek, S., Ren, H., Klee, C. B., and Bax, A. 1995. Solution structure of calcium-free calmodulin. *Nat. Struct. Biol.* 2:768–776.

Grynkiewicz, G., Poenie, M., and Tsien, R. Y. 1985. A new generation of Ca^{2+} indicators with greatly improved fluorescence properties. *J. Biol. Chem.* 260:3440–3450.

Kerr, R., Lev-Ram, V., Baird, G., Vincent, P., Tsien, R. Y., and Schafer, W. R. 2000. Optical imaging of calcium transients in neurons and pharyngeal muscle of *C. elegans*. *Neuron* 26:583–594.

Chin, D., and Means, A. R. 2000. Calmodulin: A prototypical calcium sensor. *Trends Cell Biol.* 10:322–328.

Dawson, A. P. 1997. Calcium signalling: How do IP$_3$ receptors work? *Curr. Biol.* 7:R544–R547.

Protein Kinases, Including Receptor Tyrosine Kinases

Riedel, H., Dull, T. J., Honegger, A. M., Schlessinger, J., and Ullrich, A. 1989. Cytoplasmic domains determine signal specificity, cellular routing characteristics and influence ligand binding of epidermal growth factor and insulin receptors. *EMBO J.* 8:2943–2954.

Taylor, S. S., Knighton, D. R., Zheng, J., Sowadski, J. M., Gibbs, C. S., and Zoller, M. J. 1993. A template for the protein kinase family. *Trends Biochem. Sci.* 18:84–89.

Sicheri, F., Moarefi, I., and Kuriyan, J. 1997. Crystal structure of the Src family tyrosine kinase Hck. *Nature* 385:602–609.

Waksman, G., Shoelson, S. E., Pant, N., Cowburn, D., and Kuriyan, J. 1993. Binding of a high affinity phosphotyrosyl peptide to the Src SH2 domain: Crystal structures of the complexed and peptide-free forms. *Cell* 72:779–790.

Schlessinger, J. 2000. Cell signaling by receptor tyrosine kinases. *Cell* 103:211–225.

Simon, M. A. 2000. Receptor tyrosine kinases: Specific outcomes from general signals. *Cell* 103:13–15.

Robinson, D. R., Wu, Y. M., and Lin, S. F. 2000. The protein tyrosine kinase family of the human genome. *Oncogene* 19:5548–5557.

Hubbard, S. R. 1999. Structural analysis of receptor tyrosine kinases. *Prog. Biophys. Mol. Biol.* 71:343–358.

Carter-Su, C., and Smit, L. S. 1998. Signaling via JAK tyrosine kinases: Growth hormone receptor as a model system. *Recent Prog. Horm. Res.* 53:61–82.

Insulin Signaling Pathway

Khan, A. H., and Pessin, J. E. 2002. Insulin regulation of glucose uptake: A complex interplay of intracellular signalling pathways. *Diabetologia* 45:1475–1483.

Bevan, P. 2001. Insulin signalling. *J. Cell Sci.* 114:1429–1430.

De Meyts, P., and Whittaker, J. 2002. Structural biology of insulin and IGF1 receptors: Implications for drug design. *Nat. Rev. Drug Discov.* 1:769–783.

Dhe-Paganon, S., Ottinger, E. A., Nolte, R. T., Eck, M. J., and Shoelson, S. E. 1999. Crystal structure of the pleckstrin homology-phosphotyrosine binding (PH-PTB) targeting region of insulin receptor substrate 1. *Proc. Natl. Acad. Sci. U.S.A.* 96:8378–8383.

Domin, J., and Waterfield, M. D. 1997. Using structure to define the function of phosphoinositide 3-kinase family members. *FEBS Lett.* 410:91–95.

Hubbard, S. R. 1997. Crystal structure of the activated insulin receptor tyrosine kinase in complex with peptide substrate and ATP analog. *EMBO J.* 16:5572–5581.

Hubbard, S. R., Wei, L., Ellis, L., and Hendrickson, W. A. 1994. Crystal structure of the tyrosine kinase domain of the human insulin receptor. *Nature* 372:746–754.

EGF Signaling Pathway

Burgess, A. W., Cho, H. S., Eigenbrot, C., Ferguson, K. M., Garrett, T. P., Leahy, D. J., Lemmon, M. A., Sliwkowski, M. X., Ward, C. W., and Yokoyama, S. 2003. An open-and-shut case? Recent insights into the activation of EGF/ErbB receptors. *Mol. Cell* 12:541–552.

Cho, H. S., Mason, K., Ramyar, K. X., Stanley, A. M., Gabelli, S. B., Denney, D. W., Jr., and Leahy, D. J. 2003. Structure of the extracellular region of HER2 alone and in complex with the Herceptin Fab. *Nature* 421:756–760.

Chong, H., Vikis, H. G., and Guan, K. L. 2003. Mechanisms of regulating the Raf kinase family. *Cell. Signal.* 15:463–469.

Stamos, J., Sliwkowski, M. X., and Eigenbrot, C. 2002. Structure of the epidermal growth factor receptor kinase domain alone and in complex with a 4-anilinoquinazoline inhibitor. *J. Biol. Chem.* 277:46265–46272.

Ras

Milburn, M. V., Tong, L., deVos, A. M., Brunger, A., Yamaizumi, Z., Nishimura, S., and Kim, S. H. 1990. Molecular switch for signal transduction: Structural differences between active and inactive forms of protooncogenic Ras proteins. *Science* 247:939–945.

Boriack-Sjodin, P. A., Margarit, S. M., Bar-Sagi, D., and Kuriyan, J. 1998. The structural basis of the activation of Ras by Sos. *Nature* 394:337–343.

Maignan, S., Guilloteau, J. P., Fromage, N., Arnoux, B., Becquart, J., and Ducruix, A. 1995. Crystal structure of the mammalian Grb2 adaptor. *Science* 268:291–293.

Takai, Y., Sasaki, T., and Matozaki, T. 2001. Small GTP-binding proteins. *Physiol. Rev.* 81:153–208.

Cancer

Druker, B. J., Sawyers, C. L., Kantarjian, H., Resta, D. J., Reese, S. F., Ford, J. M., Capdeville, R., and Talpaz, M. 2001. Activity of a specific inhibitor of the BCR-ABL tyrosine kinase in the blast crisis of chronic myeloid leukemia and acute lymphoblastic leukemia with the Philadelphia chromosome. *N. Engl. J. Med.* 344:1038–1042.

Vogelstein, B., and Kinzler, K. W. 1993. The multistep nature of cancer. *Trends Genet.* 9:138–141.

Ellis, C. A., and Clark, G. 2000. The importance of being K-Ras. *Cell. Signal.* 12:425–434.

Hanahan, D., and Weinberg, R. A. 2000. The hallmarks of cancer. *Cell* 100:57–70.

McCormick, F. 1999. Signalling networks that cause cancer. *Trends Cell Biol.* 9:M53–M56.

Chapter 15

Where to Start

Stipanuk, M. H. (Ed.). 2006. *Biochemical, Physiological, Molecular Aspects of Human Nutrition.* Saunders-Elsevier.

McGrane, M. M., Yun, J. S., Patel, Y. M., and Hanson, R. W. 1992. Metabolic control of gene expression: In vivo studies with transgenic mice. *Trends Biochem. Sci.* 17:40–44.

Westheimer, F. H. 1987. Why nature chose phosphates. *Science* 235:1173–1178.

Books

Atkins, P., and de Paula, J. 2005. *Physical Chemistry for the Life Sciences.* W. H. Freeman and Company.

Harold, F. M. 1986. *The Vital Force: A Study of Bioenergetics.* W. H. Freeman and Company.

Krebs, H. A., and Kornberg, H. L. 1957. *Energy Transformations in Living Matter.* Springer Verlag.

Nicholls, D. G., and Ferguson, S. J. 2002. *Bioenergetics 3* (3d ed.). Academic Press.

Frayn, K. N. 2010. *Metabolic Regulation: A Human Perspective* (3d ed.). Wiley-Blackwell.

Fell, D. 1997. *Understanding the Control of Metabolism.* Portland Press.

Harris, D. A. 1995. *Bioenergetics at a Glance.* Blackwell Scientific.

Von Baeyer, H. C. 1999. *Warmth Disperses and Time Passes: A History of Heat.* Modern Library.

Thermodynamics

Alberty, R. A. 1993. Levels of thermodynamic treatment of biochemical reaction systems. *Biophys. J.* 65:1243–1254.

Alberty, R. A., and Goldberg, R. N. 1992. Standard thermodynamic formation properties for the adenosine 5′-triphosphate series. *Biochemistry* 31:10610–10615.

Alberty, R. A. 1968. Effect of pH and metal ion concentration on the equilibrium hydrolysis of adenosine triphosphate to adenosine diphosphate. *J. Biol. Chem.* 243:1337–1343.

Goldberg, R. N. 1984. *Compiled Thermodynamic Data Sources for Aqueous and Biochemical Systems: An Annotated Bibliography (1930–1983).* National Bureau of Standards Special Publication 685, U.S. Government Printing Office.

Frey, P. A., and Arabshahi, A. 1995. Standard free energy change for the hydrolysis of the α,β-phosphoanhydride bridge in ATP. *Biochemistry* 34:11307–11310.

Bioenergetics and Metabolism

Schilling, C. H., Letscher, D., and Palsson, B. O. 2000. Theory for the systemic definition of metabolic pathways and their use in interpreting metabolic function from a pathway-oriented perspective. *J. Theor. Biol.* 203:229–248.

DeCoursey, T. E., and Cherny, V. V. 2000. Common themes and problems of bioenergetics and voltage-gated proton channels. *Biochim. Biophys. Acta* 1458:104–119.

Giersch, C. 2000. Mathematical modelling of metabolism. *Curr. Opin. Plant Biol.* 3:249–253.

Rees, D. C., and Howard, J. B. 1999. Structural bioenergetics and energy transduction mechanisms. *J. Mol. Biol.* 293:343–350.

Regulation of Metabolism

Kemp, G. J. 2000. Studying metabolic regulation in human muscle. *Biochem. Soc. Trans.* 28:100–103.

Towle, H. C., Kaytor, E. N., and Shih, H. M. 1996. Metabolic regulation of hepatic gene expression. *Biochem. Soc. Trans.* 24:364–368.

Hofmeyr, J. H. 1995. Metabolic regulation: A control analytic perspective. *J. Bioenerg. Biomembr.* 27:479–490.

Historical Aspects

Kalckar, H. M. 1991. 50 years of biological research: From oxidative phosphorylation to energy requiring transport regulation. *Annu. Rev. Biochem.* 60:1–37.

Kalckar, H. M. (Ed.). 1969. *Biological Phosphorylations.* Prentice Hall.

Fruton, J. S. 1972. *Molecules and Life.* Wiley-Interscience.

Lipmann, F. 1971. *Wanderings of a Biochemist.* Wiley-Interscience.

Chapter 16

Where to Start

Knowles, J. R. 1991. Enzyme catalysis: Not different, just better. *Nature* 350:121–124.

Granner, D., and Pilkis, S. 1990. The genes of hepatic glucose metabolism. *J. Biol. Chem.* 265:10173–10176.

McGrane, M. M., Yun, J. S., Patel, Y. M., and Hanson, R. W. 1992. Metabolic control of gene expression: In vivo studies with transgenic mice. *Trends Biochem. Sci.* 17:40–44.

Pilkis, S. J., and Granner, D. K. 1992. Molecular physiology of the regulation of hepatic gluconeogenesis and glycolysis. *Annu. Rev. Physiol.* 54:885–909.

Books

Frayn, K. N. 2010. *Metabolic Regulation: A Human Perspective* (3d ed.). Wiley-Blackwell.

Fell, D. 1997. *Understanding the Control of Metabolism.* Portland.

Fersht, A. 1999. *Structure and Mechanism in Protein Science: A Guide to Enzyme Catalysis and Protein Folding.* W. H. Freeman and Company.

Poortmans, J. R. (Ed.). 2004. *Principles of Exercise Biochemistry.* Krager.

Structure of Glycolytic and Gluconeogenic Enzymes

Ferreras, C., Hernández, E. D., Martínez-Costa, O. H., and Aragón, J. J. 2009. Subunit interactions and composition of the fructose 6-phosphate catalytic site and the fructose 2,6-bisphosphate allosteric site of mammalian phosphofructokinase. *J. Biol. Chem.* 284:9124–9131.

Hines, J. K., Chen, X., Nix, J. C., Fromm, H. J., and Honzatko. R. B. 2007. Structures of mammalian and bacterial fructose-1, 6-bisphosphatase reveal the basis for synergism in AMP/fructose-2, 6-bisphosphate inhibition. *J. Biol. Chem.* 282:36121–36131.

Ferreira-da-Silva, F., Pereira, P. J., Gales, L., Roessle, M., Svergun, D. I., Moradas-Ferreira, P., and Damas, A. M. 2006. The crystal and solution structures of glyceraldehyde-3-phosphate dehydrogenase reveal different quaternary structures. *J. Biol. Chem.* 281:33433–33440.

Kim, S.-G., Manes, N. P., El-Maghrabi, M. R., and Lee, Y.-H. 2006. Crystal structure of the hypoxia-inducible form of 6-phospho-fructo-2-kinase/fructose-2,6-phosphatase (PFKFB3): A possible target for cancer therapy. *J. Biol. Chem.* 281:2939–2944.

Aleshin, A. E., Kirby, C., Liu, X., Bourenkov, G. P., Bartunik, H. D., Fromm, H. J., and Honzatko, R. B. 2000. Crystal structures of mutant monomeric hexokinase I reveal multiple ADP binding sites and conformational changes relevant to allosteric regulation. *J. Mol. Biol.* 296:1001–1015.

Jeffery, C. J., Bahnson, B. J., Chien, W., Ringe, D., and Petsko, G. A. 2000. Crystal structure of rabbit phosphoglucose isomerase, a glycolytic enzyme that moonlights as neuroleukin, autocrine motility factor, and differentiation mediator. *Biochemistry* 39:955–964.

Schirmer, T., and Evans, P. R. 1990. Structural basis of the allosteric behaviour of phosphofructokinase. *Nature* 343:140–145.

Cooper, S. J., Leonard, G. A., McSweeney, S. M., Thompson, A. W., Naismith, J. H., Qamar, S., Plater, A., Berry, A., and Hunter, W. N. 1996. The crystal structure of a class II fructose-1,6-bisphosphate aldolase shows a novel binuclear metal-binding active site embedded in a familiar fold. *Structure* 4:1303–1315.

Davenport, R. C., Bash, P. A., Seaton, B. A., Karplus, M., Petsko, G. A., and Ringe, D. 1991. Structure of the triosephosphate isomerase–phosphoglycolohydroxamate complex: An analogue of the intermediate on the reaction pathway. *Biochemistry* 30:5821–5826.

Bernstein, B. E., and Hol, W. G. 1998. Crystal structures of substrates and products bound to the phosphoglycerate kinase active site reveal the catalytic mechanism. *Biochemistry* 37:4429–4436.

Rigden, D. J., Alexeev, D., Phillips, S. E. V., and Fothergill-Gilmore, L. A. 1998. The 2.3 Å X-ray crystal structure of *S. cerevisiae* phosphoglycerate mutase. *J. Mol. Biol.* 276:449–459.

Zhang, E., Brewer, J. M., Minor, W., Carreira, L. A., and Lebioda, L. 1997. Mechanism of enolase: The crystal structure of asymmetric dimer enolase-2-phospho-D-glycerate/enolase-phosphoenolpyruvate at 2.0 Å resolution. *Biochemistry* 36:12526–12534.

Mattevi, A., Valentini, G., Rizzi, M., Speranza, M. L., Bolognesi, M., and Coda, A. 1995. Crystal structure of *Escherichia coli* pyruvate kinase type I: Molecular basis of the allosteric transition. *Structure* 3:729–741.

Hasemann, C. A., Istvan E. S., Uyeda, K., and Deisenhofer, J. 1996. The crystal structure of the bifunctional enzyme 6-phosphofructo-2-kinase/fructose-2,6-biphosphatase reveals distinct domain homologies. *Structure* 4:1017–1029.

Tari, L. W., Matte, A., Pugazhenthi, U., Goldie, H., and Delbaere, L. T. J. 1996. Snapshot of an enzyme reaction intermediate in the structure of the ATP-Mg^{2+}-oxalate ternary complex of *Escherichia coli* PEP carboxykinase. *Nat. Struct. Biol.* 3:355–363.

Catalytic Mechanisms

Soukri, A., Mougin, A., Corbier, C., Wonacott, A., Branlant, C., and Branlant, G. 1989. Role of the histidine 176 residue in glyceraldehyde-3-phosphate dehydrogenase as probed by site-directed mutagenesis. *Biochemistry* 28:2586–2592.

Bash, P. A., Field, M. J., Davenport, R. C., Petsko, G. A., Ringe, D., and Karplus, M. 1991. Computer simulation and analysis of the reaction pathway of triosephosphate isomerase. *Biochemistry* 30:5826–5832.

Knowles, J. R., and Albery, W. J. 1977. Perfection in enzyme catalysis: The energetics of triosephosphate isomerase. *Acc. Chem. Res.* 10:105–111.

Rose, I. A. 1981. Chemistry of proton abstraction by glycolytic enzymes (aldolase, isomerases, and pyruvate kinase). *Philos. Trans. R. Soc. Lond. B Biol. Sci.* 293:131–144.

Regulation

Anderka, O., Boyken, J., Aschenbach, U., Batzer, A., Boscheinen, O., and Schmoll, D. 2008. Biophysical characterization of the interaction between hepatic glucokinase and its regulatory protein: Impact of physiological and pharmacological effectors. *J. Biol. Chem.* 283:31333–31340.

Iancu, C. V., Mukund, S., Fromm, H. J., and Honzatko, R. B. 2005. R-state AMP complex reveals initial steps of the quaternary transition of fructose-1,6-bisphosphatase. *J. Biol. Chem.* 280:19737–19745.

Wilson, J. E. 2003. Isozymes of mammalian hexokinase: Structure, function and subcellular location. *J. Exp. Biol.* 206:2049–2057.

SELECTED READINGS

Lee, Y. H., Li, Y., Uyeda, K., and Hasemann, C. A. 2003. Tissue-specific structure/function differentiation of the five isoforms of 6-phosphofructo-2-kinase/fructose-2,6-bisphosphatase. *J. Biol. Chem.* 278:523–530.

Depre, C., Rider, M. H., and Hue, L. 1998. Mechanisms of control of heart glycolysis. *Eur. J. Biochem.* 258:277–290.

Harrington, G. N., and Bush, D. R. 2003. The bifunctional role of hexokinase in metabolism and glucose signaling. *Plant Cell* 15:2493–2496.

Gleeson, T. T. 1996. Post-exercise lactate metabolism: A comparative review of sites, pathways, and regulation. *Annu. Rev. Physiol.* 58:556–581.

Nordlie, R. C., Foster, J. D., and Lange, A. J. 1999. Regulation of glucose production by the liver. *Annu. Rev. Nutr.* 19:379–406.

Jitrapakdee, S., and Wallace, J. C. 1999. Structure, function and regulation of pyruvate carboxylase. *Biochem. J.* 340:1–16.

Pilkis, S. J., and Claus, T. H. 1991. Hepatic gluconeogenesis/glycolysis: Regulation and structure/function relationships of substrate cycle enzymes. *Annu. Rev. Nutr.* 11:465–515.

Plaxton, W. C. 1996. The organization and regulation of plant glycolysis. *Annu. Rev. Plant Physiol. Plant Mol. Biol.* 47:185–214.

van de Werve, G., Lange, A., Newgard, C., Mechin, M. C., Li, Y., and Berteloot, A. 2000. New lessons in the regulation of glucose metabolism taught by the glucose 6-phosphatase system. *Eur. J. Biochem.* 267:1533–1549.

Sugar Transporters

Blodgett, D. M., Graybill, C. and Carruthers, A. 2008. Analysis of glucose transporter topology and structural dynamics. *J. Biol. Chem.* 283: 36416–36424.

Huang, S., and Czech, M. P. 2007. The GLUT4 glucose transporter. *Cell Metab.* 5:237–252.

Czech, M. P., and Corvera, S. 1999. Signaling mechanisms that regulate glucose transport. *J Biol. Chem.* 274:1865–1868.

Silverman, M. 1991. Structure and function of hexose transporters. *Annu. Rev. Biochem.* 60:757–794.

Thorens, B., Charron, M. J., and Lodish, H. F. 1990. Molecular physiology of glucose transporters. *Diabetes Care* 13:209–218.

Glycolysis and Cancer

Vander Heiden, M. G., Cantley, L. C., and Thompson, C. B. 2009. Understanding the Warburg effect: The metabolic requirements of cell proliferation. *Science* 324:1029–1033.

Mathupala, S. P., Ko, Y. H., and Pedersen, P. L. 2009. Hexokinase-2 bound to mitochondria: Cancer's stygian link to the "Warburg effect" and a pivotal target for effective therapy. *Sem. Cancer Biol.* 19:17–24.

Kroemer, G. K., and Pouyssegur, J. 2008. Tumor cell metabolism: Cancer's Achilles' heel. *Cancer Cell* 12:472–482.

Hsu, P. P., and Sabatini, D. M. 2008. Cancer cell metabolism: Warburg and beyond. *Cell* 134:703–707.

Dang, C. V., and Semenza, G. L. 1999. Oncogenic alterations of metabolism. *Trends Biochem. Sci.* 24:68–72.

Genetic Diseases

Scriver, C. R., Beaudet, A. L., Valle, D., Sly, W. S., Childs, B., Kinzler, K., and Vogelstein, B. (Eds.). 2001. *The Metabolic and Molecular Basis of Inherited Disease* (8th ed.). McGraw-Hill.

Evolution

Dandekar, T., Schuster, S., Snel, B., Huynen, M., and Bork, P. 1999. Pathway alignment: Application to the comparative analysis of glycolytic enzymes. *Biochem. J.* 343:115–124.

Heinrich, R., Melendez-Hevia, E., Montero, F., Nuno, J. C., Stephani, A., and Waddell, T. G. 1999. The structural design of glycolysis: An evolutionary approach. *Biochem. Soc. Trans.* 27:294–298.

Walmsley, A. R., Barrett, M. P., Bringaud, F., and Gould, G. W. 1998. Sugar transporters from bacteria, parasites and mammals: Structure-activity relationships. *Trends Biochem. Sci.* 23:476–480.

Maes, D., Zeelen, J. P., Thanki, N., Beaucamp, N., Alvarez, M., Thi, M. H., Backmann, J., Martial, J. A., Wyns, L., Jaenicke, R., and Wierenga, R. K. 1999. The crystal structure of triosephosphate isomerase (TIM) from *Thermotoga maritima:* A comparative thermostability structural analysis of ten different TIM structures. *Proteins* 37:441–453.

Historical Aspects

Friedmann, H. C. 2004. From *Butyribacterium* to *E. coli:* An essay on unity in biochemistry. *Perspect. Biol. Med.* 47:47–66.

Fruton, J. S. 1999. *Proteins, Enzymes, Genes: The Interplay of Chemistry and Biology.* Yale University Press.

Kalckar, H. M. (Ed.). 1969. Biological Phosphorylations: Development of Concepts. Prentice Hall.

Chapter 17

Where to Start

Sugden, M. C., and Holness, M. J. 2003. Recent advances in mechanisms regulating glucose oxidation at the level of the pyruvate dehydrogenase complex by PDKs. *Am. J. Physiol. Endocrinol. Metab.* 284:E855–E862.

Owen, O. E., Kalhan, S. C., and Hanson, R. W. 2002. The key role of anaplerosis and cataplerosis for citric acid function. *J. Biol. Chem.* 277:30409–30412.

Pyruvate Dehydrogenase Complex

Hiromasa, Y., Fujisawa, T., Aso, Y., and Roche, T. E. 2004. Organization of the cores of the mammalian pyruvate dehydrogenase complex formed by E2 and E2 plus the E3-binding proteins and their capacities to bind the E1 and E3 components. *J. Biol Chem.* 279:6921–6933.

Izard, T., Ævarsson, A., Allen, M. D., Westphal, A. H., Perham, R. N., De Kok, A., and Hol, W. G. 1999. Principles of quasi-equivalence and Euclidean geometry govern the assembly of cubic and dodecahedral cores of pyruvate dehydrogenase complexes. *Proc. Natl. Acad. Sci. U.S.A.* 96:1240–1245.

Domingo, G. J., Chauhan, H. J., Lessard, I. A., Fuller, C., and Perham, R. N. 1999. Self-assembly and catalytic activity of the pyruvate dehydrogenase multienzyme complex from *Bacillus stearothermophilus.* *Eur. J. Biochem.* 266:1136–1146.

Jones, D. D., Horne, H. J., Reche, P. A., and Perham, R. N. 2000. Structural determinants of post-translational modification and catalytic specificity for the lipoyl domains of the pyruvate dehydrogenase multienzyme complex of *Escherichia coli.* *J. Mol. Biol.* 295:289–306.

Structure of Citric Acid Cycle Enzymes

Fraser, M. E. Hayakawa, K., Hume, M. S., Ryan, D. G., and Brownie, E. R. 2006. Interactions of GTP with the ATP-grasp domain of GTP-specific succinyl-CoA synthetase. *J. Biol. Chem.* 281:11058–11065.

Yankovskaya, V., Horsefield, R., Törnroth, S., Luna-Chavez, C., Miyoshi, H., Léger, C., Byrne, B., Cecchini, G., and Iowata, S. 2003. Architecture of succinate dehydrogenase and reactive oxygen species generation. *Science* 299:700–704.

Chapman, A. D., Cortes, A., Dafforn, T. R., Clarke, A. R., and Brady, R. L. 1999. Structural basis of substrate specificity in malate dehydrogenases: Crystal structure of a ternary complex of porcine cytoplasmic malate dehydrogenase, α-ketomalonate and tetrahydoNAD. *J. Mol. Biol.* 285:703–712.

Fraser, M. E., James, M. N., Bridger, W. A., and Wolodko, W. T. 1999. A detailed structural description of *Escherichia coli* succinyl-CoA synthetase. *J. Mol. Biol.* 285:1633–1653. [Published erratum appears in May 7, 1999, issue of *J. Mol. Biol.* 288(3):501.]

Lloyd, S. J., Lauble, H., Prasad, G. S., and Stout, C. D. 1999. The mechanism of aconitase: 1.8 Å resolution crystal structure of the S642a:citrate complex. *Protein Sci.* 8:2655–2662.

Remington, S. J. 1992. Structure and mechanism of citrate synthase. *Curr. Top. Cell. Regul.* 33:209–229.

Rose, I. A. 1998. How fumarase recycles after the malate $\longrightarrow$ fumarate reaction: Insights into the reaction mechanism. *Biochemistry* 37: 17651–17658.

Organization of the Citric Acid Cycle

Lambeth, D. O., Tews, K. N., Adkins, S., Frohlich, D., and Milavetz, B. I. 2004. Expression of two succinyl-CoA specificities in mammalian tissues. *J. Biol. Chem.* 279:36621–36624.

Velot, C., Mixon, M. B., Teige, M., and Srere, P. A. 1997. Model of a quinary structure between Krebs TCA cycle enzymes: A model for the metabolon. *Biochemistry* 36:14271–14276.

Haggie, P. M., and Brindle, K. M. 1999. Mitochondrial citrate synthase is immobilized in vivo. *J. Biol. Chem.* 274:3941–3945.

Morgunov, I., and Srere, P. A. 1998. Interaction between citrate synthase and malate dehydrogenase: Substrate channeling of oxaloacetate. *J. Biol. Chem.* 273:29540–29544.

Regulation

Phillips, D., Aponte, A. M., French, S. A., Chess, D. J., and Balaban, R. S. 2009. Succinyl-CoA synthetase is a phosphate target for the activation of mitochondrial metabolism. *Biochemistry* 48: 7140–7149.

Taylor, A. B., Hu, G., Hart, P. J., and McAlister-Henn, L. 2008. Allosteric motions in structures of yeast NAD^+-specific isocitrate dehydrogenase. *J. Biol. Chem.* 283: 10872–10880.

Green, T., Grigorian, A., Klyuyeva, A., Tuganova, A., Luo, M., and Popov, K. M. 2008. Structural and functional insights into the molecular mechanisms responsible for the regulation of pyruvate dehydrogenase kinase. *J. Biol. Chem.* 283: 15789–15798.

Hiromasa, Y., and Roche, T. E. 2003. Facilitated interaction between the pyruvate dehydrogenase kinase isoform 2 and the dihydrolipoyl acetyltransferases. *J. Biol. Chem.* 278:33681–33693.

Jitrapakdee, S., and Wallace, J. C. 1999. Structure, function and regulation of pyruvate carboxylase. *Biochem. J.* 340:1–16.

The Citric Acid Cycle and Cancer

Thompson, C. B. 2009. Metabolic enzymes as oncogenes or tumor suppressors. *New Engl. J. Med.* 360:813–815.

McFate, T., Mohyeldin, A., Lu, H., Thakar, J., Henriques, J., Halim, N. D., Wu, H., Schell, M. J., Tsang, T. M., Teahan, O., Zhou, S., Califano, J. A., Jeoung, M. N., Harris, R. A., and Verma, A. 2008. Pyruvate dehydrogenase complex activity controls metabolic and malignant phenotype in cancer cells. *J. Biol. Chem.* 283: 22700–22708.

Gogvadze, V., Orrenius, S., and Zhivotovsky, B. 2008. Mitochondria in cancer cells: What is so special about them? *Trends Cell Biol.* 18:165–173.

Evolutionary Aspects

Meléndez-Hevia, E., Waddell, T. G., and Cascante, M. 1996. The puzzle of the Krebs citric acid cycle: Assembling the pieces of chemically feasible reactions, and opportunism in the design of metabolic pathways in evolution. *J. Mol. Evol.* 43:293–303.

Baldwin, J. E., and Krebs, H. 1981. The evolution of metabolic cycles. *Nature* 291:381–382.

Gest, H. 1987. Evolutionary roots of the citric acid cycle in prokaryotes. *Biochem. Soc. Symp.* 54:3–16.

Weitzman, P. D. J. 1981. Unity and diversity in some bacterial citric acid cycle enzymes. *Adv. Microbiol. Physiol.* 22:185–244.

Discovery of the Citric Acid Cycle

Kornberg, H. 2000. Krebs and his trinity of cycles. *Nat. Rev. Mol. Cell. Biol.* 1:225–228.

Krebs, H. A., and Johnson, W. A. 1937. The role of citric acid in intermediate metabolism in animal tissues. *Enzymologia* 4:148–156.

Krebs, H. A. 1970. The history of the tricarboxylic acid cycle. *Perspect. Biol. Med.* 14:154–170.

Krebs, H. A., and Martin, A. 1981. *Reminiscences and Reflections.* Clarendon Press.

Chapter 18

Where to Start

Guarente, L. 2008. Mitochondria: A nexus for aging, calorie restriction, and sirtuins? *Cell* 132:171–176.

Wallace, D. C. 2007. Why do we still have a maternally inherited mitochondrial DNA? Insights from evolutionary medicine. *Annu. Rev. Biochem.* 76:781–821.

Brandt, U. 2006. Energy converting NADH:quinone oxidoreductase (Complex I). *Annu Rev Biochem.* 75:69–92.

Hosler, J. P., Ferguson-Miller, S., and Mills, D. A. 2006. Energy transduction: Proton transfer through the respiratory complexes. *Annu. Rev. Biochem.* 75:165–187.

Gray, M. W., Burger, G., and Lang, B. F. 1999. Mitochondrial evolution. *Science* 283:1476–1481.

Shultz, B. E., and Chan, S. I. 2001. Structures and proton-pumping strategies of mitochondrial respiratory enzymes. *Annu. Rev. Biophys. Biomol. Struct.* 30:23–65.

Books

Scheffler, I. E. 2007. *Mitochondria.* Wiley.

Lane, N. 2005. *Power, Sex, Suicide: Mitochondria and the Meaning of Life.* Oxford.

Nicholls, D. G., and Ferguson, S. J. 2002. *Bioenergetics 3.* Academic Press.

Electron-Transport Chain

Qin, L., Liu, J., Mills, D. A., Proshlyakov, D. A., Hiser, C., and Ferguson-Miller, S. 2009. Redox-dependent conformational changes in cytochrome *c* oxidase suggest a gating mechanism for proton uptake. *Biochemistry* 48:5121–5130.

Lill, R. 2009. Function and biogenesis of iron–sulphur proteins. *Nature* 460:831–838.

Cooley, C. W., Lee, D.-W., and Daldal, F. 2009. Across membrane communication between the Q_o and Q_i active sites of cytochrome bc_1. *Biochemistry* 48:1888–1899.

Verkhovskaya, M. L., Belevich, N., Euro, L., Wikström, M., and Verkhovsky, M. I. 2008. Real-time electron transfer in respiratory complex I. *Proc. Natl. Acad. Sci. U.S.A.* 105:3763–3767.

Berrisford, J. M., and Sazanov, L. A. 2009. Structural basis for the mechanism of respiratory complex I. *J. Biol. Chem.* 284:29773–29783.

Acín-Pérez, R., Fernández-Silva, P., Peleato, M. L., Pérez-Martos, A., and Enriquez, J. A. 2008. Respiratory active mitochondrial supercomplexes. *Molecular Cell* 32:529–539.

Kruse, S. E., Watt, W. C., Marcinek, D. J., Kapur, R. P., Schenkman, K. A., and Palmiter, R. D. 2008. Mice with mitochondrial Complex I deficiency develop a fatal encephalomyopathy. *Cell Metab.* 7:312–320.

Belevich, I., Verkhovsky, M. I., and Wikström, M. 2007. Proton-coupled electron transfer drives the proton pump of cytochrome *c* oxidase. *Nature* 440:829–832.

Sun, F., Huo, X., Zhai, Y., Wang, A., Xu, J., Su, D., Bartlam, M., and Rai, Z. 2005. Crystal structure of mitochondrial respiratory membrane protein complex II. *Cell* 121:1043–1057.

Crofts, A. R. 2004. The cytochrome bc_1 complex: Function in the context of structure. *Annu. Rev. Physiol.* 66:689–733.

Bianchi, C., Genova, M. L., Castelli, G. P., and Lenaz, G. 2004. The mitochondrial respiratory chain is partially organized in a supramolecular complex. *J. Biol. Chem.* 279:36562–36569.

Ugalde, C., Vogel, R., Huijbens, R., van den Heuvel, B., Smeitink, J., and Nijtmans, L. 2004. Human mitochondrial Complex I assembles through a combination of evolutionary conserved modules: A framework to interpret Complex I deficiencies. *Hum. Mol. Genet.* 13:2461–2472.

Yagi, T., and Matsuno-Yagi, A. 2003. The proton-translocating NADH-quinone oxidoreductase in the respiratory chain: The secret unlocked. *Biochemistry* 42:2266–2274.

Cecchini, G. 2003. Function and structure of Complex II of the respiratory chain. *Annu. Rev. Biochem.* 72:77–109.

Lange, C., and Hunte, C. 2002. Crystal structure of the yeast cytochrome bc_1 complex with its bound substrate cytochrome *c*. *Proc. Natl. Acad. Sci. U.S.A.* 99:2800–2805.

ATP Synthase

Wittig, I., and Hermann, S. 2009. Supramolecular organization of ATP synthase and respiratory chain in mitochondrial membranes. *Biochim. Biophys. Acta* 1787:672–680.

Junge, W., Sielaff, H., and Engelbrecht S. 2009. Torque generation and elastic power transmission in the rotary F_0F_1-ATPase. *Nature* 459:364–370.

von Ballmoos, C., Cook, G. M., and Dimroth, P. 2008. Unique rotary ATP synthase and its biological diversity. *Annu. Rev. Biophys.* 37:43–64.

Adachi, K., Oiwa, K., Nishizaka, T., Furuike, S., Noji, H., Itoh, H., Yoshida, M., and Kinosita, K., Jr. 2007. Coupling of rotation and catalysis in F_1-ATPase revealed by single-molecule imaging and manipulation. *Cell* 130:309–321.

Chen, C., Ko, Y., Delannoy, M., Ludtke, S. J., Chiu, W., and Pedersen, P. L. 2004. Mitochondrial ATP synthasome: Three-dimensional structure by electron microscopy of the ATP synthase in complex formation with the carriers for P_i and ADP/ATP. *J. Biol. Chem.* 279:31761–31768.

Noji, H., and Yoshida, M. 2001. The rotary machine in the cell: ATP synthase. *J. Biol. Chem.* 276:1665–1668.

Yasuda, R., Noji, H., Kinosita, K., Jr., and Yoshida, M. 1998. F_1-ATPase is a highly efficient molecular motor that rotates with discrete 120 degree steps. *Cell* 93:1117–1124.

Kinosita, K., Jr., Yasuda, R., Noji, H., Ishiwata, S., and Yoshida, M. 1998. F_1-ATPase: A rotary motor made of a single molecule. *Cell* 93:21–24.

Noji, H., Yasuda, R., Yoshida, M., and Kinosita, K., Jr., 1997. Direct observation of the rotation of F_1-ATPase. *Nature* 386:299–302.

Tsunoda, S. P., Aggeler, R., Yoshida, M., and Capaldi, R. A. 2001. Rotation of the *c* subunit oligomer in fully functional $F_1 F_0$ ATP synthase. *Proc. Natl. Acad. Sci. U.S.A.* 987:898–902.

Gibbons, C., Montgomery, M. G., Leslie, A. G. W., and Walker, J. 2000. The structure of the central stalk in F_1-ATPase at 2.4 Å resolution. *Nat. Struct. Biol.* 7:1055–1061.

Sambongi, Y., Iko, Y., Tanabe, M., Omote, H., Iwamoto-Kihara, A., Ueda, I., Yanagida, T., Wada, Y., and Futai, M. 1999. Mechanical rotation of the *c* subunit oligomer in ATP synthase (F_0F_1): Direct observation. *Science* 286:1722–1724.

Translocators and Channels

van Marken Lichtenbelt, W. D., Vanhommerig, J. W., Smulders, N. M., Drossaerts, J. M., Kemerink, G. J., Bouvy, N. D., Schrauwen, P., and Teule, G. J. 2009. Cold-activated brown adipose tissue in healthy men. *N. Engl. J. Med.* 360:1500–1508.

Cypess, A. M., Sanaz Lehman, S., Gethin Williams, G., Tal, I., Rodman, D., Goldfine, A. B., Kuo, F. C., Palmer, E. L., Tseng, Y.-H., Doria, A., Kolodny, G. M., and Kahn, C. R. 2009. Identification and importance of brown adipose tissue in adult humans. *N. Engl. J. Med.* 360:1509–1517.

Virtanen, K. A., Lidell, M. E., Orava, J., Heglind, M., Westergren, R., Niemi, T., Taittonen, M., Laine, J., Savisto, N.-J., Enerbäck, S., and Nuutila, P. 2009. Functional brown adipose tissue in healthy adults. *N. Engl. J. Med.* 360:1518–1525.

Bayrhuber, M., Meins, T., Habeck, M., Becker, S., Giller, K., Villinger, S., Vonrhein, C., Griesinger, C., Zweckstetter, M., and Zeth, K. 2008. Structure of the human voltage-dependent anion channel. *Proc. Natl. Acad. Sci. U.S.A.* 105:15370–15375.

Bamber, L., Harding, M., Monné, M., Slotboom, D.-J. and Kunji, E. R. 2007. The yeast mitochoondrial ADP/ATP carrier functions as a monomer in mitochondrial membranes. *Proc. Natl. Acad. Sci. U. S. A.* 10:10830–10843.

Pebay-Peyroula, E., Dahout, C., Kahn, R., Trézéguet, V., Lauquin, G. J.-M., and Brandolin, G. 2003. Structure of mitochondrial ADP/ATP carrier in complex with carboxyatractyloside. *Nature* 246: 39–44.

Nicholls, D. G., and Rial, E. 1999. A history of the first uncoupling protein, UCP1. *J. Bioenerg. Biomembr.* 31:399–406.

Ricquier, D., and Bouillaud, F. 2000. The uncoupling protein homologues: UCP1, UCP2, UCP3, StUCP and AtUCP. *Biochem. J.* 345:161–179.

Reactive Oxygen Species, Superoxide Dismutase, and Catalase

Forman, H. J., Maiorino, M., and Ursini, F. 2010. Signaling functions of reactive oxygen species. *Biochemistry* 49:835–842.

Murphy, M. P. 2009. How mitochondria produce reactive oxygen species. *Biochem. J.* 417:1–13.

Leitch, J. M., Yick, P. J., and Culotta, V. V. 2009. The right to choose: Multiple pathways for activating copper, zinc superoxide dismutase. *J. Biol. Chem.* 284: 24679–24683.

Winterbourn, C. C. 2008. Reconciling the chemistry and biology of reactive oxygen species. *Nat. Chem. Biol.* 4:278–286.

Veal, E. A., Day, A. M., and Morgan, B. A. 2007. Hydrogen peroxide sensing and signaling. *Mol. Cell* 26:1–14.

Stone, J. R., and Yang, S. 2006. Hydrogen peroxide: A signaling messenger. *Antioxid. Redox Signal.* 8(3–4):243–270.

Acker, H. 2005. The oxygen sensing signal cascade under the influence of reactive oxygen species. *Phil. Trans. R. Soc. B* 360:2201–2210.

Valentine, J. S., Doucette, P. A., and Potter S. Z. 2005. Copper-zinc superoxide dismutase and amyotrophic lateral sclerosis. *Annu. Rev. Biochem.* 74:563–593.

Culotta, V. C. 2000. Superoxide dismutase, oxidative stress, and cell metabolism. *Curr. Top. Cell Regul.* 36:117–132.

Morrison, B. M., Morrison, J. H., and Gordon, J. W. 1998. Superoxide dismutase and neurofilament transgenic models of amyotrophic lateral sclerosis. *J. Exp. Zool.* 282:32–47.

Tainer, J. A., Getzoff, E. D., Richardson, J. S., and Richardson, D. C. 1983. Structure and mechanism of copper, zinc superoxide dismutase. *Nature* 306:284–287.

Reid, T. J., Murthy, M. R., Sicignano, A., Tanaka, N., Musick, W. D., and Rossmann, M. G. 1981. Structure and heme environment of beef liver catalase at 2.5 Å resolution. *Proc. Natl. Acad. Sci. U. S. A.* 78:4767–4771.

Stallings, W. C., Pattridge, K. A., Strong, R. K., and Ludwig, M. L. 1984. Manganese and iron superoxide dismutases are structural homologs. *J. Biol. Chem.* 259:10695–10699.

Hsieh, Y., Guan, Y., Tu, C., Bratt, P. J., Angerhofer, A., Lepock, J. R., Hickey, M. J., Tainer, J. A., Nick, H. S., and Silverman, D. N. 1998. Probing the active site of human manganese superoxide dismutase: The role of glutamine 143. *Biochemistry* 37:4731–4739.

Mitochondrial Diseases

Mitochondria Disease. 2009. A compendium of nine articles on mitochondrial diseases. *Biochem. Biophys. Acta Mol. Basis Disease* 1792:1095–1167.

Cicchetti, F., Drouin-Ouellet, J., and Gross, R. E. 2009. Environmental toxins and Parkinson's disease: What have we learned from pesticide-induced animal models? *Trends Pharm. Sci.* 30:475–483.

DiMauro, S., and Schon, E. A. 2003. Mitochondrial respiratory-chain disease. *New Engl. J. Med.* 348:2656–2668.

Smeitink, J., van den Heuvel, L., and DiMauro, S. 2001. The genetics and pathology of oxidative phosphorylation. *Nat. Rev. Genet.* 2:342–352.

Wallace, D. C. 1999. Mitochondrial diseases in man and mouse. *Science* 283:1482–1488.

Apoptosis

Qi, S., Pang, Y., Hu, Q., Liu, Q., Li, H., Zhou, Y., He, T., Liang, Q., Liu, Y., Yuan, X., Luo, G., Li, H., Wang, J., Yan, N., and Shi, Y. 2010.Crystal structure of the *Caenorhabditis elegans* apoptosome reveals an octameric assembly of CED-4. *Cell* 141:446–457.

Chan, D. C. 2006. Mitochondria: Dynamic organelles in disease, aging, and development. *Cell* 125:1241–1252.

Green, D. R. 2005. Apoptotic pathways: Ten minutes to dead. *Cell* 121:671–674.

Joza, N., Susin, S. A., Daugas, E., Stanford, W. L., Cho, S. K., Li, C. Y. J., Sasaki, T., Elia, A. J., Cheng, H.-Y. M., Ravagnan, L., Ferri, K. F., Zamzami, N., Wakeham, A., Hakem, R., Yoshida, H., Kong, Y.-Y., Mak, T. W., Zúñiga-Pflücker, J. C., Kroemer, G., and Penninger, J. M. 2001. Essential role of the mitochondrial apoptosis-inducing factor in programmed cell death. *Nature* 410:549–554.

Desagher, S., and Martinou, J. C. 2000. Mitochondria as the central control point of apoptosis. *Trends Cell Biol.* 10:369–377.

Hengartner, M. O. 2000. The biochemistry of apoptosis. *Nature* 407:770–776.

Historical Aspects

Prebble, J., and Weber, B. 2003. *Wandering in the Gardens of the Mind: Peter Mitchell and the Making of Glynn.* Oxford.

Mitchell, P. 1979. Keilin's respiratory chain concept and its chemiosmotic consequences. *Science* 206:1148–1159.

Preeble, J. 2002. Peter Mitchell and the ox phos wars. *Trends Biochem. Sci.* 27:209–212.

Mitchell, P. 1976. Vectorial chemistry and the molecular mechanics of chemiosmotic coupling: Power transmission by proticity. *Biochem. Soc. Trans.* 4:399–430.

Racker, E. 1980. From Pasteur to Mitchell: A hundred years of bioenergetics. *Fed. Proc.* 39:210–215.

Kalckar, H. M. 1991. Fifty years of biological research: From oxidative phosphorylation to energy requiring transport and regulation. *Annu. Rev. Biochem.* 60:1–37.

Chapter 19

Where to Start

Huber, R. 1989. A structural basis of light energy and electron transfer in biology. *EMBO J.* 8:2125–2147.

Deisenhofer, J., and Michel, H. 1989. The photosynthetic reaction centre from the purple bacterium *Rhodopseudomonas viridis.* *EMBO J.* 8:2149–2170.

Barber, J., and Andersson, B. 1994. Revealing the blueprint of photosynthesis. *Nature* 370:31–34.

Books and General Reviews

Nelson, N., and Yocum, C. 2006. Structure and functions of photosystems I and II. *Annu. Rev. Plant Biol.* 57:521–565.

Merchant, S., and Sawaya, M. R. 2005. The light reactions: A guide to recent acquisitions for the picture gallery. *Plant Cell* 17:648–663.

Blankenship, R. E. 2002. *Molecular Mechanisms of Photosynthesis.* Wiley-Blackwell.

Raghavendra, A. S. 2000. *Photosynthesis: A Comprehensive Treatise.* Cambridge University Press.

Nicholls, D. G., and Ferguson, S. J. 2002. *Bioenergetics* (3d ed.). Academic Press.

Electron-Transfer Mechanisms

Beratan, D., and Skourtis, S. 1998. Electron transfer mechanisms. *Curr. Opin. Chem. Biol.* 2:235–243.

Moser, C. C., Keske, J. M., Warncke, K., Farid, R. S., and Dutton, P. L. 1992. Nature of biological electron transfer. *Nature* 355:796–802.

Boxer, S. G. 1990. Mechanisms of long-distance electron transfer in proteins: Lessons from photosynthetic reaction centers. *Annu. Rev. Biophys. Biophys. Chem.* 19:267–299.

Photosystem II

Kirchhoff, H., Tremmel, I., Haase, W., and Kubitscheck, U. 2004. Supramolecular photosystem II organization in grana of thylakoid membranes: Evidence for a structured arrangement. *Biochemistry* 43:9204–9213.

Diner, B. A., and Rappaport, F. 2002. Structure, dynamics, and energetics of the primary photochemistry of photosystem II of oxygenic photosynthesis. *Annu. Rev. Plant Biol.* 54:551–580.

Zouni, A., Witt, H. T., Kern, J., Fromme, P., Krauss, N., Saenger, W., and Orth, P. 2001. Crystal structure of photosystem II from *Synechococcus elongatus* at 3.8 Å resolution. *Nature* 409:739–743.

Rhee, K. H. 2001. Photosystem II: The solid structural era. *Annu. Rev. Biophys. Biomolec. Struct.* 30:307–328.

Deisenhofer, J., and Michel, H. 1991. High-resolution structures of photosynthetic reaction centers. *Annu. Rev. Biophys. Biophys. Chem.* 20:247–266.

Oxygen Evolution

Barber, J. 2008. Crystal structure of the oxygen-evolving complex of photosystem II. *Inorg. Chem.* 47:1700–1710.

Pushkar, Y., Yano, J., Sauer, K., Boussac, A., and Yachandra, V. K. 2008. Structural changes in the Mn_4Ca cluster and the mechanism of photosynthetic water splitting. *Proc. Natl. Acad. Sci. U.S.A.* 105:1879–1884.

Renger, G. 2007. Oxidative photosynthetic water splitting: Energetics, kinetics and mechanism. *Photosynth. Res.* 92:407–425.

Renger, G., and Kühn, P. 2007. Reaction pattern and mechanism of light induced oxidative water splitting in photosynthesis. *Biochim. Biophys. Acta* 1767: 458-471.

Ferreira, K. N., Iverson, T. M., Maghlaoui, K., Barber, J., and Iwata, S. 2004. Architecture of the photosynthetic oxygen-evolving center. *Science* 303:1831–1838.

Hoganson, C. W., and Babcock, G. T. 1997. A metalloradical mechanism for the generation of oxygen from water in photosynthesis. *Science* 277:1953–1956.

Yamachandra, V. K., DeRose, V. J., Latimer, M. J., Mukerji, I., Sauer, K., and Klein, M. P. 1993. Where plants make oxygen: A structural model for the photosynthetic oxygen-evolving manganese complex. *Science* 260:675–679.

Peloquin, J. M., and Britt, R. D. 2001. EPR/ENDOR characterization of the physical and electronic structure of the OEC Mn cluster. *Biochim. Biophys. Acta* 1503:96–111.

Photosystem I and Cytochrome *bf*

Iwai, M., Takizawa, K., Tokutsu, R., Okamuro, A., Takahashi, Y., and Minagawa, J. 2010. Isolation of the elusive supercomplex that drives cyclic electron flow in photosynthesis. *Nature* 464:1210–1214.

Amunts, A., Drory, O., and Nelson, N. 2007. The structure of photosystem I supercomplex at 3.4 Å resolution. *Nature* 447:58–63.

Cramer, W. A., Zhang, H., Yan, J., Kurisu, G., and Smith, J. L. 2004. Evolution of photosynthesis: Time-independent structure of the cytochrome b_6f complex. *Biochemistry* 43:5921–5929.

Kargul, J., Nield, J., and Barber, J. 2003. Three-dimensional reconstruction of a light-harvesting complex I-photosystem I (LHCI-PSI) supercomplex from the green alga *Chlamydomonas reinhardtii.* *J. Biol. Chem.* 278:16135–16141.

Schubert, W. D., Klukas, O., Saenger, W., Witt, H. T., Fromme, P., and Krauss, N. 1998. A common ancestor for oxygenic and anoxygenic photosynthetic systems: A comparison based on the structural model of photosystem I. *J. Mol. Biol.* 280:297–314.

Fotiadis, D., Muller, D. J., Tsiotis, G., Hasler, L., Tittmann, P., Mini, T., Jeno, P., Gross, H., and Engel, A. 1998. Surface analysis of the photosystem I complex by electron and atomic force microscopy. *J. Mol. Biol.* 283:83–94.

Klukas, O., Schubert, W. D., Jordan, P., Krauss, N., Fromme, P., Witt, H. T., and Saenger, W. 1999. Photosystem I, an improved model of the stromal subunits PsaC, PsaD, and PsaE. *J. Biol. Chem.* 274:7351–7360.

Jensen, P. E., Gilpin, M., Knoetzel, J., and Scheller, H. V. 2000. The PSI-K subunit of photosystem I is involved in the interaction between light-harvesting complex I and the photosystem I reaction center core. *J. Biol. Chem.* 275:24701–24708.

Kitmitto, A., Mustafa, A. O., Holzenburg, A., and Ford, R. C. 1998. Three-dimensional structure of higher plant photosystem I determined by electron crystallography. *J. Biol. Chem.* 273:29592–29599.

Krauss, N., Hinrichs, W., Witt, I., Fromme, P., Pritzkow, W., Dauter, Z., Betzel, C., Wilson, K. S., Witt, H. T., and Saenger, W. 1993. Three-dimensional structure of system I photosynthesis at 6 Å resolution. *Nature* 361:326–331.

Malkin, R. 1992. Cytochrome bc_1 and $b_6 f$ complexes of photosynthetic membranes. *Photosynth. Res.* 33:121–136.

Karplus, P. A., Daniels, M. J., and Herriott, J. R. 1991. Atomic structure of ferredoxin-NADP$^+$ reductase: Prototype for a structurally novel flavoenzyme family. *Science* 251:60–66.

ATP Synthase

Vollmar, M., Schlieper, D., Winn, D., Büchner, C., and Groth, G. 2009. Structure of the c14 rotor ring of the proton translocating chloroplast ATP synthase. *J. Biol. Chem.* 284:18228–18235.

Varco-Merth, B., Fromme, R., Wang, M., and Fromme, P. 2008. Crystallization of the c14-rotor of the chloroplast ATP synthase reveals that it contains pigments. *Biochim. Biophys. Acta* 1777:605–612.

Richter, M. L., Hein, R., and Huchzermeyer, B. 2000. Important subunit interactions in the chloroplast ATP synthase. *Biochim. Biophys. Acta* 1458:326–329.

Oster, G., and Wang, H. 1999. ATP synthase: Two motors, two fuels. *Structure* 7:R67–R72.

Weber, J., and Senior, A. E. 2000. ATP synthase: What we know about ATP hydrolysis and what we do not know about ATP synthesis. *Biochim. Biophys. Acta* 1458:300–309.

Light-Harvesting Assemblies

Melkozernov, A. N., Barber, J., and Blankenship, R. E. 2006. Light harvesting in photosystem I supercomplexes. *Biochemistry* 45:331–345.

Conroy, M. J., Westerhuis, W. H., Parkes-Loach, P. S., Loach, P. A., Hunter, C. N., and Williamson, M. P. 2000. The solution structure of *Rhodobacter sphaeroides* LH1β reveals two helical domains separated by a more flexible region: Structural consequences for the LH1 complex. *J. Mol. Biol.* 298:83–94.

Koepke, J., Hu, X., Muenke, C., Schulten, K., and Michel, H. 1996. The crystal structure of the light-harvesting complex II (B800–850) from *Rhodospirillum molischianum*. *Structure* 4:581–597.

Grossman, A. R., Bhaya, D., Apt, K. E., and Kehoe, D. M. 1995. Light-harvesting complexes in oxygenic photosynthesis: Diversity, control, and evolution. *Annu. Rev. Genet.* 29:231–288.

Kühlbrandt, W., Wang, D.-N., and Fujiyoshi, Y. 1994. Atomic model of plant light-harvesting complex by electron crystallography. *Nature* 367:614–621.

Evolution

Chen, M., and Zhang, Y. 2008. Tracking the molecular evolution of photosynthesis through characterization of atomic contents of the photosynthetic units. *Photosynth. Res.* 97:255–261.

Iverson, T. M. 2006. Evolution and unique bioenergetic mechanisms in oxygenic photosynthesis. *Curr. Opin. Chem. Biol.* 10(2):91–100.

Cavalier-Smith, T. 2002. Chloroplast evolution: Secondary symbiogenesis and multiple losses. *Curr. Biol.* 12:R62–64.

Nelson, N., and Ben-Shem, A. 2005. The structure of photosystem I and evolution of photosynthesis. *BioEssays* 27:914–922.

Green, B. R. 2001. Was "molecular opportunism" a factor in the evolution of different photosynthetic light-harvesting pigment systems? *Proc. Natl. Acad. Sci. U.S.A.* 98:2119–2121.

Dismukes, G. C., Klimov, V. V., Baranov, S. V., Nozlov, Y. N., Das Gupta, J., and Tyryshkin, A. 2001. The origin of atmospheric oxygen on Earth: The innovation of oxygenic photosynthesis. *Proc. Natl. Acad. Sci. U.S.A.* 98:2170–2175.

Moreira, D., Le Guyader, H., and Phillippe, H. 2000. The origin of red algae and the evolution of chloroplasts. *Nature* 405:69–72.

Cavalier-Smith, T. 2000. Membrane heredity and early chloroplast evolution. *Trends Plant Sci.* 5:174–182.

Blankenship, R. E., and Hartman, H. 1998. The origin and evolution of oxygenic photosynthesis. *Trends Biochem. Sci.* 23:94–97.

Chapter 20

Where to Start

Ellis, R. J. 2010. Tackling unintelligent design. *Nature* 463: 164–165.

Gutteridge, S., and Pierce, J. 2006. A unified theory for the basis of the limitations of the primary reaction of photosynthetic CO_2 fixation: Was Dr. Pangloss right? *Proc. Natl. Acad. Sci. U.S.A.* 103: 7203–7204.

Horecker, B. L. 1976. Unravelling the pentose phosphate pathway. In *Reflections on Biochemistry* (pp. 65–72), edited by A. Kornberg, L. Cornudella, B. L. Horecker, and J. Oro. Pergamon.

Levi, P. 1984. Carbon. In *The Periodic Table*. Random House.

Books and General Reviews

Parry, M. A. J., Andralojc, P. J., Mitchell, R. A. C., Madgwick, P. J., and Keys, A. J. 2003. Manipulation of rubisco: The amount, activity, function and regulation. *J. Exp. Bot.* 54:1321–1333.

Spreitzer, R. J., and Salvucci, M. E. 2002. Rubisco: Structure, regulatory interactions, and possibilities for a better enzyme. *Annu. Rev. Plant Biol.* 53:449–475.

Wood, T. 1985. *The Pentose Phosphate Pathway*. Academic Press.

Buchanan, B. B., Gruissem, W., and Jones, R. L. 2000. *Biochemistry and Molecular Biology of Plants*. American Society of Plant Physiologists.

Enzymes and Reaction Mechanisms

Harrison, D. H., Runquist, J. A., Holub, A., and Miziorko, H. M. 1998. The crystal structure of phosphoribulokinase from *Rhodobacter sphaeroides* reveals a fold similar to that of adenylate kinase. *Biochemistry* 37:5074–5085.

Miziorko, H. M. 2000. Phosphoribulokinase: Current perspectives on the structure/function basis for regulation and catalysis. *Adv. Enzymol. Relat. Areas Mol. Biol.* 74:95–127.

Thorell, S., Gergely, P., Jr., Banki, K., Perl, A., and Schneider, G. 2000. The three-dimensional structure of human transaldolase. *FEBS Lett.* 475:205–208.

Carbon Dioxide Fixation and Rubisco

Satagopan, S., Scott, S. S., Smith, T. G., and Tabita, F. R. 2009. A rubisco mutant that confers growth under a normally "inhibitory" oxygen concentration. *Biochemistry* 48: 9076–9083.

Tcherkez, G. G. B., Farquhar, G. D., and Andrews, J. T. 2006. Despite slow catalysis and confused substrate specificity, all ribulose bisphosphate carboxylases may be nearly perfectly optimized. *Proc. Natl. Acad. Sci. U.S.A.* 103: 7246–7251.

Sugawara, H., Yamamoto, H., Shibata, N., Inoue, T., Okada, S., Miyake, C., Yokota, A., and Kai, Y. 1999. Crystal structure of carboxylase reaction-oriented ribulose 1,5-bisphosphate carboxylase/oxygenase from a thermophilic red alga, *Galdieria partita. J. Biol. Chem.* 274:15655–15661.

Hansen, S., Vollan, V. B., Hough, E., and Andersen, K. 1999. The crystal structure of rubisco from *Alcaligenes eutrophus* reveals a novel central eight-stranded β-barrel formed by β-strands from four subunits. *J. Mol. Biol.* 288:609–621.

Knight, S., Andersson, I., and Brändén, C. I. 1990. Crystallographic analysis of ribulose 1,5-bisphosphate carboxylase from spinach at 2.4 Å resolution: Subunit interactions and active site. *J. Mol. Biol.* 215:113–160.

Taylor, T. C., and Andersson, I. 1997. The structure of the complex between rubisco and its natural substrate ribulose 1,5-bisphosphate. *J. Mol. Biol.* 265:432–444.

Cleland, W. W., Andrews, T. J., Gutteridge, S., Hartman, F. C., and Lorimer, G. H. 1998. Mechanism of rubisco: The carbamate as general base. *Chem. Rev.* 98:549–561.

Buchanan, B. B. 1992. Carbon dioxide assimilation in oxygenic and anoxygenic photosynthesis. *Photosynth. Res.* 33:147–162.

Hatch, M. D. 1987. C_4 photosynthesis: A unique blend of modified biochemistry, anatomy, and ultrastructure. *Biochim. Biophys. Acta* 895:81–106.

Regulation

Lebreton, S., Andreescu, S., Graciet, E., and Gontero, B. 2006. Mapping of the interaction site of CP12 with glyceraldehyde-3-phosphate dehydrogenase from *Chlamydomonas reinhardtii*. Functional consequences for glyceraldehyde-3-phosphate dehydrogenase. *FEBS J.* 273:3358–3369.

Graciet, E., Lebreton, S., and Gontero, B. 2004. The emergence of new regulatory mechanisms in the Benson-Calvin pathway via protein-protein interactions: A glyceraldehyde-3-phosphate dehydrogenase/CP12/phosphoribulokinase complex. *J. Exp. Bot.* 55:1245–1254.

Balmer, Y., Koller, A., del Val, G., Manieri, W., Schürmann, P., and Buchanan, B. B. 2003. Proteomics gives insight into the regulatory function of chloroplast thioredoxins. *Proc. Natl. Acad. Sci. U.S.A.* 100:370–375.

Rokka, A., Zhang, L., and Aro, E.-M. 2001. Rubisco activase: An enzyme with a temperature-dependent dual function? *Plant J.* 25:463– 472.

Zhang, N., and Portis, A. R., Jr. 1999. Mechanism of light regulation of rubisco: A specific role for the larger rubisco activase isoform involving reductive activation by thioredoxin-f. *Proc. Natl. Acad. Sci. U.S.A.* 96:9438–9443.

Wedel, N., Soll, J., and Paap, B. K. 1997. CP12 provides a new mode of light regulation of Calvin cycle activity in higher plants. *Proc. Natl. Acad. Sci. U.S.A.* 94:10479–10484.

Avilan, L., Lebreton, S., and Gontero, B. 2000. Thioredoxin activation of phosphoribulokinase in a bi-enzyme complex from *Chlamydomonas reinhardtii* chloroplasts. *J. Biol. Chem.* 275:9447–9451.

Irihimovitch, V., and Shapira, M. 2000. Glutathione redox potential modulated by reactive oxygen species regulates translation of rubisco large subunit in the chloroplast. *J. Biol. Chem.* 275:16289– 16295.

Glucose 6-phosphate Dehydrogenase

Wang, X.-T., and Engel, P. C. 2009. Clinical mutants of human glucose 6-phosphate dehydrogenase: Impairment of $NADP^+$ binding affects both folding and stability. *Biochim. Biophys. Acta* 1792: 804–809.

Au, S. W., Gover, S., Lam, V. M., and Adams, M. J. 2000. Human glucose-6-phosphate dehydrogenase: The crystal structure reveals a structural NADP(+) molecule and provides insights into enzyme deficiency. *Struct. Fold. Des.* 8:293–303.

Salvemini, F., Franze, A., Iervolino, A., Filosa, S., Salzano, S., and Ursini, M. V. 1999. Enhanced glutathione levels and oxidoresistance mediated by increased glucose-6-phosphate dehydrogenase expression. *J. Biol. Chem.* 274:2750–2757.

Tian, W. N., Braunstein, L. D., Apse, K., Pang, J., Rose, M., Tian, X., and Stanton, R. C. 1999. Importance of glucose-6-phos-phate dehydrogenase activity in cell death. *Am. J. Physiol.* 276:C1121–C1131.

Tian, W. N., Braunstein, L. D., Pang, J., Stuhlmeier, K. M., Xi, Q. C., Tian, X., and Stanton, R. C. 1998. Importance of glucose-6-phosphate dehydrogenase activity for cell growth. *J. Biol. Chem.* 273:10609–10617.

Ursini, M. V., Parrella, A., Rosa, G., Salzano, S., and Martini, G. 1997. Enhanced expression of glucose-6-phosphate dehydrogenase in human cells sustaining oxidative stress. *Biochem. J.* 323:801–806.

Evolution

Deschamps, P., Haferkamp, I., d'Hulst, C., Neuhaus, H. E., and Ball, S. G. 2008. The relocation of starch metabolism to chloroplasts: when, why and how. *Trends Plant Sci.* 13: 574–582.

Coy, J. F., Dubel, S., Kioschis, P., Thomas, K., Micklem, G., Delius, H., and Poustka, A. 1996. Molecular cloning of tissue-specific transcripts of a transketolase-related gene: Implications for the evolution of new vertebrate genes. *Genomics* 32:309–316.

Schenk, G., Layfield, R., Candy, J. M., Duggleby, R. G., and Nixon, P. F. 1997. Molecular evolutionary analysis of the thiamine-diphosphate-dependent enzyme, transketolase. *J. Mol. Evol.* 44:552–572.

Notaro, R., Afolayan, A., and Luzzatto L. 2000. Human mutations in glucose 6-phosphate dehydrogenase reflect evolutionary history. *FASEB J.* 14:485–494.

Wedel, N., and Soll, J. 1998. Evolutionary conserved light regulation of Calvin cycle activity by NADPH-mediated reversible phosphoribulokinase/CP12/glyceraldehyde-3-phosphate dehydrogenase complex dissociation. *Proc. Natl. Acad. Sci. U.S.A.* 95:9699–9704.

Martin, W., and Schnarrenberger, C. 1997. The evolution of the Calvin cycle from prokaryotic to eukaryotic chromosomes: A case study of functional redundancy in ancient pathways through endosymbiosis. *Curr. Genet.* 32:1–18.

Ku, M. S., Kano-Murakami, Y., and Matsuoka, M. 1996. Evolution and expression of C_4 photosynthesis genes. *Plant Physiol.* 111:949–957.

Pereto, J. G., Velasco, A. M., Becerra, A., and Lazcano, A. 1999. Comparative biochemistry of CO_2 fixation and the evolution of autotrophy. *Int. Microbiol.* 2:3–10.

Chapter 21

Where to Start

Krebs, E. G. 1993. Protein phosphorylation and cellular regulation I. *Biosci. Rep.* 13:127–142.

Fischer, E. H. 1993. Protein phosphorylation and cellular regulation II. *Angew. Chem. Int. Ed.* 32:1130–1137.

Johnson, L. N. 1992. Glycogen phosphorylase: Control by phosphorylation and allosteric effectors. *FASEB J.* 6:2274–2282.

Browner, M. F., and Fletterick, R. J. 1992. Phosphorylase: A biological transducer. *Trends Biochem. Sci.* 17:66–71.

Books and General Reviews

Agius, L. 2008. Glucokinase and molecular aspects of liver glycogen metabolism. *Biochem. J.* 414:1–18.

Greenberg, C. C., Jurczak, M. J., Danos, A. M., and Brady, M. J. 2006. Glycogen branches out: New perspectives on the role of glycogen metabolism in the integration of metabolic pathways. *Am. J. Physiol. Endocrinol. Metab.* 291:E1–E8.

Shulman, R. G., and Rothman, D. L. 1996. Enzymatic phosphorylation of muscle glycogen synthase: A mechanism for maintenance of metabolic homeostasis. *Proc. Natl. Acad. Sci. U.S.A.* 93:7491–7495.

Shulman, G. I., and Landau, B. R. 1992. Pathways of glycogen repletion. *Physiol. Rev.* 72:1019–1035.

X-ray Crystallographic Studies

Horcajada, C., Guinovart, J. J., Fita, I., and Ferrer, J. C. 2006. Crystal structure of an archaeal glycogen synthase: Insights into oligomerization and substrate binding of eukaryotic glycogen synthases. *J. Biol. Chem.* 281:2923–2931.

Buschiazzo, A., Ugalde, J. E., Guerin, M. E., Shepard, W., Ugalde, R. A., and Alzari, P. M. 2004. Crystal structure of glycogen synthase: Homologous enzymes catalyze glycogen synthesis and degradation. *EMBO J.* 23:3196–3205.

Gibbons, B. J., Roach, P. J., and Hurley, T. D. 2002. Cyrstal structure of the autocatalytic initiator of glycogen biosynthesis, glycogenin. *J. Mol. Biol.* 319:463–477.

Sprang, S. R., Withers, S. G., Goldsmith, E. J., Fletterick, R. J., and Madsen, N. B. 1991. Structural basis for the activation of glycogen phosphorylase *b* by adenosine monophosphate. *Science* 254:1367–1371.

Johnson, L. N., and Barford, D. 1990. Glycogen phosphorylase: The structural basis of the allosteric response and comparison with other allosteric proteins. *J. Biol. Chem.* 265:2409–2412.

Browner, M. F., Fauman, E. B., and Fletterick, R. J. 1992. Tracking conformational states in allosteric transitions of phosphorylase. *Biochemistry* 31:11297–11304.

Martin, J. L., Johnson, L. N., and Withers, S. G. 1990. Comparison of the binding of glucose and glucose 1-phosphate derivatives to T-state glycogen phosphorylase *b*. *Biochemistry* 29:10745–10757.

Priming of Glycogen Synthesis

Lomako, J., Lomako, W. M., and Whelan, W. J. 2004. Glycogenin: The primer for mammalian and yeast glycogen synthesis. *Biochim. Biophys. Acta* 1673:45–55.

Lin, A., Mu, J., Yang, J., and Roach, P. J. 1999. Self-glucosylation of glycogenin, the initiator of glycogen biosynthesis, involves an inter-subunit reaction. *Arch. Biochem. Biophys.* 363:163–170.

Roach, P. J., and Skurat, A. V. 1997. Self-glucosylating initiator proteins and their role in glycogen biosynthesis. *Prog. Nucleic Acid Res. Mol. Biol.* 57:289–316.

Smythe, C., and Cohen, P. 1991. The discovery of glycogenin and the priming mechanism for glycogen biogenesis. *Eur. J. Biochem.* 200:625–631.

Catalytic Mechanisms

Skamnaki, V. T., Owen, D. J., Noble, M. E., Lowe, E. D., Lowe, G., Oikonomakos, N. G., and Johnson, L. N. 1999. Catalytic mechanism of phosphorylase kinase probed by mutational studies. *Biochemistry* 38:14718–14730.

Buchbinder, J. L., and Fletterick, R. J. 1996. Role of the active site gate of glycogen phosphorylase in allosteric inhibition and substrate binding. *J. Biol. Chem.* 271:22305–22309.

Palm, D., Klein, H. W., Schinzel, R., Buehner, M., and Helmreich, E. J. M. 1990. The role of pyridoxal 5'-phosphate in glycogen phosphorylase catalysis. *Biochemistry* 29:1099–1107.

Regulation of Glycogen Metabolism

Boulatnikov, I. G., Peters, J. L., Nadeau, O. W., Sage, J. M., Daniels, P. J., Kumar, P., Walsh, D. A., and Carlson, G. M. 2009. Expressed phosphorylase *b* kinase and its αγδ subcomplex as regulatory models for the rabbit skeletal muscle holoenzyme. *Biochemistry* 48:10183–10191.

Ros, S., García-Rocha, M., Domínguez, J., Ferrer, J. C., and Guinovart, J. J. 2009. Control of liver glycogen synthase activity and intracellular distribution by phosphorylation. *J. Biol. Chem.* 284:6370–6378.

Danos, A. M., Osmanovic, S., and Brady, M. J. 2009. Differential regulation of glycogenolysis by mutant protein phosphatase-1 glycogen-targeting subunits. *J. Biol. Chem.* 284:19544–19553.

Pautsch, A., Stadler, N., Wissdorf, O., Langkopf, E., Moreth, M., and Streicher, R. 2008. Molecular recognition of the protein phosphatase 1 glycogen targeting subunit by glycogen phosphorylase. *J. Biol. Chem.* 283:8913–8918.

Jope, R. S., and Johnson, G. V. W. 2004. The glamour and gloom of glycogen synthase kinase-3. *Trends Biochem. Sci.* 29:95–102.

Doble, B. W., and Woodgett, J. R. 2003. GSK-3: Tricks of the trade for a multi-tasking kinase. *J. Cell Sci.* 116:1175–1186.

Pederson, B. A., Cheng, C., Wilson, W. A., and Roach, P. J. 2000. Regulation of glycogen synthase: Identification of residues involved in regulation by the allosteric ligand glucose-6-P and by phosphorylation. *J. Biol. Chem.* 275:27753–27761.

Melendez, R., Melendez-Hevia, E., and Canela, E. I. 1999. The fractal structure of glycogen: A clever solution to optimize cell metabolism. *Biophys. J.* 77:1327–1332.

Franch, J., Aslesen, R., and Jensen, J. 1999. Regulation of glycogen synthesis in rat skeletal muscle after glycogen-depleting contractile activity: Effects of adrenaline on glycogen synthesis and activation of glycogen synthase and glycogen phosphorylase. *Biochem. J.* 344(pt.1):231–235.

Aggen, J. B., Nairn, A. C., and Chamberlin, R. 2000. Regulation of protein phosphatase-1. *Chem. Biol.* 7:R13–R23.

Egloff, M. P., Johnson, D. F., Moorhead, G., Cohen, P. T., Cohen, P., and Barford, D. 1997. Structural basis for the recognition of regulatory subunits by the catalytic subunit of protein phosphatase 1. *EMBO J.* 16:1876–1887.

Wu, J., Liu, J., Thompson, I., Oliver, C. J., Shenolikar, S., and Brautigan, D. L. 1998. A conserved domain for glycogen binding in protein phosphatase-1 targeting subunits. *FEBS Lett.* 439:185–191.

Genetic Diseases

Nyhan, W. L., Barshop, B. A., and Ozand, P. T. 2005. *Atlas of Metabolic Diseases.* (2d ed., pp. 373–408). Hodder Arnold.

Chen, Y.-T. 2001. Glycogen storage diseases. In *The Metabolic and Molecular Bases of Inherited Diseases* (8th ed., pp. 1521–1552), edited by C. R. Scriver., W. S. Sly, B. Childs, A. L. Beaudet, D. Valle, K. W. Kinzler, and B. Vogelstein. McGraw-Hill.

Burchell, A., and Waddell, I. D. 1991. The molecular basis of the hepatic microsomal glucose-6-phosphatase system. *Biochim. Biophys. Acta* 1092:129–137.

Lei, K. J., Shelley, L. L., Pan, C. J., Sidbury, J. B., and Chou, J. Y. 1993. Mutations in the glucose-6-phosphatase gene that cause glycogen storage disease type Ia. *Science* 262:580–583.

Ross, B. D., Radda, G. K., Gadian, D. G., Rocker, G., Esiri, M., and Falconer-Smith, J. 1981. Examination of a case of suspected McArdle's syndrome by ^{31}P NMR. *N. Engl. J. Med.* 304:1338–1342.

Evolution

Holm, L., and Sander, C. 1995. Evolutionary link between glycogen phosphorylase and a DNA modifying enzyme. *EMBO J.* 14:1287–1293.

Hudson, J. W., Golding, G. B., and Crerar, M. M. 1993. Evolution of allosteric control in glycogen phosphorylase. *J. Mol. Biol.* 234:700–721.

Rath, V. L., and Fletterick, R. J. 1994. Parallel evolution in two homologues of phosphorylase. *Nat. Struct. Biol.* 1:681–690.

Melendez, R., Melendez-Hevia, E., and Cascante, M. 1997. How did glycogen structure evolve to satisfy the requirement for rapid mobilization of glucose? A problem of physical constraints in structure building. *J. Mol. Evol.* 45:446–455.

Rath, V. L., Lin, K., Hwang, P. K., and Fletterick, R. J. 1996. The evolution of an allosteric site in phosphorylase. *Structure* 4:463–473.

Chapter 22

Where to Start

Rinaldo, P., Matern, D., and Bennet, M. J. 2002. Fatty acid oxidation disorders. *Annu. Rev. Physiol.* 64:477–502.

Rasmussen, B. B., and Wolfe, R. R. 1999. Regulation of fatty acid oxidation in skeletal muscle. *Annu. Rev. Nutr.* 19:463–484.

Semenkovich, C. F. 1997. Regulation of fatty acid synthase (FAS). *Prog. Lipid Res.* 36:43–53.

Sul, H. S., Smas, C. M., Wang, D., and Chen, L. 1998. Regulation of fat synthesis and adipose differentiation. *Prog. Nucleic Acid Res. Mol. Biol.* 60:317–345.

Wolf, G. 1996. Nutritional and hormonal regulation of fatty acid synthase. *Nutr. Rev.* 54:122–123.

Books

Vance, D. E., and Vance, J. E. (Eds.). 2008. *Biochemistry of Lipids, Lipoproteins, and Membranes.* Elsevier.

Stipanuk, M. H. (Ed.). 2006. *Biochemical and Physiological Aspects of Human Nutrition.* Saunders.

Fatty Acid Oxidation

Ahmadian, M., Duncan, R. E., and Sul, H. S. 2009. The skinny on fat: Lipolysis and fatty acid utilization in adipocytes. *Trends Endocrinol. Metab.* 20:424–428.

Farese, R. V., Jr., and Walther, T. C. 2009. Lipid droplets finally get a little R-E-S-P-E-C-T. *Cell* 139:855–860.

Goodman, J. L. 2008.The gregarious lipid droplet. *J. Biol. Chem.* 283:28005–28009.

Saha, P. K., Kojima, H., Marinez-Botas, J., Sunehag, A. L., and Chan, L. 2004. Metabolic adaptations in absence of perilipin. *J. Biol. Chem.* 279:35150–35158.

Barycki, J. J., O'Brien, L. K., Strauss, A. W., and Banaszak, L. J. 2000. Sequestration of the active site by interdomain shifting: Crystallographic and spectroscopic evidence for distinct conformations of L-3-hydroxyacyl-CoA dehydrogenase. *J. Biol. Chem.* 275:27186–27196.

Ramsay, R. R. 2000. The carnitine acyltransferases: Modulators of acyl-CoA-dependent reactions. *Biochem. Soc. Trans.* 28:182–186.

Eaton, S., Bartlett, K., and Pourfarzam, M. 1996. Mammalian mitochondrial β-oxidation. *Biochem. J.* 320:345–357.

Thorpe, C., and Kim, J. J. 1995. Structure and mechanism of action of the acyl-CoA dehydrogenases. *FASEB J.* 9:718–725.

Fatty Acid Synthesis

Maier, T., Leibundgut, M., and Ban, N. 2008. The crystal structure of a mammalian fatty acid synthase. *Science* 321:1315–1322.

Kuhajda, F. P. 2006. Fatty acid synthase and cancer: New application of an old pathway. *Cancer Res.* 66:5977–5980.

Ming, D., Kong, Y., Wakil, S. J., Brink, J., and Ma, J. 2002. Domain movements in human fatty acid synthase by quantized elastic deformational model. *Proc. Natl. Acad. Sci. U.S.A.* 99:7895–7899.

Zhang, Y.-M., Rao, M. S., Heath, R. J., Price, A. C., Olson, A. J., Rock, C. O., and White, S. W. 2001. Identification and analysis of the acyl carrier protein (ACP) docking site on β-ketoacyl-ACP synthase III. *J. Biol. Chem.* 276:8231–8238.

Davies, C., Heath, R. J., White, S. W., and Rock, C. O. 2000. The 1.8 Å crystal structure and active-site architecture of β-ketoacyl-acyl carrier protein synthase III (FabH) from *Escherichia coli. Struct. Fold. Design* 8:185–195.

Denton, R. M., Heesom, K. J., Moule, S. K., Edgell, N. J., and Burnett, P. 1997. Signalling pathways involved in the stimulation of fatty acid synthesis by insulin. *Biochem. Soc. Trans.* 25:1238–1242.

Loftus, T. M., Jaworsky, D. E., Frehywot, G. L., Townsend, C. A., Ronnett, G. V., Lane, M. D., and Kuhajda, F. P. 2000. Reduced food intake and body weight in mice treated with fatty acid synthase inhibitors. *Science* 288:2379–2381.

Acetyl CoA Carboxylase

Brownsey, R. W., Boone, A. N., Elliott, J. E., Kulpa, J. E., and Lee, W. M. 2006. Regulation of acetyl-CoA carboxylase. *Biochem. Soc. Trans.* 34:223–227.

Munday, M. R. 2002. Regulation of acetyl CoA carboxylase. *Biochem. Soc. Trans.* 30: 1059–1064.

Thoden, J. B., Blanchard, C. Z., Holden, H. M., and Waldrop, G. L. 2000. Movement of the biotin carboxylase B-domain as a result of ATP binding. *J. Biol. Chem.* 275:16183–16190.

Eicosanoids

Harizi, H., Corcuff, J.-B., and Gualde, N. 2008. Arachidonic-acid-derived eicosanoids: Roles in biology and immunopathology. *Trends Mol. Med.* 14:461–469.

Nakamura, M. T., and Nara, T. Y. 2004. Structure, function, and dietary regulation of Δ6, Δ5, and Δ9 desaturases. *Annu. Rev. Nutr.* 24:345–376.

Malkowski, M. G., Ginell, S. L., Smith, W. L., and Garavito, R. M. 2000. The productive conformation of arachidonic acid bound to prostaglandin synthase. *Science* 289:1933–1937.

Smith, T., McCracken, J., Shin, Y.-K., and DeWitt, D. 2000. Arachidonic acid and nonsteroidal anti-inflammatory drugs induce conformational changes in the human prostaglandin endoperoxide H2 synthase-2 (cyclooxygenase-2). *J. Biol. Chem.* 275:40407–40415.

Kalgutkar, A. S., Crews, B. C., Rowlinson, S. W., Garner, C., Seibert, K., and Marnett L. J. 1998. Aspirin-like molecules that covalently inactivate cyclooxygenase-2. *Science* 280:1268–1270.

Lands, W. E. 1991. Biosynthesis of prostaglandins. *Annu. Rev. Nutr.* 11:41–60.

Sigal, E. 1991. The molecular biology of mammalian arachidonic acid metabolism. *Am. J. Physiol.* 260:L13–L28.

Weissmann, G. 1991. Aspirin. *Sci. Am.* 264(1):84–90.

Vane, J. R., Flower, R. J., and Botting, R. M. 1990. History of aspirin and its mechanism of action. *Stroke* (12 suppl.):IV12–IV23.

Genetic Diseases

Nyhan, W. L., Barshop, B. A., and Ozand, P. T. 2005. *Atlas of Metabolic Diseases* (2d ed., pp. 339–300). Hodder Arnold.

Roe, C. R., and Coates, P. M. 2001. Mitochondrial fatty acid oxidation disorders. In *The Metabolic and Molecular Bases of Inherited Diseases* (8th ed., pp. 2297–2326), edited by C. R. Scriver., W. S. Sly, B. Childs, A. L. Beaudet, D. Valle, K. W. Kinzler, and B. Vogelstein. McGraw-Hill.

Brivet, M., Boutron, A., Slama, A., Costa, C., Thuillier, L., Demaugre, F., Rabier, D., Saudubray, J. M., and Bonnefont, J. P. 1999. Defects in activation and transport of fatty acids. *J. Inherit. Metab. Dis.* 22:428–441.

Wanders, R. J., van Grunsven, E. G., and Jansen, G. A. 2000. Lipid metabolism in peroxisomes: Enzymology, functions and dysfunctions of the fatty acid α-and β-oxidation systems in humans. *Biochem. Soc. Trans.* 28:141–149.

Wanders, R. J., Vreken, P., den Boer, M. E., Wijburg, F. A., van Gennip, A. H., and Ijist, L. 1999. Disorders of mitochondrial fatty acyl-CoA β-oxidation. *J. Inherit. Metab. Dis.* 22:442–487.

Kerner, J., and Hoppel, C. 1998. Genetic disorders of carnitine metabolism and their nutritional management. *Annu. Rev. Nutr.* 18:179–206.

Bartlett, K., and Pourfarzam, M. 1998. Recent developments in the detection of inherited disorders of mitochondrial β-oxidation. *Biochem. Soc. Trans.* 26:145–152.

Pollitt, R. J. 1995. Disorders of mitochondrial long-chain fatty acid oxidation. *J. Inherit. Metab. Dis.* 18:473–490.

Chapter 23

Where to Start

Ubiquitin-Mediated Protein Regulation. 2009. *Annu. Rev. Biochem.* 78: A series of reviews on the various roles of ubiquitin.

Torchinsky, Y. M. 1989. Transamination: Its discovery, biological and chemical aspects. *Trends Biochem. Sci.* 12:115–117.

Eisensmith, R. C., and Woo, S. L. C. 1991. Phenylketonuria and the phenylalanine hydroxylase gene. *Mol. Biol. Med.* 8:3–18.

Schwartz, A. L., and Ciechanover, A. 1999. The ubiquitin-proteasome pathway and pathogenesis of human diseases. *Annu. Rev. Med.* 50:57–74.

Watford, M. 2003. The urea cycle. *Biochem. Mol. Biol. Ed.* 31:289–297.

SELECTED READINGS

Books

Bender, D. A. 1985. *Amino Acid Metabolism* (2d ed.). Wiley.

Lippard, S. J., and Berg, J. M. 1994. *Principles of Bioinorganic Chemistry*. University Science Books.

Walsh, C. 1979. *Enzymatic Reaction Mechanisms*. W. H. Freeman and Company.

Christen, P., and Metzler, D. E. 1985. *Transaminases*. Wiley.

Ubiquitin and the Proteasome

Greer, P. L., Hanayama, R., Bloodgood, B. L., Mardinly, A. R., Lipton, D. M., Flavell, S.W., Kim, T.-K., Griffith, E. C., Waldon, Z., Maehr, R., Ploegh, H. L., Chowdhury, S., Worley, P. F., Steen, J., and Greenberg, M. E. 2010. The Angelman syndrome protein Ube3A regulates synapse development by ubiquitinating Arc. *Cell* 140: 704–716.

Peth, A., Besche, H. C., and Goldberg A. L. 2009. Ubiquitinated proteins activate the proteasome by binding to Usp14/Ubp6, which causes 20S gate opening. *Mol. Cell* 36: 794–804.

Cheng, Y. 2009. Toward an atomic model of the 26S proteasome. *Curr. Opin. Struct. Biol.* 19:203–208.

Lin, G., Li, D., Carvalho, L. P. S., Deng, H., Tao, H., Vogt, G., Wu, K., Schneider, J., Chidawanyika, T., Warren, J. D., Li, H., and Nathan, C. 2009. Inhibitors selective for mycobacterial versus human proteasomes. *Nature* 461: 621–626.

Wang, K. H., Roman-Hernandez, G., Grant, R. A., Sauer, R. T., and Baker, T. A. 2008. The molecular basis of N-end rule recognition. *Mol. Cell* 32: 406–414.

da Fonseca, P. C. A., and Morris, E. P. 2008. Structure of the human 26S proteasome: Subunit radial displacements open the gate into the proteolytic core. *J. Biol. Chem.* 283: 23305–23314.

Cooper, E. M., Hudson, A. W., Amos, J., Wagstaff, J., and Howley, P. M. 2004. Biochemical analysis of Angelman syndrome-associated mutation in the E3 ubiquitin ligase E6-associated protein. *J. Biol. Chem.* 279:41208–41217.

Giasson, B. I. and Lee, V. M.-Y. 2003. Are ubiquitination pathways central to Parkinson's disease? *Cell* 114:1–8.

Pagano, M., and Benmaamar, R. 2003. When protein destruction runs amok, malignancy is on the loose. *Cancer Cell* 4:251–256.

Thrower, J. S., Hoffman, L., Rechsteiner, M., and Pickart, C. M. 2000. Recognition of the polyubiquitin proteolytic signal. *EMBO J.* 19:94–102.

Hochstrasser, M. 2000. Evolution and function of ubiquitin-like protein-conjugation systems. *Nat. Cell Biol.* 2:E153–E157.

Pyridoxal Phosphate-Dependent Enzymes

Eliot, A. C., and Kirsch, J. F. 2004. Pyridoxal phosphate enzymes: Mechanistic, structural, and evolutionary considerations. *Annu. Rev. Biochem.* 73:383–415.

Mehta, P. K., and Christen, P. 2000. The molecular evolution of pyridoxal-5′-phosphate-dependent enzymes. *Adv. Enzymol. Relat. Areas Mol. Biol.* 74:129–184.

Schneider, G., Kack, H., and Lindqvist, Y. 2000. The manifold of vitamin B$_6$ dependent enzymes. *Structure Fold Des.* 8:R1–R6.

Urea Cycle Enzymes

Morris, S. M., Jr. 2002. Regulation of enzymes of the urea cycle and arginine metabolism. *Annu. Rev. Nutr.* 22:87–105.

Huang, X., and Raushel, F. M. 2000. Restricted passage of reaction intermediates through the ammonia tunnel of carbamoyl phosphate synthetase. *J. Biol. Chem.* 275:26233–26240.

Lawson, F. S., Charlebois, R. L., and Dillon, J. A. 1996. Phylogenetic analysis of carbamoylphosphate synthetase genes: Complex evolutionary history includes an internal duplication within a gene which can root the tree of life. *Mol. Biol. Evol.* 13:970–977.

McCudden, C. R., and Powers-Lee, S. G. 1996. Required allosteric effector site for N-acetylglutamate on carbamoyl-phosphate synthetase I. *J. Biol. Chem.* 271:18285–18294.

Amino Acid Degradation

Li, M., Smith, C. J., Walker, M. T., and Smith, T. J. 2009. Novel inhibitors complexed with glutamate dehydrogenase: allosteric regulation by control of protein dynamics. *J. Biol. Chem.* 284:22988–23000.

Smith, T. J., and Stanley, C. A. 2008. Untangling the glutamate dehydrogenase allosteric nightmare. *Trends Biochem. Sci.* 33: 557–564.

Fusetti, F., Erlandsen, H., Flatmark, T., and Stevens, R. C. 1998. Structure of tetrameric human phenylalanine hydroxylase and its implications for phenylketonuria. *J. Biol. Chem.* 273:16962–16967.

Titus, G. P., Mueller, H. A., Burgner, J., Rodriguez De Cordoba, S., Penalva, M. A., and Timm, D. E. 2000. Crystal structure of human homogentisate dioxygenase. *Nat. Struct. Biol.* 7:542–546.

Erlandsen, H., and Stevens, R. C. 1999. The structural basis of phenylketonuria. *Mol. Genet. Metab.* 68:103–125.

Genetic Diseases

Jayakumar, A. R., Liu, M., Moriyama, M. Ramakrishnan, R., Forbush III, B., Reddy, P. V. V., and Norenberg, M.D. 2008. Na-K-Cl cotransporter-1 in the mechanism of ammonia-induced astrocyte swelling. *J. Biol. Chem.* 283: 33874–33882.

Scriver, C. R., and Sly, W. S. (Eds.), Childs, B., Beaudet, A. L.,Valle, D., Kinzler, K. W., and Vogelstein, B. 2001. *The Metabolic Basis of Inherited Disease* (8th ed.). McGraw-Hill.

Historical Aspects and the Process of Discovery

Cooper, A. J. L., and Meister, A. 1989. An appreciation of Professor Alexander E. Braunstein: The discovery and scope of enzymatic transamination. *Biochimie* 71:387–404.

Garrod, A. E. 1909. *Inborn Errors in Metabolism*. Oxford University Press (reprinted in 1963 with a supplement by H. Harris).

Childs, B. 1970. Sir Archibald Garrod's conception of chemical individuality: A modern appreciation. *N. Engl. J. Med.* 282:71–78.

Holmes, F. L. 1980. Hans Krebs and the discovery of the ornithine cycle. *Fed. Proc.* 39:216–225.

Chapter 24

Where to Start

Kim, J., and Rees, D. C. 1989. Nitrogenase and biological nitrogen fixation. *Biochemistry* 33:389–397.

Christen, P., Jaussi, R., Juretic, N., Mehta, P. K., Hale, T. I., and Ziak, M. 1990. Evolutionary and biosynthetic aspects of aspartate aminotransferase isoenzymes and other aminotransferases. *Ann. N. Y. Acad. Sci.* 585:331–338.

Schneider, G., Kack, H., and Lindqvist, Y. 2000. The manifold of vitamin B6 dependent enzymes. *Structure Fold Des.* 8:R1–R6.

Rhee, S. G., Chock, P. B., and Stadtman, E. R. 1989. Regulation of *Escherichia coli* glutamine synthetase. *Adv. Enzymol. Mol. Biol.* 62:37–92.

Shemin, D. 1989. An illustration of the use of isotopes: The biosynthesis of porphyrins. *Bioessays* 10:30–35.

Books

Bender, D. A. 1985. *Amino Acid Metabolism* (2d ed.). Wiley.

Jordan, P. M. (Ed.). 1991. *Biosynthesis of Tetrapyrroles*. Elsevier.

Scriver, C. R. (Ed.), Sly, W. S. (Ed.), Childs, B., Beaudet, A. L., Valle, D., Kinzler, K. W., and Vogelstein, B. 2001. *The Metabolic Basis of Inherited Disease* (8th ed.). McGraw-Hill.

Meister, A. 1965. *Biochemistry of the Amino Acids* (vols. 1 and 2, 2d ed.). Academic Press.

McMurry, J. E., and Begley, T. P. 2005. *The Organic Chemistry of Biological Pathways*. Roberts and Company.

Blakley, R. L., and Benkovic, S. J. 1989. *Folates and Pterins* (vol. 2). Wiley.

Walsh, C. 1979. *Enzymatic Reaction Mechanisms*. W. H. Freeman and Company.

Nitrogen Fixation

Seefeldt, L. C., Hoffman, B. M., and Dean, D. R. 2009. Mechanism of Mo-dependent nitrogenase. *Annu. Rev. Biochem.* 79:701–722.

Halbleib, C. M., and Ludden, P. W. 2000. Regulation of biological nitrogen fixation. *J. Nutr.* 130:1081–1084.

Einsle, O., Tezcan, F. A., Andrade, S. L., Schmid, B., Yoshida, M., Howard, J. B., and Rees, D. C. 2002. Nitrogenase MoFe-protein at 1.16 Å resolution: A central ligand in the FeMo-cofactor. *Science* 297:1696–1700.

Benton, P. M., Laryukhin, M., Mayer, S. M., Hoffman, B. M., Dean, D. R., and Seefeldt, L. C. 2003. Localization of a substrate binding site on the FeMo-cofactor in nitrogenase: Trapping propargyl alcohol with an α-70-substituted MoFe protein. *Biochemistry* 42: 9102–9109.

Peters, J. W., Fisher, K., and Dean, D. R. 1995. Nitrogenase structure and function: A biochemical-genetic perspective. *Annu. Rev. Microbiol.* 49:335–366.

Leigh, G. J. 1995. The mechanism of dinitrogen reduction by molybdenum nitrogenases. *Eur. J. Biochem.* 229:14–20.

Georgiadis, M. M., Komiya, H., Chakrabarti, P., Woo, D., Kornuc, J. J., and Rees, D. C. 1992. Crystallographic structure of the nitrogenase iron protein from *Azotobacter vinelandii*. *Science* 257:1653–1659.

Regulation of Amino Acid Biosynthesis

Eisenberg, D., Gill, H. S., Pfluegl, G. M., and Rotstein, S. H. 2000. Structure-function relationships of glutamine synthetases. *Biochim. Biophys. Acta* 1477:122–145.

Purich, D. L. 1998. Advances in the enzymology of glutamine synthesis. *Adv. Enzymol. Relat. Areas Mol. Biol.* 72:9–42.

Yamashita, M. M., Almassy, R. J., Janson, C. A., Cascio, D., and Eisenberg, D. 1989. Refined atomic model of glutamine synthetase at 3.5 Å resolution. *J. Biol. Chem.* 264:17681–17690.

Schuller, D. J., Grant, G. A., and Banaszak, L. J. 1995. The allosteric ligand site in the V_{max}-type cooperative enzyme phosphoglycerate dehydrogenase. *Nat. Struct. Biol.* 2:69–76.

Rhee, S. G., Park, R., Chock, P. B., and Stadtman, E. R. 1978. Allosteric regulation of monocyclic interconvertible enzyme cascade systems: Use of *Escherichia coli* glutamine synthetase as an experimental model. *Proc. Natl. Acad. Sci. U.S.A.* 75:3138–3142.

Wessel, P. M., Graciet, E., Douce, R., and Dumas, R. 2000. Evidence for two distinct effector-binding sites in threonine deaminase by site-directed mutagenesis, kinetic, and binding experiments. *Biochemistry* 39:15136–15143.

James, C. L., and Viola, R. E. 2002. Production and characterization of bifunctional enzymes: Domain swapping to produce new bifunctional enzymes in the aspartate pathway. *Biochemistry* 41: 3720–3725.

Xu, Y., Carr, P. D., Huber, T., Vasudevan, S. G., and Ollis, D. L. 2001. The structure of the P_{II}-ATP complex. *Eur. J. Biochem.* 268: 2028–2037.

Krappmann, S., Lipscomb, W. N., and Braus, G. H. 2000. Coevolution of transcriptional and allosteric regulation at the chorismate metabolic branch point of *Saccharomyces cerevisiae*. *Proc. Natl. Acad. Sci. U.S.A.* 97:13585–13590.

Aromatic Amino Acid Biosynthesis

Brown, K. A., Carpenter, E. P., Watson, K. A., Coggins, J. R., Hawkins, A. R., Koch, M. H., and Svergun, D. I. 2003. Twists and turns: A tale of two shikimate-pathway enzymes. *Biochem. Soc. Trans.* 31:543–547.

Pan, P., Woehl, E., and Dunn, M. F. 1997. Protein architecture, dynamics and allostery in tryptophan synthase channeling. *Trends Biochem. Sci.* 22:22–27.

Sachpatzidis, A., Dealwis, C., Lubetsky, J. B., Liang, P. H., Anderson, K. S., and Lolis, E. 1999. Crystallographic studies of phosphonate-based α-reaction transition-state analogues complexed to tryptophan synthase. *Biochemistry* 38:12665–12674.

Weyand, M., and Schlichting, I. 1999. Crystal structure of wild-type tryptophan synthase complexed with the natural substrate indole-3-glycerol phosphate. *Biochemistry* 38:16469–16480.

Crawford, I. P. 1989. Evolution of a biosynthetic pathway: The tryptophan paradigm. *Annu. Rev. Microbiol.* 43:567–600.

Carpenter, E. P., Hawkins, A. R., Frost, J. W., and Brown, K. A. 1998. Structure of dehydroquinate synthase reveals an active site capable of multistep catalysis. *Nature* 394:299–302.

Schlichting, I., Yang, X. J., Miles, E. W., Kim, A. Y., and Anderson, K. S. 1994. Structural and kinetic analysis of a channel-impaired mutant of tryptophan synthase. *J. Biol. Chem.* 269:26591–26593.

Glutathione

Edwards, R., Dixon, D. P., and Walbot, V. 2000. Plant glutathione S-transferases: Enzymes with multiple functions in sickness and in health. *Trends Plant Sci.* 5:193–198.

Lu, S. C. 2000. Regulation of glutathione synthesis. *Curr. Top. Cell Regul.* 36:95–116.

Schulz, J. B., Lindenau, J., Seyfried, J., and Dichgans, J. 2000. Glutathione, oxidative stress and neurodegeneration. *Eur. J. Biochem.* 267:4904–4911.

Lu, S. C. 1999. Regulation of hepatic glutathione synthesis: Current concepts and controversies. *FASEB J.* 13:1169–1183.

Salinas, A. E., and Wong, M. G. 1991. Glutathione S-transferases: A review. *Curr. Med. Chem.* 6:279–309.

Ethylene and Nitric Oxide

Nisoli, E., Falcone, S., Tonello, C., Cozzi, V., Palomba, L., Fiorani, M., Pisconti, A., Brunelli, S., Cardile, A., Francolini, M., Cantoni, O., Carruba, M. O., Moncada, S., and Clementi, E. 2004. Mitochondrial biogenesis by NO yields functionally active mitochondria in mammals. *Proc. Natl. Acad. Sci U.S.A.* 101:16507–16512.

Bretscher, L. E., Li, H., Poulos, T. L. and Griffith, O. W. 2003. Structural characterization and kinetics of nitric oxide synthase inhibition by novel N^5-(iminoalkyl)- and N^5-(iminoalkenyl)-ornithines. *J. Biol. Chem.* 278:46789–46797.

Haendeler, J., Zeiher, A. M., and Dimmeler, S. 1999. Nitric oxide and apoptosis. *Vitam. Horm.* 57:49–77.

Capitani, G., Hohenester, E., Feng, L., Storici, P., Kirsch, J. F., and Jansonius, J. N. 1999. Structure of 1-aminocyclopropane-1-carboxylate synthase, a key enzyme in the biosynthesis of the plant hormone ethylene. *J. Mol. Biol.* 294:745–756.

Hobbs, A. J., Higgs, A., and Moncada, S. 1999. Inhibition of nitric oxide synthase as a potential therapeutic target. *Annu. Rev. Pharmacol. Toxicol.* 39:191–220.

Stuehr, D. J. 1999. Mammalian nitric oxide synthases. *Biochim. Biophys. Acta* 1411:217–230.

Chang, C., and Shockey, J. A. 1999. The ethylene-response pathway: Signal perception to gene regulation. *Curr. Opin. Plant Biol.* 2:352–358.

Theologis, A. 1992. One rotten apple spoils the whole bushel: The role of ethylene in fruit ripening. *Cell* 70:181–184.

Biosynthesis of Porphyrins

Kaasik, K. and Lee, C. C. 2004. Reciprocal regulation of haem biosynthesis and the circadian clock in mammals. *Nature* 430:467–471.

Leeper, F. J. 1989. The biosynthesis of porphyrins, chlorophylls, and vitamin B_{12}. *Nat. Prod. Rep.* 6:171–199.

Porra, R. J., and Meisch, H.-U. 1984. The biosynthesis of chlorophyll. *Trends Biochem. Sci.* 9:99–104.

Chapter 25

Where to Start

Sutherland, J. D. 2010. Ribonucleotides. *Cold Spring Harb. Perspect. Biol.* 2:a005439.

Ordi, J., Alonso, P. L., de Zulueta, J., Esteban, J., Velasco, M., Mas, E., Campo, E., and Fernández, P. L. 2006. The severe gout of Holy Roman Emperor Charles V. *N. Eng. J. Med.* 355: 516–520.

Kappock, T. J., Ealick, S. E., and Stubbe, J. 2000. Modular evolution of the purine biosynthetic pathway. *Curr. Opin. Chem. Biol.* 4:567–572.

Jordan, A., and Reichard, P. 1998. Ribonucleotide reductases. *Annu. Rev. Biochem.* 67:71–98.

Pyrimidine Biosynthesis

Raushel, F. M., Thoden, J. B., Reinhart, G. D., and Holden, H. M. 1998. Carbamoyl phosphate synthetase: A crooked path from substrates to products. *Curr. Opin. Chem. Biol.* 2:624–632.

Huang, X., Holden, H. M., and Raushel, F. M. 2001. Channeling of substrates and intermediates in enzyme-catalyzed reactions. *Annu. Rev. Biochem.* 70:149–180.

Begley, T. P., Appleby, T. C., and Ealick, S. E. 2000. The structural basis for the remarkable proficiency of orotidine 5'-monophosphate decarboxylase. *Curr. Opin. Struct. Biol.* 10:711–718.

Traut, T. W., and Temple, B. R. 2000. The chemistry of the reaction determines the invariant amino acids during the evolution and divergence of orotidine 5'-monophosphate decarboxylase. *J. Biol. Chem.* 275:28675–28681.

Purine Biosynthesis

An, S., Kyoung, M., Allen, J. J., Shokat, K. M., and Benkovic, S. J. 2010. Dynamic regulation of a metabolic multi-enzyme complex by protein kinase CK2. *J. Biol. Chem.* 285: 11093–11099.

An, S., Kumar, R., Sheets, E. D., and Benkovic, S. J. 2008. Reversible compartmentalization of de novo purine biosynthetic complexes in living cells. *Science* 320: 103–106.

Thoden, J. B., Firestine, S., Nixon, A., Benkovic, S. J., and Holden, H. M. 2000. Molecular structure of *Escherichia coli* PurT-encoded glycinamide ribonucleotide transformylase. *Biochemistry* 39:8791– 8802.

McMillan, F. M., Cahoon, M., White, A., Hedstrom, L., Petsko, G. A., and Ringe, D. 2000. Crystal structure at 2.4 Å resolution of *Borrelia burgdorferi* inosine 5'-monophosphate dehydrogenase: Evidence of a substrate-induced hinged-lid motion by loop 6. *Biochemistry* 39:4533–4542.

Levdikov, V. M., Barynin, V. V., Grebenko, A. I., Melik-Adamyan, W. R., Lamzin, V. S., and Wilson, K. S. 1998. The structure of SAICAR synthase: An enzyme in the de novo pathway of purine nucleotide biosynthesis. *Structure* 6:363–376.

Smith, J. L., Zaluzec, E. J., Wery, J. P., Niu, L., Switzer, R. L., Zalkin, H., and Satow, Y. 1994. Structure of the allosteric regulatory enzyme of purine biosynthesis. *Science* 264:1427–1433.

Weber, G., Nagai, M., Natsumeda, Y., Ichikawa, S., Nakamura, H., Eble, J. N., Jayaram, H. N., Zhen, W. N., Paulik, E., and Hoffman, R. 1991. Regulation of de novo and salvage pathways in chemotherapy. *Adv. Enzyme Regul.* 31:45–67.

Ribonucleotide Reductases

Cotruvo, Jr., J. A., and Stubbe, J. 2010. An active dimanganese(III)-tyrosyl radical cofactor in *Escherichia coli* class Ib ribonucleotide reductase. *Biochemistry* 49:1297–1309.

Avval, F. Z., and Holmgren, A. 2009. Molecular mechanisms of thioredoxin and glutaredoxin as hydrogen donors for mammalian S phase ribonucleotide reductase. *J. Biol. Chem.* 284: 8233–8240.

Rofougaran, R., Crona M., Vodnala, M., Sjöberg, B. M., and Hofer, A. 2008. Oligomerization status directs overall activity regulation of the *Escherichia coli* class Ia ribonucleotide reductase. *J. Biol. Chem.* 283: 35310–35318.

Nordlund, P., and Reichard, P. 2006. Ribonucleotide reductases. *Annu. Rev. Biochem.* 75: 681–706.

Eklund, H., Uhlin, U., Farnegardh, M., Logan, D. T. and Nordlund, P. 2001. Structure and function of the radical enzyme ribonucleotide reductase. *Prog. Biophys. Mol. Biol.* 77:177–268.

Reichard, P. 1997. The evolution of ribonucleotide reduction. *Trends Biochem. Sci.* 22:81–85.

Stubbe, J. 2000. Ribonucleotide reductases: The link between an RNA and a DNA world? *Curr. Opin. Struct. Biol.* 10:731–736.

Logan, D. T., Andersson, J., Sjoberg, B. M., and Nordlund, P. 1999. A glycyl radical site in the crystal structure of a class III ribonucleotide reductase. *Science* 283:1499–1504.

Tauer, A., and Benner, S. A. 1997. The B_{12}-dependent ribonucleotide reductase from the archaebacterium *Thermoplasma acidophila:* An evolutionary solution to the ribonucleotide reductase conundrum. *Proc. Natl. Acad. Sci. U.S.A.* 94:53–58.

Stubbe, J., Nocera, D. G., Yee, C. S. and Chang, M. C. 2003. Radical initiation in the class I ribonucleotide reductase: Long-range proton-coupled electron transfer? *Chem. Rev.* 103:2167–2201.

Stubbe, J., and Riggs-Gelasco, P. 1998. Harnessing free radicals: Formation and function of the tyrosyl radical in ribonucleotide reductase. *Trends Biochem. Sci.* 23:438–443.

Thymidylate Synthase and Dihydrofolate Reductase

Abali, E. E., Skacel, N. E., Celikkaya, H., and Hsieh, Y.-C. 2008. Regulation of human dihydrofolate reductase activity and expression. *Vitam. Horm.* 79:267–292.

Schnell, J. R., Dyson, H. J., and Wright, P. E. 2004. Structure, dynamics, and catalytic function of dihydrofolate reductase. *Annu. Rev. Biophys. Biomol. Struct.* 33:119–140.

Li, R., Sirawaraporn, R., Chitnumsub, P., Sirawaraporn, W., Wooden, J., Athappilly, F., Turley, S., and Hol, W. G. 2000. Three-dimensional structure of *M. tuberculosis* dihydrofolate reductase reveals opportunities for the design of novel tuberculosis drugs. *J. Mol. Biol.* 295:307–323.

Liang, P. H., and Anderson, K. S. 1998. Substrate channeling and domain-domain interactions in bifunctional thymidylate synthase-dihydrofolate reductase. *Biochemistry* 37:12195–12205.

Miller, G. P., and Benkovic, S. J. 1998. Stretching exercises: Flexibility in dihydrofolate reductase catalysis. *Chem. Biol.* 5:R105–R113.

Carreras, C. W., and Santi, D. V. 1995. The catalytic mechanism and structure of thymidylate synthase. *Annu. Rev. Biochem.* 64:721– 762.

Schweitzer, B. I., Dicker, A. P., and Bertino, J. R. 1990. Dihydrofolate reductase as a therapeutic target. *FASEB J.* 4:2441–2452.

Defects in Nucleotide Biosynthesis

Aiuti, A., Cattaneo, F., Galimberti, S., Benninghoff, U., et al. 2009. Gene therapy for immunodeficiency due to adenosine deaminase deficiency. *N. Engl. J. Med.* 360:447–58.

Jurecka, A. 2009. Inborn errors of purine and pyrimidine metabolism. *J. Inherit. Metab. Dis.* 32:247–263.

Nyhan, W. L., Barshop, B. A., and Ozand, P. T. 2005. *Atlas of Metabolic Diseases.* (2d ed., pp. 429–462). Hodder Arnold.

Scriver, C. R., Sly, W. S., Childs, B., Beaudet, A. L., Valle, D., Kinzler, K. W., and Vogelstein, B. (Eds.). 2001. *The Metabolic and Molecular Bases of Inherited Diseases* (8th ed., pp. 2513–2704). McGraw-Hill.

Nyhan, W. L. 1997. The recognition of Lesch-Nyhan syndrome as an inborn error of purine metabolism. *J. Inherited Metab. Dis.* 20: 171–178.

Wong, D. F., Harris, J. C., Naidu, S., Yokoi, F., Marenco, S., Dannals, R. F., Ravert, H. T., Yaster, M., Evans, A., Rousset, O., Bryan, R. N., Gjedde, A., Kuhar, M. J., and Breese, G. R. 1996. Dopamine transporters are markedly reduced in Lesch-Nyhan disease in vivo. *Proc. Natl. Acad. Sci. U.S.A.* 93:5539–5543.

Resta, R., and Thompson, L. F. 1997. SCID: The role of adenosine deaminase deficiency. *Immunol. Today* 18:371–374.

Neychev, V. K., and Mitev, V. I. 2004. The biochemical basis of the neurobehavioral abnormalities in the Lesch-Nyhan syndrome: A hypothesis. *Med. Hypotheses* 63:131–134.

Chapter 26

Where to Start

Brown, M. S., and Goldstein, J. L. 2009. Cholesterol feedback: From Schoenheimer's bottle to Scap's MELADL. *J. Lipid Res.* 50:S15–S27.

Gimpl, G., Burger, K., and Fahrenholz, F. 2002. A closer look at the cholesterol sensor. *Trends Biochem. Sci.* 27:595–599.

Oram, J. F. 2002. Molecular basis of cholesterol homeostasis: Lessons from Tangier disease and ABCA1. *Trends Mol. Med.* 8:168–173.

Vance, D. E., and Van den Bosch, H. 2000. Cholesterol in the year 2000. *Biochim. Biophys. Acta* 1529:1–8.

Endo, A. 1992. The discovery and development of HMG-CoA reductase inhibitors. *J. Lipid Res.* 33:1569–1582.

Books

Vance, J. E., and Vance, D. E. (Eds.). 2008. *Biochemistry of Lipids, Lipoproteins and Membranes.* Elsevier.

Nyhan, W. L., Barshop, B. A., and Ozand, P. T. 2005. *Atlas of Metabolic Diseases.* (2d ed., pp. 567–696). Hodder Arnold.

Scriver, C. R., Sly, W. S., Childs, B., Beaudet, A. L., Valle, D., Kinzler, K. W., and Vogelstein, B. (Eds.). 2001. *The Metabolic and Molecular Bases of Inherited Diseases* (8th ed., pp. 2707–2960). McGraw-Hill.

Phospholipids and Sphingolipids

Carman, G. M., and Han, G.-S. 2009. Phosphatidic acid phosphatase, a key enzyme in the regulation of lipid synthesis. *J. Biol. Chem.* 284:2593–2597.

Bartke, N., and Hannun, Y. A. 2009. Bioactive sphingolipids: Metabolism and function. *J. Lipid Res.* 50:S91–S96.

Lee, J., Johnson, J., Ding, Z., Paetzel, M., and Cornell, R. B. 2009. Crystal structure of a mammalian CTP: Phosphocholine cytidylyltransferase catalytic domain reveals novel active site residues within a highly conserved nucleotidyltransferase fold. *J. Biol. Chem.* 284:33535–33548.

Nye, C. K., Hanson, R. W., and Kalhan, S. C. 2008. Glyceroneogenesis is the dominant pathway for triglyceride glycerol synthesis *in vivo* in the rat. *J. Biol. Chem.* 283:27565–27574.

Kent, C. 1995. Eukaryotic phospholipid biosynthesis. *Annu. Rev. Biochem.* 64:315–343.

Biosynthesis of Cholesterol and Steroids

Radhakrishnan, A., Goldstein, J. L., McDonald, J. G., and Brown, M. S. 2008. Switch-like control of SREBP-2 transport triggered by small changes in ER cholesterol: A delicate balance. *Cell Metab.* 8:512–521.

DeBose-Boyd, R. A. 2008. Feedback regulation of cholesterol synthesis: Sterol-accelerated ubiquitination and degradation of HMG CoA reductase. *Cell Res.* 18:609–621.

Hampton, R. Y. 2002. Proteolysis and sterol regulation. *Annu. Rev. Cell Dev. Biol.* 18:345–378.

Kelley, R. I., and Herman, G. E. 2001. Inborn errors of sterol biosynthesis. *Annu. Rev. Genom. Hum. Genet.* 2:299–341.

Istvan, E. S., and Deisenhofer, J. 2001. Structural mechanism for statin inhibition of HMG-CoA reductase. *Science* 292:1160–1164.

Ness, G. C., and Chambers, C. M. 2000. Feedback and hormonal regulation of hepatic 3-hydroxy-3-methylglutaryl coenzyme A reductase: The concept of cholesterol buffering capacity. *Proc. Soc. Exp. Biol. Med.* 224:8–19.

Libby, P., Aikawa, M., and Schonbeck, U. 2000. Cholesterol and atherosclerosis. *Biochim. Biophys. Acta* 1529:299–309.

Yokoyama, S. 2000. Release of cellular cholesterol: Molecular mechanism for cholesterol homeostasis in cells and in the body. *Biochim. Biophys. Acta* 1529:231–244.

Cronin, S. R., Khoury, A., Ferry, D. K., and Hampton, R. Y. 2000. Regulation of HMG-CoA reductase degradation requires the P-type ATPase Cod1p/Spf1p. *J. Cell Biol.* 148:915–924.

Edwards, P. A., Tabor, D., Kast, H. R., and Venkateswaran, A. 2000. Regulation of gene expression by SREBP and SCAP. *Biochim. Biophys. Acta* 1529:103–113.

Istvan, E. S., Palnitkar, M., Buchanan, S. K., and Deisenhofer, J. 2000. Crystal structure of the catalytic portion of human HMG-CoA reductase: Insights into regulation of activity and catalysis. *EMBO J.* 19:819–830.

Jeon, H., Meng, W., Takagi, J., Eck, M. J., Springer, T. A., and Blacklow, S. C. 2001. Implications for familial hypercholesterolemia from the structure of the LDL receptor YWTD-EGF domain pair. *Nat. Struct. Biol.* 8:499–504.

Lipoproteins and Their Receptors

Rye, K-A., Bursill, C. A., Lambert, G., Tabet, F., and Barter, P. J. 2009. The metabolism and anti-atherogenic properties of HDL. *J. Lipid Res.* 50:S195–S200.

Rader, D. J., Alexander, E. T., Weibel, G. L., Billheimer, J., and Rothblat, G. H. 2009. The role of reverse cholesterol transport in animals and humans and relationship to atherosclerosis. *J. Lipid Res.* 50:S189–S194.

Tall, A. R., Yvan-Charvet, L., Terasaka, N., Pagler, T., and Wang, N. 2008. HDL, ABC transporters, and cholesterol efflux: Implications for the treatment of atherosclerosis. *Cell Metab.* 7:365–375.

Jeon, H., and Blacklow, S. C. 2005. Structure and physiologic function of the low-density lipoprotein receptor. *Annu. Rev. Biochem.* 74:535–562.

Beglova, N., and Blacklow, S. C. 2005. The LDL receptor: How acid pulls the trigger. *Trends Biochem. Sci.* 30:309–316.

Brouillette, C. G., Anantharamaiah, G. M., Engler, J. A., and Borhani, D. W. 2001. Structural models of human apolipoprotein A-I: A critical analysis and review. *Biochem. Biophys. Acta* 1531:4–46.

Hevonoja, T., Pentikainen, M. O., Hyvonen, M. T., Kovanen, P. T., and Ala-Korpela, M. 2000. Structure of low density lipoprotein (LDL) particles: Basis for understanding molecular changes in modified LDL. *Biochim. Biophys. Acta* 1488:189–210.

Silver, D. L., Jiang, X. C., Arai, T., Bruce, C., and Tall, A. R. 2000. Receptors and lipid transfer proteins in HDL metabolism. *Ann. N. Y. Acad. Sci.* 902:103–111.

Nimpf, J., and Schneider, W. J. 2000. From cholesterol transport to signal transduction: Low density lipoprotein receptor, very low density lipoprotein receptor, and apolipoprotein E receptor-2. *Biochim. Biophys. Acta* 1529:287–298.

Oxygen Activation and P450 Catalysis

Stiles, A. R., McDonald, J. G., Bauman, D. R., and Russell, D. W. 2009. CYP7B1: One cytochrome P450, two human genetic diseases, and multiple physiological functions. *J. Biol. Chem.* 284:28485–28489.

Zhou, S.-F., Liu, J.-P., and Chowbay, B. 2009. Polymorphism of human cytochrome P450 enzymes and its clinical impact. *Drug Metab. Rev.* 4:89–295.

Williams, P. A., Cosme, J., Vinkovic, D. M., Ward, A., Angove, H. C., Day, P. J., Vonrhein, C., Tickle, I. J., and Jhoti, H. 2004. Crystal structure of human cytochrome P450 3A4 bound to metyrapone and progesterone. *Science* 305:683–686.

Ingelmn-Sundberg, M., Oscarson, M., and McLellan, R. A. 1999. Polymorphic human cytochrome P450 enzymes: An opportunity for individualized drug treatment. *Trends Pharmacol. Sci.* 20:342–349.

Chapter 27

Books

Wrangham, R. 2009. *Catching Fire: How Cooking Made Us Human.* Basic Books.

Stipanuk, M. H. (Ed.). 2006. *Biochemical, Physiological, & Molecular Aspects of Human Nutrition.* Saunders-Elsevier.

Fell, D. 1997. *Understanding the Control of Metabolism.* Portland Press.

Frayn, K. N. 1996. *Metabolic Regulation: A Human Perspective.* Portland Press.

Poortmans, J. R. (Ed.). 2004. *Principles of Exercise Biochemistry.* Karger.

Harris, R. A., and Crabb, D. W. 2006. Metabolic interrelationships. In *Textbook of Biochemistry with Clinical Correlations* (pp. 849–890), edited by T. M. Devlin. Wiley-Liss.

Caloric Homeostasis

Woods, S. C. 2009. The control of food intake: Behavioral versus molecular perspectives. *Cell Metab.* 9:489–498.

Figlewicz, D. P., and Benoit, S. C. 2009. Insulin, leptin, and food reward: Update 2008. *Am. J. Physiol. Integr. Comp. Physiol.* 296:R9–R19.

Israel, D., and Chua, S. Jr. 2009. Leptin receptor modulation of adiposity and fertility. *Trends Endocrinol. Metab.* 21:10–16.

Meyers, M. G., Cowley, M. A., and Münzberg, H. 2008. Mechanisms of leptin action and leptin resistance. *Annu. Rev. Physiol.* 70:537–556.

Sowers, J. R. 2008. Endocrine functions of adipose tissue: Focus on adiponectin. *Clin. Cornerstone* 9:32–38.

Brehma, B. J., and D'Alessio, D. A. 2008. Benefits of high-protein weight loss diets: Enough evidence for practice? *Curr. Opin. Endocrinol., Diabetes, Obesity* 15:416–421.

Coll, A. P., Farooqi, I. S., and O'Rahillt, S. O. 2007. The hormonal control of food intake. *Cell* 129:251–262.

Muoio, D. M., and Newgard, C. B. 2006. Obesity-related derangements in metabolic regulation. *Annu. Rev. Biochem.* 75:367–401.

Diabetes Mellitus

Zhang, B. B., Zhou, G., and Li, C. 2009. AMPK: An emerging drug target for diabetes and the metabolic syndrome. *Cell Metab.* 9:407–416.

Magkos, F., Yannakoulia, M., Chan, J. L., and Mantzoros, C. S. 2009. Management of the metabolic syndrome and type 2 diabetes through lifestyle modification. *Annu. Rev. Nutr.* 29:8.1–8.34.

Muoio, D. M., and Newgard, C. B. 2008. Molecular and metabolic mechanisms of insulin resistance and β-cell failure in type 2 diabetes. *Nat. Rev. Mol. Cell. Biol.* 9:193–205.

Leibiger, I. B., Leibiger, B., and Berggren, P.-O. 2008. Insulin signaling in the pancreatic β-cell. *Annu. Rev. Nutr.* 28:233–251.

Doria, A., Patti, M. E., and Kahn, C. R. 2008. The emerging architecture of type 2 diabetes. *Cell Metab.* 8:186–200.

Croker, B. A., Kiu, H., and Nicholson, S. E. 2008. SOCS regulation of the JAK/STAT signalling pathway. *Semin. Cell Dev. Biol.* 19:414–422.

Eizirik, D. L., Cardozo, A. K., and Cnop, M. 2008. The role of endoplasmic reticulum stress in diabetes mellitus. *Endocrinol. Rev.* 29:42–61.

Howard, J. K., and Flier, J. S. 2006. Attenuation of leptin and insulin signaling by SOCS proteins. *Trends Endocrinol. Metab.* 9:365–371.

Lowel, B. B., and Shulman, G. 2005. Mitochondrial dysfunction and type 2 diabetes. *Science* 307:384–387.

Taylor, S. I. 2001. Diabetes mellitus. In *The Metabolic Basis of Inherited Diseases* (8th ed., pp. 1433–1469), edited by C. R. Scriver, W. S. Sly, B. Childs, A. L. Beaudet, D. Valle, K. W. Kinzler, and B. Vogelstein. McGraw-Hill.

Exercise Metabolism

Hood, D. A. 2001. Contractile activity-induced mitochondrial biogenesis in skeletal muscle. *J. Appl. Physiol.* 90:1137–1157.

Shulman, R. G., and Rothman, D. L. 2001. The "glycogen shunt" in exercising muscle: A role for glycogen in muscle energetics and fatigue. *Proc. Natl. Acad. Sci. U.S.A.* 98:457–461.

Gleason, T. 1996. Post-exercise lactate metabolism: A comparative review of sites, pathways, and regulation. *Annu. Rev. Physiol.* 58:556–581.

Holloszy, J. O., and Kohrt, W. M. 1996. Regulation of carbohydrate and fat metabolism during and after exercise. *Annu. Rev. Nutr.* 16:121–138.

Hochachka, P. W., and McClelland, G. B. 1997. Cellular metabolic homeostasis during large-scale change in ATP turnover rates in muscles. *J. Exp. Biol.* 200:381–386.

Horowitz, J. F., and Klein, S. 2000. Lipid metabolism during endurance exercise. *Am. J. Clin. Nutr.* 72:558S–563S.

Wagenmakers, A. J. 1999. Muscle amino acid metabolism at rest and during exercise. *Diabetes Nutr. Metab.* 12:316–322.

Metabolic Adaptations in Starvation

Baverel, G., Ferrier, B., and Martin, M. 1995. Fuel selection by the kidney: Adaptation to starvation. *Proc. Nutr. Soc.* 54:197–212.

MacDonald, I. A., and Webber, J. 1995. Feeding, fasting and starvation: Factors affecting fuel utilization. *Proc. Nutr. Soc.* 54:267–274.

Cahill, G. F., Jr. 1976. Starvation in man. *Clin. Endocrinol. Metab.* 5:397–415.

Sugden, M. C., Holness, M. J., and Palmer, T. N. 1989. Fuel selection and carbon flux during the starved-to-fed transition. *Biochem. J.* 263:313–323.

Ethanol Metabolism

Nagy, L. E. 2004. Molecular aspects of alcohol metabolism: Transcription factors involved in early-induced liver injury. *Annu. Rev. Nutr.* 24:55–78.

Molotkov, A., and Duester, G. 2002. Retinol/ethanol drug interaction during acute alcohol intoxication involves inhibition of retinol metabolism to retinoic acid by alcohol dehydrogenase. *J. Biol. Chem.* 277:22553–22557.

Stewart, S., Jones, D., and Day, C. P. 2001. Alcoholic liver disease: New insights into mechanisms and preventive strategies. *Trends Mol. Med.* 7:408–413.

Lieber, C. S. 2000. Alcohol: Its metabolism and interaction with nutrients. *Annu. Rev. Nutr.* 20:395–430.

Niemela, O. 1999. Aldehyde-protein adducts in the liver as a result of ethanol-induced oxidative stress. *Front. Biosci.* 1:D506–D513.

Riveros-Rosas, H., Julian-Sanchez, A., and Pina, E. 1997. Enzymology of ethanol and acetaldehyde metabolism in mammals. *Arch. Med. Res.* 28:453–471.

Chapter 28

Where to Start

Johnson, A., and O'Donnell, M. 2005. Cellular DNA replicases: Components and dynamics at the replication fork. *Annu. Rev. Biochem.* 74:283–315.

Kornberg, A. 1988. DNA replication. *J. Biol. Chem.* 263:1–4.

Wang, J. C. 1982. DNA topoisomerases. *Sci. Am.* 247(1):94–109.

Lindahl, T. 1993. Instability and decay of the primary structure of DNA. *Nature* 362:709–715.

Greider, C. W., and Blackburn, E. H. 1996. Telomeres, telomerase, and cancer. *Sci. Am.* 274(2):92–97.

Books

Kornberg, A., and Baker, T. A. 1992. *DNA Replication* (2d ed.). W. H. Freeman and Company.

Bloomfield, V. A., Crothers, D., Tinoco, I., and Hearst, J. 2000. *Nucleic Acids: Structures, Properties and Functions.* University Science Books.

Friedberg, E. C., Walker, G. C., and Siede, W. 1995. *DNA Repair and Mutagenesis.* American Society for Microbiology.

Cozzarelli, N. R., and Wang, J. C. (Eds.). 1990. *DNA Topology and Its Biological Effects.* Cold Spring Harbor Laboratory Press.

DNA Topology and Topoisomerases

Graille, M., Cladiere, L., Durand, D., Lecointe, F., Gadelle, D., Quevillon-Cheruel, S., Vachette, P., Forterre, P., and van Tilbeurgh, H. 2008. Crystal structure of an intact type II DNA topoisomerase: Insights into DNA transfer mechanisms. *Structure* 16:360–370.

Charvin, G., Strick, T. R., Bensimon, D., and Croquette, V. 2005. Tracking topoisomerase activity at the single-molecule level. *Annu. Rev. Biophys. Biomol. Struct.* 34:201–219.

Sikder, D., Unniraman, S., Bhaduri, T., and Nagaraja, V. 2001. Functional cooperation between topoisomerase I and single strand DNA-binding protein. *J. Mol. Biol.* 306:669–679.

Yang, Z., and Champoux, J. J. 2001. The role of histidine 632 in catalysis by human topoisomerase I. *J. Biol. Chem.* 276:677–685.

Fortune, J. M., and Osheroff, N. 2000. Topoisomerase II as a target for anticancer drugs: When enzymes stop being nice. *Prog. Nucleic Acid Res. Mol. Biol.* 64:221−253.

Isaacs, R. J., Davies, S. L., Sandri, M. I., Redwood, C., Wells, N. J., and Hickson, I. D. 1998. Physiological regulation of eukaryotic topoisomerase II. *Biochim. Biophys. Acta* 1400:121−137.

Wang, J. C. 1996. DNA topoisomerases. *Annu. Rev. Biochem.* 65:635−692.

Wang, J. C. 1998. Moving one DNA double helix through another by a type II DNA topoisomerase: The story of a simple molecular machine. *Q. Rev. Biophys.* 31:107−144.

Baird, C. L., Harkins, T. T., Morris, S. K., and Lindsley, J. E. 1999. Topoisomerase II drives DNA transport by hydrolyzing one ATP. *Proc. Natl. Acad. Sci. U.S.A.* 96:13685−13690.

Vologodskii, A. V., Levene, S. D., Klenin, K. V., Frank, K. M., and Cozzarelli, N. R. 1992. Conformational and thermodynamic properties of supercoiled DNA. *J. Mol. Biol.* 227:1224−1243.

Fisher, L. M., Austin, C. A., Hopewell, R., Margerrison, M., Oram, M., Patel, S., Wigley, D. B., Davies, G. J., Dodson, E. J., Maxwell, A., and Dodson, G. 1991. Crystal structure of an N-terminal fragment of the DNA gyrase B protein. *Nature* 351:624−629.

Mechanism of Replication

Davey, M. J., and O'Donnell, M. 2000. Mechanisms of DNA replication. *Curr. Opin. Chem. Biol.* 4:581−586.

Keck, J. L., and Berger, J. M. 2000. DNA replication at high resolution. *Chem. Biol.* 7:R63−R71.

Kunkel, T. A., and Bebenek, K. 2000. DNA replication fidelity. *Annu. Rev. Biochem.* 69:497−529.

Waga, S., and Stillman, B. 1998. The DNA replication fork in eukaryotic cells. *Annu. Rev. Biochem.* 67:721−751.

Marians, K. J. 1992. Prokaryotic DNA replication. *Annu. Rev. Biochem.* 61:673−719.

DNA Polymerases and Other Enzymes of Replication

Singleton, M. R., Sawaya, M. R., Ellenberger, T., and Wigley, D. B. 2000. Crystal structure of T7 gene 4 ring helicase indicates a mechanism for sequential hydrolysis of nucleotides. *Cell* 101:589−600.

Donmez, I., and Patel, S. S. 2006. Mechanisms of a ring shaped helicase. *Nucleic Acids Res.* 34:4216−4224.

Johnson, D. S., Bai, L., Smith, B. Y., Patel, S. S., and Wang, M. D. 2007. Single-molecule studies reveal dynamics of DNA unwinding by the ring-shaped T7 helicase. *Cell* 129:1299−1309.

Lee, S. J., Qimron, U., and Richardson, C. C. 2008. Communication between subunits critical to DNA binding by hexameric helicase of bacteriophage T7. *Proc. Natl. Acad. Sci. U.S.A.* 105:8908−8913.

Toth, E. A., Li, Y., Sawaya, M. R., Cheng, Y., and Ellenberger, T. 2003. The crystal structure of the bifunctional primase-helicase of bacteriophage T7. *Mol. Cell* 12:1113−1123.

Hubscher, U., Maga, G., and Spadari, S. 2002. Eukaryotic DNA polymerases. *Annu. Rev. Biochem.* 71:133−163.

Doublié, S., Tabor, S., Long, A. M., Richardson, C. C., and Ellenberger, T. 1998. Crystal structure of a bacteriophage T7 DNA replication complex at 2.2 Å resolution. *Nature* 391:251−258.

Arezi, B., and Kuchta, R. D. 2000. Eukaryotic DNA primase. *Trends Biochem. Sci.* 25:572−576.

Jager, J., and Pata, J. D. 1999. Getting a grip: Polymerases and their substrate complexes. *Curr. Opin. Struct. Biol.* 9:21−28.

Steitz, T. A. 1999. DNA polymerases: Structural diversity and common mechanisms. *J. Biol. Chem.* 274:17395−17398.

Beese, L. S., Derbyshire, V., and Steitz, T. A. 1993. Structure of DNA polymerase I Klenow fragment bound to duplex DNA. *Science* 260:352−355.

McHenry, C. S. 1991. DNA polymerase III holoenzyme: Components, structure, and mechanism of a true replicative complex. *J. Biol. Chem.* 266:19127−19130.

Kong, X. P., Onrust, R., O'Donnell, M., and Kuriyan, J. 1992. Three-dimensional structure of the β subunit of *E. coli* DNA polymerase III holoenzyme: A sliding DNA clamp. *Cell* 69:425−437.

Polesky, A. H., Steitz, T. A., Grindley, N. D., and Joyce, C. M. 1990. Identification of residues critical for the polymerase activity of the Klenow fragment of DNA polymerase I from *Escherichia coli*. *J. Biol. Chem.* 265:14579−14591.

Lee, J. Y., Chang, C., Song, H. K., Moon, J., Yang, J. K., Kim, H. K., Kwon, S. T., and Suh, S. W. 2000. Crystal structure of NAD$^+$ dependent DNA ligase: Modular architecture and functional implications. *EMBO J.* 19:1119−1129.

Timson, D. J., and Wigley, D. B. 1999. Functional domains of an NAD$^+$-dependent DNA ligase. *J. Mol. Biol.* 285:73−83.

Doherty, A. J., and Wigley, D. B. 1999. Functional domains of an ATP-dependent DNA ligase. *J. Mol. Biol.* 285:63−71.

von Hippel, P. H., and Delagoutte, E. 2001. A general model for nucleic acid helicases and their "coupling" within macromolecular machines. *Cell* 104:177−190.

Tye, B. K., and Sawyer, S. 2000. The hexameric eukaryotic MCM helicase: Building symmetry from nonidentical parts. *J. Biol. Chem.* 275:34833−34836.

Marians, K. J. 2000. Crawling and wiggling on DNA: Structural insights to the mechanism of DNA unwinding by helicases. *Struct. Fold. Des.* 5:R227−R235.

Soultanas, P., and Wigley, D. B. 2000. DNA helicases: "Inching forward." *Curr. Opin. Struct. Biol.* 10:124−128.

de Lange, T. 2009. How telomeres solve the end-protection problem. *Science* 326:948−952.

Bachand, F., and Autexier, C. 2001. Functional regions of human telomerase reverse transcriptase and human telomerase RNA required for telomerase activity and RNA-protein interactions. *Mol. Cell Biol.* 21:1888−1897.

Bryan, T. M., and Cech, T. R. 1999. Telomerase and the maintenance of chromosome ends. *Curr. Opin. Cell Biol.* 11:318−324.

Griffith, J. D., Comeau, L., Rosenfield, S., Stansel, R. M., Bianchi, A., Moss, H., and de Lange, T. 1999. Mammalian telomeres end in a large duplex loop. *Cell* 97:503−514.

McEachern, M. J., Krauskopf, A., and Blackburn, E. H. 2000. Telomeres and their control. *Annu. Rev. Genet.* 34:331−358.

Mutations and DNA Repair

Yang, W. 2003. Damage repair DNA polymerases Y. *Curr. Opin. Struct. Biol.* 13:23−30.

Wood, R. D., Mitchell, M., Sgouros, J., and Lindahl, T. 2001. Human DNA repair genes. *Science* 291:1284−1289.

Shin, D. S., Chahwan, C., Huffman, J. L., and Tainer, J. A. 2004. Structure and function of the double-strand break repair machinery. *DNA Repair (Amst.)* 3:863−873.

Michelson, R. J., and Weinert, T. 2000. Closing the gaps among a web of DNA repair disorders. *Bioessays* 22:966−969.

Aravind, L., Walker, D. R., and Koonin, E. V. 1999. Conserved domains in DNA repair proteins and evolution of repair systems. *Nucleic Acids Res.* 27:1223−1242.

Mol, C. D., Parikh, S. S., Putnam, C. D., Lo, T. P., and Tainer, J. A. 1999. DNA repair mechanisms for the recognition and removal of damaged DNA bases. *Annu. Rev. Biophys. Biomol. Struct.* 28:101−128.

Parikh, S. S., Mol, C. D., and Tainer, J. A. 1997. Base excision repair enzyme family portrait: Integrating the structure and chemistry of an entire DNA repair pathway. *Structure* 5:1543−1550.

Vassylyev, D. G., and Morikawa, K. 1997. DNA-repair enzymes. *Curr. Opin. Struct. Biol.* 7:103−109.

Verdine, G. L., and Bruner, S. D. 1997. How do DNA repair proteins locate damaged bases in the genome? *Chem. Biol.* 4:329−334.

Bowater, R. P., and Wells, R. D. 2000. The intrinsically unstable life of DNA triplet repeats associated with human hereditary disorders. *Prog. Nucleic Acid Res. Mol. Biol.* 66:159−202.

Cummings, C. J., and Zoghbi, H. Y. 2000. Fourteen and counting: Unraveling trinucleotide repeat diseases. *Hum. Mol. Genet.* 9:909–916.

Defective DNA Repair and Cancer

Berneburg, M., and Lehmann, A. R. 2001. Xeroderma pigmentosum and related disorders: Defects in DNA repair and transcription. *Adv. Genet.* 43:71–102.

Lambert, M. W., and Lambert, W. C. 1999. DNA repair and chromatin structure in genetic diseases. *Prog. Nucleic Acid Res. Mol. Biol.* 63:257–310.

Buys, C. H. 2000. Telomeres, telomerase, and cancer. *N. Engl. J. Med.* 342:1282–1283.

Urquidi, V., Tarin, D., and Goodison, S. 2000. Role of telomerase in cell senescence and oncogenesis. *Annu. Rev. Med.* 51:65–79.

Lynch, H. T., Smyrk, T. C., Watson, P., Lanspa, S. J., Lynch, J. F., Lynch, P. M., Cavalieri, R. J., and Boland, C. R. 1993. Genetics, natural history, tumor spectrum, and pathology of hereditary non-polyposis colorectal cancer: An updated review. *Gastroenterology* 104:1535–1549.

Fishel, R., Lescoe, M. K., Rao, M. R. S., Copeland, N. G., Jenkins, N. A., Garber, J., Kane, M., and Kolodner, R. 1993. The human mutator gene homolog *MSH2* and its association with hereditary nonpolyposis colon cancer. *Cell* 75:1027–1038.

Ames, B. N., and Gold, L. S. 1991. Endogenous mutagens and the causes of aging and cancer. *Mutat. Res.* 250:3–16.

Ames, B. N. 1979. Identifying environmental chemicals causing mutations and cancer. *Science* 204:587–593.

Recombination and Recombinases

Singleton, M. R., Dillingham, M. S., Gaudier, M., Kowalczykowski, S. C., and Wigley, D. B. 2004. Crystal structure of RecBCD enzyme reveals a machine for processing DNA breaks. *Nature* 432:187–193.

Spies, M., Bianco, P. R., Dillingham, M. S., Handa, N., Baskin, R. J., and Kowalczykowski, S. C. 2003. A molecular throttle: The recombination hotspot chi controls DNA translocation by the RecBCD helicase. *Cell* 114:647–654.

Kowalczykowski, S. C. 2000. Initiation of genetic recombination and recombination-dependent replication. *Trends Biochem. Sci.* 25:156–165.

Prevost, C., and Takahashi, M. 2003. Geometry of the DNA strands within the RecA nucleofilament: Role in homologous recombination. *Q. Rev. Biophys.* 36:429–453.

Van Duyne, G. D. 2001. A structural view of Cre-loxP site-specific recombination. *Annu. Rev. Biophys. Biomol. Struct.* 30:87–104.

Chen, Y., Narendra, U., Iype, L. E., Cox, M. M., and Rice, P. A. 2000. Crystal structure of a Flp recombinase-Holliday junction complex: Assembly of an active oligomer by helix swapping. *Mol. Cell* 6:885–897.

Craig, N. L. 1997. Target site selection in transposition. *Annu. Rev. Biochem.* 66:437–474.

Gopaul, D. N., Guo, F., and Van Duyne, G. D. 1998. Structure of the Holliday junction intermediate in Cre-loxP site-specific recombination. *EMBO J.* 17:4175–4187.

Gopaul, D. N., and Duyne, G. D. 1999. Structure and mechanism in site-specific recombination. *Curr. Opin. Struct. Biol.* 9:14–20.

Chapter 29

Where to Start

Kornberg, R. D. 2007. The molecular basis of eukaryotic transcription. *Proc. Natl. Acad. Sci. U.S.A.* 104:12955–12961.

Woychik, N. A. 1998. Fractions to functions: RNA polymerase II thirty years later. *Cold Spring Harbor Symp. Quant. Biol.* 63:311–317.

Losick, R. 1998. Summary: Three decades after sigma. *Cold Spring Harbor Symp. Quant. Biol.* 63:653–666.

Ast, G. 2005. The alternative genome. *Sci. Am.* 292(4):40–47.

Sharp, P. A. 1994. Split genes and RNA splicing (Nobel Lecture). *Angew. Chem. Int. Ed. Engl.* 33:1229–1240.

Cech, T. R. 1990. Nobel lecture: Self-splicing and enzymatic activity of an intervening sequence RNA from *Tetrahymena. Biosci. Rep.* 10:239–261.

Villa, T., Pleiss, J. A., and Guthrie, C. 2002. Spliceosomal snRNAs: Mg^{2+} dependent chemistry at the catalytic core? *Cell* 109:149–152.

Books

Lewin, B. 2007. *Genes* (9th ed.). Jones and Bartlett.

Kornberg, A., and Baker, T. A. 1992. *DNA Replication* (2d ed.). W. H. Freeman and Company.

Lodish, H., Berk, A., Matsudaira, P., Krieger, M., Kaiser, C. A., Scott, M. P., Bretscher, A., Plough, H., and Darnell, J. 2008. *Molecular Cell Biology* (6th ed.). W. H. Freeman and Company.

Watson, J. D., Baker, T. A., Bell, S. P., Gann, A., Levine, M., and Losick, R. 2004. *Molecular Biology of the Gene* (5th ed.). Pearson/Benjamin Cummings.

Gesteland, R. F., Cech, T., and Atkins, J. F. 2006. *The RNA World: The Nature of Modern RNA Suggests a Prebiotic RNA* (3d ed.) Cold Spring Harbor Laboratory Press.

RNA Polymerases

Liu, X., Bushnell, D. A., Wang, D., Calero, G., and Kornberg, R. D. 2010. Structure of an RNA polymerase II-TFIIB complex and the transcription initiation mechanism. *Science* 327:206–209.

Wang, D., Bushnell, D. A., Huang, X., Westover, K. D., Levitt, M., and Kornberg, R. D. 2009. Structural basis of transcription: Backtracked RNA polymerase II at 3.4 angstrom resolution. *Science* 324:1203–1206.

Darst, S. A. 2001. Bacterial RNA polymerase. *Curr. Opin. Struct. Biol.* 11:155–162.

Ross, W., Gosink, K. K., Salomon, J., Igarashi, K., Zou, C., Ishihama, A., Severinov, K., and Gourse, R. L. 1993. A third recognition element in bacterial promoters: DNA binding by the alpha subunit of RNA polymerase. *Science* 262:1407–1413.

Cramer, P., Bushnell, D. A., and Kornberg, R. D. 2001. Structural basis of transcription: RNA polymerase II at 2.8 Å resolution. *Science* 292:1863–1875.

Gnatt, A. L., Cramer, P., Fu, J., Bushnell, D. A., and Kornberg, R. D. 2001. Structural basis of transcription: An RNA polymerase II elongation complex at 3.3 Å resolution. *Science* 292:1876–1882.

Zhang, G., Campbell, E. A., Minakhin, L., Richter, C., Severinov, K., and Darst, S. A. 1999. Crystal structure of *Thermus aquaticus* core RNA polymerase at 3.3 Å resolution. *Cell* 98:811–824.

Campbell, E. A., Korzheva, N., Mustaev, A., Murakami, K., Nair, S., Goldfarb, A., and Darst, S. A. 2001. Structural mechanism for rifampicin inhibition of bacterial RNA polymerase. *Cell* 104:901–912.

Darst, S. A. 2004. New inhibitors targeting bacterial RNA polymerase. *Trends Biochem. Sci.* 29:159–160.

Cheetham, G. M., and Steitz, T. A. 1999. Structure of a transcribing T7 RNA polymerase initiation complex. *Science* 286:2305–2309.

Ebright, R. H. 2000. RNA polymerase: Structural similarities between bacterial RNA polymerase and eukaryotic RNA polymerase II. *J. Mol. Biol.* 304:687–698.

Paule, M. R., and White, R. J. 2000. Survey and summary: Transcription by RNA polymerases I and III. *Nucleic Acids Res.* 28:1283–1298.

Initiation and Elongation

Murakami, K. S., and Darst, S. A. 2003. Bacterial RNA polymerases: The whole story. *Curr. Opin. Struct. Biol.* 13:31–39.

Buratowski, S. 2000. Snapshots of RNA polymerase II transcription initiation. *Curr. Opin. Cell Biol.* 12:320–325.

Conaway, J. W., and Conaway, R. C. 1999. Transcription elongation and human disease. *Annu. Rev. Biochem.* 68:301–319.

Conaway, J. W., Shilatifard, A., Dvir, A., and Conaway, R. C. 2000. Control of elongation by RNA polymerase II. *Trends Biochem. Sci.* 25:375–380.

Korzheva, N., Mustaev, A., Kozlov, M., Malhotra, A., Nikiforov, V., Goldfarb, A., and Darst, S. A. 2000. A structural model of transcription elongation. *Science* 289:619–625.

Reines, D., Conaway, R. C., and Conaway, J. W. 1999. Mechanism and regulation of transcriptional elongation by RNA polymerase II. *Curr. Opin. Cell Biol.* 11:342–346.

Promoters, Enhancers, and Transcription Factors

Merika, M., and Thanos, D. 2001. Enhanceosomes. *Curr. Opin. Genet. Dev.* 11:205–208.

Park, J. M., Gim, B. S., Kim, J. M., Yoon, J. H., Kim, H. S., Kang, J. G., and Kim, Y. J. 2001. *Drosophila* mediator complex is broadly utilized by diverse gene-specific transcription factors at different types of core promoters. *Mol. Cell. Biol.* 21:2312–2323.

Smale, S. T., and Kadonaga, J. T. 2003. The RNA polymerase II core promoter. *Annu. Rev. Biochem.* 72:449–479.

Gourse, R. L., Ross, W., and Gaal, T. 2000. Ups and downs in bacterial transcription initiation: The role of the alpha subunit of RNA polymerase in promoter recognition. *Mol. Microbiol.* 37:687–695.

Fiering, S., Whitelaw, E., and Martin, D. I. 2000. To be or not to be active: The stochastic nature of enhancer action. *Bioessays* 22:381–387.

Hampsey, M., and Reinberg, D. 1999. RNA polymerase II as a control panel for multiple coactivator complexes. *Curr. Opin. Genet. Dev.* 9:132–139.

Chen, L. 1999. Combinatorial gene regulation by eukaryotic transcription factors. *Curr. Opin. Struct. Biol.* 9:48–55.

Muller, C. W. 2001. Transcription factors: Global and detailed views. *Curr. Opin. Struct. Biol.* 11:26–32.

Reese, J. C. 2003. Basal transcription factors. *Curr. Opin. Genet. Dev.* 13:114–118.

Kadonaga, J. T. 2004. Regulation of RNA polymerase II transcription by sequence-specific DNA binding factors. *Cell* 116:247–257.

Harrison, S. C. 1991. A structural taxonomy of DNA-binding domains. *Nature* 353:715–719.

Sakurai, H., and Fukasawa, T. 2000. Functional connections between mediator components and general transcription factors of *Saccharomyces cerevisiae*. *J. Biol. Chem.* 275:37251–37256.

Droge, P., and Muller-Hill, B. 2001. High local protein concentrations at promoters: Strategies in prokaryotic and eukaryotic cells. *Bioessays* 23:179–183.

Smale, S. T., Jain, A., Kaufmann, J., Emami, K. H., Lo, K., and Garraway, I. P. 1998. The initiator element: A paradigm for core promoter heterogeneity within metazoan protein-coding genes. *Cold Spring Harbor Symp. Quant. Biol.* 63:21–31.

Kim, Y., Geiger, J. H., Hahn, S., and Sigler, P. B., 1993. Crystal structure of a yeast TBP/TATA-box complex. *Nature* 365:512–520.

Kim, J. L., Nikolov, D. B., and Burley, S. K., 1993. Co-crystal structure of TBP recognizing the minor groove of a TATA element. *Nature* 365:520–527.

White, R. J., and Jackson, S. P. 1992. The TATA-binding protein: A central role in transcription by RNA polymerases I, II and III. *Trends Genet.* 8:284–288.

Martinez, E. 2002. Multi-protein complexes in eukaryotic gene transcription. *Plant Mol. Biol.* 50:925–947.

Meinhart, A., Kamenski, T., Hoeppner, S., Baumli, S., and Cramer, P. 2005. A structural perspective of CTD function. *Genes Dev.* 19:1401–1415.

Palancade, B., and Bensaude, O. 2003. Investigating RNA polymerase II carboxyl-terminal domain (CTD) phosphorylation. *Eur. J. Biochem.* 270:3859–3870.

Termination

Burgess, B. R., and Richardson, J. P. 2001. RNA passes through the hole of the protein hexamer in the complex with *Escherichia coli* Rho factor. *J. Biol. Chem.* 276:4182–4189.

Yu, X., Horiguchi, T., Shigesada, K., and Egelman, E. H. 2000. Three-dimensional reconstruction of transcription termination factor rho: Orientation of the N-terminal domain and visualization of an RNA-binding site. *J. Mol. Biol.* 299:1279–1287.

Stitt, B. L. 2001. *Escherichia coli* transcription termination factor Rho binds and hydrolyzes ATP using a single class of three sites. *Biochemistry* 40:2276–2281.

Henkin, T. M. 2000. Transcription termination control in bacteria. *Curr. Opin. Microbiol.* 3:149–153.

Gusarov, I., and Nudler, E. 1999. The mechanism of intrinsic transcription termination. *Mol. Cell* 3:495–504.

Riboswitches

Barrick, J. E., and Breaker, R. R. 2007. The distributions, mechanisms, and structures of metabolite-binding riboswitches. *Genome Biol.* 8:R239.

Cheah, M. T., Wachter, A., Sudarsan, N., and Breaker, R. R. 2007. Control of alternative RNA splicing and gene expression by eukaryotic riboswitches. *Nature* 447:497–500.

Serganov, A., Huang, L., and Patel, D. J. 2009. Coenzyme recognition and gene regulation by a flavin mononucleotide riboswitch. *Nature* 458:233–237.

Noncoding RNA

Peculis, B. A. 2002. Ribosome biogenesis: Ribosomal RNA synthesis as a package deal. *Curr. Biol.* 12:R623–R624.

Decatur, W. A., and Fournier, M. J. 2002. rRNA modifications and ribosome function. *Trends Biochem. Sci.* 27:344–351.

Hopper, A. K., and Phizicky, E. M. 2003. tRNA transfers to the limelight. *Genes Dev.* 17:162–180.

Weiner, A. M. 2004. tRNA maturation: RNA polymerization without a nucleic acid template. *Curr. Biol.* 14:R883–R885.

5'-Cap Formation and Polyadenylation

Shatkin, A. J., and Manley, J. L. 2000. The ends of the affair: Capping and polyadenylation. *Nat. Struct. Biol.* 7:838–842.

Bentley, D. L. 2005. Rules of engagement: Co-transcriptional recruitment of pre-mRNA processing factors. *Curr. Opin. Cell Biol.* 17:251–256.

Aguilera, A. 2005. Cotranscriptional mRNP assembly: From the DNA to the nuclear pore. *Curr. Opin. Cell Biol.* 17:242–250.

Ro-Choi, T. S. 1999. Nuclear snRNA and nuclear function (discovery of 5' cap structures in RNA). *Crit. Rev. Eukaryotic Gene Expr.* 9:107–158.

Bard, J., Zhelkovsky, A. M., Helmling, S., Earnest, T. N., Moore, C. L., and Bohm, A. 2000. Structure of yeast poly(A) polymerase alone and in complex with 3'-dATP. *Science* 289:1346–1349.

Martin, G., Keller, W., and Doublie, S. 2000. Crystal structure of mammalian poly(A) polymerase in complex with an analog of ATP. *EMBO J.* 19:4193–4203.

Zhao, J., Hyman, L., and Moore, C. 1999. Formation of mRNA 3' ends in eukaryotes: Mechanism, regulation, and interrelationships with other steps in mRNA synthesis. *Microbiol. Mol. Biol. Rev.* 63:405–445.

Minvielle-Sebastia, L., and Keller, W. 1999. mRNA polyadenylation and its coupling to other RNA processing reactions and to transcription. *Curr. Opin. Cell Biol.* 11:352–357.

Small Regulatory RNAs

Winter, J., Jung, S., Keller, S., Gregory, R. I., and Diederichs, S. 2009. Many roads to maturity: MicroRNA biogenesis pathways and their regulation. *Nat. Cell Biol.* 11:228–234.

Ruvkun, G., Wightman, B., and Ha, I. 2004. The 20 years it took to recognize the importance of tiny RNAs. *Cell* 116:S93–S96.

SELECTED READINGS

RNA Editing

Gott, J. M., and Emeson, R. B. 2000. Functions and mechanisms of RNA editing. *Annu. Rev. Genet.* 34:499–531.

Simpson, L., Thiemann, O. H., Savill, N. J., Alfonzo, J. D., and Maslov, D. A. 2000. Evolution of RNA editing in trypanosome mitochondria. *Proc. Natl. Acad. Sci. U.S.A.* 97:6986–6993.

Chester, A., Scott, J., Anant, S., and Navaratnam, N. 2000. RNA editing: Cytidine to uridine conversion in apolipoprotein B mRNA. *Biochim. Biophys. Acta* 1494:1–3.

Maas, S., and Rich, A. 2000. Changing genetic information through RNA editing. *Bioessays* 22:790–802.

Splicing of mRNA Precursors

Caceres, J. F., and Kornblihtt, A. R. 2002. Alternative splicing: Multiple control mechanisms and involvement in human disease. *Trends Genet.* 18:186–193.

Faustino, N. A., and Cooper, T. A. 2003. Pre-mRNA splicing and human disease. *Genes Dev.* 17:419–437.

Lou, H., and Gagel, R. F. 1998. Alternative RNA processing: Its role in regulating expression of calcitonin/calcitonin gene-related peptide. *J. Endocrinol.* 156:401–405.

Matlin, A. J., Clark, F., and Smith, C. W. 2005. Understanding alternative splicing: Towards a cellular code. *Nat. Rev. Mol. Cell Biol.* 6:386–398.

McKie, A. B., McHale, J. C., Keen, T. J., Tarttelin, E. E., Goliath, R., et al. 2001. Mutations in the pre-mRNA splicing factor gene PRPC8 in autosomal dominant retinitis pigmentosa (RP13). *Hum. Mol. Genet.* 10:1555–1562.

Nilsen, T. W. 2003. The spliceosome: The most complex macromolecular machine in the cell? *Bioessays* 25:1147–1149.

Rund, D., and Rachmilewitz, E. 2005. β-Thalassemia. *N. Engl. J. Med.* 353:1135–1146.

Patel, A. A., and Steitz, J. A. 2003. Splicing double: Insights from the second spliceosome. *Nat. Rev. Mol. Cell Biol.* 4:960–970.

Sharp, P. A. 2005. The discovery of split genes and RNA splicing. *Trends Biochem. Sci.* 30:279–281.

Valadkhan, S., and Manley, J. L. 2001. Splicing-related catalysis by protein-free snRNAs. *Nature* 413:701–707.

Zhou, Z., Licklider, L. J., Gygi, S. P., and Reed, R. 2002. Comprehensive proteomic analysis of the human spliceosome. *Nature* 419:182–185.

Stark, H., Dube, P., Luhrmann, R., and Kastner, B. 2001. Arrangement of RNA and proteins in the spliceosomal U1 small nuclear ribonucleoprotein particle. *Nature* 409:539–542.

Strehler, E. E., and Zacharias, D. A. 2001. Role of alternative splicing in generating isoform diversity among plasma membrane calcium pumps. *Physiol. Rev.* 81:21–50.

Graveley, B. R. 2001. Alternative splicing: Increasing diversity in the proteomic world. *Trends Genet.* 17:100–107.

Newman, A. 1998. RNA splicing. *Curr. Biol.* 8:R903–R905.

Reed, R. 2000. Mechanisms of fidelity in pre-mRNA splicing. *Curr. Opin. Cell Biol.* 12:340–345.

Sleeman, J. E., and Lamond, A. I. 1999. Nuclear organization of pre-mRNA splicing factors. *Curr. Opin. Cell Biol.* 11:372–377.

Black, D. L. 2000. Protein diversity from alternative splicing: A challenge for bioinformatics and post-genome biology. *Cell* 103:367–370.

Collins, C. A., and Guthrie, C. 2000. The question remains: Is the spliceosome a ribozyme? *Nat. Struct. Biol.* 7:850–854.

Self-Splicing and RNA Catalysis

Adams, P. L., Stanley, M. R., Kosek, A. B., Wang, J., and Strobel, S. A. 2004. Crystal structure of a self-splicing group I intron with both exons. *Nature* 430:45–50.

Adams, P. L., Stanley, M. R., Gill, M. L., Kosek, A. B., Wang, J., and Strobel, S. A. 2004. Crystal structure of a group I intron splicing intermediate. *RNA* 10:1867–1887.

Stahley, M. R., and Strobel, S. A. 2005. Structural evidence for a two-metal-ion mechanism of group I intron splicing. *Science* 309:1587–1590.

Carola, C., and Eckstein, F. 1999. Nucleic acid enzymes. *Curr. Opin. Chem. Biol.* 3:274–283.

Doherty, E. A., and Doudna, J. A. 2000. Ribozyme structures and mechanisms. *Annu. Rev. Biochem.* 69:597–615.

Fedor, M. J. 2000. Structure and function of the hairpin ribozyme. *J. Mol. Biol.* 297:269–291.

Hanna, R., and Doudna, J. A. 2000. Metal ions in ribozyme folding and catalysis. *Curr. Opin. Chem. Biol.* 4:166–170.

Scott, W. G. 1998. RNA catalysis. *Curr. Opin. Struct. Biol.* 8:720–726.

Chapter 30

Where to Start

Williamson, J. R. 2009. The ribosome at atomic resolution. *Cell* 139:1041–1043.

Noller, H. F. 2005. RNA structure: Reading the ribosome. *Science* 309:1508–1514.

Dahlberg, A. E. 2001. Ribosome structure: The ribosome in action. *Science* 292:868–869.

Ibba, M., Curnow, A. W., and Söll, D. 1997. Aminoacyl-tRNA synthesis: Divergent routes to a common goal. *Trends Biochem. Sci.* 22:39–42.

Koonin, E. V., and Novozhilov, A. S. 2009. Origin and evolution of the genetic code: The universal enigma. *IUBMB Life* 61:99–111.

Schimmel, P., and Ribas de Pouplana, L. 2000. Footprints of aminoacyl-tRNA synthetases are everywhere. *Trends Biochem. Sci.* 25:207–209.

Books

Cold Spring Harbor Symposia on Quantitative Biology. 2001. Volume 66, *The Ribosome*. Cold Spring Harbor Laboratory Press.

Gesteland, R. F., Atkins, J. F., and Cech, T. (Eds.). 2005. *The RNA World*, 3d ed. Cold Spring Harbor Laboratory Press.

Garrett, R., Douthwaite, S. R., Liljas, A., Matheson, A. T, Moore, P. B., and Noller, H. F. 2000. *The Ribosome: Structure, Function, Antibiotics, and Cellular Interactions.* The American Society for Microbiology.

Aminoacyl-tRNA Synthetases

Kaminska, M., Havrylenko, S., Decottignies, P., Le Maréchal, P., Negrutskii, B., and Mirande, M. 2009. Dynamic organization of aminoacyl-tRNA synthetase complexes in the cytoplasm of human cells. *J. Biol. Chem.* 284:13746–13754.

Park, S. G., Schimmel, P., and Kim, S. 2008. Aminoacyl tRNA synthetases and their connections to disease. *Proc. Natl. Acad. Sci. U.S.A.* 105:11043–11049.

Ibba, M., and Söll, D. 2000. Aminoacyl-tRNA synthesis. *Annu. Rev. Biochem.* 69:617–650.

Sankaranarayanan, R., Dock-Bregeon, A. C., Rees, B., Bovee, M., Caillet, J., Romby, P., Francklyn, C. S., and Moras, D. 2000. Zinc ion mediated amino acid discrimination by threonyl-tRNA synthetase. *Nat. Struct. Biol.* 7:461–465.

Sankaranarayanan, R., Dock-Bregeon, A. C., Romby, P., Caillet, J., Springer, M., Rees, B., Ehresmann, C., Ehresmann, B., and Moras, D. 1999. The structure of threonyl-tRNA synthetase-tRNAThr complex enlightens its repressor activity and reveals an essential zinc ion in the active site. *Cell* 97:371–381.

Dock-Bregeon, A., Sankaranarayanan, R., Romby, P., Caillet, J., Springer, M., Rees, B., Francklyn, C. S., Ehresmann, C., and Moras, D. 2000. Transfer RNA-mediated editing in threonyl-tRNA synthetase: The class II solution to the double discrimination problem. *Cell* 103:877–884.

de Pouplana, L. R., and Schimmel, P. 2000. A view into the origin of life: Aminoacyl-tRNA synthetases. *Cell. Mol. Life Sci.* 57:865–870.

Transfer RNA

Ibba, M., Becker, H. D., Stathopoulos, C., Tumbula, D. L., and Söll, D. 2000. The adaptor hypothesis revisited. *Trends Biochem. Sci.* 25:311–316.

Weisblum, B. 1999. Back to Camelot: Defining the specific role of tRNA in protein synthesis. *Trends Biochem. Sci.* 24:247–250.

Ribosomes and Ribosomal RNAs

Jin, H., Kelley, A. C., Loakes, D., and Ramakrishnan, V. 2010. Structure of the 70S ribosome bound to release factor 2 and a substrate analog provides insights into catalysis of peptide release. *Proc. Natl. Acad. Sci. U.S.A.* 107:8593–8598.

Rodnina, M. V., and Wintermeyer, W. 2009. Recent mechanistic insights into eukaryotic ribosomes. *Curr. Opin. Cell Biol.* 21:435–443.

Dinman, J. D. 2008. The eukaryotic ribosome: Current status and challenges. *J. Biol. Chem.* 284:11761–11765.

Wen, J.-D., Lancaster, L., Hodges, C., Zeri, A.-C., Yoshimura, S. H., Noller, H. F., Bustamante, C., and Tinoco, I., Jr. 2008. Following translation by single ribosomes one codon at a time. *Nature* 452:598–603.

Korostelev, A., and Noller, H. F. 2007. The ribosome in focus: New structures bring insights. *Trends Biochem. Sci.* 32:434–441.

Brandt, F., Etchells, S. A., Ortiz, J. O., Elcock, A. H., Hartl, F. U., and Baumeister, W. 2009. The native 3D organization of bacterial polysomes. *Cell* 136:261–271.

Schuwirth, B. S., Borovinskaya, M. A., Hau, C. W., Zhang, W., Vila-Sanjurjo, A., Holton, J. M., and Cate, J. H. 2005. Structures of the bacterial ribosome at 3.5 Å resolution. *Science* 310:827–834.

Yonath, A., and Franceschi, F. 1998. Functional universality and evolutionary diversity: Insights from the structure of the ribosome. *Structure* 6:679–684.

Ban, N., Nissen, P., Hansen, J., Moore, P. B., and Steitz, T. A. 2000. The complete atomic structure of the large ribosomal subunit at 2.4 Å resolution. *Science* 289:905–920.

Carter, A. P., Clemons, W. M., Brodersen, D. E., Morgan-Warren, R. J., Wimberly, B. T., and Ramakrishnan, V. 2000. Functional insights from the structure of the 30S ribosomal subunit and its interactions with antibiotics. *Nature* 407:340–348.

Wimberly, B. T., Brodersen, D. E., Clemons, W. M., Morgan-Warren, R. J., Carter, A. P., Vonrhein, C., Hartsch, T., and Ramakrishnan, V. 2000. Structure of the 30S ribosomal subunit. *Nature* 407:327–339.

Initiation Factors

Søgaard, B., Sørensen, H. P., Mortensen, K. K., and Sperling-Petersen, H. U. 2005. Initiation of protein synthesis in bacteria. *Microbiol. Mol. Biol. Rev.* 69:101–123.

Carter, A. P., Clemons, W. M., Jr., Brodersen, D. E., Morgan-Warren, R. J., Hartsch, T., Wimberly, B. T., and Ramakrishnan, V. 2001. Crystal structure of an initiation factor bound to the 30S ribosomal subunit. *Science* 291:498–501.

Guenneugues, M., Caserta, E., Brandi, L., Spurio, R., Meunier, S., Pon, C. L., Boelens, R., and Gualerzi, C. O. 2000. Mapping the fMet-tRNA$_f^{Met}$ binding site of initiation factor IF2. *EMBO J.* 19:5233–5240.

Meunier, S., Spurio, R., Czisch, M., Wechselberger, R., Guenneugues, M., Gualerzi, C. O., and Boelens, R. 2000. Structure of the fMet-tRNA$_f^{Met}$-binding domain of *B. stearothermophilus* initiation factor IF2. *EMBO J.* 19:1918–1926.

Elongation Factors

Schuette, J.-C., Murphy, F. V., IV, Kelley, A. C., Weir, J. R., Giesebrecht, J., Connell, S. R., Loerke, J., Mielke, T., Zhang, W., Penczek, P. A., Ramakrishnan, V., and Spahn, C. M. T. 2009. GTPase activation of elongation factor EF-Tu by the ribosome during decoding. *EMBO J.* 28:755–765.

Stark, H., Rodnina, M. V., Wieden, H. J., van Heel, M., and Wintermeyer, W. 2000. Large-scale movement of elongation factor G and extensive conformational change of the ribosome during translocation. *Cell* 100:301–309.

Baensch, M., Frank, R., and Kohl, J. 1998. Conservation of the amino-terminal epitope of elongation factor Tu in Eubacteria and Archaea. *Microbiology* 144:2241–2246.

Krasny, L., Mesters, J. R., Tieleman, L. N., Kraal, B., Fucik, V., Hilgenfeld, R., and Jonak, J. 1998. Structure and expression of elongation factor Tu from *Bacillus stearothermophilus*. *J. Mol. Biol.* 283:371–381.

Pape, T., Wintermeyer, W., and Rodnina, M. V. 1998. Complete kinetic mechanism of elongation factor Tu-dependent binding of aminoacyl-tRNA to the A site of the *E. coli* ribosome. *EMBO J.* 17:7490–7497.

Piepenburg, O., Pape, T., Pleiss, J. A., Wintermeyer, W., Uhlenbeck, O. C., and Rodnina, M. V. 2000. Intact aminoacyl-tRNA is required to trigger GTP hydrolysis by elongation factor Tu on the ribosome. *Biochemistry* 39:1734–1738.

Peptide-Bond Formation and Translocation

Uemura, S., Aitken, C. E., Korlach, J., Flusberg, B. A., Turner, S. W., and Puglisi, J. D. 2010. Real-time tRNA transit on single translating ribosomes at codon resolution. *Nature* 464:1012–1018.

Beringer, M., and Rodnina, M. V. 2007. The ribosomal peptidyl transferase. *Mol. Cell* 26:311–321.

Yarus, M., and Welch, M. 2000. Peptidyl transferase: Ancient and exiguous. *Chem. Biol.* 7:R187–R190.

Vladimirov, S. N., Druzina, Z., Wang, R., and Cooperman, B. S. 2000. Identification of 50S components neighboring 23S rRNA nucleotides A2448 and U2604 within the peptidyl transferase center of *Escherichia coli* ribosomes. *Biochemistry* 39:183–193.

Frank, J., and Agrawal, R. K. 2000. A ratchet-like inter-subunit reorganization of the ribosome during translocation. *Nature* 406:318–322.

Termination

Weixlbaumer, A., Jin, H., Neubauer, C., Voorhees, R. M., Petry, S., Kelley, A. C., and Ramakrishnan, V. 2008. Insights into translational termination from the structure of RF2 bound to the ribosome. *Science* 322:953–956.

Trobro, S., and Åqvist, S. 2007. A model for how ribosomal release factors induce peptidyl-tRNA cleavage in termination of protein synthesis. *Mol. Cell* 27:758–766.

Korosteleva, A., Asaharaa, H., Lancastera, L., Laurberga, M., Hirschia, A., Zhua, J., Trakhanova, S., Scotta, W. G., and Noller, H. F. 2008. Crystal structure of a translation termination complex formed with release factor RF2. *Proc. Natl. Acad. Sci. U.S.A.* 105:19684–19689.

Wilson, D. N., Schluenzen, F., Harms, J. M., Yoshida, T., Ohkubo, T., Albrecht, A., Buerger, J., Kobayashi, Y., and Fucini, P. 2005. X-ray crystallography study on ribosome recycling: The mechanism of binding and action of RRF on the 50S ribosomal subunit. *EMBO J.* 24:251–260.

Kisselev, L. L., and Buckingham, R. H. 2000. Translational termination comes of age. *Trends Biochem. Sci.* 25:561–566.

Fidelity and Proofreading

Zaher, H. S., and Green, R. 2009. Quality control by the ribosome following peptide bond formation. *Nature* 457:161–166.

Zaher, H. S., and Green, R. 2009. Fidelity at the molecular level: Lessons from protein synthesis. *Cell* 136:746–762.

Ogle, J. M., and Ramakrishnan, V. 2005. Structural insights into translational fidelity. *Annu. Rev. Biochem.* 74:129–177.

Ibba, M., and Söll, D. 1999. Quality control mechanisms during translation. *Science* 286:1893–1897.

Rodnina, M. V., and Wintermeyer, W. 2001. Ribosome fidelity: tRNA discrimination, proofreading and induced fit. *Trends Biochem. Sci.* 26:124–130.

SELECTED READINGS

Eukaryotic Protein Synthesis

Rhoads, R. E. 2009. eIF4E: New family members, new binding partners, new roles. *J. Biol. Chem.* 284:16711–16715.

Marintchev, A., Edmonds, K. A., Marintcheva, B., Hendrickson, E., Oberer, M., Suzuki, C., Herdy, B., Sonenberg, N., and Wagner, G. 2009. Topology and regulation of the human eIF4A/4G/4H helicase complex in translation initiation. *Cell* 136:447–460.

Fitzgerald, K. D., and Semler, B. L. 2009. Bridging IRES elements in mRNAs to the eukaryotic translation apparatus. *Biochim. Biophys. Acta* 1789:518–528.

Mitchell, S. F., and Lorsch, J. R. 2008. Should I stay or should I go? Eukaryotic translation initiation factors 1 and 1A control start codon recognition. *J. Biol. Chem.* 283:27345–27349.

Amrani, A., Ghosh, S., Mangus, D. A., and Jacobson, A. 2008. Translation factors promote the formation of two states of the closed-loop mRNP. *Nature* 453:1276–1280.

Sachs, A. B., and Varani, G. 2000. Eukaryotic translation initiation: There are (at least) two sides to every story. *Nat. Struct. Biol.* 7:356–361.

Kozak, M. 1999. Initiation of translation in prokaryotes and eukaryotes. *Gene* 234:187–208.

Bushell, M., Wood, W., Clemens, M. J., and Morley, S. J. 2000. Changes in integrity and association of eukaryotic protein synthesis initiation factors during apoptosis. *Eur. J. Biochem.* 267:1083–1091.

Das, S., Ghosh, R., and Maitra, U. 2001. Eukaryotic translation initiation factor 5 functions as a GTPase-activating protein. *J. Biol. Chem.* 276:6720–6726.

Lee, J. H., Choi, S. K., Roll-Mecak, A., Burley, S. K., and Dever, T. E. 1999. Universal conservation in translation initiation revealed by human and archaeal homologs of bacterial translation initiation factor IF2. *Proc. Natl. Acad. Sci. U.S.A.* 96:4342–4347.

Pestova, T. V., and Hellen, C. U. 2000. The structure and function of initiation factors in eukaryotic protein synthesis. *Cell. Mol. Life Sci.* 57:651–674.

Antibiotics and Toxins

Belova, L., Tenson, T., Xiong, L., McNicholas, P. M., and Mankin, A. S. 2001. A novel site of antibiotic action in the ribosome: Interaction of evernimicin with the large ribosomal subunit. *Proc. Natl. Acad. Sci. U.S.A.* 98:3726–3731.

Brodersen, D. E., Clemons, W. M., Jr., Carter, A. P., Morgan-Warren, R. J., Wimberly, B. T., and Ramakrishnan, V. 2000. The structural basis for the action of the antibiotics tetracycline, pactamycin, and hygromycin B on the 30S ribosomal subunit. *Cell* 103:1143–1154.

Porse, B. T., and Garrett, R. A. 1999. Ribosomal mechanics, antibiotics, and GTP hydrolysis. *Cell* 97:423–426.

Lord, M. J., Jolliffe, N. A., Marsden, C. J., Pateman, C. S., Smith, D. S., Spooner, R. A., Watson, P. D., and Roberts, L. M. 2003. Ricin: Mechanisms of toxicity. *Toxicol. Rev.* 22:53–64.

Protein Transport Across Membranes

Janda, C. Y., Li, J., Oubridge, C., Hernández, H., Robinson, C. V., and Nagai, K. 2010. Recognition of a signal peptide by the signal recognition particle. *Nature* 465:507–510.

Cross, B. C. S., Sinning, I., Luirink, J., and High, S. 2009. Delivering proteins for export from the cytosol. *Nat. Rev. Mol. Cell. Biol.* 10:255–264.

Shan, S., Schmid, S. L., and Zhang, X. 2009. Signal recognition particle (SRP) and SRP receptor: A new paradigm for multistate regulatory GTPases. *Biochemistry* 48:6696–6704.

Johnson, A. E. 2009. The structural and functional coupling of two molecular machines, the ribosome and the translocon. *J. Cell Biol.* 185:765–767.

Pool, R. P. 2009. A trans-membrane segment inside the ribosome exit tunnel triggers RAMP4 recruitment to the Sec61p translocase. *J. Cell Biol.* 185:889–902.

Egea, P. F., Stroud, R. M., and Walter, P. 2005. Targeting proteins to membranes: Structure of the signal recognition particle. *Curr. Opin. Struct. Biol.* 15:213–220.

Halic, M., and Beckmann, R. 2005. The signal recognition particle and its interactions during protein targeting. *Curr. Opin. Struct. Biol.* 15:116–125.

Doudna, J. A., and Batey, R. T. 2004. Structural insights into the signal recognition particle. *Annu. Rev. Biochem.* 73:539–557.

Schnell, D. J., and Hebert, D. N. 2003. Protein translocons: Multifunctional mediators of protein translocation across membranes. *Cell* 112:491–505.

Chapter 31

Where to Start

Pabo, C. O., and Sauer, R. T. 1984. Protein–DNA recognition. *Annu. Rev. Biochem.* 53:293–321.

Ptashne, M., Johnson, A. D., and Pabo, C. O. 1982. A genetic switch in a bacterial virus. *Sci. Am.* 247:128–140.

Ptashne, M., Jeffrey, A., Johnson, A. D., Maurer, R., Meyer, B. J., Pabo, C. O., Roberts, T. M., and Sauer, R. T. 1980. How the lambda repressor and Cro work. *Cell* 19:1–11.

Books

Ptashne, M. 2004. *A Genetic Switch: Phage λ Revisited* (3d ed.). Cold Spring Harbor Laboratory Press.

McKnight, S. L., and Yamamoto, K. R. (Eds.). 1992. *Transcriptional Regulation* (vols. 1 and 2). Cold Spring Harbor Laboratory Press.

Lodish, H., Berk, A., Matsudaira, P., Kaiser, C. A., Krieger, M., Scott, M. P., Zipursky, S. L., and Darnell, J., 2008. *Molecular Cell Biology* (6th ed.). W. H. Freeman and Company.

DNA-Binding Proteins

Balaeff, A., Mahadevan, L. and Schulten, K. 2004. Structural basis for cooperative DNA binding by CAP and *lac* repressor. *Structure* 12:123–132.

Bell, C. E., and Lewis, M. 2001. The Lac repressor: A second generation of structural and functional studies. *Curr. Opin. Struct. Biol.* 11:19–25.

Lewis, M., Chang, G., Horton, N. C., Kercher, M. A., Pace, H. C., Schumacher, M. A., Brennan, R. G., and Lu, P. 1996. Crystal structure of the lactose operon repressor and its complexes with DNA and inducer. *Science* 271:1247–1254.

Niu, W., Kim, Y., Tau, G., Heyduk, T., and Ebright, R. H. 1996. Transcription activation at class II CAP-dependent promoters: Two interactions between CAP and RNA polymerase. *Cell* 87:1123–1134.

Schultz, S. C., Shields, G. C., and Steitz, T. A. 1991. Crystal structure of a CAP-DNA complex: The DNA is bent by 90 degrees. *Science* 253:1001–1007.

Parkinson, G., Wilson, C., Gunasekera, A., Ebright, Y. W., Ebright, R. E., and Berman, H. M. 1996. Structure of the CAP-DNA complex at 2.5 Å resolution: A complete picture of the protein–DNA interface. *J. Mol. Biol.* 260:395–408.

Busby, S., and Ebright, R. H. 1999. Transcription activation by catabolite activator protein (CAP). *J. Mol. Biol.* 293:199–213.

Somers, W. S., and Phillips, S. E. 1992. Crystal structure of the met repressor-operator complex at 2.8 Å resolution reveals DNA recognition by β-strands. *Nature* 359:387–393.

Gene-Regulatory Circuits

Johnson, A. D., Poteete, A. R., Lauer, G., Sauer, R. T., Ackers, G. K., and Ptashne, M. 1981. Lambda repressor and Cro: Components of an efficient molecular switch. *Nature* 294:217–223.

Stayrook, S., Jaru-Ampornpan, P., Ni, J., Hochschild, A., and Lewis, M. 2008. Crystal structure of the lambda repressor and a model for pairwise cooperative operator binding. *Nature* 452:1022–1025.

Arkin, A., Ross, J., and McAdams, H. H. 1998. Stochastic kinetic analysis of developmental pathway bifurcation in phage lambda-infected *Escherichia coli* cells. *Genetics* 149:1633–1648.

Posttranscriptional Regulation
Kolter, R., and Yanofsky, C. 1982. Attenuation in amino acid biosynthetic operons. *Annu. Rev. Genet.* 16:113–134.

Yanofsky, C. 1981. Attenuation in the control of expression of bacterial operons. *Nature* 289:751–758.

Miller, M. B., and Bassler, B. L. 2001. Quorum sensing in bacteria. *Annu. Rev. Microbiol.* 55:165–199.

Zhang, R. G., Pappas, T., Brace, J. L., Miller, P. C., Oulmassov, T., Molyneaux, J. M., Anderson, J. C., Bashkin, J. K., Winans, S. C., and Joachimiak, A. 2002. Structure of a bacterial quorum-sensing transcription factor complexed with pheromone and DNA. *Nature* 417:971–974.

Soberon-Chavez, G., Aguirre-Ramirez, M., and Ordonez, L. 2005. Is *Pseudomonas aeruginosa* only "sensing quorum"? *Crit. Rev. Microbiol.* 31:171–182.

Historical Aspects
Lewis, M. 2005. The lac repressor. *C. R. Biol.* 328:521–548.

Jacob, F., and Monod, J. 1961. Genetic regulatory mechanisms in the synthesis of proteins. *J. Mol. Biol.* 3:318–356.

Ptashne, M., and Gilbert, W. 1970. Genetic repressors. *Sci. Am.* 222(6):36–44.

Lwoff, A., and Ullmann, A. (Eds.). 1979. *Origins of Molecular Biology: A Tribute to Jacques Monod*. Academic Press.

Judson, H. 1996. *The Eighth Day of Creation: Makers of the Revolution in Biology*. Cold Spring Harbor Laboratory Press.

Chapter 32

Where to Start
Kornberg, R. D. 2007. The molecular basis of eukaryotic transcription. *Proc. Natl. Acad. Sci. U.S.A.* 104:12955–12961.

Pabo, C. O., and Sauer, R. T. 1984. Protein–DNA recognition. *Annu. Rev. Biochem.* 53:293–321.

Struhl, K. 1989. Helix-turn-helix, zinc-finger, and leucine-zipper motifs for eukaryotic transcriptional regulatory proteins. *Trends Biochem. Sci.* 14:137–140.

Struhl, K. 1999. Fundamentally different logic of gene regulation in eukaryotes and prokaryotes. *Cell* 98:1–4.

Korzus, E., Torchia, J., Rose, D. W., Xu, L., Kurokawa, R., McInerney, E. M., Mullen, T. M., Glass, C. K., and Rosenfeld, M. G. 1998. Transcription factor-specific requirements for coactivators and their acetyltransferase functions. *Science* 279:703–707.

Aalfs, J. D., and Kingston, R. E. 2000. What does "chromatin remodeling" mean? *Trends Biochem. Sci.* 25:548–555.

Books
McKnight, S. L., and Yamamoto, K. R. (Eds.). 1992. *Transcriptional Regulation* (vols. 1 and 2). Cold Spring Harbor Laboratory Press.

Latchman, D. S. 2004. *Eukaryotic Transcription Factors* (4th ed.). Academic Press.

Wolffe, A. 1992. *Chromatin Structure and Function*. Academic Press.

Lodish, H., Berk, A., Matsudaira, P., Kaiser, C. A., Krieger, M., Scott, M. P., Zipursky, S. L., and Darnell, J., 2008. *Molecular Cell Biology* (6th ed.). W. H. Freeman and Company.

Chromatin and Chromatin Remodeling
Lorch, Y., Maier-Davis, B., and Kornberg, R. D. 2010. Mechanism of chromatin remodeling. *Proc. Natl. Acad. Sci. U.S.A.* 107:3458–3462.

Tang, L., Nogales, E., and Ciferri, C. 2010. Structure and function of SWI/SNF chromatin remodeling complexes and mechanistic implications for transcription. *Prog. Biophys. Mol. Biol.* 102:122–128.

Jenuwein, T., and Allis, C. D. 2001. Translating the histone code. *Science* 293:1074–1080.

Jiang, C., and Pugh, B. F. 2009. Nucleosome positioning and gene regulation: Advances through genomics. *Nat. Rev. Genet.* 10:161–172.

Barski, A., Cuddapah, S., Cui, K., Roh, T. Y., Schones, D. E., Wang, Z., Wei, G., Chepelev, I., and Zhao, K. 2007. High-resolution profiling of histone methylations in the human genome. *Cell* 129:823–837.

Weintraub, H., Larsen, A., and Groudine, M. 1981. β-Globin-gene switching during the development of chicken embryos: Expression and chromosome structure. *Cell* 24:333–344.

Ren, B., Robert, F., Wyrick, J. J., Aparicio, O., Jennings, E. G., Simon, I., Zeitlinger, J., Schreiber, J., Hannett, N., Kanin, E., Volkert, T. L., Wilson, C. J., Bell, S. P., and Young, R. A. 2000. Genome-wide location and function of DNA-binding proteins. *Science* 290:2306–2309.

Goodrich, J. A., and Tjian, R. 1994. TBP-TAF complexes: Selectivity factors for eukaryotic transcription. *Curr. Opin. Cell. Biol.* 6:403–409.

Bird, A. P., and Wolffe, A. P. 1999. Methylation-induced repression: Belts, braces, and chromatin. *Cell* 99:451–454.

Cairns, B. R. 1998. Chromatin remodeling machines: Similar motors, ulterior motives. *Trends Biochem. Sci.* 23:20–25.

Albright, S. R., and Tjian, R. 2000. TAFs revisited: More data reveal new twists and confirm old ideas. *Gene* 242:1–13.

Urnov, F. D., and Wolffe, A. P. 2001. Chromatin remodeling and transcriptional activation: The cast (in order of appearance). *Oncogene* 20:2991–3006.

Luger, K., Mader, A. W., Richmond, R. K., Sargent, D. F., and Richmond, T. J. 1997. Crystal structure of the nucleosome core particle at 2.8 Å resolution. *Nature* 389:251–260.

Arents, G., and Moudrianakis, E. N. 1995. The histone fold: A ubiquitous architectural motif utilized in DNA compaction and protein dimerization. *Proc. Natl. Acad. Sci. U.S.A.* 92:11170–11174.

Baxevanis, A. D., Arents, G., Moudrianakis, E. N., and Landsman, D. 1995. A variety of DNA-binding and multimeric proteins contain the histone fold motif. *Nucleic Acids Res.* 23:2685–2691.

Transcription Factors
Green, M. R. 2005. Eukaryotic transcription activation: Right on target. *Mol. Cell* 18:399–402.

Kornberg, R. D. 2005. Mediator and the mechanism of transcriptional activation. *Trends Biochem. Sci.* 30:235–239.

Clements, A., Rojas, J. R., Trievel, R. C., Wang, L., Berger, S. L., and Marmorstein, R. 1999. Crystal structure of the histone acetyltransferase domain of the human PCAF transcriptional regulator bound to coenzyme A. *EMBO J.* 18:3521–3532.

Deckert, J., and Struhl, K. 2001. Histone acetylation at promoters is differentially affected by specific activators and repressors. *Mol. Cell. Biol.* 21:2726–2735.

Dutnall, R. N., Tafrov, S. T., Sternglanz, R., and Ramakrishnan, V. 1998. Structure of the histone acetyltransferase Hat1: A paradigm for the GCN5-related N-acetyltransferase superfamily. *Cell* 94:427–438.

Finnin, M. S., Donigian, J. R., Cohen, A., Richon, V. M., Rifkind, R. A., Marks, P. A., Breslow, R., and Pavletich, N. P. 1999. Structures of a histone deacetylase homologue bound to the TSA and SAHA inhibitors. *Nature* 401:188–193.

Finnin, M. S., Donigian, J. R., and Pavletich, N. P. 2001. Structure of the histone deacetylase SIR2. *Nat. Struct. Biol.* 8:621–625.

Jacobson, R. H., Ladurner, A. G., King, D. S., and Tjian, R. 2000. Structure and function of a human TAFII250 double bromodomain module. *Science* 288:1422–1425.

Rojas, J. R., Trievel, R. C., Zhou, J., Mo, Y., Li, X., Berger, S. L., Allis, C. D., and Marmorstein, R. 1999. Structure of *Tetrahymena* GCN5 bound to coenzyme A and a histone H3 peptide. *Nature* 401:93–98.

SELECTED READINGS

Induced Pluripotent Stem Cells

Takahashi, K., Tanabe, K., Ohnuki, M., Narita, M., Ichisaka, T., Tomoda, K., and Yamanaka, S. 2007. Induction of pluripotent stem cells from adult human fibroblasts by defined factors. *Cell* 131:861–872.

Takahashi, K., and Yamanaka, S. 2006. Induction of pluripotent stem cells from mouse embryonic and adult fibroblast cultures by defined factors. *Cell* 126:663–676.

Park, I. H., Arora, N., Huo, H., Maherali, N., Ahfeldt, T., Shimamura, A., Lensch, M. W., Cowan, C., Hochedlinger, K., and Daley, G. Q. 2008. Disease-specific induced pluripotent stem cells. *Cell* 134:877–886.

Yamanaka, S. 2009. A fresh look at iPS cells. *Cell* 137:13–17.

Yu, J., Hu, K., Smuga-Otto, K., Tian, S., Stewart, R., Slukvin, I. I., and Thomson, J. A. 2009. Human induced pluripotent stem cells free of vector and transgene sequences. *Science* 324:797–801.

Nuclear Hormone Receptors

Downes, M., Verdecia, M. A., Roecker, A. J., Hughes, R., Hogenesch, J. B., Kast-Woelbern, H. R., Bowman, M. E., Ferrer, J. L., Anisfeld, A. M., Edwards, P. A., Rosenfeld, J. M., Alvarez, J. G., Noel, J. P., Nicolaou, K. C., and Evans, R. M. 2003. A chemical, genetic, and structural analysis of the nuclear bile acid receptor FXR. *Mol. Cell* 11:1079–1092.

Evans, R. M. 2005. The nuclear receptor superfamily: A Rosetta stone for physiology. *Mol. Endocrinol.* 19:1429–1438.

Xu, W., Cho, H., Kadam, S., Banayo, E. M., Anderson, S., Yates, J. R., 3d, Emerson, B. M., and Evans, R. M. 2004. A methylation-mediator complex in hormone signaling. *Genes Dev.* 18:144–156.

Evans, R. M. 1988. The steroid and thyroid hormone receptor super-family. *Science* 240:889–895.

Yamamoto, K. R. 1985. Steroid receptor regulated transcription of specific genes and gene networks. *Annu. Rev. Genet.* 19:209–252.

Tanenbaum, D. M., Wang, Y., Williams, S. P., and Sigler, P. B. 1998. Crystallographic comparison of the estrogen and progesterone receptor's ligand binding domains. *Proc. Natl. Acad. Sci. U.S.A.* 95:5998–6003.

Schwabe, J. W., Chapman, L., Finch, J. T., and Rhodes, D. 1993. The crystal structure of the estrogen receptor DNA-binding domain bound to DNA: How receptors discriminate between their response elements. *Cell* 75:567–578.

Shiau, A. K., Barstad, D., Loria, P. M., Cheng, L., Kushner, P. J., Agard, D. A., and Greene, G. L. 1998. The structural basis of estrogen receptor/coactivator recognition and the antagonism of this interaction by tamoxifen. *Cell* 95:927–937.

Collingwood, T. N., Urnov, F. D., and Wolffe, A. P. 1999. Nuclear receptors: Coactivators, corepressors and chromatin remodeling in the control of transcription. *J. Mol. Endocrinol.* 23:255–275.

Posttranscriptional Regulation

Rouault, T. A., Stout, C. D., Kaptain, S., Harford, J. B., and Klausner, R. D. 1991. Structural relationship between an iron-regulated RNA-binding protein (IRE-BP) and aconitase: Functional implications. *Cell* 64:881–883.

Klausner, R. D., Rouault, T. A., and Harford, J. B. 1993. Regulating the fate of mRNA: The control of cellular iron metabolism. *Cell* 72:19–28.

Gruer, M. J., Artymiuk, P. J., and Guest, J. R. 1997. The aconitase family: Three structural variations on a common theme. *Trends Biochem. Sci.* 22:3–6.

Theil, E. C. 1994. Iron regulatory elements (IREs): A family of mRNA non-coding sequences. *Biochem. J.* 304:1–11.

MicroRNAs

Ruvkun, G. 2008. The perfect storm of tiny RNAs. *Nat. Med.* 14:1041–1045.

Sethupathy, P., and Collins, F. S. 2008. MicroRNA target site polymorphisms and human disease. *Trends Genet.* 24:489–497.

Adams, B. D., Cowee, D. M., and White, B. A. 2009. The role of miR-206 in the epidermal growth factor (EGF) induced repression of estrogen receptor-α (ERα) signaling and a luminal phenotype in MCF-7 breast cancer cells. *Mol. Endocrinol.* 23:1215–1230.

Jegga, A. G., Chen, J., Gowrisankar, S., Deshmukh, M. A., Gudivada, R., Kong, S., Kaimal, V., and Aronow, B. J. 2007. GenomeTrafac: A whole genome resource for the detection of transcription factor binding site clusters associated with conventional and microRNA encoding genes conserved between mouse and human gene orthologs. *Nucleic Acids Res.* 35:D116–D121.

Chapter 33

Where to Start

Axel, R. 1995. The molecular logic of smell. *Sci. Am.* 273(4):154–159.

Dulac, C. 2000. The physiology of taste, vintage 2000. *Cell* 100:607–610.

Yarmolinsky, D. A., Zuker, C. S., and Ryba, N. J. (2009) Common sense about taste: From mammals to insects. *Cell* 139:234–244.

Stryer, L. 1996. Vision: From photon to perception. *Proc. Natl. Acad. Sci. U.S.A.* 93:557–559.

Hudspeth, A. J. 1989. How the ear's works work. *Nature* 341:397–404.

Olfaction

Buck, L., and Axel, R. 1991. A novel multigene family may encode odorant receptors: A molecular basis for odor recognition. *Cell* 65:175–187.

Saito, H., Chi, Q., Zhuang, H., Matsunami, H., and Mainland, J. D. 2009. Odor coding by a mammalian receptor repertoire. *Sci. Signal.* 2:ra9.

Malnic, B., Hirono, J., Sato, T., and Buck, L. B. 1999. Combinatorial receptor codes for odors. *Cell* 96:713–723.

Zou, D. J., Chesler, A., and Firestein, S. 2009. How the olfactory bulb got its glomeruli: A just so story? *Nat. Rev. Neurosci.* 10:611–618.

De la Cruz, O., Blekhman, R., Zhang, X., Nicolae, D., Firestein, S., and Gilad, Y. 2009. A signature of evolutionary constraint on a subset of ectopically expressed olfactory receptor genes. *Mol. Biol. Evol.* 26:491–494.

Mombaerts, P., Wang, F., Dulac, C., Chao, S. K., Nemes, A., Mendelsohn, M., Edmondson, J., and Axel, R. 1996. Visualizing an olfactory sensory map. *Cell* 87:675–686.

Buck, L. 2005. Unraveling the sense of smell (Nobel lecture). *Angew. Chem. Int. Ed. Engl.* 44:6128–6140.

Belluscio, L., Gold, G. H., Nemes, A., and Axel, R. 1998. Mice deficient in G(olf) are anosmic. *Neuron* 20:69–81.

Vosshall, L. B., Wong, A. M., and Axel, R. 2000. An olfactory sensory map in the fly brain. *Cell* 102:147–159.

Lewcock, J. W., and Reed, R. R. 2003. A feedback mechanism regulates monoallelic odorant receptor expression. *Proc. Natl. Acad. Sci. U.S.A.* 101:1069–1074.

Reed, R. R. 2004. After the holy grail: Establishing a molecular mechanism for mammalian olfaction. *Cell* 116:329–336.

Taste

Chandrashekar, J., Yarmolinsky, D., von Buchholtz, L., Oka, Y., Sly, W., Ryba, N. J., and Zuker, C. S. 2009. The taste of carbonation. *Science* 326:443–445.

Zhao, G. Q., Zhang, Y., Hoon, M. A., Chandrashekar, J., Erlenbach, I., Ryba, N. J. P., and Zuker, C. S. 2003. The receptors for mammalian sweet and umami taste. *Cell* 115:255–266.

Herness, M. S., and Gilbertson, T. A. 1999. Cellular mechanisms of taste transduction. *Annu. Rev. Physiol.* 61:873–900.

Adler, E., Hoon, M. A., Mueller, K. L., Chandrashekar, J., Ryba, N. J., and Zuker, C. S. 2000. A novel family of mammalian taste receptors. *Cell* 100:693–702.

Chandrashekar, J., Mueller, K. L., Hoon, M. A., Adler, E., Feng, L., Guo, W., Zuker, C. S., and Ryba, N. J. 2000. T2Rs function as bitter taste receptors. *Cell* 100:703–711.

Mano, I., and Driscoll, M. 1999. DEG/ENaC channels: A touchy superfamily that watches its salt. *Bioessays* 21:568–578.

Benos, D. J., and Stanton, B. A. 1999. Functional domains within the degenerin/epithelial sodium channel (Deg/ENaC) superfamily of ion channels. *J. Physiol. (Lond.)* 520(part 3):631–644.

McLaughlin, S. K., McKinnon, P. J., and Margolskee, R. F. 1992. Gustducin is a taste-cell-specific G protein closely related to the transducins. *Nature* 357:563–569.

Nelson, G., Hoon, M. A., Chandrashekar, J., Zhang, Y., Ryba, N. J., and Zuker, C. S. 2001. Mammalian sweet taste receptors. *Cell* 106:381–390.

Vision

Stryer, L. 1988. Molecular basis of visual excitation. *Cold Spring Harbor Symp. Quant. Biol.* 53:283–294.

Jastrzebska, B., Tsybovsky, Y., and Palczewski, K. 2010. Complexes between photoactivated rhodopsin and transducin: Progress and questions. *Biochem. J.* 428:1–10.

Wald, G. 1968. The molecular basis of visual excitation. *Nature* 219:800–807.

Ames, J. B., Dizhoor, A. M., Ikura, M., Palczewski, K., and Stryer, L. 1999. Three-dimensional structure of guanylyl cyclase activating protein-2, a calcium-sensitive modulator of photoreceptor guanylyl cyclases. *J. Biol. Chem.* 274:19329–19337.

Nathans, J. 1994. In the eye of the beholder: Visual pigments and inherited variation in human vision. *Cell* 78:357–360.

Nathans, J. 1999. The evolution and physiology of human color vision: Insights from molecular genetic studies of visual pigments. *Neuron* 24:299–312.

Palczewski, K., Kumasaka, T., Hori, T., Behnke, C. A., Motoshima, H., Fox, B. A., LeTrong, I., Teller, D. C., Okada, T., Stenkamp, R. E., Yamamoto, M., and Miyano, M. 2000. Crystal structure of rhodopsin: A G protein-coupled receptor. *Science* 289:739–745.

Filipek, S, Teller, D. C., Palczewski, K., and Stemkamp, R. 2003. The crystallographic model of rhodopsin and its use in studies of other G protein-coupled receptors. *Annu. Rev. Biophys. Biomol. Struct.* 32:375–397.

Hearing

Furness, D. N., Hackney, C. M., and Evans, M. G. 2010. Localisation of the mechanotransducer channels in mammalian cochlear hair cells provides clues to their gating. *J. Physiol.* 588:765–772.

Lim, K., and Park, S. 2009. A mechanical model of the gating spring mechanism of stereocilia. *J. Biomech.* 42:2158–2164.

Siemens, J., Lillo, C., Dumont, R. A., Reynolds, A., Williams, D. S., Gillespie, P. G., and Muller, U. 2004. Cadherin 23 is a component of the tip link in hair-cell stereocilia. *Nature* 428:950–955.

Spinelli, K. J., and Gillespie, P. G. 2009. Bottoms up: Transduction channels at tip link bases. *Nat. Neurosci.* 12:529–530.

Hudspeth, A. J. 1997. How hearing happens. *Neuron* 19:947–950.

Pickles, J. O., and Corey, D. P. 1992. Mechanoelectrical transduction by hair cells. *Trends Neurosci.* 15:254–259.

Walker, R. G., Willingham, A. T., and Zuker, C. S. 2000. A *Drosophila* mechanosensory transduction channel. *Science* 287:2229–2234.

Hudspeth, A. J., Choe, Y., Mehta, A. D., and Martin, P. 2000. Putting ion channels to work: Mechanoelectrical transduction, adaptation, and amplification by hair cells. *Proc. Natl. Acad. Sci. U.S.A.* 97:11765–11772.

Touch and Pain Reception

Myers, B. R., Bohlen, C. J., and Julius, D. 2008. A yeast genetic screen reveals a critical role for the pore helix domain in TRP channel gating. *Neuron* 58:362–373.

Lishko, P. V., Procko, E., Jin, X., Phelps, C. B., and Gaudet, R. 2007. The ankyrin repeats of TRPV1 bind multiple ligands and modulate channel sensitivity. *Neuron* 54:905–918.

Franco-Obregon, A., and Clapham, D. E. 1998. Touch channels sense blood pressure. *Neuron* 21:1224–1226.

Caterina, M. J., Schumacher, M. A., Tominaga, M., Rosen, T. A., Levine, J. D., and Julius, D. 1997. The capsaicin receptor: A heat-activated ion channel in the pain pathway. *Nature* 389:816–824.

Tominaga, M., Caterina, M. J., Malmberg, A. B., Rosen, T. A., Gilbert, H., Skinner, K., Raumann, B. E., Basbaum, A. I., and Julius, D. 1998. The cloned capsaicin receptor integrates multiple pain-producing stimuli. *Neuron* 21:531–543.

Caterina, M. J., and Julius, D. 1999. Sense and specificity: A molecular identity for nociceptors. *Curr. Opin. Neurobiol.* 9:525–530.

Clapham, D. E. 2003. TRP channels as cellular sensors. *Nature* 426:517–524.

Chapter 34

Where to Start

Nossal, G. J. V. 1993. Life, death, and the immune system. *Sci. Am.* 269(3):53–62.

Tonegawa, S. 1985. The molecules of the immune system. *Sci. Am.* 253(4):122–131.

Leder, P. 1982. The genetics of antibody diversity. *Sci. Am.* 246(5):102–115.

Bromley, S. K., Burack, W. R., Johnson, K. G., Somersalo, K., Sims, T. N., Sumen, C., Davis, M. M., Shaw, A. S., Allen, P. M., and Dustin, M. L. 2001. The immunological synapse. *Annu. Rev. Immunol.* 19:375–396.

Books

Kindt, T. J., Goldsby, R. A., and Osborne, B. A. 2007. *Kuby Immunology* (6th ed.). W. H. Freeman and Company.

Abbas, A. K., and Lichtman, A. H. 2003. *Cellular and Molecular Immunology* (5th ed). Saunders.

Cold Spring Harbor Symposia on Quantitative Biology, 1989. Volume 54. Immunological Recognition.

Nisinoff, A. 1985. *Introduction to Molecular Immunology* (2d ed.). Sinauer.

Weir, D. M. (Ed.). 1996. *Handbook of Experimental Immunology* (5th ed.). Oxford University Press.

Janeway, C. A., Travers, P., Walport, M., and Shlomchik, M. 2005. *Immunobiology* (6th ed.). Garland Science.

Innate Immune System

Janeway, C. A., Jr., and Medzhitov, R. 2002. Innate immune recognition. *Annu. Rev. Immunol.* 20:197–216.

Choe, J., Kelker, M. S., and Wilson, I. A. 2005. Crystal structure of human toll-like receptor 3 (TLR3) ectodomain. *Science* 309:581–585.

Khalturin, K., Panzer, Z., Cooper, M. D., and Bosch, T. C. 2004. Recognition strategies in the innate immune system of ancestral chordates. *Mol. Immunol.* 41:1077–1087.

Beutler, B., and Rietschel, E. T. 2003. Innate immune sensing and its roots: The story of endotoxin. *Nat. Rev. Immunol.* 3:169–176.

Xu, Y., Tao, X., Shen, B., Horng, T., Medzhitov, R., Manley, J. L., and Tong, L. 2000. Structural basis for signal transduction by the Toll/interleukin-1 receptor domains. *Nature* 408:111–115.

Structure of Antibodies and Antibody-Antigen Complexes

Davies, D. R., Padlan, E. A., and Sheriff, S. 1990. Antibody-antigen complexes. *Annu. Rev. Biochem.* 59:439–473.

Poljak, R. J. 1991. Structure of antibodies and their complexes with antigens. *Mol. Immunol.* 28:1341–1345.

Davies, D. R., and Cohen, G. H. 1996. Interactions of protein antigens with antibodies. *Proc. Natl. Acad. Sci. U.S.A.* 93:7–12.

Marquart, M., Deisenhofer, J., Huber, R., and Palm, W. 1980. Crystallographic refinement and atomic models of the intact immunoglobulin molecule Kol and its antigen-binding fragment at 3.0 Å and 1.9 Å resolution. *J. Mol. Biol.* 141:369–391.

Silverton, E. W., Navia, M. A., and Davies, D. R. 1977. Three-dimensional structure of an intact human immunoglobulin. *Proc. Natl. Acad. Sci. U.S.A.* 74:5140–5144.

Padlan, E. A., Silverton, E. W., Sheriff, S., Cohen, G. H., Smith, G. S., and Davies, D. R. 1989. Structure of an antibody-antigen complex: Crystal structure of the HyHEL-10 Fab lysozyme complex. *Proc. Natl. Acad. Sci. U.S.A.* 86:5938–5942.

Rini, J., Schultze-Gahmen, U., and Wilson, I. A. 1992. Structural evidence for induced fit as a mechanism for antibody-antigen recognition. *Science* 255:959–965.

Fischmann, T. O., Bentley, G. A., Bhat, T. N., Boulot, G., Mariuzza, R. A., Phillips, S. E., Tello, D., and Poljak, R. J. 1991. Crystallographic refinement of the three-dimensional structure of the FabD1.3-lysozyme complex at 2.5-Å resolution. *J. Biol. Chem.* 266:12915–12920.

Burton, D. R. 1990. Antibody: The flexible adaptor molecule. *Trends Biochem. Sci.* 15:64–69.

Saphire, E. O., Parren P. W., Pantophlet, R., Zwick, M. B., Morris, G. M., Rudd, P. M., Dwek, R. A., Stanfield, R. L., Burton, D. R., and Wilson, I. A. 2001. Crystal structure of a neutralizing human IgG against HIV-1: A template for vaccine design. *Science* 293:1155–1159.

Calarese, D. A., Scanlan, C. N., Zwick, M. B., Deechongkit, S., Mimura, Y., Kunert R., Zhu, P., Wormald, M. R., Stanfield, R. L., Roux, K. H., Kelly, J. W., Rudd, P. M., Dwek, R. A., Katinger, H., Burton, D. R., and Wilson, I. A. 2003. Antibody domain exchange is an immunological solution to carbohydrate cluster recognition. *Science* 300:2065–2071.

Generation of Diversity

Tonegawa, S. 1988. Somatic generation of immune diversity. *Biosci. Rep.* 8:3–26.

Honjo, T., and Habu, S. 1985. Origin of immune diversity: Genetic variation and selection. *Annu. Rev. Biochem.* 54:803–830.

Gellert, M., and McBlane, J. F. 1995. Steps along the pathway of VDJ recombination. *Philos. Trans. R. Soc. Lond. B Biol. Sci.* 347:43–47.

Harris, R. S., Kong, Q., and Maizels, N. 1999. Somatic hypermutation and the three R's: Repair, replication and recombination. *Mutat. Res.* 436:157–178.

Lewis, S. M., and Wu, G. E. 1997. The origins of V(D)J recombination. *Cell* 88:159–162.

Ramsden, D. A., van Gent, D. C., and Gellert, M. 1997. Specificity in V(D)J recombination: New lessons from biochemistry and genetics. *Curr. Opin. Immunol.* 9:114–120.

Roth, D. B., and Craig, N. L. 1998. VDJ recombination: A transposase goes to work. *Cell* 94:411–414.

Sadofsky, M. J. 2001. The RAG proteins in V(D)J recombination: More than just a nuclease. *Nucleic Acids Res.* 29:1399–1409.

MHC Proteins and Antigen Processing

Bjorkman, P. J., and Parham, P. 1990. Structure, function, and diversity of class I major histocompatibility complex molecules. *Annu. Rev. Biochem.* 59:253–288.

Goldberg, A. L., and Rock, K. L. 1992. Proteolysis, proteasomes, and antigen presentation. *Nature* 357:375–379.

Madden, D. R., Gorga, J. C., Strominger, J. L., and Wiley, D. C. 1992. The three-dimensional structure of HLA-B27 at 2.1 Å resolution suggests a general mechanism for tight binding to MHC. *Cell* 70:1035–1048.

Fremont, D. H., Matsumura, M., Stura, E. A., Peterson, P. A., and Wilson, I. A. 1992. Crystal structures of two viral peptides in complex with murine MHC class I H-2Kb. *Science* 257:880–881.

Matsumura, M., Fremont, D. H., Peterson, P. A., and Wilson, I. A. 1992. Emerging principles for the recognition of peptide antigens by MHC class I. *Science* 257:927–934.

Brown, J. H., Jardetzky, T. S., Gorga, J. C., Stern, L. J., Urban, R. G., Strominger, J. L., and Wiley, D. C. 1993. Three-dimensional structure of the human class II histocompatibility antigen HLA-DR1. *Nature* 364:33–39.

Saper, M. A., Bjorkman, P. J., and Wiley, D. C. 1991. Refined structure of the human histocompatibility antigen HLA-A2 at 2.6 Å resolution. *J. Mol. Biol.* 219:277–319.

Madden, D. R., Gorga, J. C., Strominger, J. L., and Wiley, D. C. 1991. The structure of HLA-B27 reveals nonamer self-peptides bound in an extended conformation. *Nature* 353:321–325.

Cresswell, P., Bangia, N., Dick, T., and Diedrich, G. 1999. The nature of the MHC class I peptide loading complex. *Immunol. Rev.* 172:21–28.

Madden, D. R., Garboczi, D. N., and Wiley, D. C. 1993. The antigenic identity of peptide-MHC complexes: A comparison of the conformations of five viral peptides presented by HLA-A2. *Cell* 75:693–708.

T-Cell Receptors and Signaling Complexes

Hennecke, J., and Wiley, D. C. 2001. T-cell receptor-MHC interactions up close. *Cell* 104:1–4.

Ding, Y. H., Smith, K. J., Garboczi, D. N., Utz, U., Biddison, W. E., and Wiley, D. C. 1998. Two human T cell receptors bind in a similar diagonal mode to the HLA-A2/Tax peptide complex using different TCR amino acids. *Immunity* 8:403–411.

Reinherz, E. L., Tan, K., Tang, L., Kern, P., Liu, J., Xiong, Y., Hussey, R. E., Smolyar, A., Hare, B., Zhang, R., Joachimiak, A., Chang, H. C., Wagner, G., and Wang, J. 1999. The crystal structure of a T-cell receptor in complex with peptide and MHC class II. *Science* 286:1913–1921.

Davis, M. M., and Bjorkman, P. J. 1988. T-cell antigen receptor genes and T-cell recognition. *Nature* 334:395–402.

Cochran, J. R., Cameron, T. O., and Stern, L. J. 2000. The relationship of MHC-peptide binding and T cell activation probed using chemically defined MHC class II oligomers. *Immunity* 12:241–250.

Garcia, K. C., Teyton, L., and Wilson, I. A. 1999. Structural basis of T cell recognition. *Annu. Rev. Immunol.* 17:369–397.

Garcia, K. C., Degano, M., Stanfield, R. L., Brunmark, A., Jackson, M. R., Peterson, P. A., Teyton, L. A., and Wilson, I. A. 1996. An αβ T-cell receptor structure at 2.5 Å and its orientation in the TCR-MHC complex. *Science* 274:209–219.

Garboczi, D. N., Ghosh, P., Utz, U., Fan, Q. R., Biddison, W. E., Wiley, D. C. 1996. Structure of the complex between human T-cell receptor, viral peptide and HLA-A2. *Nature* 384:134–141.

Gaul, B. S., Harrison, M. L., Geahlen, R. L., Burton, R. A., and Post, C. B. 2000. Substrate recognition by the Lyn protein-tyrosine kinase: NMR structure of the immunoreceptor tyrosine-based activation motif signaling region of the B cell antigen receptor. *J. Biol. Chem.* 275:16174–16182.

Kern, P. S., Teng, M. K., Smolyar, A., Liu, J. H., Liu, J., Hussey, R. E., Spoerl, R., Chang, H. C., Reinherz, E. L., and Wang, J. H. 1998. Structural basis of CD8 coreceptor function revealed by crystallographic analysis of a murine CD8 αβ ectodomain fragment in complex with H-2Kb. *Immunity* 9:519–530.

Konig, R., Fleury, S., and Germain, R. N. 1996. The structural basis of CD4-MHC class II interactions: Coreceptor contributions to T cell receptor antigen recognition and oligomerization-dependent signal transduction. *Curr. Top. Microbiol. Immunol.* 205:19–46.

Davis, M. M., Boniface, J. J., Reich, Z., Lyons, D., Hampl, J., Arden, B., and Chien, Y. 1998. Ligand recognition by αβ T-cell receptors. *Annu. Rev. Immunol.* 16:523–544.

Janeway, C. J. 1992. The T cell receptor as a multicomponent signalling machine: CD4/CD8 coreceptors and CD45 in T cell activation. *Annu. Rev. Immunol.* 10:645–674.

Podack, E. R., and Kupfer, A. 1991. T-cell effector functions: Mechanisms for delivery of cytotoxicity and help. *Annu. Rev. Cell Biol.* 7:479–504.

Davis, M. M. 1990. T cell receptor gene diversity and selection. *Annu. Rev. Biochem.* 59:475–496.

Leahy, D. J., Axel, R., and Hendrickson, W. A. 1992. Crystal structure of a soluble form of the human T cell coreceptor CD8 at 2.6 Å resolution. *Cell* 68:1145–1162.

Bots, M., and Medema, J. P. 2006. Granzymes at a glance. *J. Cell. Sci.* 119:5011–5014.

Lowin, B., Hahne, M., Mattmann, C., and Tschopp, J. 1994. Cytolytic T-cell cytotoxicity is mediated through perforin and Fas lytic pathways. *Nature* 370:650–652.

Rudolph, M. G., and Wilson, I. A. 2002. The specificity of TCR/pMHC interaction. *Curr. Opin. Immunol.* 14:52–65.

HIV and AIDS

Fauci, A. S. 1988. The human immunodeficiency virus: Infectivity and mechanisms of pathogenesis. *Science* 239:617–622.

Gallo, R. C., and Montagnier, L. 1988. AIDS in 1988. *Sci. Am.* 259(4):41–48.

Kwong, P. D., Wyatt, R., Robinson, J., Sweet, R. W., Sodroski, J., and Hendrickson, W. A. 1998. Structure of an HIV gp120 envelope glycoprotein in complex with the CD4 receptor and a neutralizing human antibody. *Nature* 393:648–659.

Vaccines

Johnston, M. I. and Fauci, A. S. 2007. An HIV vaccine—evolving concepts. *N. Engl. J. Med.* 356:2073–2081.

Burton, D. R., Desrosiers, R. C., Doms, R. W., Koff, W. C., Kwong, P. D., Moore, J. P., Nabel, G. J., Sodroski, J., Wilson, I. A., and Wyatt, R. T. 2004. HIV vaccine design and the neutralizing antibody problem. *Nature Immunol.* 5:233–236.

Ada, G. 2001. Vaccines and vaccination. *N. Engl. J. Med.* 345:1042–1053.

Behbehani, A. M. 1983. The smallpox story: Life and death of an old disease. *Microbiol. Rev.* 47:455–509.

Discovery of Major Concepts

Ada, G. L., and Nossal, G. 1987. The clonal selection theory. *Sci. Am.* 257(2):62–69.

Porter, R. R. 1973. Structural studies of immunoglobulins. *Science* 180:713–716.

Edelman, G. M. 1973. Antibody structure and molecular immunology. *Science* 180:830–840.

Kohler, G. 1986. Derivation and diversification of monoclonal antibodies. *Science* 233:1281–1286.

Milstein, C. 1986. From antibody structure to immunological diversification of immune response. *Science* 231:1261–1268.

Janeway, C. A., Jr. 1989. Approaching the asymptote? Evolution and revolution in immunology. *Cold Spring Harbor Symp. Quant. Biol.* 54:1–13.

Jerne, N. K. 1971. Somatic generation of immune recognition. *Eur. J. Immunol.* 1:1–9.

Chapter 35

Where to Start

Gennerich, A., and Vale, R. D. 2009. Walking the walk: How kinesin and dynein coordinate their steps. *Curr. Opin. Cell Biol.* 21:59–67.

Vale, R. D. 2003. The molecular motor toolbox for intracellular transport. *Cell* 112:467–480.

Vale, R. D., and Milligan, R. A. 2000. The way things move: Looking under the hood of molecular motor proteins. *Science* 288:88–95.

Vale, R. D. 1996. Switches, latches, and amplifiers: Common themes of G proteins and molecular motors. *J. Cell Biol.* 135:291–302.

Mehta, A. D., Rief, M., Spudich, J. A., Smith, D. A., and Simmons, R. M. 1999. Single-molecule biomechanics with optical methods. *Science* 283:1689–1695.

Schuster, S. C., and Khan, S. 1994. The bacterial flagellar motor. *Annu. Rev. Biophys. Biomol. Struct.* 23:509–539.

Books

Howard, J. 2001. *Mechanics of Motor Proteins and the Cytosketon.* Sinauer.

Squire, J. M. 1986. *Muscle Design, Diversity, and Disease.* Benjamin Cummings.

Pollack, G. H., and Sugi, H. (Eds.). 1984. *Contractile Mechanisms in Muscle.* Plenum.

Myosin and Actin

Lorenz, M., and Holmes, K. C. 2010. The actin-myosin interface. *Proc. Natl. Acad. Sci. U.S.A.* 107:12529–12534.

Yang, Y., Gourinath, S., Kovacs, M., Nyitray, L., Reutzel, R., Himmel, D. M., O'Neall-Hennessey, E., Reshetnikova, L., Szent-Györgyi, A. G., Brown, J. H., and Cohen, C. 2007. Rigor-like structures from muscle myosins reveal key mechanical elements in the transduction pathways of this allosteric motor. *Structure* 15:553–564.

Himmel, D. M., Mui, S., O'Neall-Hennessey, E., Szent-Györgyi, A. G., and Cohen, C. 2009. The on-off switch in regulated myosins: Different triggers but related mechanisms. *J. Mol. Biol.* 394:496–505.

Houdusse, A., Gaucher, J. F., Krementsova, E., Mui, S., Trybus, K. M., and Cohen, C. 2006. Crystal structure of apo-calmodulin bound to the first two IQ motifs of myosin V reveals essential recognition features. *Proc. Natl. Acad. Sci. U.S.A.* 103:19326–19331.

Li, X. E., Holmes, K. C., Lehman, W., Jung, H., and Fischer, S. 2010. The shape and flexibility of tropomyosin coiled coils: Implications for actin filament assembly and regulation. *J. Mol. Biol.* 395:327–339.

Fischer, S., Windshugel, B., Horak, D., Holmes, K. C., and Smith, J. C. 2005. Structural mechanism of the recovery stroke in the myosin molecular motor. *Proc. Natl. Acad. Sci. U.S.A.* 102:6873–6878.

Holmes, K. C., Angert, I., Kull, F. J., Jahn, W., and Schroder, R. R. 2003. Electron cryo-microscopy shows how strong binding of myosin to actin releases nucleotide. *Nature* 425:423–427.

Holmes, K. C., Schroder, R. R., Sweeney, H. L., and Houdusse, A. 2004. The structure of the rigor complex and its implications for the power stroke. *Philos. Trans. R. Soc. Lond. B Biol. Sci.* 359:1819–1828.

Purcell, T. J., Morris, C., Spudich, J. A., and Sweeney, H. L. 2002. Role of the lever arm in the processive stepping of myosin V. *Proc. Natl. Acad. Sci. U.S.A.* 99:14159–14164.

Purcell, T. J., Sweeney, H. L., and Spudich, J. A. 2005. A force-dependent state controls the coordination of processive myosin V. *Proc. Natl. Acad. Sci. U.S.A.* 102:13873–13878.

Holmes, K. C. 1997. The swinging lever-arm hypothesis of muscle contraction. *Curr. Biol.* 7:R112–R118.

Berg, J. S., Powell, B. C., and Cheney, R. E. 2001. A millennial myosin census. *Mol. Biol. Cell* 12:780–794.

Houdusse, A., Kalabokis, V. N., Himmel, D., Szent-Györgyi, A. G., and Cohen, C. 1999. Atomic structure of scallop myosin subfragment S1 complexed with MgADP: A novel conformation of the myosin head. *Cell* 97:459–470.

Houdusse, A., Szent-Györgyi, A. G., and Cohen, C. 2000. Three conformational states of scallop myosin S1. *Proc. Natl. Acad. Sci. U.S.A.* 97:11238–11243.

Uyeda, T. Q., Abramson, P. D., and Spudich, J. A. 1996. The neck region of the myosin motor domain acts as a lever arm to generate movement. *Proc. Natl. Acad. Sci. U.S.A.* 93:4459–4464.

Mehta, A. D., Rock, R. S., Rief, M., Spudich, J. A., Mooseker, M. S., and Cheney, R. E. 1999. Myosin-V is a processive actin-based motor. *Nature* 400:590–593.

Otterbein, L. R., Graceffa, P., and Dominguez, R. 2001. The crystal structure of uncomplexed actin in the ADP state. *Science* 293:708–711.

SELECTED READINGS

Holmes, K. C., Popp, D., Gebhard, W., and Kabsch, W. 1990. Atomic model of the actin filament. *Nature* 347:44–49.

Schutt, C. E., Myslik, J. C., Rozycki, M. D., Goonesekere, N. C., and Lindberg, U. 1993. The structure of crystalline profilin-β-actin. *Nature* 365:810–816.

van den Ent, F., Amos, L. A., and Lowe, J. 2001. Prokaryotic origin of the actin cytoskeleton. *Nature* 413:39–44.

Schutt, C. E., and Lindberg, U. 1998. Muscle contraction as a Markov process I: Energetics of the process. *Acta Physiol. Scand.* 163:307–323.

Rief, M., Rock, R. S., Mehta, A. D., Mooseker, M. S., Cheney, R. E., and Spudich, J. A. 2000. Myosin-V stepping kinetics: A molecular model for processivity. *Proc. Natl. Acad. Sci. U.S.A.* 97:9482–9486.

Friedman, T. B., Sellers, J. R., and Avraham, K. B. 1999. Unconventional myosins and the genetics of hearing loss. *Am. J. Med. Genet.* 89:147–157.

Kinesin, Dynein, and Microtubules

Yildiz, A., Tomishige, M., Gennerich, A., and Vale, R. D. 2008. Intramolecular strain coordinates kinesin stepping behavior along microtubules. *Cell* 134:1030–1041.

Yildiz, A., Tomishige, M., Vale, R. D., and Selvin, P. R. 2004. Kinesin walks hand-over-hand. *Science* 303:676–678.

Rogers, G. C., Rogers, S. L., Schwimmer, T. A., Ems-McClung, S. C., Walczak, C. E., Vale, R. D., Scholey, J. M., and Sharp, D. J. 2004. Two mitotic kinesins cooperate to drive sister chromatid separation during anaphase. *Nature* 427:364–370.

Vale, R. D., and Fletterick, R. J. 1997. The design plan of kinesin motors. *Annu. Rev. Cell. Dev. Biol.* 13:745–777.

Kull, F. J., Sablin, E. P., Lau, R., Fletterick, R. J., and Vale, R. D. 1996. Crystal structure of the kinesin motor domain reveals a structural similarity to myosin. *Nature* 380:550–555.

Kikkawa, M., Sablin, E. P., Okada, Y., Yajima, H., Fletterick, R. J., and Hirokawa, N. 2001. Switch-based mechanism of kinesin motors. *Nature* 411:439–445.

Wade, R. H., and Kozielski, F. 2000. Structural links to kinesin directionality and movement. *Nat. Struct. Biol.* 7:456–460.

Yun, M., Zhang, X., Park, C. G., Park, H. W., and Endow, S. A. 2001. A structural pathway for activation of the kinesin motor ATPase. *EMBO J.* 20:2611–2618.

Kozielski, F., De Bonis, S., Burmeister, W. P., Cohen-Addad, C., and Wade, R. H. 1999. The crystal structure of the minus-end-directed microtubule motor protein ncd reveals variable dimer conformations. *Struct. Fold. Des.* 7:1407–1416.

Lowe, J., Li, H., Downing, K. H., and Nogales, E. 2001. Refined structure of αβ-tubulin at 3.5 Å resolution. *J. Mol. Biol.* 313:1045–1057.

Nogales, E., Downing, K. H., Amos, L. A., and Lowe, J. 1998. Tubulin and FtsZ form a distinct family of GTPases. *Nat. Struct. Biol.* 5:451–458.

Zhao, C., Takita, J., Tanaka, Y., Setou, M., Nakagawa, T., Takeda, S., Yang, H. W., Terada, S., Nakata, T., Takei, Y., Saito, M., Tsuji, S., Hayashi, Y., and Hirokawa, N. 2001. Charcot-Marie-Tooth disease type 2A caused by mutation in a microtubule motor KIF1Bβ. *Cell* 105:587–597.

Asai, D. J., and Koonce, M. P. 2001. The dynein heavy chain: Structure, mechanics and evolution. *Trends Cell Biol.* 11:196–202.

Mocz, G., and Gibbons, I. R. 2001. Model for the motor component of dynein heavy chain based on homology to the AAA family of oligomeric ATPases. *Structure* 9:93–103.

Bacterial Motion and Chemotaxis

Baker, M. D., Wolanin, P. M., and Stock, J. B. 2006. Systems biology of bacterial chemotaxis. *Curr. Opin. Microbiol.* 9:187–192.

Wolanin, P. M., Baker, M. D., Francis, N. R., Thomas, D. R., DeRosier, D. J., and Stock, J. B. 2006. Self-assembly of receptor/signaling complexes in bacterial chemotaxis. *Proc. Natl. Acad. Sci. U.S.A.* 103:14313–14318.

Sowa, Y., Rowe, A. D., Leake, M. C., Yakushi, T., Homma, M., Ishijima, A., and Berry, R. M. 2005. Direct observation of steps in rotation of the bacterial flagellar motor. *Nature* 437:916–919.

Berg, H. C. 2000. Constraints on models for the flagellar rotary motor. *Philos. Trans. R. Soc. Lond. B Biol. Sci.* 355:491–501.

DeRosier, D. J. 1998. The turn of the screw: The bacterial flagellar motor. *Cell* 93:17–20.

Ryu, W. S., Berry, R. M., and Berg, H. C. 2000. Torque-generating units of the flagellar motor of *Escherichia coli* have a high duty ratio. *Nature* 403:444–447.

Lloyd, S. A., Whitby, F. G., Blair, D. F., and Hill, C. P. 1999. Structure of the C-terminal domain of FliG, a component of the rotor in the bacterial flagellar motor. *Nature* 400:472–475.

Purcell, E. M. 1977. Life at low Reynolds number. *Am. J. Physiol.* 45:3–11.

Macnab, R. M., and Parkinson, J. S. 1991. Genetic analysis of the bacterial flagellum. *Trends Genet.* 7:196–200.

Historical Aspects

Huxley, H. E. 1965. The mechanism of muscular contraction. *Sci. Am.* 213(6):18–27.

Summers, K. E., and Gibbons, I. R. 1971. ATP-induced sliding of tubules in trypsin-treated flagella of sea-urchin sperm. *Proc. Natl. Acad. Sci. U.S.A.* 68:3092–3096.

Macnab, R. M., and Koshland, D. E., Jr. 1972. The gradient-sensing mechanism in bacterial chemotaxis. *Proc. Natl. Acad. Sci. U.S.A.* 69:2509–2512.

Taylor, E. W. 2001. 1999 E. B. Wilson lecture: The cell as molecular machine. *Mol. Biol. Cell* 12:251–254.

Chapter 36

Books

Kenakin, T. P. 2006. *A Pharmacology Primer: Theory, Applications, and Methods* (2d ed.). Academic Press.

Brunton, L., Lazo, J., and Parker, K. 2005. *Goodman and Gilman's The Pharmacological Basis of Therapeutics* (11th ed.). McGraw-Hill Professional.

Walsh, C. T., and Schwartz-Bloom, R. D. 2004. *Levine's Pharmacology: Drug Actions and Reactions* (7th ed.). Taylor and Francis Group.

Silverman, R. B. 2004. *Organic Chemistry of Drug Design and Drug Action*. Academic Press.

Walsh, C. 2003. *Antibiotics: Actions, Origins, Resistance*. ASM Press.

ADME and Toxicity

Caldwell, J., Gardner, I., and Swales, N. 1995. An introduction to drug disposition: The basic principles of absorption, distribution, metabolism, and excretion. *Toxicol. Pathol.* 23:102–114.

Lee, W., and Kim, R. B. 2004. Transporters and renal drug elimination. *Annu. Rev. Pharmacol. Toxicol.* 44:137–166.

Lin, J., Sahakian, D. C., de Morais, S. M., Xu, J. J., Polzer, R. J., and Winter, S. M. 2003. The role of absorption, distribution, metabolism, excretion and toxicity in drug discovery. *Curr. Top. Med. Chem.* 3:1125–1154.

Poggesi, I. 2004. Predicting human pharmacokinetics from preclinical data. *Curr. Opin. Drug Discov. Devel.* 7:100–111.

Case Histories

Flower, R. J. 2003. The development of COX2 inhibitors. *Nat. Rev. Drug Discov.* 2:179–191.

Tobert, J. A. 2003. Lovastatin and beyond: The history of the HMG-CoA reductase inhibitors. *Nat. Rev. Drug Discov.* 2:517–526.

Vacca, J. P., Dorsey, B. D., Schleif, W. A., Levin, R. B., McDaniel, S. L., Darke, P. L., Zugay, J., Quintero, J. C., Blahy, O. M., Roth, E., et al. 1994. L-735,524: An orally bioavailable human immunodeficiency virus type 1 protease inhibitor. *Proc. Natl. Acad. Sci. U.S.A.* 91:4096–4100.

Wong, S., and Witte, O. N. 2004. The BCR-ABL story: Bench to bedside and back. *Annu. Rev. Immunol.* 22:247–306.

Structure-Based Drug Design

Kuntz, I. D. 1992. Structure-based strategies for drug design and discovery. *Science* 257:1078–1082.

Dorsey, B. D., Levin, R. B., McDaniel, S. L., Vacca, J. P., Guare, J. P., Darke, P. L., Zugay, J. A., Emini, E. A., Schleif, W. A., Quintero, J. C., et al. 1994. L-735,524: The design of a potent and orally bioavailable HIV protease inhibitor. *J. Med. Chem.* 37:3443–3451.

Chen, Z., Li, Y., Chen, E., Hall, D. L., Darke, P. L., Culberson, C., Shafer, J. A., and Kuo, L. C. 1994. Crystal structure at 1.9-Å resolution of human immunodeficiency virus (HIV) II protease complexed with L-735,524, an orally bioavailable inhibitor of the HIV proteases. *J. Biol. Chem.* 269:26344–26348.

Combinatorial Chemistry

Baldwin, J. J. 1996. Design, synthesis and use of binary encoded synthetic chemical libraries. *Mol. Divers.* 2:81–88.

Burke, M. D., Berger, E. M., and Schreiber, S. L. 2003. Generating diverse skeletons of small molecules combinatorially. *Science* 302:613–618.

Edwards, P. J., and Morrell, A. I. 2002. Solid-phase compound library synthesis in drug design and development. *Curr. Opin. Drug Discov. Devel.* 5:594–605.

Genomics

Zambrowicz, B. P., and Sands, A. T. 2003. Knockouts model the 100 best-selling drugs: Will they model the next 100? *Nat. Rev. Drug Discov.* 2:38–51.

Salemme, F. R. 2003. Chemical genomics as an emerging paradigm for postgenomic drug discovery. *Pharmacogenomics* 4:257–267.

Michelson, S., and Joho, K. 2000. Drug discovery, drug development and the emerging world of pharmacogenomics: Prospecting for information in a data-rich landscape. *Curr. Opin. Mol. Ther.* 2:651–654.

Weinshilboum, R., and Wang, L. 2004. Pharmacogenomics: Bench to bedside. *Nat. Rev. Drug Discov.* 3:739–748.

INDEX

Note: Page numbers followed by f, t, and b refer to figures, tables, and boxed material, respectively. **Boldface** page numbers indicate structural formulas and ribbon diagrams.

ACIDITY CONSTANTS

pK_a values of some acids

Acid	pK' (at 25°C)
Acetic acid	4.76
Acetoacetic acid	3.58
Ammonium ion	9.25
Ascorbic acid, pK_1	4.10
pK_2	11.79
Benzoic acid	4.20
n-Butyric acid	4.81
Cacodylic acid	6.19
Citric acid, pK_1	3.14
pK_2	4.77
pK_3	6.39
Ethylammonium ion	10.81
Formic acid	3.75
Glycine, pK_1	2.35
pK_2	9.78
Imidazolium ion	6.95
Lactic acid	3.86
Maleic acid, pK_1	1.83
pK_2	6.07

Acid	pK' (at 25°C)
Malic acid, pK_1	3.40
pK_2	5.11
Phenol	9.89
Phosphoric acid, pK_1	2.12
pK_2	7.21
pK_3	12.67
Pyridinium ion	5.25
Pyrophosphoric acid, pK_1	0.85
pK_2	1.49
pK_3	5.77
pK_4	8.22
Succinic acid, pK_1	4.21
pK_2	5.64
Trimethylammonium ion	9.79
Tris (hydroxymethyl) aminomethane	8.08
Water*	15.74

*$[H^+][OH^-] = 10^{-14}$; $[H_2O] = 55.5$ M.

Typical pK_a values of ionizable groups in proteins

Group	Acid	$\rightleftharpoons$	Base	Typical pK_a
Terminal α-carboxyl group				3.1
Aspartic acid Glutamic acid				4.1
Histidine				6.0
Terminal α-amino group				8.0

Group	Acid	$\rightleftharpoons$	Base	Typical pK_a
Cysteine				8.3
Tyrosine				10.4
Lysine				10.0
Arginine				12.5

Note: pK_a values depend on temperature, ionic strength, and the microenvironment of the ionizable group.

STANDARD BOND LENGTHS

Bond	Structure	Length (Å)
C—H	R_2CH_2	1.07
	Aromatic	1.08
	RCH_3	1.10
C—C	Hydrocarbon	1.54
	Aromatic	1.40
C=C	Ethylene	1.33
C≡C	Acetylene	1.20
C—N	RNH_2	1.47
	O=C—N	1.34
C—O	Alcohol	1.43
	Ester	1.36
C=O	Aldehyde	1.22
	Amide	1.24
C—S	R_2S	1.82
N—H	Amide	0.99
O—H	Alcohol	0.97
O—O	O_2	1.21
P—O	Ester	1.56
S—H	Thiol	1.33
S—S	Disulfide	2.05